Fossil Plants and Spores: modern techniques

edited by

T. P. JONES
Department of Earth Sciences, Cardiff University, Wales, UK

and

N. P. ROWE
Laboratoire de Paléobotanique, Université de Montpellier, France

1999
Published by
The Geological Society
London

THE GEOLOGICAL SOCIETY

The Geological Society of London was founded in 1807 and is the oldest geological society in the world. It received its Royal Charter in 1825 for the purpose of 'investigating the mineral structure of the Earth' and is now Britain's national society for geology.

Both a learned society and a professional body, the Geological Society is recognized by the Department of Trade and Industry (DTI) as the chartering authority for geoscience, able to award Chartered Geologist status upon appropriately qualified Fellows. The Society has a membership of 8600, of whom about 1500 live outside the UK.

Fellowship of the Society is open to persons holding a recognized honours degree in geology or a cognate subject and who have at least two years' relevant postgraduate experience, or not less than six years' relevant experience in geology or a cognate subject. A Fellow with a minimum of five years' relevant postgraduate experience in the practice of geology may apply for chartered status. Successful applicants are entitled to use the designatory postnominal CGeol (Chartered Geologist). Fellows of the Society may use the letters FGS. Other grades of membership are available to members not yet qualifying for Fellowship.

The Society has its own Publishing House based in Bath, UK. It produces the Society's international journals, books and maps, and is the European distributor for publications of the American Association of Petroleum Geologists (AAPG), the Society for Sedimentary Geology (SEPM) and the Geological Society of America (GSA). Members of the Society can buy books at considerable discounts. The Publishing House has an online bookshop (*http://bookshop.geolsoc.org.uk*).

Further information on Society membership may be obtained from the Membership Services Manager, The Geological Society, Burlington House, Piccadilly, London W1V 0JU (Email: *enquiries@geolsoc.org.uk*; tel: +44 (0)171 434 9944).

The Society's Web Site can be found at *http://www.geolsoc.org.uk/*. The Society is a Registered Charity, number 210161.

Published by The Geological Society from:
The Geological Society Publishing House
Unit 7, Brassmill Enterprise Centre
Brassmill Lane
Bath BA1 3JN, UK

(*Orders*: Tel. +44 (0)1225 445046
Fax +44 (0)1225 442836)
Online bookshop: *http://bookshop.geolsoc.org.uk*

First published 1999

The publishers make no representation, express or implied, with regard to the accuracy of the information contained in this book and cannot accept any legal responsibility for any errors or omissions that may be made.

British Library Cataloguing in Publication Data
A catalogue record for this book is available from the British Library.

ISBN 1-86239-035-5 (hbk)
ISBN 1-86239-041-X (sbk)

Typeset by E & M Graphics, Midsomer Norton, Bath, UK

Printed by Cambridge University Press Printing House, Cambridge, UK

Distributors

USA
AAPG Bookstore
PO Box 979
Tulsa
OK 74101-0979
USA
Orders: Tel. + 1 918 584-2555
Fax +1 918 560-2652
Email *bookstore@aapg.org*

Australia
Australian Mineral Foundation Bookshop
63 Conyngham Street
Glenside
South Australia 5065
Australia
Orders: Tel. +61 88 379-0444
Fax +61 88 379-4634
Email *bookshop@amf.com.au*

India
Affiliated East-West Press PVT Ltd
G-1/16 Ansari Road, Daryaganj,
New Delhi 110 002
India
Orders: Tel. +91 11 327-9113
Fax +91 11 326-0538

Japan
Kanda Book Trading Co.
Cityhouse Tama 204
Tsurumaki 1-3-10
Tama-shi
Tokyo 206-0034
Japan
Orders: Tel. +81 (0)423 57-7650
Fax +81 (0)423 57-7651

Contents

Contributors

John M. Anderson
National Botanical Institute, Private Bag X101, Pretoria 0001, South Africa

Lindsey Axe
Department of Earth Sciences, Cardiff University, Cardiff CF1 3YE, UK
Email   axe@cardiff.ac.uk

Mike G. L. Baillie
Palaeoecology Centre, School of Geosciences, Queen's University, Belfast, N. Ireland BT7 1NN, UK
Email   m.baillie@qub.ac.uk

Richard M. Bateman
Royal Botanic Garden, 20A Inverleith Row, Edinburgh EH3 5LR, UK
Email   richardb@rbge.org.uk

David J. Batten
Institute of Geography and Earth Sciences, University of Wales, Aberystwyth SY23 3DB UK
Email   dqb@aber.ac.uk

Dave J. Beerling
Department of Animal and Plant Sciences, University of Sheffield, Sheffield S10 2TN, UK
Email   D.J. Beerling@Sheffield.ac.uk

Christopher M. Berry
Department of Earth Sciences, Cardiff University, Cardiff CF1 3YE, UK
Email   C.Berry@cardiff.ac.uk

Kelly A. Bérubé
School of Biosciences, Cardiff University CF1 3YE, UK
Email   berube@cardiff.ac.uk

Hervé Bocherens
Laboratoire de Biogéochimie Isotopique, CNRS-INRA-UPMC UMR 162, Université P. et M. Curie, case 120, 4 Place Jussieu, 75252 Paris Cedex 05, France
Email   bocheren@ccr.jussieu.fr

Michael C. Boulter
Palaeobiology Research Unit, University of East London, Romford Road, London E15 4LZ, UK
Email   boulter@uel.ac.uk

Angela A. Bruch
Institut und Museum für Geologie und Paläontologie, Sigwartstr. 10, 72076 Tübingen, Germany.
Email   angela.bruch@uni-tuebingen.de

Bill Chaloner
Department of Geology, Royal Holloway, University of London, Egham, Surrey TW20 0EX, UK
Email   w.chaloner@rhbnc.ac.uk

Geoffrey Clayton
Department of Geology, Trinity College, Dublin 2, Ireland
Email   gclayton@tcd.ie

Christopher J. Cleal
Department of Biodiversity and Systematic Biology, National Museums and Galleries of Wales, Cathays Park, Cardiff CF1 3NP, UK
Email   chris_cleal@compuserve.com

Margaret E. Collinson
Department of Geology, Royal Holloway, University of London, Egham, Surrey TW20 0EX, UK
Email   m.collinson@gl.rhbnc.ac.uk

Peter Coxon
Department of Geography, Trinity College, Dublin 2, Ireland
Email   pcoxon@tcd.ie

Geoffrey T. Creber
Department of Geology, Royal Holloway University of London, Egham, Surrey TW20 0EX, UK
Email   g.creber@rhbnc.ac.uk

Thomas Denk
Swedish Museum of Natural History, Paleobotany, Box 5000 7, Stockholm S-10405, Sweden
Email   tlomas.denk@nrm.se

William A. Dimichele
Department of Paleobiology, National Museum of Natural History, Smithsonian Institution, Washington, DC 20560, USA
Email   dimichele.bill@nmnh.si.edu

John G. Douglas
41 Grieve Street, Warrnambool 3280, Australia
Email   douglas@standard.net.au

Muriel Fairon-Demaret
Université de Liège au Sart Tilman,
Paléobotanique et Paléopalynologie, Bât B18, B-
4000 Liège, Belgium
Email   M.Fairon@ulg.ac.be

David K. Ferguson
Palaeontological Institute, Geocentre, University
of Vienna, Althanstrasse 14, A-1090 Vienna,
Austria
Email   David.Kay.Ferguson@univie.ac.at

Isabel Figueiral
ESA 5059, CNRS, Institut de Botanique, 163 Rue
A. Broussonet, 34090 Montpellier, France
Email   figueir@crit.univ-montp2.fr

Tiffany S. Foster
Department of Palaeontology, The Natural History
Museum, Cromwell Rd. London SW7 5BD UK
Email   tf@nhm.ac.uk

Jane E. Francis
School of Earth Sciences, University of Leeds,
Leeds LS2 9JT, UK
Email   j.francis@earth.leeds.ac.uk

Jean Galtier
Laboratoire de Paléobotanique, Institut des
Sciences de L'Evolution, (UMR 5554 CNRS),
Université de Montpellier 2, 34095 Montpellier
Cedex 05, France
Email   galtier@isem.univ-montp2.fr

Robert A. Gastaldo
Department of Geology, 210 Petrie Hall, Auburn
University, AL 36849-5305, USA
Email   gastara@mail.auburn.edu

Philippe Gerrienne
Paléobotanique, Bât. B18, Sart Tilman, Université
de Liège, B-4000 Liège, Belgium
Email   p.gerrienne@ulg.ac.be

Ian J. Glasspool
Geology Department, Royal Holloway University
of London, Egham, Surrey
TW20 0EX, UK
Email   I.Glasspool@rhbnc.ac.uk

Edward M. Golenberg
Department of Biological Sciences, Wayne State
University, Detroit, Michigan 48202, USA
Email   egolenb@biology.biosci.wayne.edu

Antonio-J. González Barrioz
Consejería de Medio Ambiente, Junta de
Andalucía, Tomás de Aquino, s/n, 14004 Córdoba,
Spain.

Hagen Hass
Abteilung Paläobotanik, Westfälische Wilhelms-
Universität Münster, Hindenburgplatz 57-59, D-
48143 Münster, Germany.

Pat Hatcher
The Ohio State University, Newman and Wolfram
Lab., 100 West 18th Avenue, Columbus, OH
43210, USA
Email   hatcher@chemistry.ohio-state.edu

Alan R. Hemsley
Department of Earth Sciences, Cardiff University,
Cardiff CF1 3YE, UK
Email   hemsleyar@cardiff.ac.uk

Jason Hilton
Department of Earth Sciences, Cardiff University,
Cardiff CF1 3YE, UK
Email   Hilton@cardiff.ac.uk

Christa-Charlotte Hofmann
Palaeontological Institute, Geocentre, University
of Vienna, Althanstrasse 14, A-1090 Vienna,
Austria
Email   christa.hofmann@univie.ac.at

Carol L. Hotton
National Center for Biotechnology Information,
National Library of Medicine, National Institutes
of Health, Bethesda, MD 20894, USA
Email   hotton@ncbi.nlm.nih.gov

Rupert A. Housley
Department of Archaeology, University of
Glasgow, Gregory Building, Glasgow G12 8QQ,
UK
Email   rah@archaeology.arts.gla.ac.uk.

Stephen T. Jackson
Department of Botany, Aven Nelson Building,
University of Wyoming, Laramie, WY 82071
USA
Email   jackson@uwyo.edu

Tim P. Jones
Department of Earth Sciences, Cardiff University,
Cardiff CF1 3YE, UK
Email   jonestp@cardiff.ac.uk

Paul Kenrick
The Natural History Museum, Cromwell Road,
London SW7 5BD, UK
Email   p.kenrick@nhm.ac.uk

Hans Kerp
Abteilung Paläobotanik, Westfälische Wilhelms-
Universität Münster, Hindenburgplatz 57-59, D-
48143 Münster, Germany
Email   kerp@uni-muenster.de

Michael Krings
Abteilung Paläobotanik, Westfälische Wilhelms-
Universität Münster, Hindenburgplatz 57-59, D-
48143 Münster, Germany
Email   krings@uni-muenster.de

Wolfram M. Kürschner
Laboratory of Palaeobotany and Palynology,
Utrecht University, Budapestlaan 4, 3584 CD
Utrecht, The Netherlands
Email   W.Kurschner@biol.ruu.nl

Cheng-Sen Li
Institute of Botany, Chinese Academy of Sciences,
Xiangshan, Beijing 100093, China
Email   lics@ns.ibcas.ac.cn

Gary E. Maciel
Department of Chemistry, Colorado State
University, Fort Collins, CO 80523 USA

André Mariotti
Laboratoire de Biogéochimie Isotopique, CNRS-
INRA-UPMC UMR 162, Université P. et M. Curie,
case 120, 4 Place Jussieu, 75252 Paris Cedex 05,
France
Email   mariotti@ccr.jussieu.fr

John E. A. Marshall
School of Ocean and Earth Science, University of
Southampton, Southampton Oceanography Centre,
Waterfront Campus, European Way, Southampton
SO14 3ZH, UK
E mail   jeam@mail.soc.soton.ac.uk

Volker Mosbrugger
Institute of Geology and Palaeontology, University
of Tübingen, Sigwartstrasse 10
D-72076 Tübingen, Germany
Email   volker.mosbrugger@uni-tuebingen.de

Gary J. Nichols
Department of Geology, Royal Holloway,
University of London, Egham, Surrey TW20 0EX,
UK
Email   nichols@gl.rhbnc.ac.uk

Robert R. Ogilvie
Department of Education and Culture, Nova
Scotia Museum, Halifax, Nova Scotia, Canada,
B3H 3A6
Email   educnsm.ogilvirr@gov.ns.ca

Vicky H. Pan
The Energy Institute, 405 Academic
Activities Building, The Pennsylvania
State University, University Park, PA 16802,
USA

Toni Pearson
Calderstones, 59, Park Road, Limpsfield, Oxted,
Surrey RH8 OAN, UK
Email   ap45@tutor.open.ac.uk

James H. J. Penny
Department of Biology, Monkton Combe School,
Bath BA2 7HG, UK
Email   jamespenny@aol.com

Tom L. Phillips
Department of Plant Biology, University of
Illinois, 505 South Goodwin Avenue, Urbana,
Illinois 61801, USA

Imogen Poole
Department of Earth Sciences, University of
Leeds, Leeds LS2 9JT, UK
Email   I.Poole@earth.leeds.ac.uk

Jörg Pross
Institut und Museum für Geologie und
Paläontologie, Sigwartstr. 10, 72076 Tübingen,
Germany
Email   joerg.pross@uni-tuebingen.de

Peter McA Rees
Dept. of Earth Sciences, The Open University,
Walton Hall, Milton Keynes MK7 6AA, UK
Email   P.M.Rees@open.ac.uk

Gregory J. Retallack
Department of Geological Sciences, University
of Oregon, Eugene, Oregon 97403-1272,
USA
Email   greg_retallack@ccmail.uoregon.edu

Nick P. Rowe
Laboratoire de Paléobotanique, Institut des
Sciences de L'Evolution, (UMR 5554 CNRS),
Université de Montpellier 2, 34095 Montpellier
Cedex 05, France
Email   rowe@isem.univ-montp2.fr

Gerhard H. Schleser
Forschungszentrum Jülich GmbH, Institut für
Erdöl und Organische Geochemie (ICG-4),
Isotopengeochemie und Paläoklima, D-52425
Jülich, Germany
Email   g.schleser@fz-juelich.de

Andrew C. Scott
Department of Geology, Royal Holloway,
University of London, Egham, Surrey TW20 0EX,
UK
Email   scott@sun1.gl.rhbnc.ac.uk

Cedric H. Shute
Department of Palaeontology, The Natural History
Museum, Cromwell Rd. London SW7 5BD, UK
Email   chs@nhm.ac.uk

Thomas Speck
Botanischer Garten, Albert-Ludwigs-Universität
Freiburg, Schänzlestrasse 1, D-79104 Freiburg,
Germany
Email   speckth@sun2.ruf.uni-freiburg.de

Robert A. Spicer
Department of Earth Sciences, The Open
University, Milton Keynes MK7 6AA, UK
Email   R.A.Spicer@open.ac.uk

William E. Stein
Department of Biological Sciences, State
University of New York, Binghamton, NY 13902-
6000, USA
Email   stein@binghamton.edu

Thomas N. Taylor
Department of Ecology and Evolutionary Biology,
Museum and Biodiversity Research Center,
University of Kansas, Lawrence, KS 66045 USA
Email   ttaylor@falcon.cc.ukans.edu

Fred F. Titchener
Department of Geology, Royal Holloway,
University of London, Egham, Surrey TW20 0EX,
UK
Email   PHFB061@vms.rhbnc.ac.uk

Alfred Traverse
Department of Geosciences, the Pennsylvania
State University, University Park, PA 16802, USA
Email   traverse@ems.psu.edu

Pim F. van Bergen
Organic Geochemistry Group, Faculty of Earth

Sciences, Utrecht University, PO Box 80021, 3508
TA Utrecht, The Netherlands
Email   p.vanbergen@geo.uu.nl

Johanna H. A. Van Konijnenburg-Van Cittert
Laboratory of Palaeobotany and Palynology,
University of Utrecht, Budapestlaan 4, 3584 CD
Utrecht, The Netherlands
Email   jtvk@kgk.nl

Robert H. Wagner
Jardín Botánico de Córdoba, Avenida de Linneo,
s/n, 14004 Córdoba, Spain

Charles H. Wellman
Centre for Palynology, The University of
Sheffield, Dainton Building, Brook Hill, Sheffield
S3 7HF, UK
Email   c.wellman@sheffield.ac.uk

George Willcox
Institut de Préhistoire Orientale, UPR 7537,
CNRS, Jalès, 07460 Berrias, France
Email   ipocnrs@wanadoo.fr

Ben J. Williamson
Department of Earth Sciences, University of
Bristol, Wills Memorial Buildings, Queens Road,
Bristol, BS8 1RJ
Email   Ben.Williamson@bristol.ac.uk

Jack A. Wolfe
Department of Geosciences, University of
Arizona, Tucson, AZ 85721, USA
Email   jwolfe@geo.arizona.edu

Barbara L. Yule
School of Ocean and Earth Science, University of
Southampton, Southampton Oceanography Centre,
Waterfront Campus, European Way, Southampton
SO14 3ZH, UK

Alfred M. Ziegler
Dept. of Geophysical Sciences, University of
Chicago, 5734 S. Ellis Avenue, Chicago, Illinois
60637, USA
Email   Ziegler@geol.uchicago.edu

References to this volume

It is recommended that reference to all or part of this book should be made in one of the following ways:

JONES, T. P. & ROWE, N. P. (eds) 1999. *Fossil Plants and Spores: modern techniques*. Geological
Society, London.

FIGUEIRAL, I, & WILLCOX, G. 1999. Archaeobotany: collecting and analytical techniques for sub-fossils.
In: JONES, T. P. & ROWE, N. P. (eds) *Fossil Plants and Spores: modern techniques*. Geological Society,
London, 00–00.

Introduction

TIM P. JONES & NICK P. ROWE

In recent years the study of fossil plants, spores and pollen has produced an abundance of new methods and modifications of old ones. Many of these have been specifically designed for fossil plants, but could be adapted for other branches of palaeontology and related subjects. This volume represents a 'recipe book' of methods and conceptual approaches aimed specifically at fossils derived from plant material. One of the aims of this volume was also to include information of the sort that you might get to hear about personally but not find in the literature. As well as providing an update of tried and tested methods and their improvements, we have also included some of the most recent innovations, particularly in the fields of biogeochemical analysis and palaeoclimatology. The chapters in each section are written by specialists in their fields and include detailed accounts of the methods, in addition to the problems and how to solve them. Many chapters give precise methods and approaches used in the authors' laboratories; a common reviewer's response was to exclaim 'that's not how we do it' followed by a barrage of personal preferences, sometimes at odds with one or more chapters of the volume. Chapters dealing with more conceptual approaches, of course, suffered some of the same treatment and, short of enlarging the volume itself beyond an acceptable size and affordable price, we were forced to compromise. So, while this book may be seen as a showpiece of tested methods and approaches, we do encourage our readers to experiment rather than sticking rigidly to the methods as described; there is, after all, more than one way to skin a cat. Our layout of the sections is designed to follow a logical sequence of locating, collecting, extracting, analysing and preserving plant fossils and palynomorphs.

Part One deals with locating, collecting and extraction techniques. The first chapter discusses the basics of locating and collecting fossil plants, with a selection of tips and hints based on personal experiences (i.e. 'farmers and vicious dogs'). The next five chapters deal with extracting plant macrofossils and palynomorphs from their sediments. Such techniques have undergone some changes in view of the growing interest in different 'types' of fossil material such as mesodebris, cuticle fragments and charcoal. Part Two consists of six chapters, and considers techniques related to surface morphology, with the emphases placed on

preparation of the fossils, observation and interpretation, photography, light microscopy, and scanning electron microscopy. Part Three deals with the anatomy and internal structure of plants and spores, and includes a wide range of sectioning and embedding techniques. Part Four, on plant ultrastructure, deals mainly with the preparation of material for transmission electron microscopy. We are delighted to give Alan Hemsley & Ian Glasspool the opportunity to publish what they describe as the worst ultra-thin sections and micrographs they have ever produced.

Part Five contains perhaps the most rapidly developing field in fossil plant research – geochemical and biogeochemical analyses. It begins with a brief chapter on the collecting, handling and storage of materials for geochemical analysis to avoid problems of contamination. This is followed by a chapter on stable carbon isotopes, $^{13}C : ^{12}C$, which are being used increasingly for studying palaeoclimates and for palaeoenvironmental research. Further geochemical techniques deal with the identification of biomacromolecules, recognizing the chemical composition of macrofossils and palynomorphs, and understanding the chemical transformations and preservation biases during diagenesis. Another chapter in this section deals with the revolutionary and controversial field of extracting, purifying and verifying DNA from plant fossils. Finally, two additional chapters deal with geothermal maturation and spore coloration, as well as the use of geochemical signals, in determining the provenance of plant fossils. Since many of the techniques described in this section require specialist equipment with dedicated operators, we have tried to highlight the underlying principles behind the techniques, and how to understand and interpret the results.

Part Six deals with the computerized handling of plant fossil data, the problematic subject of naming fragmentary and differently preserved plant fossils, and the curation of fossils in museum collections. Part Seven contains eight chapters on sedimentology, taphonomy and stratigraphy. These contributions include techniques for looking at modern settings or experiments, as a means of interpreting the past. We have included chapters on methods that deal with fossils from clastic sediments and permineralized peats (coal balls). The last two chapters demonstrate the importance of plants in

JONES, T. P. & ROWE, N. P. 1999. Introduction. *In*: JONES, T. P. & ROWE, N. P. (eds) *Fossil Plants and Spores: modern techniques*. Geological Society, London, 1–2.

stratigraphy. Part Eight is devoted to palaeo-climatology, and the diverse ways fossil plants can be used to reconstruct ancient climates. We have included analyses based on leaf form variability, databases based on floral variation and palaeo-latitude, tree ring growth and the variation of stomatal indices according to environmental change.

Part Nine is a mixed bag, containing ten chapters on 'palaeoecology'. Some situations require unique approaches and this final chapter deals with a range of them, almost as 'case studies'. These include methods dealing with lake and coastal peat deposits, calcareous algae, archaeobotanical inves-tigations, dendrochronology, ^{14}C and $^{13}C : ^{12}C$, animal–plant interactions, and animal diets. A final section, outlining the national laws on collecting fossils from a selection of countries world-wide, follows.

On a more humorous note, it was a great source of amusement to see how various domestic household items have been described in some of the chapters. Palaeobotanists and palynologists are certainly great 'improvisers'. Two of our special favourites were 'disposable wooden applicators' = lollipop (popsicle) sticks, and 'airtight polyethylene containers = Tupperware. Rather curiously, a large number of techniques involve nail polish/varnish (?). And, finally, when a technique is described as requiring 'patience, skill, and even self control ... '; what does that really mean ?

Safety

This book contains a large number of techniques which involve highly dangerous machinery and chemicals. Always follow manufacturers' instructions and regulatory working practices (e.g. COSHH in the UK). Wherever possible, work involving dangerous reagents should be undertaken in a fume cupboard. Check all protocols with your safety advisers before trying them, and make sure you know what to do and who to contact in the event of an accident.

Acknowledgements

We would like to acknowledge the support and encouragement of our wives during the course of this project and we thank the very large numbers of our colleagues who reviewed these chapters. And finally, a big thank you to all our contributors who have survived our editing and made this project possible.

Part One   Extraction Techniques

1. Locating and collecting

N. P. ROWE & T. P. JONES

In this chapter we provide some broad guidance on general aspects of locating and collecting fossil plant material. Although much of this might be obvious to experienced field workers, there are not really any reference sources where methods specifically applicable to fossil plants are available to people new to the field. We focus largely on macrofossil material because of the diverse range of circumstances in which such material may be found and collected. Some recent analytical techniques, particularly geochemical analyses, require special care when collecting material and this is discussed by van Bergen (Chapter 28).

Before excavation and collection from a site the collector must be aware of the ownership, laws and legality of accessing localities, collecting the material and taking it away. The reader is referred to the chapter in this volume on laws and ownership of fossil plants for guidance on the kinds of laws existing in a selection of countries world-wide. In our experience, when approaching landowners for permission to collect, there is no better alternative than following up preliminary letters requesting permission by diplomatically and enthusiastically explaining on site what you are collecting and why. Many people, from farmers accompanied by vicious dogs, to executives of quarrying companies, are interested in fossils and on the whole are perfectly happy to allow access for collecting. Of course there are exceptions and, if the site is worth the trouble, obtaining permission for collecting and removing material could be a long process. Given the activities of some commercial collectors and the increasing financial interest in fossils, it is advisable to emphasize to the landowner the scientific aims of your activities.

Finding and recording locations

Surveying and scouting for new locations is an important aspect of palaeobotany field work whatever the type of investigation. When appraising an area it is preferable to inspect closely all the available exposures of the most promising lithology rather than stopping and collecting from the first one at which you find fossils. At locations where the rocks have been weathered to form a scree, it is advisable to scan this initially for evidence of fossil material, and then match the lithology and contents with *in situ* blocks above. Screes provide a large sample of fractured and weathered surfaces for initially recognizing fossils and this is a usually a better way of making a 'first contact' than spending a lot of time hammering away at rocks that might yield nothing. The same approach can be applied to many locations such as coastal sites, and blocks beneath sea cliffs, loose blocks in river beds and hillside scarps. It is always preferable to locate the source of loose material. Many well known fossils are known only from loose blocks where *in situ* material, potentially yielding bigger and better fossils was close by. Recognition of exposures can be difficult in certain locations when revisiting sites. Compass bearings should be taken on conspicuous landmarks; more recently, satellite-aided locating devices can be used for pinpointing locations. Photographs at varying distances of the site right up to the fossil-bearing horizon are extremely useful for relocating the site. Polaroid photos stuck into field notes and annotated at the site are a very useful method for recording precise location details and sample locations. When photographing the locations of fossil-bearing horizons, different light conditions will have drastic effects on the results, which may be crucial for demonstrating important layers on the photograph. Low angle direct sunlight can cause excessive shadowing; diffuse light, such as under cloudy conditions, is often much better. Wide-angled lenses can distort the vertical and lateral distances of overall views of locations and exposures. This must be borne in mind if such photographs are going to be used for accurately tracing the stratigraphy. Such photographs are best taken from a distance with a telephoto lens.

Recognizing fossils and lithologies

In contrast to the fact that only certain types of facies are likely to generate pollen and spores (see below), there are no strict rules for the types of facies yielding macrofossils. Meso- and macro-fossils may be found in many sediments, and their occurrences vary widely depending upon the differing sedimentological settings and taphonomic processes. These might be highly unexpected, including lithologies such as offshore black marine shales and volcanic ashes. Indeed, fossil plant charcoal has even been collected from igneous and high-grade metamorphic rocks.

ROWE, N. P. & JONES, T. P. 1999. Locating and collecting. *In*: JONES, T. P. & ROWE, N. P. (eds) *Fossil Plants and Spores: modern techniques*. Geological Society, London, 5–8.

Locating compression or permineralized fossils generally requires different approaches from the outset. Horizons containing compressions are most easily discovered by exposing surfaces parallel to the bedding plane and can be difficult to spot if the outcrop is exposed perpendicular to the bedding. Compression/impression fossils are readily spotted from scree accumulations, even if poorly preserved and weathered. Higher quality fossils might not be identified at first, but lithologies yielding fragments may signal the vicinity of higher quality material which might be confined to a single horizon.

Permineralized and petrified plants can be much harder to detect when not appropriately exposed. Even large-scale fossils such as trunks, stumps and branches might not be obvious at first sight if not cleanly exposed. Identification of smaller-scale permineralized fossils in most facies requires extremely acute observation and those that are not concentrated in obvious concretions such as coal balls, can be extremely difficult to locate. Permineralizations are often only visible if the rock surface is clean and 'suitably' weathered: once you have spotted one you are then likely to locate more. Under ideal circumstances, the matrix surface would be cleanly weathered and a different colour to that of the permineralized plant material; the plant fossils might be fractured and exposed perpendicular to the bedding plane and may even be inspected with a ×10 or ×20 hand lens to establish whether anatomical details are preserved.

Locating and collecting palynological samples in the field is more straightforward. A rock will either contain or not contain spores and pollen and workers rarely set up field laboratories in the field to check this (see Chapter 51). A degree of certainty exists about rocks likely to contain preserved pollen and spores. Palynomorphs are generally only located in sedimentary rocks and are most common in rocks with silt-sized particles. They are generally rare or not present in limestones, red beds or deeply weathered rocks, metamorphosed rocks, dolomites and volcanics. Good field advice is given in Traverse (1988, pp. 475–477), where the most likely lithology is described as 'fudgy' when the texture of the matrix is sampled between the fieldworker's teeth and is neither 'creamy' (too fine) or 'gritty' (too course). Most references indicate that recent exposures or freshly cut surfaces will provide the best samples with the least risk of oxidation by weathering and contamination from recent palynomorphs. Authors such as Traverse (1988) suggest that 10 g of a productive siltstone will provide sufficient material.

Excavating and removing material

Having located what is believed to be a worthwhile site, the degree of excavation depends very much on the scale and type of study required. 'Large-scale projects', such as detailed quantitative counts of macrofossils for ecological studies, will require large exposed surfaces and almost certainly require the extensive removal of overlying rocks (overburden). When collecting compressions or permineralizations, the size of the fossils themselves should govern the size of the block you attempt to excavate: a first of many constraints in reconstructing whole plants. Time spent clearing overburden is well worth it and highly preferable to levering out blocks pinned down by the rocks above. When forced to do the latter, bedding planes within the block can separate and this can easily damage any fossil material and, furthermore, you might never reach the end of the fossil.

Once optimistic that blocks collected in the field might yield abundant fossils, it is often best to split them further back in the lab. For compressions, this can avoid unnecessarily exposing delicate compression surfaces, and with permineralizations, reduces the risk of losing attached parts which might be only visible when the whole block is sawn or sectioned. When collecting on a small scale, or for initially establishing what is at a locality, it is necessary to split open the fossil-bearing horizons. In these cases the part and counterpart have to be adequately wrapped and protected prior to transport.

Excavating material from *in situ* locations must be carried out with due respect to the environment, the long-term value of the site itself, and within the agreed limits of your activities with the landowner. If considerable excavation is required the scree and cleared vegetation etc. should be tidied.

Excavating methods

Large-scale excavations requiring the removal of considerable overburden require contracting a mechanical digger. It is a good idea to explain carefully to the excavation company an outline of the proposed work before the driver arrives on site with the vehicle. An important consideration is whether the machine will be required to dig away overburden using a bucket or break up hard rocks using a hammer attachment. Also, be sure to instruct the driver to dig towards the fossil exposure very carefully, leaving just enough overburden to clear manually. Sometimes blocks of overburden can be removed with 4-wheel drive cars or trucks fitted with a power winch. Relatively loose blocks can sometimes be shifted with a tow rope, or an 'A-frame' can be constructed to lift, rather than drag, away the overburden. Loose blocks can also be shifted aside or down a slope with a simple hand-operated car-jack placed behind the block. For reasons of safety, such improvised means of clearing overburden must be considered very carefully beforehand.

An effective way of removing jointed blocks is with a heavy-duty steel crow bar (up to 2 m length), these can be remarkably efficient at shifting blocks up to a metre or two in dimensions. Smaller blocks can be removed effectively with a smaller crow bar (jemmy) or hand-held chisels. Loosening blocks with crow bars and gently levering them up and away is recommended, rather than swinging at overlying layers with a pick-axe or sledge hammer. Alternatively, bedded blocks can be loosened and then removed with a heavy lump hammer and chisel; the size and weight of these generally depends on the massiveness of the material. Once the overburden has been removed and before the collecting begins, the exposed facies should be clearly marked. This can be done by spray-painting, colour-coding, or marking with (coloured) chalks. Detailed field sketches, polaroids and photographs should be taken for orientating blocks back in the laboratory.

Depending on the type of study, blocks containing fossils may be split either in the field during excavation or taken back whole to the laboratory. Blocks containing compressions are generally split along the bedding planes with hammer and chisel or chisel-edged hammer. Well-bedded sediments can be split very precisely and in such cases compression fossils can be uncovered from precisely split blocks millimetre by millimetre. Relatively thin slabs up to 20 or 30 mm thick can be trimmed around the compression fossil with a clamp or vice fitted with blades. Initially exposing and locating permineralized plants is less straightforward, as striking the matrix surrounding the permineralized axis might not split parallel to the fossil and the specimen might easily shatter. Permineralized specimens are best left in blocks until sectioned with a rock saw in the lab. Having said this, it is important to make sure when collecting, that all the blocks containing a long branch for example, have been collected. If blocks containing permineralized plants are fragmenting during extraction it is essential to scrutinize carefully the broken surfaces to check whether permineralized material extends into adjacent blocks.

Bedding planes and blocks containing compressions and permineralizations might be easily broken or only held together weakly by the surrounding matrix. It can be very difficult to remove such material piece by piece and a good way of extracting the entire ensemble is to fill the cracks with 'super-glue' (see Appendix); this will dry in a few minutes and works relatively well, even if the material is damp (but not entirely wet).

Such glues are now marketed under the brand name of 'Paleo-bond' (see Appendix). This technique is especially useful if a vertical or overhanging surface is unstable and likely to fall to pieces if disturbed. By just applying the glue to the cracks means that not all of the fossil is contaminated by adhesive; this is an advantage over other methods such as embedding the fragmentary area in plaster of Paris or fibreglass resin which will contaminate material for geochemical study and ruin fine surface details for SEM. With larger fragment-prone blocks, particularly containing permineralized material, the whole ensemble can be painted with fibre-glass resin; this is particularly useful when there are relatively large cracks and gaps between adjacent blocks which would not be adequately filled by the super-glue. Fragmentary blocks glued *in situ* can be tapped out carefully or levered out with a crow bar or chisel. Levering is always preferable to tapping which can jolt pieces of the specimen away. Blocks can also be removed or cut away using a builder's masonry saw. These are also useful if plant fossils, particularly extensive permineralizations, are deposited within massive beds of hard sediment. In such cases, specimens near the surface can also be chipped away with a hammer and chisel but this is unlikely to recover specimens of any size and is also likely to damage the material extracted. Rock saws and the level of noise they produce can, however, bring the researcher a lot of unwanted attention. When hammering against rock and/or chisels, adequate precaution (eye protection, gloves, hard hat) must be taken against fragments flying from the rock or the flakes of metal from the chisel end or hammer. Higher quality hammers and chisels are preferred; a number of companies now manufacture geological hammers of different weights and shapes in which 'one piece' shafts and heads are made of specially hardened steel (e.g. Estwing, see Appendix). Not all plant fossils are found in consolidated rock and a flat-bladed knife or spatula can be useful for removing fossils from soft sediments, marls, and even soft limestones. Larger slabs or blocks of soft sediment which don't shatter on impact, can be cut out with a broad-bladed mattock.

All the material collected, especially cleaved compressions, must be adequately wrapped and protected as soon as possible: dirt and sand can spoil delicate surfaces and organic material such as cuticle can peel away from the fossil surface. Delicate material should be wrapped carefully in soft tissue or kitchen roll before further wrapping in newspaper or 'bubble-pack' for extra safety. Rigid stackable boxes are ideal for safely transporting wrapped specimens and for safely packing into vehicles. Parts and counterparts of compression fossils should never be 're-assembled' and then packed: the 'near fit' of the articulated surfaces when put together like this can wreck some of the fine details. Such specimens are always best packed separately with a wad of tissue to protect the freshly exposed surfaces. Complex blocks of articulated compressions or permineralized fossil plants, which have not been glued together, should ideally be photographed *in situ* and then each part carefully labelled and wrapped separately. Many localities yield material which is damp when collected and may split far more easily than when dry. Blocks collected in the field for splitting later in the lab can be rehydrated by placing the blocks between layers of wet newspaper for several days. This is especially useful for finely splitting blocks of compressions along poorly formed bedding planes.

2. Extraction of lignitic and fusainized plant fragments from unconsolidated sandy and clay-rich sediments

JAMES H. J. PENNY

The allochthonous lignitic, fusainized and charcoalified fragments discussed here fall into the general category of mesofossils, a term defined by Hughes (1994) as '...intermediate size plant fossils such as megaspores and small seeds..... requiring microscopic study'. The fossils which are recovered may be compressed or mineralized, and include small fragments of wood with cuticles, leaves, megaspores and seeds, as well as insect material. They represent a potentially fruitful but relatively untapped resource (Hughes 1994). There is no clear rule describing the size range of these mesofossils, but specimens usually range from around 0.25 mm up to a few millimetres. All specimens require microscopic study and SEM is desirable. Mesofossils provide useful clues to support and link megafossil and palynological evidence in the reconstruction of fossil floras and the characterization of the environments in which they grew. Angiosperm flowers recovered by Friis and co-workers are of particular interest (e.g. Friis & Skarby 1981; Friis 1984). Anthers of these flowers contain pollen which confirms the identification of dispersed semitectate pollen genera, while their floral anatomy has been used to give vital evidence in the interpretation of early patterns of angiosperm diversification. Furthermore, the new knowledge of fossil floral structure provided by these fossils gives strong evidence for a well-developed entomophilous relationship between insects and angiosperms before the end of the Cretaceous (Friis 1985). All the techniques involved require the use of fine sieves.

Sample collection

Suitable samples include unconsolidated sandy and clay-rich sediments. For example, Friis (1984) collected from fluviatile sands and clays from a kaolin quarry in southern Sweden. Friis *et al.* (1988) obtained clay samples from the Patapsco Formation (Potomac Group) USA, while Oldham (1976) studied samples from Wealden plant debris beds in Dorset, Sussex and the Isle of Wight, UK, which included siltstones and claystones. Oldham noted that the best specimens came from sediments that are 'soft enough to cut with a knife' and also explained that while plant material can be found in

most grades of sediment, coarse sediments tend to yield poorly-preserved specimens. Thus fine-grained sediments make the best hunting grounds, especially when they are poorly consolidated. Such sediments include lacustrine or fluviatile fine sands, silts and clays, plant debris beds and fine delta deposits. The fossils may be clearly visible in hand specimens. Plant debris beds often include larger material such as cones and logs (Oldham 1976).

Samples should therefore be collected from soft, fine sediments and also need to be excavated rather than taken from weathered (and possibly contaminated) surfaces of outcrops.

Preliminary treatment

A range of strategies is available but these are not universally applied. Oldham (1976) soaked samples of medium- to fine-grained siltstones and mudstones in 10 volume hydrogen peroxide for an hour to break up the sediment before sieving. Hydrogen peroxide decomposes spontaneously, generating oxygen gas bubbles within the matrix and consequently helping to force it apart. Specimen damage may occur, especially for larger three-dimensional examples. A milder alternative is to soak the samples in water, which disaggregates them effectively, if somewhat more slowly. Silt and clay-rich samples which have been allowed to dry in air often break down very quickly when placed in water. Use of hot water can accelerate this process. It is perfectly feasible to break up large samples by bulk maceration using covered buckets at this stage. The result is a disaggregated mixture of mineral particles and fossil material.

A method for separating fossils from shales was reported by Harris (1926), who 'immersed (shales) for a few days in strong nitric acid containing about 5% potassium chlorate' (Schulze's solution). The acid was then completely removed using running water and the shale then treated with dilute sodium hydroxide.

Sieving

When the sample is completely disaggregated it is washed through a fine sieve of mesh size between

Penny, J. H. J. 1999. Extraction of lignitic and fusainized plant fragments from unconsolidated sandy and clay-rich sediments. *In*: JONES, T. P. & ROWE, N. P. (eds) *Fossil Plants and Spores: modern techniques*. Geological Society, London, 9–10.

125 µm (Friis *et al.* 1988) and 250 µm (Oldham 1976). Large amounts of water should be used and gentle swirling of the contents of the sieve assist the flow rate. A domestic showerhead connected to the water pipe provides a constant gentle stream of water which helps to wash material through the sieve. Specimens are then recovered from the mesh of the sieve by further rinsing with water. It is useful to use nylon meshes, which can be bought in larger sizes and cut to fit purpose-built holders. A further advantage is to use sieves stacked in series with progressively smaller mesh sizes in order to avoid the clogging problems associated with overloading of very fine meshes. Patience is required and specimens should be removed from the sieve frequently. The most common difficulty occurs when the mesh becomes clogged with small sediment particles. Attempts to accelerate the sieving process by using physical manipulation should be avoided, because they may damage the fossils or distort the mesh, resulting in loss of the specimens.

Cleaning and demineralization

Where necessary, the specimens can be further cleaned from mineral material by acid treatment. Since hydrofluoric acid (HF) is involved, great care is required in handling this reagent.

Place the picked fossils into polypropylene or nalgene (i.e. HF resistant) containers. Add the HF, a little at a time to avoid sudden reactions which may lead to excessive frothing and overflow of the acid, until they are fully submerged. The time required for demineralization varies from sample to sample, but may involve up to three days in 60% HF (Oldham 1976). Lightly mineralized specimens may appear clean after as little as four hours in 20% HF. The acid must then be thoroughly washed out of the samples, either using running water or repeated water changes with centrifugation. Litmus paper is a useful test for complete acid removal. It is also possible to use a subsequent wash in hydrochloric acid (HCl). Drinnan *et al.* (1990) used 10% HCl for this. Once again, complete removal of the acid with water is required. The order of acid treatments should be carefully considered. Meso-fossil authors (e.g. Drinnan *et al.* 1990) report the use of HF then HCl but palynologists normally precede the HF stage with an HCl treatment (e.g. Penny 1986). This is done in order to avoid the subsequent formation of secondary fluorides such as CaF_2 and MgF_2. Where mesofossils are collected from carbonate-rich sediments it may therefore be advisable to use a pre-treatment with HCl. Palynologists use 50% HCl for this but lower concentrations are advisable where there is a risk of vigorous effervescence and consequent damage to mesofossil specimens. If HCl is used, it must be thoroughly washed out of the sample before HF treatment by using water. It is possible to apply this demineralization to the bulk sample before picking specimens, but this carries the risk of inadvertent damage to fossils, especially as bulk treatments tend by their very nature to be more heavy-handed.

Oxidation

This is not always necessary, for example for three-dimensional specimens which are destined for SEM study. However, cuticle fragments benefit from oxidation treatment. Concentrated nitric acid is added and the specimens left for a time which varies between samples. Oldham (1976) found a twenty-four hour period to be the optimum. Cuticle specimens can also be cleaned by oxidation in Schulze's solution (70% nitric acid saturated with potassium chlorate) which shortens the treatment time considerably in many cases. Oxidation is followed by washing in water to remove the acid, then treatment with 5% ammonium hydroxide for ten minutes to remove soluble oxidation products. Oxidation is a process which carries the risk of specimen damage or collapse. It is therefore sensible to examine specimens carefully before proceeding. After a final wash in water the specimens are ready for mounting and observation. Alternatively the specimens may be allowed to dry in air before examination. Specimens that have been dried often become very fragile and may curl (e.g. cuticles).

3. Extracting plant mesofossils and megafossils by bulk acid maceration

CHARLES H. WELLMAN & LINDSEY AXE

Relatively large fragments of fossil plants (mesofossils and megafossils) can often be isolated intact from their enclosing matrix using bulk acid maceration techniques. Such fossils are formed via a number of different preservational modes. Usually only gross morphological features are preserved, and anatomical detail is lost, although in some cases fine detail of conducting tissues, cuticles and spores is retained (e.g. Krings & Kerp 1997b). Nonetheless, certain modes of preservation preserve exquisite cellular detail, and the fossils can be analysed using light microscopy (LM), scanning electron microscopy (SEM), and transmission electron microscopy (TEM), revealing detailed morphological, anatomical and ultra-structural information. Some of the most spectacular and informative plant fossils known exhibit exceptional preservation of this type, and were isolated using bulk acid maceration techniques. Notable examples include Late Silurian – Early Devonian rhyniophytes and rhyniophytoids (e.g. Edwards 1996; Fig. 3.1), Early Devonian trimerophytes (Doran 1980), Carboniferous conifer leaves (Scott 1974), Cretaceous bryophytes (Herendeen et al. 1996), fern leaves (Alvin 1974), angiosperm flowers and fruits (e.g. Friis & Skarby 1981; Crane & Herendeen 1996) and Eocene angiosperm flowers and leaves (Basinger & Christophel 1985). However, such fossils are usually extremely fragile, and special techniques have been developed to avoid their destruction during preparation and analysis, and to ensure they survive long-term storage. Furthermore, comprehensive analysis of such fossils usually involves destructive techniques, in that they must be broken apart in order to reveal certain anatomical features, such that parts of the specimens are destroyed and many features that were originally visible are obliterated (e.g. Wellman et al. 1996). Consequently the fossils need to be fully documented as they are analysed, with careful curation of the acquired data (descriptions, quantitative data and photographic/electronic images).

Modes of preservation

Maceration involves the release of organic matter via acid digestion of the enclosing matrix (see Chapter 2). Plant fossils comprising recalcitrant organic materials that survive acid maceration techniques include adpressions and petrifactions; these form via a number of preservational processes, including coalification (with or without compression), charcoalification and permineralization (see reviews by Schopf 1975; Scott & Collinson 1983; Bateman 1991). The boundary between two-dimensional adpressions and three-dimensional petrifactions is taken as a reduction to 20% of the original thickness (Shute & Cleal 1987). This is approximately the amount of compression required to eliminate intracellular spaces from most tissues. Adpressions are not anatomically preserved unlike certain types of petrifaction (e.g. permineralization).

Adpression fossils form as a consequence of two inter-related processes – physical compression and progressive compositional changes resulting from loss of volatile organic components from the organic matter (coalification or devolatilization). The fossils are flattened and, although gross morphology is evident, anatomical detail is lost. Nonetheless certain features survive; for example, compressed sporangia often retain compressed spores, and conducting tissues and cuticles are often discernible (e.g. Krings & Kerp 1997b). Adpression fossils comprise organic material that is black, amorphous and brittle. Due to the fragility of the organic material they usually fragment during maceration.

Petrifactions comprise either volatilized organic material (preserved via permineralization), coalified material or charcoalified material. The reasons why fossils comprising the latter two are preserved uncompressed are unclear, but is probably because either the matrix is uncompacted or they have been physically supported by early diagenetic mineralization. Volatilized organic material preserved via permineralization is usually too fragile to be recovered by bulk acid maceration. However, coalified or charcoalified petrifactions are often sufficiently rigid to withstand acid maceration, allowing isolation of such fossils using this technique. In some cases the fossils are clearly coalified or lignified (not charcoalified). Their mode of preservation is unclear, although rapid desiccation and burial are likely (i.e. they were

WELLMAN, C. H. & AXE, L. 1999. Extracting plant mesofossils and megafossils by bulk acid maceration. *In*: JONES, T. P. & ROWE, N. P. (eds) *Fossil Plants and Spores: modern techniques*. Geological Society, London, 11–14.

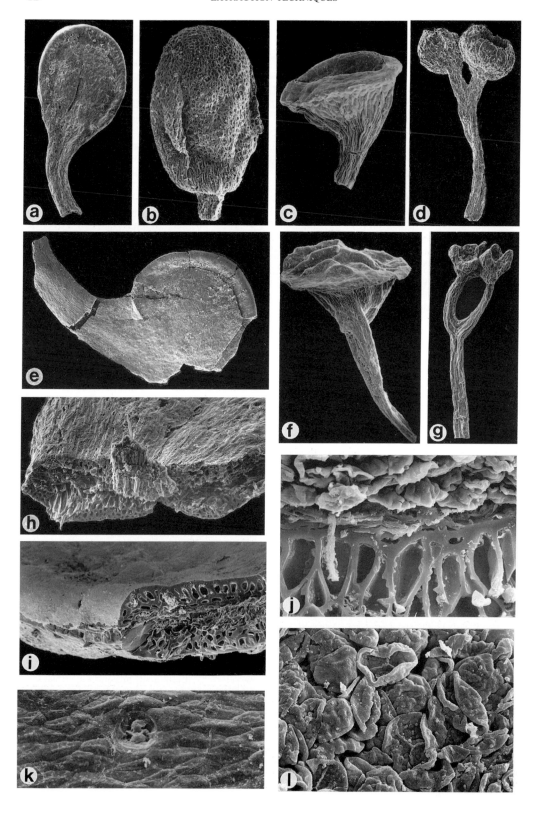

mummified). In other cases the fossils appear to comprise of fusain. Some authors believe that such fossils comprise pyrofusain and were formed by charcoalification due to burning prior to burial (e.g. Scott 1989). Others believe they comprise biofusain formed diagenetically via geothermal devolatilization after burial (e.g. Schopf 1975).

Examples of exceptionally preserved fossils, retaining anatomical detail, are interpeted as being preserved in a variety of ways. The Late Silurian – Early Devonian rhyniophytes and rhyniophytoids described by Edwards and co-workers (Rogerson *et al.* 1993; Edwards *et al.* 1994, 1995a, 1996b; Edwards 1996; Wellman *et al.* 1996, 1998) comprise sporangia, spore masses and axes, usually less than 5 mm in maximum dimension (Fig. 3.1). The fossils are preserved in loosely consolidated siltstones and appear to be coalified but are relatively uncompressed. It is unclear why they escaped compression, as structural support from diagenetic mineralization seems unlikely. Doran (1980) described the trimerophyte *Psilophyton crenulatum* preserved as semi-compressed coalifications in a secondarily silicified tuff matrix. The specimens are relatively large (commonly up to 7 cm in length) and spectacular, virtually complete, plants can be macerated from the matrix. The Eocene flowers described by Basinger & Christophel (1985) are preserved in a clay lens and are uncompressed, 5–10 mm in maximum dimension, and are thought to comprise lignite preserved by mummification. Co-occurring leaves are somewhat larger and are believed to be similarly preserved. Notable example of fossils reputedly charcoalified by wildfire prior to burial are Carboniferous leaves (Scott 1974) and Cretaceous bryophytes (Herendeen *et al.* 1996), fern leaves (Alvin 1974) and angiosperm flowers and fruits (e.g. Friis & Skarby 1981; Crane & Herendeen 1996).

Isolation techniques

Acid maceration techniques used to isolate smaller palynomorphs are rather harsh and tend to destroy larger plant fragments. Techniques are therefore modified so that the process is less destructive. The severity of maceration required is dependent on the extent of consolidation of the matrix. If the matrix is unconsolidated, or only very loosely consolidated, the fossils can be recovered immediately via wet sieving. In order to promote dissociation of the matrix it can be soaked in various agents. Basinger & Christophel (1985) used dilute hydrogen peroxide (H_2O_2) to disaggregate weakly consolidated Eocene sediments. Dr Andrew Jeram (pers. comm.) uses dilute potassium hydroxide (KOH) for several days followed by 30% hydrogen peroxide (H_2O_2) for up to 20 days to break down weakly consolidated Devonian siltstones and Carboniferous shales (see also Jeram 1994). Once released the fossils are washed first in hydrochloric acid (HCl) and then in hydrofluoric acid (HF) in order to remove any adhering inorganic materials. If, however, the matrix is consolidated, fossils must be recovered using the harsher technique of HCl/HF acid maceration (see below).

HCl/HF acid maceration protocol

Since the mid-1980s we have been isolating mesofossils from loosely consolidated siltstones of Late Silurian – Early Devonian age from localities in the Welsh Borderland. During this period we have gradually adapted an HCl/HF acid maceration technique originally developed for the recovery of palynomorphs (Wellman *et al.* 1996).

Because the fossils are often relatively large (generally in the order of hundreds of micrometres up to a few millimetres), we avoid excessive crushing of the sediment and process relatively large fragments of matrix (up to 2×2 cm). The rock matrix is digested in large (1 litre capacity) plastic beakers by first adding HCl (one day), then decanting off the HCl and adding distilled water (one day), and finally decanting off the water and adding 40% HF. We never fill the beakers above the 400 ml level when using HF as the reaction can be violent and the acid occasionally boils. Because relatively large fragments of matrix are treated, complete digestion and release of the fossils may take several days, and it is often necessary to change the HF several times. The residues are periodically stirred, but this process is performed

---

Fig. 3.1. SEM images of Early Devonian rhyniophytoid plant mesofossils, from a stream section to the north of Brown Clee Hill, Shropshire, UK, isolated by bulk HCl/HF acid maceration: (**a–g**) individual plants. Magnifications (**a**) × 20; (**b**) × 50; (**c**) × 60; (**d**) × 60; (**e**) × 12; (**f**) × 60; (**g**) × 40. (**h–l**) Sequence of images demonstrating features analysed following the fragmentation of the specimen illustrated in Fig. (3.1e): (**h**) fragmentation of the axis produces a cross-section revealing cellular detail of the conducting tissue and sterome (× 100); (**i,j**) fragmentation of the sporangium revealing details of the cellular construction of the sporangium wall and *in situ* spores (× 150 and × 475 respectively); (**k**) close up of the plant surface revealing stomata and surrounding cells (× 270), (**l**) close up of *in situ* spores revealed following fragmentation of the sporangium (× 750).

gently in order to prevent unnecessary agitation of the fossils.

After the rock has broken down, as much acid as possible is poured off taking care not to lose any residue. In order to neutralize any residual acid remaining with the residue, the beakers are repeatedly filled with distilled water, which is decanted once the residue has settled. This process is performed once or twice a day until the residue-containing fluid is neutralized (checked using pH paper accurate over the range of 1–6). We avoid any further treatment such as centrifugation and heavy liquid separation which might damage the fossils. Finally, the residue is washed through 250 μm polyester mesh (see Appendix 3). The >250 μm fraction is washed into a petri dish and can be examined under a dissecting microscope. If we wish to study the palynomorph fraction, we perform a heavy liquid separation on the <250 μm fraction. It is centrifuged for 20 minutes at 1000 rpm using sodium polytungstate (Appendix 3) dissolved in sufficient water to make up a solution with a specific gravity of 2.0 (Savage 1988).

A problem we encounter with our macerates is the large amounts of cuticle present. If we air dry the samples, the cuticle tends to drape around the other organic matter and glue everything together. We remove it by swirling the residue in a petri dish, whereupon the thin sheets of cuticle float for a longer period of time than the other coalified debris, and are pipetted off whilst viewing under a dissecting microscope. Once removed, in order to avoid desiccation and/or microbial attack, the cuticle is stored in 5% HCl in screw-capped bottles. If it is left to air dry, it desiccates rapidly and tends to fragment, curl up and clump together. The acid is added to prevent microbial attack. Once the bulk of the cuticle has been removed, the remaining macerate can be air dried in a petri dish, and examined under a dissecting microscope. Sometimes further HF treatment is necessary if undissolved lumps of sediment remain or if there is mineral matter still adhering to the fossils. Usually this only requires overnight treatment, and the acid is easily removed by washing the macerate through a 250 μm polyester mesh, whereupon it is once more left to air dry in a petri dish. The macerate is then sorted by viewing under a dissecting microscope and any fossils of interest are removed using a dampened fine brush and transferred to a clean petri dish.

When observed using SEM many of our mesofossils are found to contain large quantities of pyrite which can obscure anatomical detail. The pyrite can be removed by placing the entire macerate in a large beaker in a fume cupboard, and adding fuming 95% nitric acid for between 15 and 60 minutes. The reaction tends to be quite violent and must be monitored and diluted with water if necessary. After treatment the acid is removed by washing the macerate through a 250 μm polyester mesh and leaving it to air dry in a petri dish. However, we have found that preservation state often varies considerably, both between and within samples, and certain types of specimen tend to disintegrate during nitric acid treatment. Consequently we now tend to treat our mesofossils individually, if necessary, after initial examination using SEM. Nitric acid treatment of individual specimens is undertaken in a petri dish where it can be closely monitored and terminated when appropriate.

4. Small palynomorphs

DAVID J. BATTEN

Assemblages of small palynomorphs (spores, pollen grains, dinoflagellate cysts, acritarchs, prasinophyte algae and other organic-walled bodies <200 µm in diameter) recovered from rocks or unconsolidated sediments are commonly referred to in the literature as having been extracted by standard palynological techniques. Several papers and chapters in books have been devoted to methods of sample preparation including those by Gray (1965), Barss & Williams (1973), Bates *et al.* (1978), Doher (1980), Batten & Morrison (1983), Evitt (1984), Phipps & Playford (1984), Traverse (1988) and Wood *et al.* (1996). Along with many of the other publications cited therein, they provide a wealth of observations on basic technique and the variations that have been employed by palynologists. Reference should be made to them for additional information or more detailed discussion of aspects of the two methods described below that have been adopted by users of the palynological laboratories at the University of Wales, Aberystwyth. These are based on personal experience of, and preferences resulting from, many years of processing samples for their acid-resistant organic content.

For the majority of pre-Quaternary samples, standard palynological techniques are usually taken to mean, at the very least, digestion of the inorganic matrix in which the palynomorphs are embedded using dilute hydrochloric (HCl) and 40% or 58–62% hydrofluoric (HF) acids. They are also likely to imply several of the following:

(1) crushing of a rock prior to immersion in HCl;
(2) neutralization of samples after mineral digestion by diluting the acid and decanting or, more commonly, centrifuging several times;
(3) separation of any remaining mineral detritus from the organic residue using a heavy liquid (e.g. zinc bromide solution, $ZnBr_2$);
(4) oxidation (e.g. with nitric acid, HNO_3) to clear some of the unwanted organic debris associated with the palynomorphs and to lighten their colour;
(5) treatment with a dilute alkali (e.g. ammonium hydroxide, NH_4OH) to neutralize humic acids;
(6) ultrasonic vibration to disperse aggregations of particles, particularly those adhering to palynomorphs;
(7) sieving or filtering to remove finely particulate

matter so that the palynomorphs are present in greater concentrations and less likely to be smothered by extraneous matter when mounted on a microscope slide, hence rendering them easier to study.

Palynomorphs could also be routinely extracted from most Quaternary samples and modern surface sediments by this general procedure (e.g. Farr 1989), but they are not. Instead they are usually recovered by a technique that involves other chemicals including, typically, a combination of acetic anhydride $[(CH_3CO)_2O]$ and concentrated sulphuric acid (H_2SO_4). This 'acetolysis mixture' was used originally to clear cellulose, sticky outer substances (pollenkitt), and other non-sporo-pollenin matter from pollen and spores isolated from fresh and herbarium material, but it has subsequently become part of a standard method for recovering palynological assemblages from Pleistocene and Holocene deposits.

Although the two approaches to sample processing for small palynomorphs have been almost universally adopted, novice preparators will find that the procedural details described in the literature or passed on orally differ quite widely according to personal preferences, the requirements of particular projects, and the types of rock or sediment involved. Some methods are undoubtedly more effective than others in enabling the recovery of high quality assemblages that are truly representative of a sedimentary deposit. A considerable amount of knowledge and skill is required. Poor technique will lead to microscope slides that are not only difficult to study but also unsatisfactory because the data obtained from them will be unreliable.

For both methods, good laboratory practice is essential. All containers used should be carefully labelled, and all stages of the procedure for each sample should be recorded in a log book, on record sheets, and/or in a computer database. Retrieval of slides and unmounted residues is easier if the basis for labelling and cataloguing is preparation rather than sample numbers. They can then be stored in numerical (chronological) order of processing. In case of subsequent accidental damage to, or removal of, labels it is advisable to use a diamond 'pencil' to scratch preparation numbers on all glass slides and residue containers.

BATTEN, D. J. 1999. Small palynomorphs. *In*: JONES, T. P. & ROWE, N. P. (eds) *Fossil Plants and Spores: modern techniques.* Geological Society, London, 15–19.

It makes sense to process several samples at once to save time. A clean laboratory and great care is always necessary in order to prevent contamination of samples from the atmosphere, water or other preparations. Safety in the laboratory is paramount. Every potentially hazardous protocol and method of waste disposal must be discussed with the safety officer of the institute. It is essential that all requirements are strictly followed, and that emergency procedures necessary for dealing with accidental spillage of dangerous chemicals are understood before the extraction of palynomorphs from samples is attempted. Protective clothing must always be worn, and most of the chemical treatment should be carried out in a fume cupboard. This applies especially to HF, oxidation and acetolysis stages when it is essential to wear protective rubber gloves, sleeves and apron, and a face shield. The fan and water-wash system (spray pump within fume cupboard) should not be switched off at any time when HF is in use, no matter how dilute the acid. For more detailed comments on safety in the laboratory and treatments required for neutralizing commonly used acids and other chemicals, see Wood *et al.* (1996).

Recovery of small palynomorphs from sedimentary rocks and unconsolidated sediments of all ages

1. Possible surface contaminants must be removed; hence, core, side-wall core and outcrop samples should be scrubbed in water unless they consist of unconsolidated sediment. Drill cuttings and very small indurated samples may be rinsed in a beaker of water or washed on a fine-mesh screen.
2. Indurated samples are normally crushed to pea-sized pieces.
3. An appropriate amount is weighed and placed in a labelled, polypropylene beaker. Usually 5 or 10 g is sufficient, but more should be used if the sample is unlikely to yield much organic matter (e.g. sandstones, many limestones).
4. 20% HCl (more concentrated if preferred) is added slowly and the amount of effervescence that takes place, if any, is noted. For reactive samples, once the reaction has ceased and the fine particles have settled, the spent HCl is carefully decanted and fresh acid added. For samples rich in carbonates, this may be repeated and the spent acid poured away as many times as necessary. Depending on the composition of the sample, the amount of time allowed for settling before decanting may vary from 30 min to 2 h or longer (overnight). In order to ensure that fluorides do not precipitate when HF is added, the sample is then washed several (usually 4–5) times, preferably until neutral, by filling the beaker with distilled water and decanting.

5. Once neutral, most of the water is tipped away and a few (20–30) ml of 58–62% HF is added to the sample. After about 10 min the intensity of the reaction is noted. If there is no need to hurry the mineral digestion process, a further 30–50 ml of HF may be added and the sample left for several hours or overnight; the spent acid is then poured off. However, for most preparations, once the heat generated by the reaction to the first few ml of HF has reduced, it is possible to proceed directly to step 6.
6. Approximately 30 ml of concentrated HCl and 100 ml of 58–62% HF are added, and the beaker is placed in a hot-water bath at 90°C for at least 3 h, the time varying according to the size of the sample and the rate at which it breaks down. If it is not clear of all mineral matter after this treatment, the liquid is decanted and the process repeated. Once the mineral component has been removed the liquid is again poured off and the residue neutralized by washing several times as above (step 4). The sample is then transferred to either a Buchner funnel with a sintered glass disc (porosity 2) or a sieve.
7. The sintered glass funnel is fitted by means of a rubber bung to a filter flask with hand bellows attached. The sample is again washed with plenty of water. This ensures that the neutralization process is complete and at least partly removes any detritus smaller than about 8 μm in diameter, including clay minerals. It is then left in the funnel to soak in 20% HCl, overnight if time allows, after which the acid is drained off and the sample is again neutralized by flushing plenty of water through the sintered disc.
8. A slide is made of part of the residue for transmitted light examination using either glycerine jelly or a synthetic mounting medium. Prepared glycerine jelly is melted in a test tube and a small amount pipetted onto a glass slide. A few drops of the sample are stirred into it using a glass rod, and the slide is placed on a hotplate at *c.* 67°C to allow the water to evaporate. When the organic matter and glycerine jelly mixture is set it is covered with a glass coverslip.

   The synthetic medium used is Clearcol (see Appendix 3), a couple of drops of which are placed on a coverslip and mixed with a similar amount of aqueous residue. This is allowed to dry under the heat generated by the light bulb of an angle-poise lamp. Euparal (see Appendix 3) is used to seal the coverslip to the slide.

Following this stage, the quality of a preparation may need to be improved by, for example, removing some or all of the finely divided detritus and/or lightening the colour of the palynomorphs, making them easier to examine in transmitted light. The two most commonly used additional treatments are oxidation (steps 9, 10) and ultrasonic vibration (step 11). Either or both may be necessary.

9. Fuming HNO_3 is added to the sample (slowly to gauge any reaction) in the sintered glass funnel for a predetermined length of time (15 s to 2 min in the first instance). Alternatively concentrated HNO_3, Schulze's reagent (a saturated aqueous solution of potassium chlorate ($KClO_3$) and varying amounts of HNO_3) or sodium hypochlorite (bleach, $NaOCL$) is used, allowing longer reaction times. The main aim is to transform partly degraded organic matter into humic acids. The reaction is stopped by draining the acid through the sintered disc and washing with plenty of distilled water to neutralize.

10. It may be necessary to rinse the residue briefly (usually for only 1–2 min) in 5% NH_4OH, especially if it contains a large amount of woody matter, in order to neutralize the humic acids generated by the oxidation. This can also be carried out in the sintered glass funnel.

11. For ultrasonic vibration (at 50 kHz), the aqueous residue is transferred from the funnel into a polypropylene beaker which is placed in an ultrasonic bath for no longer than 2 min in the first instance. It is then put back into the funnel and washed with water to remove any fine (<8 μm) material.

12. A second slide is made in the same way as the first (step 8). After checking for content and quality, further oxidative, ultrasonic or other additional treatment is carried out as required. This may include sieving with nylon or polyester mesh screens to remove any unwanted fraction (e.g. <10 μm, <20 μm, >150 μm), and/or swirling or short centrifuging to clear away large, heavy particles. Swirling the residue in water on a large watch glass separates heavier from lighter particles which can be pipetted out. Short centrifuging also takes advantage of varying specific gravities and, hence, different settling rates; most of the lighter particles remain floating and can be decanted or siphoned off.

13. Once the required number of slides has been made, any residue remaining is stored. This is done by transferring it in water to a small labelled vial and leaving it to settle. Excess water is subsequently removed using a pipette. Glycerol (the reagent glycerine) and a couple of drops of saturated phenol solution are then added (the latter to prevent microbial activity and the growth of fungi) and the vial is sealed and stored.

Variations (sedimentary deposits of all ages)

The above procedure does not involve centrifugation to speed up the neutralizing stages or heavy liquids to separate any remaining mineral detritus (commonly together with 'large' wood fragments) from the organic residues. These can be used if desired, the latter prior to preparing the first slide and/or after oxidation has removed most pyrite crystals and other sulphide minerals. If sulphide compounds persist, treatment of the residue with 10% HNO_3 in a hot-water bath at 90°C for a few minutes should clear them. Whereas some types of oxidation may enhance the recovery of palynomorphs, as demonstrated by Eshet & Hoek (1996), great care must be taken not to destroy less robust components (e.g. Dodsworth 1995).

Many palynologists prefer sieves to sintered glass filters. Generally 5, 10 or 20 μm-mesh screens are used, the size selected varying according to the requirements of a particular study or personal preference.

Depending on the lithological composition of the samples, some stages may be omitted or must be repeated. For example, HCl and HF may have little or no effect on oil shales and coals apart from perhaps softening them, whereas these rock types generally require much longer in (fuming) HNO_3 than others if the palynomorphs they contain are to be liberated. Limestones may need very little or no treatment with HF. Sodium pyrophosphate ($Na_4P_2O_7$) may be used to deflocculate and suspend clays, which can then be decanted after centrifugation (see Quaternary section below), or removed by sieving or filtering. In some laboratories a tunable ultrasonic probe is used for 'cold boiling' organic residues (I. C. Harding, pers. comm. 1997), an effective method for clearing unwanted amorphous organic matter (AOM). A microwave oxidation technique has also been reported to help in this respect (R. A. Jones 1994).

Any oxidation or ultrasonic vibration of organic matter recovered from Holocene and modern surface sediments should be carried out especially carefully because delicate palynomorphs such as tintinnids and certain invertebrate eggs may be damaged or destroyed. To prevent this from happening, after initial treatment with HCl and HF it may be preferable merely to wash an organic residue on a fine-mesh screen to remove unwanted minute particles.

Palynomorphs that have been thermally altered to the extent that they are very dark brown or black may be unable to withstand ultrasonic treatment because they are too brittle. They may also be destroyed during oxidation, presumably because changes in the original composition of the sporo-pollenin have altered its structure. Opaque palynomorphs can be bleached using $c.$ 5% sodium hypochlorite (NaOCl) or hydrogen peroxide (H_2O_2) but, again, this can cause specimens to disintegrate.

Some palynologists, particularly those working on Quaternary material, like to inject colour, most commonly safranin, into their preparations. This can be useful if the palynomorphs are very pale or colourless and, therefore, difficult to examine and photograph, but the results may be uneven because some do not take up stain whereas others readily absorb it. An alternative to staining is to examine pale assemblages using interference and phase contrast or fluorescence microscopy, all of which can enhance features not readily seen in ordinary transmitted light (see Chapter 10).

Other mounting media may be used in preference to glycerine jelly or Clearcol. All differ to varying degrees in ease of use, refractive index and/or durability. None is better than the others. Clearcol is water miscible and dries quickly whereas some other synthetic media and Canada balsam require that the residue is first dehydrated in alcohol. Refractive indices vary; that of Elvacite, for example, is not as satisfactory as glycerine jelly, which may, however, desiccate unless the mounting of residues is done well and the coverslips are sealed to the slides with clear, hard nail varnish or paraffin wax so that no jelly is exposed to the atmosphere. Glycerine jelly slides that are well prepared may last indefinitely provided that they are stored flat, and in a room that is maintained at a fairly even, cool temperature. They are not suitable for use in tropical or subtropical climates unless they are kept in air-conditioned surroundings, because the jelly will melt.

All residues must be completely neutral before slides are made and unmounted material is stored, otherwise chemical reactions may continue and degrade or even destroy the palynomorphs and/or lead to the formation of crystals.

Alternative procedure for Quaternary deposits

1. A 1 cm^3 sample is commonly sufficient for the recovery of a workable assemblage of Quaternary palynomorphs (but see below). This is placed in a 50 ml polypropylene centrifuge tube and a *Lycopodium* or *Eucalyptus* tablet (see Appendix 3) is added (for determination of absolute pollen frequencies) followed by $c.$ 10 ml of 10% HCl. When effervescence (if any) has ceased $c.$ 20 ml more acid is added and the tube is placed in a hot-water bath at 90°C to speed up any additional reaction. Following centrifugation at $c.$ 3000 rpm and decanting, this procedure is repeated until there is no further effervescence. The sample is then washed in distilled water until it is neutral, again centrifuging to hasten the process. With each wash a little methanol is added to the distilled water in order to reduce specific gravity and surface tension; this applies to all steps of the procedure apart from 7 and 8.

2. About 10 ml of 10% potassium or sodium hydroxide (KOH or NaOH) is added to the sample, which is then placed in a hot-water bath at 90°C for 2–5 min (longer for peat samples) and stirred occasionally. On subsequent centrifugation, the colour of the supernatant is recorded on a five-point scale (from light to dark) as a measure of humification before it is decanted. Further washing is necessary until the supernatant is colourless.

3. If there is much coarse mineral or organic matter in the sample, it is washed through a screen with a mesh-size of usually 150 or 180 µm. The residue retained on the screen is transferred to a petri dish and checked under a binocular microscope for seeds, moss fragments, charcoal and other material, relative abundances being recorded; it is then stored wet in a glass or plastic vial.

4. If clay minerals are abundant $c.$ 30 ml of 5% $Na_4P_2O_7$ is added to the sample, which is then stirred and placed in a hot-water bath, again at 90°C, for 10–20 min, centrifuged and the supernatant poured off. This procedure is repeated until the supernatant is free of clays (normally 3–5 times), and is followed by washing with distilled water.

5. If the sample contains mineral detritus, it is treated initially with just 10 ml of 58–62% HF in case of violent reaction, followed by 10 ml of concentrated HCl. It is then topped up with more HF, placed in a hot-water bath (temperature as before) for 30 min to 2 h depending on the composition of the sample, and stirred occasionally with a polypropylene rod. It is allowed to cool prior to centrifuging and decanting. Further HCl and HF may be added, and the 2–3 h digestion procedure repeated as necessary until all mineral is removed, after which the sample is neutralized. The addition of methanol to the surface of the mixture prior to centrifuging helps prevent acidic fumes from escaping.

6. About 10 ml of glacial acetic acid (CH_3COOH) is added to the residue which is stirred, centrifuged and decanted. This dehydrates the sample, an essential prerequisite to step 7 because water reacts explosively with the acetolysis mixture.

7. One part (e.g. 20 ml) concentrated H_2SO_4 is added very slowly to nine parts (e.g. 180 ml) acetic anhydride [$(CH_3CO)_2O$] in a clean, dry, 250 ml polypropylene beaker, stirring constantly. Then 10 ml of this mixture (which has to be freshly made because it does not keep) is added cautiously to each sample being acetolysed, and the tubes are placed in a hot-water bath at 90°C for 2 min, stirring once after 1 min. On removal from the bath each tube is filled with CH_3COOH, centrifuged and the supernatant poured off.

8. A further 10 ml of CH_3COOH is added, followed by centrifuging and decantation to remove the soluble cellulose acetate products of acetolysis.

9. After further washing in distilled water until the pH is neutral (usually at least 5 times), the residue is transferred to a 15 ml conical centrifuge tube from which microscope slides are made and residues stored using the method outlined above for sedimentary samples of all ages.

Variations (Quaternary material)

This procedure is generally satisfactory for silts and muds that are comparatively rich in organic matter but, as for preparations of pre-Quaternary material, inevitably there have to be modifications to accommodate, for example, deposits containing very little, or practically nothing but, organic matter. For the former, samples much larger than 1 cm^3 must be processed. The cost of the chemicals involved in dealing with these may be reduced if some of the mineral component is first removed by sieving to clear sand grains and clay particles. The treatment of peats on the other hand may be largely restricted to the acetolysis stage.

Examples of lesser modifications to the procedure are as follows. After step 4 the sample may be washed again with 10% HCl. If it contains much pyrite or other sulphides, *c*. 30 ml of 10% HNO_3 can be added after step 5; the sample is then placed in a hot-water bath (once more at 90°C) for not more than 2 min, after which it is washed in distilled water. Should the residue still contain clay minerals, it may be resuspended in $Na_4P_2O_7$ after step 9 and sieved through a nylon screen of 5 µm mesh-size. The residue remaining on the screen is washed back into the 15 ml tube with distilled water and centrifuged.

To conclude, no matter which general procedure is adopted and how many modifications are made, it should not be rushed. It is essential that all steps are carefully documented and completed properly so that there is no danger of losing potentially valuable components of a sample. The results achieved on modifying the technique should be carefully monitored because the quality of the preparations and, therefore, the data generated can vary markedly and affect the conclusions drawn.

I am indebted to Lorraine Morrison for advice and comments on the manuscript.

5. Large palynomorphs and debris

TONI PEARSON & ANDREW C. SCOTT

Many sedimentary rocks contain 'large' palyno-morphs, a coarse organic fraction in the 180 μm–5 mm size range. These may be overlooked in normal palynological preparations, either because the rock was crushed too finely before acid treatment and sieving, resulting in the palyno-morphs being sieved out, or too little material was examined on the slide. This size fraction can contain a range of identifiable organic remains, including megaspores. Traverse (1988) defines palynomorphs as 'microscopic, resistant-walled organic bodies' and palynodebris as 'palynomorph-sized particles other than palynomorphs, e.g. wood fragments'.

Field collection and processing techniques

A wide variety of rocks contain large palyno-morphs. Plant and animal debris may be abundant in silty and even sandy sediments as well as in mudstones. Carbonates, cherts, volcanogenic sedi-ments and coals may all yield abundant palyno-debris. Palynomorphs are found in marine and non-marine rocks, although they are more common in the latter. As with the collection of rocks for traditional palynomorph preparation, rocks that are grey or green are usually more productive than those which are red or brown (Traverse 1988). It is worth collecting a range of lithologies from any given location. Even sediments that are normally unfossiliferous, such as coarse green volcanic ash, have yielded abundant palynodebris. Figure 5.1 is a flow chart showing basic procedures for processing large palynomorphs and debris.

Field collection

Sample collection is dependent upon the type of research being undertaken. If only one horizon is of interest, or the potential of a given facies for palynology is being assessed, just one or two samples will suffice. However, when undertaking large-scale palaeoenvironmental studies, a detailed and well considered sampling programme needs to be devised. Regularly spaced samples should be taken, changes in facies noted and additional samples taken from the new lithologies (Highton *et al*. 1991). Continuous sampling will give a very high resolution palaeoenvironmental profile. A minimum sample weight of 100 g is usual but in some cases samples of up to 1 kg may be needed. Cores are ideal for sampling. Weathered surfaces of the exposures should be cleaned back before collection and loose rubble cleared away. Areas polluted by modern contaminants should also be avoided. Fresh rock samples should be placed in bags with reference numbers safely and clearly included, ideally both outside and inside the bag. Bags may be made of either strong plastic or cloth. Aluminium foil can be used to keep friable rock specimens intact.

Friable horizons, such as plant debris beds (Scott 1978, Bed 20f), are problematic in that clean specimens must be obtained whilst avoiding contamination from adjacent horizons. To over-come this, large blocks of rock may be extracted from the outcrops for later sampling in the laboratory. This is done using spades, chisels or power saws. If there is a danger that the block may break up, it can be embedded in plaster of Paris at the collection site. Alternatively, the excavated block may be wrapped in strong aluminium foil (with the top, bed number and locality marked) for transport. In the laboratory, the foil-wrapped block is embedded in plaster of Paris and, when dry, sliced perpendicular to the bedding with a rock saw. Individual horizons can then be sampled. For coals, in particular, one half can be used to make polished blocks for petrographic study and the other half used for maceration.

For most preliminary investigations, between 10–50 g of sediment is sufficient. When processing coals, an initial sample of 10 g may be enough, but, for other rock types, up to 50 g may be required to obtain satisfactory results. If a specimen is of special interest, larger samples (up to 500 g) may be processed. Where specific plant organs are being sought (e.g. flowers or seeds) samples may be up to 1 kg, and on occasion even more. It is important to consider the time spent preparing and processing large amounts of material, compared with the advantages obtained from a larger dataset.

Preparation of samples

A wide range of processing techniques can be used to extract palynodebris, and the best practice can only be identified by experience and experiment. The three main categories of material to be

PEARSON, A. & SCOTT, A. C. 1999. Large palynomorphs and debris. *In*: JONES, T. P. & ROWE, N. P. (eds) *Fossil Plants and Spores: modern techniques*. Geological Society, London, 20–25.

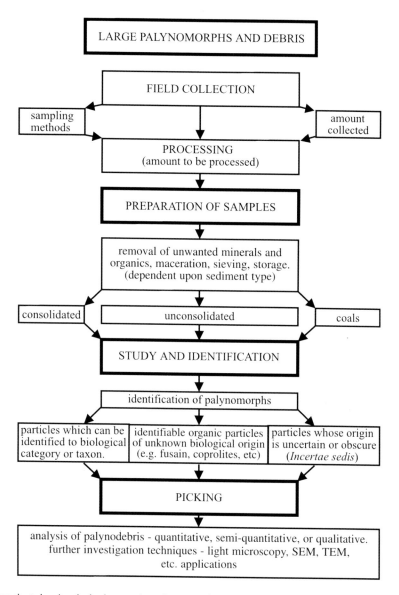

Fig. 5.1. Flow chart showing the basic procedures for processing large palynomorphs and debris.

considered are unconsolidated sediments, consolidated sediments and coals (Fig. 5.1).

Unconsolidated sediment
In some cases the organic and inorganic fractions can be separated simply by wet sieving. Nests of sieves are used, with the finest being 180 μm. If the sediment does not sieve completely, it may be necessary to dry it first and then use hot water to

assist the breakdown. This procedure may be repeated several times. To encourage the breakdown of clays and fine-grained sediments, it may be necessary to add 10% hydrogen peroxide (H_2O_2). If effervescence occurs, the sediment should be left for several hours until it appears to have broken down. The material may then be wet-sieved, and the palynodebris obtained gently rinsed a number of times in clean distilled water to remove all traces of hydrogen peroxide.

Consolidated sediment

Clastic sediments and cherts need both physical and chemical treatments. The rock should be crushed to fragments measuring between 0.5–1 cm in size. If large cuticle specimens are required, larger rock fragments should be processed. A few drops of 10% hydrochloric acid (HCl) are added to the sample to see if any carbonate is present; if so, effervescence will be seen. The calcareous rock should be placed in a glass beaker in a fume cupboard and covered with 10% HCl. When effervescence has ceased, any remaining rock fragments may be treated with concentrated HCl. Once all effervescence has stopped, the remaining HCl must be neutralized. When the matrix has broken down or dissolved, the residue can be wet-sieved. If too much clastic sediment remains, the liquid is decanted, the residue transferred to a polypropylene bottle and 40% hydrofluoric acid (HF) added. Ensure that the polypropylene bottle has a 'breather' hole in the lid. The sample is left for several days. The acid is then diluted, decanted and neutralized. After checking that the solutions are neutral, the wet residue is sieved. If larger amounts of material are being treated, organic residue floating on the top of the HF can be removed periodically by careful decanting. Again, care should be taken to ensure that solutions are neutral. The remaining clastic material may be left in the HF to be diluted and decanted at a later date.

Certain shale samples may require the use of kerosene (paraffin) to help break them down. The sample is completely dried and kerosene added; this causes rapid expansion of the clays. The resultant 'sludge' can then be sieved as described above.

Coals

For the extraction of palynodebris, coal fragments should ideally be 0.5–1 cm in diameter. Larger fragments require a longer maceration time. Approximately 10 g of coal is put into a glass flask, and 100 ml of concentrated nitric acid (HNO_3) is added. If the liquid turns brown within one hour, the maceration has begun, and it can be left for several days. If, however, the liquid remains clear, crystals of potassium chlorate ($KClO_3$) are added until crystals remain undissolved (i.e. the solution is saturated). If the reaction is violent and the mixture becomes very hot, the flask must be put

into a cold-water bath. The macerating liquid can then be left for several days. The acid mixture is poured off and distilled water added to the macerated coal. At this stage the 'sediment' can be washed in a 180 µm sieve and put into a large beaker. Approximately 250 ml of 10% ammonium hydroxide solution is added; the mixture is stirred (it should go dark brown/black) and left overnight. The mixture is sieved again under a running tap to obtain the final extracted palaeodebris. Lignites usually require much less oxidation time; low volatile bituminous coals may need longer treatment or the use of fuming nitric acid (see details of coal maceration, Bruch & Pross, Chapter 6).

Storage of residues

Residues may be stored wet or dry; this is a matter of preference and largely dependent upon the preferred picking method. Dry samples should be stored in air-tight glass or plastic bottles. Wet samples should be stored in air-tight jars in distilled water with a fungal inhibitor, such as phenol or thymol, or slightly acidified with HCl to prevent fungal growth. Short-term storage of the residues in refrigerators is also recommended. Remember that the fungal inhibitors could affect geochemical analyses. If material is to be studied geochemically the use of chemicals for the breakdown of the sediment and storage of the residues needs to be considered carefully (see Chapter 25).

Identification of palynomorphs

Figure 5.2 demonstrates typical examples of palynomorphs. Palynomorphs may be placed into three categories.

(1) Particles which have distinctive features and can be identified either to a biological category or specific taxon. This category includes mega-spores, some cuticles and a range of plant reproductive structures.

(2) Particles which are identifiable as organic and yield information as to their origin but are not identifiable to a botanical category or specific taxon, such as fusain, resin rodlets and coprolite contents.

Fig. 5.2. Scanning electron micrographs of organic debris in the 180 µm–5 mm range from the Late Carboniferous (d,f,g,i,j) and Early–Mid Cretaceous (a,b,c,e,h). (**a**) Fusain (fossil wood charcoal) showing characteristic three-dimensional anatomical preservation. (**b**) Charred flower. (**c**) Charred fern pinnule. (**d**) Arthropod (Euryperid) cuticle. (**e**) Plant (Conifer) cuticle showing epidermal walls and stomata. (**f**) Pteridosperm sporangia. (**g**) Pollen in (f). (**h**) Termite coprolite. (**i**) Pollen and spores in arthropod coprolite. (**j**) Lycopsid megaspore (*Setosisporites*).

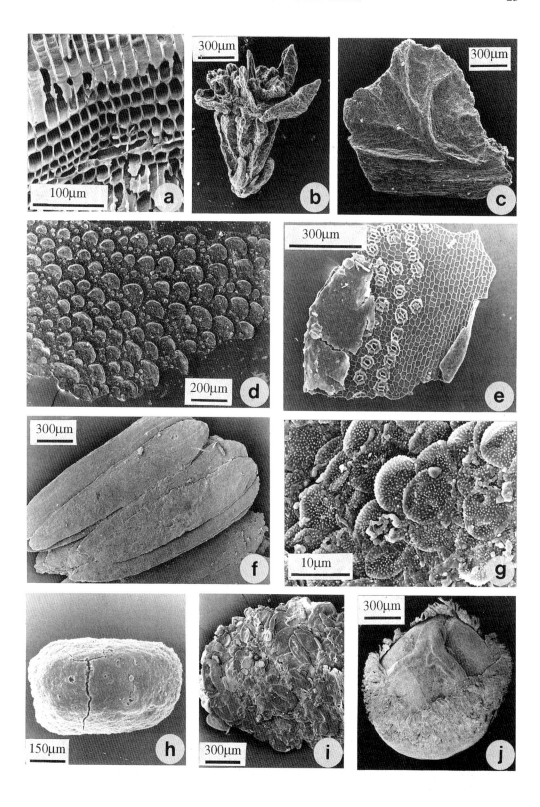

(3) Particles whose origin is uncertain or obscure; these are termed *incertae sedis* (Fig. 5.1). There is usually a mass of unidentifiable organic matter in the residue and this is termed amorphous organic matter (AOM). For a detailed atlas of organic particles see the three-volume work of Jansonius & Macgregor (1996).

Picking

Organic residues are best picked from petri dishes under a low-power binocular microscope using a fine brush. While some workers prefer to pick samples dry, others prefer to pick wet, as this prevents clumping of material. A small amount of residue is poured into the dish and distilled water added. Too much residue makes both searching and picking difficult. The contents of the petri dish should be swirled around several times and picked over for all identifiable particles. It is good practice not to discard any residue as some categories are easily overlooked and, with experience, samples may be re-picked and new specimens found at a later date. Megaspores, coprolites, fusain, etc., are best picked using a fine 00 or 000 brush and/or a mounted needle. The picked specimens are stored in distilled water or in a dry cavity slide. Specimens for examination with a scanning electron microscope (SEM) may be stuck directly onto a stub (see Chapter 12). Specimens for chemical analysis should be stored in distilled water without added fungicide and freeze-dried or air-dried. Cuticles are best stored in bottles of distilled water. They can then be removed at a later date and mounted on glass slides or directly onto SEM stubs. If only HF or HCl were used in the preparation of samples, further oxidation with HNO_3 may be necessary. In this instance, only a few hours of treatment is necessary (see Chapter 11).

Analysis of palynodebris

Palynodebris may be studied either (1) quantitatively, (2) semi-quantitatively or (3) qualitatively; therefore the type of study being undertaken must be carefully considered before beginning the analysis.

(1) Quantitative studies are numerical studies, whereby the actual numbers of any given category are recorded. All the recovered residue may be picked, all particles may be picked from a measured sample (e.g. 10 g), or a pre-determined number of particles of the category under investigation, e.g. megaspores,

may be picked with notes being made of the rate of appearance of new species. Quantitative studies may include only one category of palaeodebris or, alternatively, for a detailed palaeoenvironmental analysis, all categories must be recorded. The abundance of certain categories, e.g. vitrain in samples, often makes this impractical.

(2) Semi-quantitative studies assign 'abundance scales', where the distribution may be described as 'present', 'common', 'frequent' or 'abundant' depending on pre-determined criteria (Batten 1973). Again, either all the sample may be examined, or a pre-determined amount of the residue.

(3) Qualitative studies are an assessment of the preservation state, (poor, fair, good, abraded, etc.), and sizes of the particles. This type of analysis has applications when attempting to determine the taphonomic history of the palynodebris, especially whether it is transported or *in situ*.

Palynodebris studies can generate large amounts of numerical data for statistical analyses, and a degree of pre-planning is recommended before starting. There are a myriad of statistical and data analyses available for geologists; Davis (1986) is recommended as a comprehensive guide on this subject. Since the results will most probably consist of depth against components matrices, useful statistical analyses of these multivariate data might include: tests of significance, cluster analysis, principal components analysis, as well as a basic statistical description. There is also a bewildering array of statistical software packages available on modern PCs, with many of these packages not compatible in terms of data input. Pre-planning should include the following: ensuring the data acquisition (e.g. Image Analysis) and data processing (statistical) packages are compatible; structuring your data matrices or spreadsheets so that the data-processing packages can read them (ideally these data spreadsheets should also be able to be imported into word processing packages to construct data tables); considering the long-term electronic storage of your data.

Investigation techniques

Once fossils have been picked from palynodebris assemblages they may be investigated using a wide variety of different techniques. These techniques include: light microscopy, scanning and transmission electron microscopy, image analysis and chemical methods. Readers are recommended to read the relevant chapters in this book for further information.

Applications

One of the most important uses of palynodebris is for taphonomic and palaeoecological studies. Studies on palynodebris from coal seam profiles can add significantly to traditional palynological investigations (see Bartram 1987; Willard *et al.* 1995; Calder *et al.* 1996) where closely spaced sampling prevents averaging effects. Sampling of clastic facies has also yielded palaeoecological data (Batten 1969; Scott 1978). The botanical affinities of the organic particles are required to make precise palaeoecological interpretations. Megaspores from palynodebris preparations have been used widely to date sediment and coal samples (Batten & Kovach 1990). Megaspores are also useful for the forensic identification of coals (e.g. the identification of coal shipments to power stations). Plant fossils from this mesofossil fraction have been widely used in evolutionary studies. This is particularly the case with reproductive organs and disseminules such as flowers and seeds (Collinson 1980, Friis & Skarby 1981). Results have industrial applications. The development of three-dimensional models of terrestrial palynofacies for comparison with off-shore rocks of a similar age, gives greater predictive power for use in coal and oil exploration, and development (Highton *et al.* 1991).

6. Palynomorph extraction from peat, lignite and coal

ANGELA A. BRUCH & JÖRG PROSS

In palynological research, the application of different extraction techniques can lead to considerable differences in the results. In this chapter, we focus on the extraction of palynomorphs from peat, lignite and coal. Since these sediments have formed in a wide range of environments, are made up of a variety of constituents, and have reached different stages of alteration from their original composition, no universal processing method is applicable. Different samples may react differently under the same treatment, thus rendering palynomorph extraction a highly individual process, even if the basic techniques remain essentially the same. The directions given here are therefore not intended to be mandatory; rather they aim to provide an understanding of the principles of palynomorph extraction from peat, lignite and coal, as well as an overview of the methods described in the literature.

Principles

Peat, lignite and coal consist predominantly of the remains of vascular plants. These were originally comprised of cellulose and hemicelluloses (50–80% by weight), lignin (15–30%), and lipids such as cutin and suberin in the living plants. Under aerobic conditions all organic matter except lignin is depolymerized relatively quickly by biological activity. Lignin is chemically very stable and under natural conditions can only be degraded by white-rot fungi (e.g. Goñi et al. 1993). When anaerobic conditions exist, many organic complexes decompose only partly, forming peat, lignite and coal, dependent upon the degree of peatification and coalification to which they have been subjected.

Depending on the nature of the original material, peats, lignites and coals consist of a variety of compounds, such as lignin-related complexes, carbohydrates, fats, waxes and alcohols. In order to extract pollen and spores from these chemically very heterogeneous materials, a range of different methods is required. They are all based on the fact that the exines of pollen and spores, which consist of biopolymers commonly termed sporopollenin (Zetzsche & Vicari 1931; Brooks & Shaw 1978; Kawase & Takahashi 1995), are generally less susceptible to degradation through chemical processes than the other constituents. Relatively robust lignin, lignin-like complexes and highly-altered organic substances can be removed by oxidation processes. Alkali-soluble components (humic acids) are extracted using alkaline solutions, and others such as the derived carbohydrates (cellulose and hemicelluloses) are removed by acetolysis. Bituminous substances (lipids and lipoids), which may be strongly enriched in some organic sediments, can be dissolved by treatment with volatile organic solvents.

Oxidation

Oxidation is required to remove the more insoluble and inert organic components, such as those derived from lignin. Since their presence is a function of the degree of coalification the material has undergone, oxidation is not generally required for peat (Fig. 6.1). For oxidation, a broad variety of reagents is available (see Gray 1965, for a detailed review). In order of increasing reactivity, nitric acid (HNO_3), Schulze solution ($HNO_3 + KClO_3$ [potassium chlorate]), and fuming nitric acid are most often used. Other oxidants proposed by different authors include hydrogen peroxide (H_2O_2) (e.g. Poulsen et al. 1990), ozone (O_3) (Brooks & Elsik 1974), and combinations of different reagents, which may also yield good results. For example, Zetzsche & Kälin (1932) recommend the halogenation of higher rank coal with bromine (Br_2), which reportedly improves the resistance of pollen and spore exines to the oxidation process. However, such special treatments are probably unnecessary for most coals.

Generally, for a given oxidant the strength of the reaction depends on the maturity of the material, becoming weaker for more coalified and, therefore, more inert material. However, Smith & Butterworth (1967) in an analysis of the oxidation time using fuming nitric acid or Schulze solution found no general relationship between coal rank and oxidation time. This stresses again the need to treat each sample individually. A relatively new method which radically reduces reaction times is microwave digestion: here oxidation is accelerated by microwave heating and conducted at atmospheric pressure or in a pressurized vessel (R. A. Jones 1994; T. Jones, pers. comm. 1997). Oxidation can also affect the palynomorphs remaining in the sample's residue. If the oxidant is too strong or remains in contact with the sample for too long, pollen and spores will be oxidized along with the

BRUCH, A. A. & PROSS, J. 1999. Palynomorph extraction from peat, lignite and coal.
In: JONES, T. P. & ROWE, N. P. (eds) *Fossil Plants and Spores: modern techniques.*
Geological Society, London, 26–30.

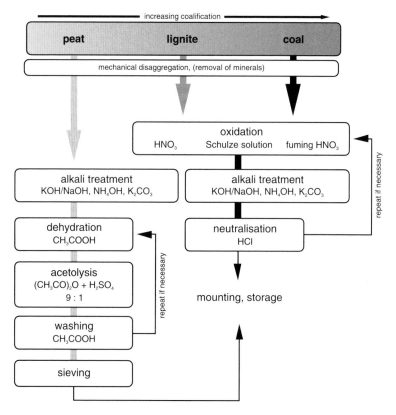

Fig. 6.1. Schematic flow chart for the palynological processing of organic sediments. It is necessary to clean with water between all processes, exept before and after acetolyis; but for greater clarity these steps are omitted.

other organic detritus. Moreover, different palyno-morphs exhibit varying resistance to oxidation (e.g. Smith & Butterworth 1967; Dodsworth 1995), and their sizes are also subject to changes (e.g. Butterworth & Williams 1954).

Alkali treatment

Alkalis are used to remove the humic acids which have formed during the decomposition of the original material, and to eliminate the alkali-soluble products, the 'artificially regenerated humic acids' of Traverse (1988) resulting from the oxidation. The humic acids react with alkalis forming water and water-soluble salts, and these can be removed by washing with water. For palynomorph extraction from coals, the treatment with alkalis follows oxidation. If the sample material consists of peat or low rank lignite, however, it can be omitted (Fig. 6.1). The alkaline reagents commonly used are, in order of decreasing reactivity, potassium hydroxide (KOH), sodium hydroxide (NaOH), ammonium hydroxide (NH_4OH) and, to a lesser extent, potas-

sium carbonate (K_2CO_3). As an alternative to alkali treatment, washing the sample with organic solvents such as alcohol or acetone–water solution to remove the oxidized humic components can be useful, especially if the residue has been over-oxidized (e.g. Gray 1965).

In order to avoid destruction of the pollen and spore exines, the concentrations of the alkali solutions should always remain below 10% (Faegri & Iversen 1950), and monitoring of the residue during the treatment is highly advised. Besides its potentially destructive effects, alkali treatment can also cause an increase in the size of palynomorphs (Moore *et al.* 1991). If the alkali treatment forms the final step in the extraction process, as is usually the case with lignite and coal, we recommend the neutralization of the sample material with hydrochloric acid (HCl). Otherwise, remnants of the alkaline solution can continue to react with the material in the stored residue and even in the prepared slide, turning the storage and mounting media brown, and potentially even destroying the palynomorphs.

Acetolysis

The procedure of depolymerizing the cellulose and hemicelluloses, as well as the intine remains and protoplasmic contents of palynomorphs, by replacing the hydroxyl groups with acetyl groups is commonly termed acetolysis, although to be technically correct it should be named acetylation (Gray 1965). The main reaction of acetolysis is as follows, with sulphuric acid (H_2SO_4) serving as a catalyst. When cellulose/hemicelluloses and acetic anhydrite ($CH_3CO)_2O$ react, the hydrogen–oxygen bonds of the cellulose/hemicelluloses are broken by the replacement of hydroxyl groups with acetyl groups. This converts celluloses into cellulose triacetate (($C_6H_7O_5$) ($CH_3CO)_3$) and forms glacial acetic acid (CH_3COOH) as a by-product. Cellulose triacetate is soluble in glacial acetic acid, and therefore can be removed easily from the residue (Fig. 6.1). Since cellulose and hemicelluloses decompose relatively quickly, acetolysis is only applied to Recent to sub-fossil material. As already mentioned for both oxidation and alkali treatment, prolonged acetolysis may effect pollen size (e.g. Moore *et al.* 1991) and can destroy palynomorphs (e.g. Hesse & Waha 1989; Charman 1992). Therefore it is advisable to keep acetolysis time to a minimum and to repeat it if necessary.

Methods

The following directions for the processing of peat, lignite and coal result from personal experience and are accompanied by comments on the methods of other workers, most notably on the comprehensive review of Gray (1965). They are intended as a general guide to possible procedure, and each method certainly needs to be modified and optimized for different samples. Frequent inspection of the residue after each processing step, especially after oxidation, along with documentation of all steps will help to obtain the best possible results.

As a first step in the extraction process, each sample needs to be cleaned, crushed and, if necessary, separated from inorganic calcareous and siliceous components. These processes (and also the hazards related to the application of the reagents needed) have been described in great detail by many authors (e.g. Phipps & Playford 1985; Wood *et al.* 1996) and thus are discussed here only very briefly. Samples containing carbonates are decarbonated through a treatment with HCl, the concentration of the solution depending on the reactivity of the sample (mostly between 10 and 35%). Whereas for samples containing only calcium carbonate treatment with cold HCl is sufficient, sample material with magnesium carbonate

(dolomite) has to be heated in HCl to ensure thorough dissolution. This is necessary to avoid the precipitation of fluorides during a subsequent hydrofluoric acid (HF) treatment. Samples with high carbonate contents may require a repetition of the HCl process. For the removal of siliceous components in the sample material, treatment with HF is necessary. Since HF is an extremely aggressive and hazardous reagent, extreme caution is mandatory in this preparation step. To dissolve silica and silicates, the decarbonated sample is transferred into polypropylene beakers, and 40 to 70% HF is added for 24 to 72 h. Frequent stirring will ensure that the material from the bottom of the beaker will also be thoroughly digested. The application of hot HF accelerates the reaction process, but also produces high amounts of dangerous HF fumes and should therefore be avoided, unless preparation time is a critical factor.

The amount of sample material needed depends highly on the nature of the sediment. To isolate pollen and spores from organic material, a few grams are sufficient. For the isolation of megaspores, which generally occur in lower concentrations and have sizes greater than 100 µm, larger amounts are necessary (20–100 g of lignite or coal; see Dettmann (1965) for a review on megaspore treatment). In accordance with the different amounts of sample material required, different amounts of reagents are necessary for the preparation. Generally, the samples should be at least fully covered by the specific reagent. After each preparation step (except for acetolysis), the residue must be cleaned with water to remove all traces of the previously used reagent. Depending on the facilities available this is conducted mechanically by sieving (e.g. Cwynar *et al.* 1979), sieving in combination with an ultrasonic probe (e.g. Wood *et al.* 1996), decantation (e.g. Barss & Williams 1973) or centrifugation (e.g. Colbath 1985). Mounting and storage of the extracted palynomorphs is described by Phipps & Playford (1985) and Batten (Chapter 4). Not only the chemical, but also the mechanical treatment (e.g. centrifugation, ultrasonic treatment) can affect the palynological assemblages, which may strongly influence the palaeoecological, palaeoclimatic and stratigraphical interpretation of the data. The advantages and disadvantages of each mechanical preparation process are discussed in the papers cited above.

In the extraction of palynomorphs from peat, lignite and coal a number of highly dangerous, i.e. poisonous (Br_2, CH_3COOH, ($CH_3CO)_2O$, HCl, HNO_3, $KClO_3$, KOH, NaOH), corrosive (CH_3COOH, ($CH_3CO)_2O$, HCl, HNO_3, KOH, K_2CO_3 NaOH) and flammable (CH_3COOH, ($CH_3CO)_2O$, $KClO_3$) chemicals are involved. Protective clothing, acid- and alkali-proof gloves as well as a face-shield or glasses and a fume hood are essential during all processes dealing with these reagents. Always check with a qualified department safety officer before processing.

Peat

The treatment of peat samples with alkalis and subsequent acetolysis usually yields satisfactory results. For more mature peats, where the cellulose has been partly or even fully decomposed, processing with alkalis alone may well be sufficient. In this case, as already mentioned above, neutralization of the residue with hydrochloric acid after the alkaline treatment is vital. The following treatment has been well tested, and commonly produces good results (Fig. 6.1; partly after Gray 1965 and Moore *et al.* 1991).

Treatment with alkalis

(1) Add < 10 % aqueous KOH to 3–5 g of peat until sample is fully covered and boil for 5 min in a heat- and acid-resistant vessel (e.g. glass beaker).
(2) Add water and wash thoroughly until washing water is clear.
(3) If visual inspection reveals cellulose in the sample or protoplasmic contents in the pollen, thus making acetolysis necessary, go directly to step (5). Otherwise add HCl (30 %) to the residue to ensure that alkalis are thoroughly neutralized.
(4) Add water and wash thoroughly several times.

Acetolysis

Since the acetolysis reagent can explode if it has contact with water, all tools used, as well as the sample, have to be thoroughly dried prior to this procedure.

(5) Centrifuge residue with glacial acetic acid (CH_3COOH) for dehydration and decant supernatant.
(6) Add the freshly mixed acetolysis reagent (acetic anhydride (($CH_3CO)_2O$) + concentrated sulphuric acid (H_2SO_4) in the ratio of 9:1) into the centrifuge tube while still hot and resuspend by stirring.
(7) Place in boiling water bath (1 min after Gray (1965), 3 min after Moore *et al.* (1991), 15 min after Phipps & Playford (1985)).
(8) Centrifuge and decant very carefully into the sink with a tap running.
(9) Wash residue with glacial acetic acid, centrifuge and decant.

(10) Add water and wash thoroughly several times. If visual inspection reveals cellulose in the sample or protoplasmic contents in the pollen, repeat steps (5) to (10).
(11) Sieving to extract coarse detritus is optional, but provides a good means of concentrating the palynomorphs (a mesh size of 150 or 200 µm will allow the passage of large palynomorphs).

Lignite

The processing of lignite commonly comprises both oxidation and alkaline treatment (Fig. 6.1). For lignite with very low maturity, oxidation can sometimes be omitted. This is best tested with a method proposed by Gray (1965), i.e. by placing a small amount of the sample material on a microscope slide, adding a drop of 5–10 % alkaline solution, and examining the reaction under a microscope. If the particles break down, turning the fluid dark brown, and possibly making some palynomorphs visible, no oxidation is necessary. This procedure is also useful during the oxidation process to examine whether the material has been oxidized enough, or if further oxidation is needed. The choice of the oxidation reagent primarily depends on the coalification of the sample material. For low maturity lignite, oxidation is generally conducted with nitric acid which can be used in different concentrations, temperatures and maceration times (see Gray 1965). For more mature lignite the application of diluted Schulze solution as a stronger oxidant is recommended (see section on Coal). The treatment we use for Neogene lignites from Central Europe is outlined below.

Oxidation

(1) Add 10–20 g of sample material to 100 ml of HNO_3 (concentration 25–30%).
(2) Leave until the lignite is partly disintegrated or easily broken (the progress of the reaction can be monitored by the microscope slide alkaline test of Gray (1965) as described above).
(3) Add distilled water and leave sample for about 24 h.
(4) Wash residue thoroughly with water several times.

Treatment with alkalis

(5) Add KOH (concentration < 10%) until sample is fully covered and heat up to near boiling, or less if a reaction becomes visible, i.e. if the liquid turns brown.
(6) Add water and wash thoroughly until washing water is clear.

(7) Add HCl (concentration 30%).
(8) Add water and wash residue thoroughly several times.
(9) Repeat steps (5) to (8) if visual inspection shows that the palynomorphs are still enclosed in lumps of amorphous organic matter.

Coal

Oxidation is the most important preparation step in the processing of coal. Medium rank and even high rank coal is commonly oxidized with Schulze solution (e.g. Gray 1965; Traverse 1988). If the coal is very mature, fuming nitric acid can be used for the same purpose. However, in this case subsequent alkaline treatment is not mandatory (e.g. Smith & Butterworth 1967), but the sample material should be halogenized with Br_2 prior to oxidation (see under 'Oxidation'). Schulze solution can be produced in different ways. In the so-called wet method, one part saturated aqueous solution of potassium chlorate ($KClO_3$) and two to three parts cold concentrated (70%) or fuming (pure) nitric acid (HNO_3) are combined (Smith & Butterworth 1967). Alternatively, $KClO_3$ can be added to fuming HNO_3 until saturation is reached. This procedure will result in a stronger oxidation agent (Wille, pers. comm. 1997). The so-called dry method is based on a mixture of potassium or sodium chlorate crystals ($KClO_3$ or $NaClO_3$) and an equal amount of coal, to which the two- to threefold amount of concentrated nitric acid is added (Gray 1965; Smith & Butterworth 1967). Even if the dry method reacts faster than the wet method, it is not recommended here, because the chloric acid ($HClO_3$) generated during the reaction can explode spontaneously if concentrations exceed 30% (see Smith & Butterworth 1967). However, the application of the wet method to pyrite-rich coals may also result in explosion. Thus in proceeding either way caution is mandatory. For medium to high rank coal the following treatment commonly leads to good results (adapted from Gray 1965).

Oxidation

(1) Add 100 ml Schulze solution to 10–20 g of sample material (wet method).
(2) Monitor reaction. In case of a very violent oxidation the process may be slowed by carefully adding water. If the sample reacts only slowly, leave it for 24 h or until testing with alkaline solution (see the section on Lignite) indicates that the oxidation has been completed. Oxidation time is highly dependent on the sample material and with Schulze solution reportedly varies between less than 5 min for organic residue in certain lignites (Funkhouser & Evitt 1959), and up to 8 days in bituminous coal (Kosanke 1950). When oxidation times are very high, replacing the Schulze solution every 24 h is recommended.
(3) Add water and wash thoroughly several times until washing water is clear.

Treatment with alkalis

(4) Add KOH (concentration < 10%) and heat up to near boiling, or less if a reaction becomes visible, i.e. if the liquid turns brown.
(5) Add water and wash thoroughly until washing water is clear.
(6) Add HCl (concentration 30%).
(7) Add water and wash residue thoroughly several times.
(8) Repeat steps (4) to (7) if visual inspection shows that the palynomorphs are still enclosed in lumps of amorphous organic matter.

If, after following the above procedure, oxidation does not yield satisfying results, it may be modified by increasing the proportion of nitric acid in the Schulze solution, by carefully heating the reagent, or by increasing the reaction time. A more powerful oxidant such as fuming nitric acid can also be applied. However, all these steps should be applied very carefully since they will provide apparently barren samples, if overused.

Part Two   Morphology

7. Surface preparation of macrofossils (dégagement)

MURIEL FAIRON-DEMARET, JASON HILTON & CHRISTOPHER M. BERRY

Dégagement is the term applied to the technique of removing sediment surrounding a plant fossil using sharpened needles. The necessary degree of force is applied by lightly striking the needle with a hammer or manipulating the needle by hand. The exceptional results obtained by Leclercq, who developed this technique to perfection as early as 1951, give ample evidence of the usefulness of the process.

Even when the greatest care is taken while cleaving slabs containing fossils, it is rare to obtain plant remains which are suitably fractured through the middle and adequately exposed on both rock surfaces. Whatever the state of preservation (impression, adpression or petrifaction), a fossil is most often exposed by a fracture which is oblique and much of the specimen may remain embedded in the matrix. When three-dimensional plant parts are under consideration (e.g. branching systems), the specimen may appear demonstrative and exceptional but will almost certainly not show the organization of the entire structure. To understand the spatial, three-dimensional organization of such complex structures, preparation of both the part and the counterpart is essential. It is, therefore, frequently the case that exhibited 'show pieces' are of little real scientific value because of missing counterparts. Both complementary surfaces must be similarly treated and compared in order to obtain the complete morphology. Even though this practice was much emphasized by Leclercq (1960), the procedure is still not often fully exploited. When applied to both part and counterpart of a specimen, the dégagement technique can provide the required morphological information for well supported reconstructions.

Dégagement

The principle behind the technique of dégagement is very simple. By using needles and a light, but well balanced, hammer, the sediment embedding the specimen is gradually removed and extensive areas of the fossil are progressively uncovered. With practice, the force applied when striking the needle with the hammer can be controlled exactly and orientated more precisely than when manipulating the needles by hand. A small rubber bulb, usually used for dusting photographic lenses, can be carefully used to blow away detached particles. Gentle, well orientated streams of air are less damaging than brushing the specimen repeatedly.

It is necessary to continuously observe the work with a dissecting microscope, sometimes up to a magnification of $\times 50$, especially when dealing with very narrow segments. The lack of visible contrast between the fossil and the matrix is often a problem, and this is still more acute when working under high magnification. The use of cross-polarized illumination is useful, and is preferred to repeated application of liquids such as alcohol that may disperse or decolorize the material.

The dégagement must always proceed towards the plant fragment (never away from it) with the needle disposed obliquely, at a low angle so as not to perforate the specimen (Fig. 7.1a, b). Deep excavations require a progressive approach by preparing a succession of steps in the matrix down towards the plant (Fig. 7.1a). For more delicate specimens, such as slender axes that are three-dimensionally divided, the sediment must be removed on a grain-by-grain basis using very sharp sewing needles (Fig.7.1b) or tungsten wire sharpened to a point.

Dégagement may, at first sight, appear to be a simple technique, but it is in fact time-consuming and calls for much patience, skill and self-control. It is actually difficult to apply successfully. The quality of the results depends on personal skill as well as on the nature of the matrix, the thickness of

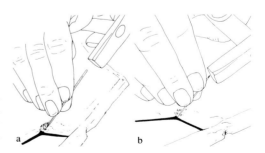

Fig.7.1. (**a**) Preparation of a succession of steps down in the matrix, using a triangular needle. Note the position and orientation of the needle. (**b**) Grain-by-grain removal of the matrix very near the specimen, using a sharp sewing needle.

FAIRON-DEMARET, M., HILTON, J. & BERRY, C. M. 1999. Surface preparation of macrofossils (dégagement). *In*: JONES, T. P. & ROWE, N. P. (eds) *Fossil Plants and Spores: modern techniques.* Geological Society, London, 33–35.

the sediment, the preservation of the specimen and the size of the particular structure being uncovered. Different sedimentary layers, even a few centimetres apart, react differently to the dégagement process and each case may require adjustment of the technique. It is therefore strongly recommended to practise dégagement on an unimportant specimen, from the same locality and horizon, to test the cohesion and characteristics of the matrix.

Needle preparation

The size and shape of the needles must be chosen carefully. For the large-scale removal of matrix, steel needles used for leather-working are the most useful (G. Weyland, see Appendix). These are triangular in cross-section and sufficiently durable to survive repeated hammer strokes. Commercially manufactured needles made of hardened steel (indicated by a blue-stained needle eye) are the most resistant. These triangular needles must be used with one of the flat sides in contact with the sediment (Fig. 7.1a) and the opposite sharp edge orientated upwards (Leclercq 1960). The edges of the triangular point are of great help when correctly used in dislodging heavily cemented particles. According to the characteristics of the sediment, the pyramidal points of these needles can be shaped to the appropriate length and thickness with carborundum paper or a fine-grained grinding stone.

Tungsten needles are most useful when preparation of a slender, delicate specimen requires a grain-by-grain removal of the matrix. Their preparation, thought not difficult, calls for a note of caution. Pure tungsten wire (see Appendix) 1.0 mm in diameter is cut into lengths (c. 120 mm). These are sharpened by etching in molten sodium nitrite in a fume cupboard. White crystals of sodium nitrite ($NaNO_2$) are heated in a small ferrous crucible suspended from a tripod above a Bunsen flame. When the crystals have melted a length of wire is held in heat-proof tongs and one end is heated in the Bunsen flame until it glows red hot. It is then dipped into the molten sodium nitrite. Here a vigorous exothermic reaction occurs and the tungsten wire is etched to a point. By practising the depth of dipping and rate of withdrawal from the molten sodium nitrite, the degree of tapering of the tip can be controlled and checked under a binocular microscope. After cooling the needles should be washed in water to remove excess sodium nitrite.

Safety

The fume cupboard fan should be on at all times when the needles are being sharpened as fumes are released. The reaction between the tungsten and sodium nitrite is highly exothermic and will therefore maintain its own heat. The flame can be withdrawn from the crucible during sharpening and reapplied only when necessary. Do not overheat the sodium nitrite – it may decompose. The BDH health and safety sheet for this chemical states 'May explode if heated'. Sodium nitrite becomes molten at 271°C and decomposes at 320°C. Therefore the heat of the Bunsen and that from the exothermic reaction needs to be balanced with the cooling effect of the fume cupboard fan. The latter can be controlled somewhat by adjusting the height of the fume cupboard door within normal safety limits. Protective gloves and full face mask must be worn. Tungsten needles are more brittle than steel needles so pressure should be applied by the hand only.

Serial dégagement

When dégagement is carried out on slender three-dimensional ramifications, extreme care is required to avoid unrecorded destruction of segments underneath. For example, while uncovering the ultimate lateral system of *Pseudosporochnus nodosus* (Berry & Fairon-Demaret 1997) it was necessary to dégage along a segment in one level of the matrix to discover at which point it gave rise to branches orientated downwards. Exposed axes and branching points were photographed and drawn by camera lucida before being picked away to uncover underlying segments. A similar treatment was applied to the counterpart. This technique is known as serial dégagement. All the photographs and drawings of each stage of the serial dégagement on both the part and counterpart were ultimately used to reconstruct the whole lateral ramified system. The best, classical demonstration of the usefulness of careful serial dégagement still remains the reconstruction of the three-dimensional fertile appendages of *Calamophyton* (Leclercq & Andrews 1960).

Consolidation

Specimens which are weakly attached to the matrix or which are extremely fragile, especially lustrous adpressions with cleat fractures (e.g. *Estinnophyton* Fairon-Demaret 1978 or *Aglosperma* Hilton & Edwards 1996), are particularly difficult to work on. The last sedimentary particles overlying the specimen often tightly adhere to it. These cannot be detached without breaking the very brittle layer of carbonaceous matter along regular and predetermined fracture planes. Unfortunately, by the end of the process, there remains only the faint impression surface below the original carbonaceous compression. As a very last resort, such a specimen may be reinforced during and after dégagement with an adhesive solution. It is recommended to first test the reinforcement technique on an unimportant fossil. Paraloid B27 consolidant granules (see Appendix) are dissolved in acetone to make a weak solution. The right concentration of granules is reached when a drop of the solution allowed to dry does not remain tacky. The dilute mixture is then added to the matrix surrounding the fossil one drop at a time, using a fine paint brush, until the glue can be seen seeping towards the fossil material. This procedure ensures that the upper surface of the fossil remains glue free while the specimen is held on the rock from underneath. In the case of accidentally applying the solution directly to the fossil, the glue can be removed by the addition of pure acetone applied to the surrounding matrix. The same technique can also be used for reinforcing more consolidated fossils after dégagement to ensure optimal preservation of the finished specimen.

Disintegration of the organic matter can also be overcome by applying a few drops of a highly diluted solution of cellulose acetate in amyl acetate on the area. The correct viscosity of the liquid is attained by progressively adding amyl acetate until a drop of the mixture can slide along a needle and spread evenly before hardening. When it is necessary to get rid of the glue, it can be removed from the specimen by carefully flooding with amyl acetate.

The above adhesive mixtures are used when actually working on specimens. In order to prevent desiccation and crumbling of fossils and to retain the original colour whilst in the field, it has proved most successful to spray the freshly exposed surfaces with a 10% solution of gum-Arabic in water (sterilized with xylol or phenol, Leclercq 1960). This mixture dries quickly and does not prevent further preparation of the specimens, as opposed to commercial transparent contact resins.

Conclusions

Dégagement is a traditional palaeobotanical technique and may appear obsolete when compared with apparently more sophisticated methods of surface excavation such as vibrotools or air abrasives. These allow removal of matrix at high speed but are nearly always too aggressive and usually result in destruction of parts of the fossil. This is especially the case for vibrotools which may easily bring about the fragmentation of plant fossils. When used carefully, dégagement is a highly effective technique which may be applied to specimens that might not survive other higher risk preparations.

8. Plant and spore compression in sediments

BILL W. CHALONER

The two most common forms of preservation of plant fossils are permineralizations and compression/impression fossils (Schopf 1975). In the former, mineral matter in solution diffuses through the plant tissue during early diagenesis, and much of the detailed anatomical structure of the tissue may be preserved in three dimensions (see Section 4, Ultrastructure). Compression fossils, on the other hand, are formed when part of a plant (leaf, stem, seed, pollen grain or spore) is buried in sediment, without significant deposition of mineral matter within the tissue. The plant material then undergoes varying degrees of flattening. This results in part from collapse of the plant tissue as it biodegrades, and in part from the compaction of the enclosing matrix under the load of sediment above. Such of the residual organic matter of the original tissue which has not been biologically degraded will then become altered to coal, to an extent depending largely on the depth of burial. This process of coalification involves loss of volatile constituents and a corresponding increase in the percentage of carbon in the residue. The whole process may be further complicated by matrix entering cavities (for example, a pith cavity in a stem) and the sediment infill becoming enclosed in the compressed plant tissue and subsequently becoming indurated to form a sedimentary 'cast' of that cavity. This chapter is concerned with the events involved in this compression process and its results.

Plant compression fossils will normally be revealed by fracture of the rock matrix exposing the coalified plant or organ lying more or less in the bedding plane (Fig. 8.1, A to C). Plant microfossils such as spores and dinoflagellate cysts represent a special case of such compression fossils. They are normally investigated by disaggregating or dissolving the matrix and studying the individual spores extracted in this way. Since individual spores and similar microfossils behave very differently from larger plant organs, they are treated separately here.

Compression of plant macrofossils

Walton (1936) published a pioneering paper describing an experimental study of how compression fossils form, but gave no details of his experimental methods. Harris (1974), writing about compression processes in spores, said of Walton's work: 'He told me that he had compressed various solid plant organs – plant stems, apples and the like in wet sand in a power press so constructed as to allow surplus water to drain away'. Rex & Chaloner (1983) attempted an experimental study of the compression process, using models of plant material in sponge and other substances. These were compressed in a device which exposed the vertical dimension of the changes occurring during the process (see also Rex 1986a, b). Rex (1985) also studied sedimentary infill of real plant organs in a series of flume experiments. Some of the results of these studies are reviewed here.

Briggs (1990) and Briggs & Williams (1981) review how the compression process influences the appearance of soft-bodied animal fossils, compare their behaviour with that of plant material and discuss the problems of restoring their original three-dimensional form from the compressed state.

Some of the terminology of plant compression fossils is set out in Fig. 8.1. This diagrammatic representation shows a leaf with hairs and a midrib on the lower surface buried in sediment (A1) and after collapse of the tissue and compaction of the sediment (A2). The plant tissue (now coal) has normally undergone far more compression than the matrix. The fracture plane which reveals the fossil within the matrix (Fig. 8.1, B1, B2) will commonly pass over one surface of the coaly layer representing the plant tissue, leaving the film of coal on one surface as a compression fossil (Fig. 8.1, B2). The other half of the fossil (the 'counterpart') generally lacking coaly matter, is here regarded as an impression fossil (Fig. 8.1, B1) although, as in that figure, it may retain the coaly residue of hairs held in the matrix. The combined specimens – the coalified 'compression fossil' plus the other half of the matrix, with its impression of the plant on the matrix surface, has been called an 'adpression fossil' by Shute & Cleal (1987). Sometimes the fracture plane revealing the compression may pass more or less through the residue of the plant, leaving coaly material on both part and counterpart (a cleaved compression, Fig. 8.1 C1, C2).

At some stage after the matrix has become more or less indurated, but before the fossil is exposed by fracture, all the coaly material (or uncoalified organic matter of the fossil) may be removed. This

CHALONER, W. 1999. Plant and spore compression in sediments. *In*: JONES, T. P. & ROWE, N. P. (eds) *Fossil Plants and Spores: modern techniques*. Geological Society, London, 36–40.

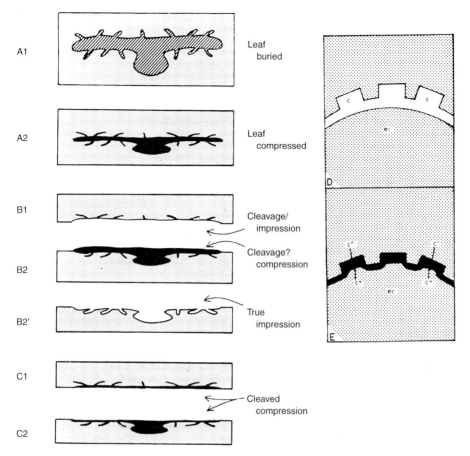

Fig. 8.1. The formation of compression and impression fossils. (**A1, A2**) A leaf with hairs and a midrib on the lower surface, buried in sediment undergoes collapse and compression. (**B1, B2**) The fossil is exposed by a cleavage plane running along the upper surface of the compressed and coalified leaf. Small topographic features, such as the hairs on the upper surface, may remain in the matrix. (**B1**) is commonly termed an impression. The term 'cleavage impression' used here emphasizes that this face was exposed by a fracture rather than by total removal of the organic matter, as in (**B2′**), which is a 'true impression'. This preserves all the details of the original surface microtopography and may be obtained by burning off the coaly matter forming the compression fossil shown in (**B2**). (**C1,C2**) Here the cleavage plane has passed through the coaly matter, giving two complementary 'cleaved compressions'. (**D, E**) This represents a cortical cylinder of a lycopod buried in sediment. Sediment filling the cortical cavity (endocortical infill) is shown by 'ei'; on collapse of the tissue and under compression, the endocortical cast (ec) shows on its outer surface features corresponding to the outer topography of the stem, despite the fact that the inner face of the original cavity was smooth (as at ei). c is the leaf base cushion; c′ is the outer surface of the compressed leaf base cushion; c″ is the bulge on the matrix surface of the endocortical cast corresponding to the cushion on the original outer surface. From Chaloner & Collinson (1975a, fig. 1) and Rex & Chaloner (1983, text-fig. 6.)

may occur very early on by biodegradation, or later by *in situ* pyrolysis in the event of deep burial, or simply by oxidation within the weathering zone if close to the surface. The effect of this removal at whatever stage is that the site of the plant material remains only as a break, a plane of weakness within the matrix, to be revealed by a fracture producing two complementary impression fossils. If there is still residual coaly material obscuring the surface of

the impression, this may be burnt off by combustion at high temperature (Chaloner & Gay 1972) to leave a clean impression on the matrix (Fig. 8.1, B2′).

Those authors report on a compression fossil giving very high fidelity replicas, which had been burnt off naturally in a coal-mine tip-heap fire which had probably occcurred spontaneously. Such 'naturally occurring' combustion of the coal of the compression fossil probably gives ideal conditions for burning off. Crookall (1929) describes burning off the coaly layer of a compression fossil to yield a clean impression surface: 'Examples of *Sigillaria* and *Lepidodendron* are often found in which the scars are obscured by a thin coaly layer: they are often excellently preserved, and only require slow heating in a red fire to burn off the coal'. I have used this means myself, and can confirm its efficacy for those with that facility available ! Such burning off of the coaly layer can certainly be achieved in a mini-furnace under laboratory conditions, but temperature and timing would need to be determined by trial and error for any particular type of material. T. Jones (pers. comm. 1997) suggests 500°C for 20 min.

Detail of the remaining impression fossil surface (its 'microtopography') may then be obtained by preparing a replica of the original plant surface. This is done by pouring latex or cellulose acetate onto the impression surface, allowing it to dry and pulling it off the matrix surface. The replica may then be coated and examined under SEM (Chaloner & Gay 1972, give details of sources). The study of such impression fossil surfaces shows that the detail of the fossil microtopography has undergone less distortion in the vertical plane than the overall collapse of the whole organ (Chaloner *et al.* 1978). Casts of stomatal pits may thus survive in the matrix surface while the stem on which they are present has been reduced to a ribbon of coal.

A more complex type of compression fossil may be produced if there is some infilling of a cavity within the plant tissue before or during the process of diagenesis. Such an infill eventually forms a 'natural cast' of the cavity within which it forms. One of the commonest examples is the pith cast of the Carboniferous stems of the genus *Calamites*. The cylinder of woody tissue which enclosed the sediment to produce such a pith cast is normally far more compressible than the sediment itself. The resulting margin of coal, representing the compressed plant tissue then lies at either side of the pith infill in the fractured matrix, a so-called 'compression rim', a term coined by Walton (1936). An example of this is shown in text-fig. 7 of Rex & Chaloner (1983). The width of the stem outline and of the pith cast (i.e. the horizontal dimension of the plant fossil) appears from experimental evidence to remain unaltered during the compression process.

Further complexity in the shape of plant compression fossils results from the interaction of the outer topography of, say, a stem with the surface of the matrix infilling a cavity within it. This is seen in the so-called endocortical casts of many Palaeozoic lycopod stems (Fig. 8.1, D, E). These are formed when the cortical cavity of the stem fills with sediment (Fig. 8.1, D). On compression the outer surface of the endocortical cast may then show a weak version of the original outer stem surface (Fig. 8.1, E, ec) with its leaf cushions (c in D), even though the inner face of the original cavity was completely smooth. This results in an endocortical cast showing a deceptive similarity to the original outer surface, in having a spiral series of blurred leaf cushions (c″ in E, formed as matrix moved into the collapsing leaf base cushion). Berry & Edwards (1995) describe a closely analagous process occurring in a fossil stem where no cavity existed, and no sedimentary infill therefore occurred. On collapse and coalification of the tissue, the topography of the upper surface was reflected in the sediment juxtaposed to the lower surface (just as in the endocortical cast described above). This produces what they describe as 'false leaf bases' in the resulting 'compound cleaved impression', where leaf bases from the upper surface appear as positive features on the sedimentary impression of the lower surface. These are just some of the many complexities of the variations in form which may result as plant tissue undergoes collapse and compression within a matrix.

Fracture pathways

The pathway taken by the fracture through the matrix which reveals a compression fossil can also have a significant effect on its appearance. Leaves borne on a stem, or the cone scales (sporophylls) forming a lepidodendrid fructification, produce planes of weakness which may offer alternative pathways of fracture of the matrix, to reveal different versions of the fossil. Leaves standing at an obtuse angle to a stem surface (Fig. 8.2, A, B) may be removed in the counterpart specimen of matrix, leaving 'false leaf scars' on the compressed stem surface (Fig. 8.2A). Only the leaves lying at either side of the compressed stem reveal what has happened. Leaves lying more nearly parallel to the stem surface will offer a fracture pathway which may then run more or less along those leaves, and so conceal the stem surface below (Fig. 8.2, C, D). Similarly, alternative fracture planes of lycopod cones may reveal either the outer surface (Fig. 8.2E, above) or pass through the centre of the cone, and reveal the axis surface and the sporangia attached to the sporophylls (Fig. 8.2E, below). In cases such as this, where there is considerable three-dimensional complexity to the compression fossil, slow and painstaking removal of the matrix by dégagement (Chapter 7) will reveal far more than is visible on the fracture surface.

An additional technique for studying compression fossils is to section the matrix containing

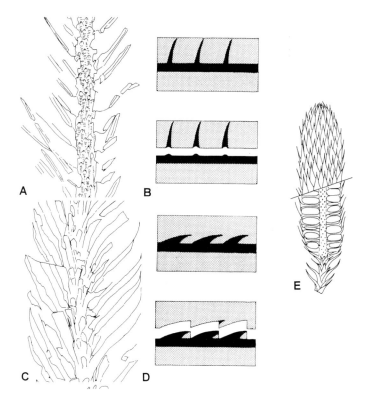

Fig. 8.2. Illustration of the effect of alternative pathways of the fracture plane on the appearance of compression fossils. (**A**), (**C**) compression fossils of leafy shoots of two species of *Lepidodendron*. (**A,B**) *Lepidodendron wortheni* Lesquereux has leaves which were straight and relatively rigid and protruded from the stem at a steep angle. (**C,D**) *Lepidodendron simile* Kidston, has sigmoid leaves which leave the stem at a more acute angle, with the apices turning more or less parallel to the stem. In (A) the fracture plane truncates the fossil leaves near their bases and runs along the stem surface producing 'false leaf scars', caused by that fracture, (B). In (C) the fracture plane has run largely along the leaf surfaces, which then obscure the stem surface beneath, (D). (**E**) *Lepidostrobus variabilis* L & H, showing two possible fracture planes which may expose such a compression fossil; (above) the fracture has run more or less over the surface of the sporophyll laminae, presenting what is in effect the original outer surface of the cone; (below) a fracture plane which has cleaved through the cone, running along the surface of the sporangia and across the cone axis, which shows false scars of the sporophylls. These two views of the cone may occur in different parts of the same specimen, as the fracture jumps from one plane of weakness to the other. From Rex & Chaloner 1983, Chaloner & Collinson 1975*b*.

the fossil in the vertical plane. The cut face may then be examined, to see the shape of the compressed plant in that dimension. If a particular plant compression fossil has been exposed on the fracture plane, the part and counterpart may be photographed and the two then stuck back together again, using Araldite or other synthetic resin. The restored compressed fossil may then be sectioned in the plane perpendicular to that of the original fracture, revealing the form of the compressed plant in the matrix. This procedure has been successfully applied to Carboniferous lycopod and pteridosperm leaves by Rex (1986*a*) and some unexpected features of the compression process elucidated in that way.

Spore compression

The properties of the tough and relatively rigid exine of fossil spores and pollen are significantly different from those of bulk cellular plant tissue, even those thought of as being relatively rigid, such as wood. On burial in sediment, while the cell contents of spores (the term is used here used to include pollen) will rapidly degrade, the outer spore wall in the form of the exine will commonly survive with little chemical alteration. It then behaves in a way which has been compared with the flattening of a table-tennis- or tennis-ball, undergoing compression, folding and even tearing in a very different way from the collapse of larger plant organs.

As with plant tissue compression, relatively little consideration has been given to the process of collapse and folding of fossil spores. Indeed, most palynologists have generally regarded such folds and tears merely as a distraction from recognizing the true nature of their fossil. As Harris (1974) aptly observed, 'I had previously thought very little about the compression of spores except to regard the secondary distortions as a nuisance, to be recognised as distortions and so to be avoided as pitfalls and to be eliminated from descriptions. I had never welcomed them as useful evidence as I try to do here'.

In that paper Harris described a series of experiments on the compression of various 'artificial spores' in the form of hollow spheres made from synthetic materials. His aim was to explain the wide range of shapes seen in the originally spherical pollen of a Jurassic gymnosperm and to elucidate the factors which control folding and splitting of spore walls in the course of compression. One of a number of significant items that he was able to show, was that the maximum diameter of a flattened (and distorted) spore could be up to 140% of the original diameter. A few other authors have discussed folding and compression phenomena seen in fossil spores (e.g. Potonié 1962; Clayton 1972; Guy-Ohlson *et al.* 1988) but Harris is the only one to have carried out such experiments.

Potonié (1962) had published earlier on the effect of folding in fossil spores and pollen which he believed could be attributed to the process of fossilization. He calls these features 'secondary folds' to distinguish them from any feature of the original spore. He went on to set out what he called the 'rules' governing the formation of such folds. He describes six distinct patterns of secondary folds which may ensue from the collapse of a more or less sub-spherical pteridophyte spore, as it flattens to a circular disc. He also points out that a more or less spherical spore can form a flattened disc without any secondary folding or tearing if the original spore wall was sufficiently thick.

Many original structural features of the spore, such as an equatorial thickening (a cingulum) will have a significant effect on the way in which it undergoes secondary folding. Such an equatorial ridge will affect the orientation that the spore takes up in the sediment, and may give that part of the spore enough rigidity to prevent secondary folding at the equator. A feature of rigidity on the proximal face of a spore, such as the lips of a triradiate mark, could also encourage the formation of two more or less parallel folds on the distal face, which may resemble a germinal furrow (colpus). In the case of thin-walled subtriangular trilete spores such as *Dictyophyllidites*, where the polar axis is about as long as the diameter, the spore may become flattened and fold with its polar axis in the plane of compression to produce what Potonié called 'triplane folding'. This peculiar folding has been made the basis of a distinct generic name, *Triplanosporites* Pflug, which Potonié regards simply as a particular configuration of *Dictyophyllidites*.

The position of secondary folding in fossil spores can actually be helpful in demonstrating the extent of attachment of a saccus to a central body, or the area of connection between a cavate wall and the inner exine. As Potonié (1962) explains, the distribution of secondary folds in *Lebachia* pollen make it clear that the saccus is free from the central body over its entire surface except for the germinal area, since folds are never seen to pass across that feature.

It is further evident from the observations of Harris and Potonié that the character of the matrix, its compressibility and especially how it controls the orientation of the spore as it becomes fossilized, can all affect the way in which a fossil spore becomes flattened and folded. Spores becoming compressed within a sporangium cannot change their position within the mass as they become flattened, and so show no preferred orientation; this is in contrast to spores settling out at a sediment-water interface, where they will tend to flatten with their longest axis (normally in the equatorial plane) parallel to the bedding.

9. Macrophotography

NICK P. ROWE

Macrophotography of fossil plant material is an essential and often difficult technique for reproducing illustrated material for publications and research. In this section macrophotography is dealt with for objects between *c.* 1 and 30 mm in size. This size range is possibly the most difficult to deal with in palaeobotany and palynology, falling between standard photographic equipment using macro lenses and the lowest magnifications possible using a compound light microscope. Photography of both morphological compression material as well as light-transparent peels and thin sections also poses specific problems in this size range. Because of the wide range of equipment now available for macrophotography, including state-of-the-art dissecting microscopes, this section will address some of the generalities involved in ensuring good photographic results whatever the equipment available, modern or old. Problems of photography in this size range involve most commonly three basic areas: sharpness of image, adequate and appropriate lighting, control of contrast.

Sharpness of image

Out-of-focus images can result from a number of causes. In my experience any macrophotography apparatus can develop faults over time, which cause either consistent or sporadically out-of-focus images. Poor focus usually results from the following reasons.

The object was incorrectly focused

In SLR (single lens reflex) camera systems, the image is viewed and focused on a focusing screen in the camera itself and this is the image which will be exposed to the film. At relatively high magnifications, many images become difficult to focus through standard camera viewfinders, and poor focus can commonly result from simply not focusing correctly. Camera systems can be fitted with a magnifier viewfinder which enlarges the image seen on the camera screen so that the object may be focused more reliably. These scopes are usually adjusted manually for the operator's vision by focusing a ring or double ring against a white background.

In non-SLR systems the image is focused via an eyepiece objective which is calibrated with the frame area of the film compartment where the image is projected. The eyepiece may be either one of the main viewing eyepieces of a stereo microscope or an eyepiece tube somewhere between the object and the film compartment; these systems can cause problems. The eyepiece lens must be calibrated for the operator's vision (by focusing cross-hairs or rings as outlined above). Problems arise from the fact that focusing of cross-hairs may be difficult (especially with older equipment) and that the calibration *between* the eyepiece and the frame holding the actual film can shift over time and use. If the part of the apparatus containing the film is not an SLR camera, you will never be really sure if the image is really in focus. If you suspect that this is the problem, it is relatively easily checked:

(i)   calibrate the eyepiece cross-hairs/ring so that it is in focus for your vision against a blank screen;
(ii) put a flat object under the apparatus and focus on it using the main focus control;
(iii) open the film compartment and place a frosted microscope slide (or microscope slide with opaque scotch tape) directly on the runners which normally support the film.

If the room is darkened it will be possible to see whether the image visible on the slide is in focus (depending on the camera/shutter model it will be necessary to keep the shutter open using the manual 'B' setting). The focus can be checked critically by viewing the image with a × 10 eyepiece objective held near the surface of the slide. If this image in the position of the film is not properly focused, adjust the main focus control until the object is in focus on the slide. At this point, re-adjust the eyepiece scope so that the image and not necessarily the ring/cross-hairs, is in focus for your vision and mark this setting on the adjustable focusing ring of the eyepiece itself so that it can be returned to (different operators might require different settings on the same apparatus!). After this calibration, it is only necessary to get the image in focus via the eyepiece and ignore the cross-hairs before exposing the film.

ROWE, N. P. 1999. Macrophotography. *In*: JONES, T. P. & ROWE, N. P. (eds) *Fossil Plants and Spores: modern techniques.* Geological Society, London, 41–46.

f *values and aperture settings*

The aperture settings of macrophotographic set-ups are particularly important for controlling the depth of field. Small apertures (high *f* settings) ensure high depth of field, while open apertures (low *f* settings) limit the depth of field. This is particularly important for three-dimensional specimens and can become difficult to get right when small specimens are in the range of one or several mm (Fig. 9.1e–f).

If the out-of-focus area of a photograph is in zones (Fig. 9.1e–f), then this is a fairly sure indication that the depth of field (Jacobson *et al.* 1979) is not great enough for the depth of the specimen. Both camera objectives and macro-photography objective lenses (Fig. 9.2) can be adjusted to open or close the aperture and adjust the depth of field. Some stereo microscope photosystems also include iris diaphragms which can adjust the aperture and *f* setting. One problem with shutting down the aperture means that you get less light into the camera, and therefore need longer exposure times. This risks exceeding the limit of the light metering/shutter system. One way of improvising around this is to tilt the specimen on a support of modelling clay so that the 'depth' of the feature of interest is at a minimum, and to focus on the mid-point of the depth observed.

Movement

Poor focus can often result from movement of the apparatus relative to the specimen during exposure. The photographic results often depend on the magnification and the sensitivity of the situation. Low magnification photos of transmitted light images of the anatomy of plant tissues are extremely sensitive to camera movement giving blurred cell outlines if the apparatus is anything other than absolutely stationary. Similarly, high contrast objects photographed at high magnification can also be highly sensitive to movement. There are many reasons for movement problems which depend on the system used and the application. Two potential causes of poor focus include movement during the winding on of the film and problems with the movement of the shutter. Many manual camera systems will put the specimen out of focus when the wind-on lever is pulled and in these cases the focus must be checked after every time the film is wound on. If the film is wound on automatically check that this movement doesn't shift the focus. The trigger mechanisms for activating the shutter vary and manually pressing the shutter button on the camera body can induce camera movement during the exposure. Either cable or electronic shutter releases are preferred

and when not available the timer release, fitted to many standard camera bodies can be used.

If problems with movement still persist, it is possible to test whether it is the shutter mechanism itself which is causing vibration during exposure. One way to entirely exclude movement is to perform the following:

(i)   adjust the light metering to an exposure time of about one second;
(ii) interrupt the light source with a piece of card – without touching the set-up;
(iii) set the shutter control to 'B' and open the camera shutter;
(iv) remove the card allowing an exposure for approximately one second and replace the card;
(v)   close the shutter.

This kind of test works on most kinds of macro systems and dissecting microscopes set-up for transmitted and incident light. Some systems allow the light on/off switch to be timed so that the exposure time can be more precisely controlled.

In the most sensitive situations such as low magnification, transmitted light images of anatomical cellular materials, this technique may be the only way of obtaining good results. If the camera shutter is inducing movement which is causing problems, try and modify the mounting of the camera and the macro-lens/objective system. Finally, I have known this kind of problem to occur in modern, expensive dissecting microscopes with all the attachments for high magnification macrophotography, but short of changing the camera system there was no way of remedying the camera shake apart from resorting to the manual method above.

Adequate and appropriate lighting

Film can be extremely sensitive to only slight visible changes of intense light at high macro-magnifications. Uneven lighting is often a problem with incident light photographs of compression surfaces. Fibre optic light sources produce a very intense light which can be focused with the aid of 'swan-neck' focusing final lenses attached to the end of each fibre optic cable. These lenses are best used with objects less than a few cm in size and beneath this can be easily adjusted for the size of the specimen. The intense light from fibre optic sources means that you have to be especially careful about the evenness of the lighting of the object when more than one fibre optic cable is illuminating the same area. 'Overlapped areas' appear much brighter on film than areas lit by single cables. For larger objects, fibre optic light sources are best used with the swan-neck lenses off

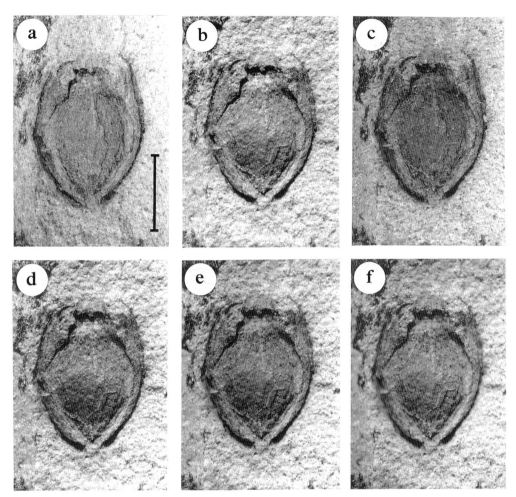

Fig. 9.1. Macrophotography of a small, three-dimensional compression/impression fossil (scale bar 1 mm). This subject is extremely difficult, combining small size, weak contrast of the impression surface and remaining organic material and a high level of three-dimensionality, all of which are important for interpretation of the fossil. The specimen is photographed using the set-up in Fig. 9.2 with a 'Schott' fibre optic light source with twin light cables, swan-neck lenses and with and without polarized light. The objective is a Leitz 16 mm, Aristophot lens (f 15–f 1) with a final magnification to the negative (Ilford PanF film) of × 10. (**a**) Non-polarized light from all four directions (f 15). The organic staining of the compression surface is poorly defined; the image is quite 'flat' with little of the information of the cast/mould structure of the fossil and there is some glaring from reflectance of the sediment surface and mineral particles. (**b**) Single polarized light filter over light source (f 15), the contrast of the organic staining of the impression surface is improved, there is much three-dimensionality of the subject. (**c**) Polarized light filters over light source and objective lens, light source cross-polarized. The organic material and impression surface appear dark, the image is quite flat with little three-dimensional information (f 15). This image is similar to pictures taken under liquids. (**d**) Polarized light filters over light source and objective lens, light not quite cross-polarized (f 15). This configuration probably gives the best combination of organic material contrast with the impression surface and three-dimensionality of the subject. (**e**) Same settings as (d). but aperture of objective set to f 2 (focused at vertical mid-point of specimen). The effect of reducing the depth of field by opening the iris diaphragm is demonstrated. The uppermost (the surface of the nucellar impression surface) and the lowermost (the left and right of the ovule and the lagenostome impression surface) surfaces are out of focus. (**f**) Same settings as (d), but aperture of objective lens set to f 1: only an oval band around the middle of the depth of field is in focus; all parts of the specimen above and below are blurred.

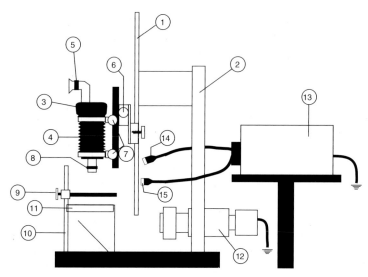

Fig. 9.2. A functional macrophotography set up as used in our laboratory. The main frame holding the camera, specimen stage and transmitted lamp housing is modified from a 'Leitz' Aristophot photographic system. The vertical steel support (1) and base (2) is stable and vibration free. An Olympus SLR, 24 × 35 mm camera body (Olympus SC35) with automatic wind-on mechanism (3) is mounted on an Olympus autobellows (4) via a 7 mm auto-extension tube. A magnifying finder ('Olympus varimagni finder') is attached (5) which can magnify the image frame to × 1.25 and × 2.5 for precise focusing. The whole camera ensemble can be moved (focused) by control (6) whereas different magnifications are set by adjusting the focal length with controls (7) on the bellows. A range of objective lenses (8) can be fitted to the bellows. We routinely use an olympus standard 50 mm macro lens for low power work. For higher magnifications we use a set of Leitz objectives all of which have an iris diaphragm to control f settings with focal lengths of 60 mm, 40 mm, 25 mm 16 mm. Using the full ranges of adjustment on the bellows system these afford magnifications of:1.3–3.0, 1.8–4.2, 3.6–9.0 and 7.0–18.0. After setting the focal length and magnification on the bellows system, the focus can be adjusted by either (6) or (9). Control (9) is part of the 'Aristophot' moveable stage and can be moved very smoothly at high magnifications. The transmitted light unit (10) consists of an angled mirror and horizontal holder for varying condenser lenses (11) and the lamp housing (12). The space in between these units allows manual exposures of photographs which might be highly sensitive to even very slight movement of even a modern camera shutter. The fibre optic system (13) is set up on a separate bench or shelf so that vibration from the fan motor does not travel through the camera system. The fibre optic cables are shown with 'swan-neck' focusing lenses (14) and screw-on polarizing filters (15). Ideally the fibre optic system can be moved and orientated in any direction around the specimen stage. This set up is highly flexible for a range of magnifications. The transmitted light box and stage can be removed and the bellows detached from the camera for low power macrophotography. The camera can also be removed and replaced by a video camera for digital image capturing.

and the lights some distance from the object to ensure even lighting.

At high magnifications, depending on the type of objective used, the distance between the objective lens and the specimen is usually small and there may be problems in positioning lights close enough to the subject. Journals normally require a certain orientation of the specimen so that they are orientated and illuminated from the upper left. This is one of the problems with using ring flashes and ring light sources which illuminate the subject evenly, although these light sources can be combined with directional light sources pointing from the upper left. For low magnification macrophotography of specimens above 3–4 cm in size, there are now many variations of domestic table-top 12V, 20W, halogen lamps which provide a uniform white light, work well with polarizing filters, and are ideal for fossil compression material. The appearance of a three-dimensional subject can change dramatically with the angle of incident light. The orientation and depth of a plant compression surface, for example, can be made invisible, visible or exaggerated just by the angle of lighting (Fig. 9.1).

Appropriate contrast

Light intensity

As with lighting, the quality of results from both incident and transmitted light macrophotography depend largely on controlling the contrast during exposure; the intensity of the light source can influence the contrast. An excessively bright and cold (predominantly blue wavelength) light source can 'bleach' the more subtle range of colours and contrasts, resulting in a flat image, whereas a less intense, warmer (more red wavelength) light might enhance such differences. This variation depends on the kind of material and is a matter of experimentation as different materials behave differently under variable light intensities. Light-coloured reflective sediments with slightly darker plant compression material would probably benefit from less intense or diffuse light for a good contrast, whereas darker non-reflective sediments might require more intense direct light to pick out the contrast differences between sediment and fossil. This difference in intensity and colour temperature varies greatly between light sources. Incandescent light sources show considerable change in colour temperature over different intensities than modern halogen light sources and so are more difficult to control and replicate similar results.

Polarizing filters

Some materials, particularly coarse-grained and micaceous sediments may reflect light directly back into the objective lens causing glare and/or hotspots (Fig. 9.1a). This can be remedied by using less intense, diffuse light, polarizing filters or submersing the material in a liquid such as water or alcohol. There are problems with using liquids which include the specimen breaking up, bubbles floating out of the specimen, particles drifting across the subject, reflectance off the liquid surface, and difficulties in obtaining a shadowed rather than 'flat' image.

Low contrast subjects such as faintly coloured plant impression surfaces on a similarly coloured sediment background may be markedly improved by using cross-polarized light. Polarizing filters fitted to the light source and over the objective lens are then rotated until the cross-polarized effect enhances the contrast between the materials. This works particularly well between organic material and clastic sediment, particularly if the organic material is only faintly staining the sediment surface. Polarizing filters can be improvised easily for most light sources. For high magnification, special polarizing filters can be attached to the swan-neck lenses of fibre optic light sources (Fig. 9.2), and these are highly recommended.

One problem with polarizing images is that the image often loses most of the shadowing or three-dimensional relief of the subject, even if the polarized light is orientated at a low angle. This situation can be remedied by carefully rotating one or more of the light source filters or the objective filter, and carefully watching the polarizing effect and shadowing change. A compromise can often be found with just the right amount or degree of cross-polarized light and non-cross-polarized shadowing (Fig. 9.1d).

For plant compressions, I have found that polarized light is far more effective than colour filters. Yellow, orange, red and green filters will generally transmit their own colour and either limit or block the colour opposite in the spectrum and thus vary the number of shades of grey recorded on the film. However, in some circumstances when polarizing light does not work, such filters can be tried, especially in cases when impression surfaces may entirely lack organic material or comprise varied colours against the sediment background. Generally speaking, orange and yellow filters can be useful for compression material.

Transmitted light macrophotography

A number of problems are associated with obtaining high definition images from the relatively low magnifications used in macrophotography. These largely depend on the size and nature of the material. Creating uniform light over a distance of more than a few millimetres to several centimetres is difficult without large diameter condenser lenses which can be positioned and focused below the object. Few modern transmitted light macro systems cater for this. The Leitz Aristophot system includes a range of large condenser lenses, which appreciably improve the light quality of large, transmitted light subjects (Fig. 9.2). Lens apertures should not be used to modify the light intensity or exposure in these circumstances, but should be set to fully open or nearly so; closing the aperture can lead to problems with defracted light. If large condenser lenses are not available, uniform lighting can be improvised by placing large transmitted light subjects on a photographer's light box.

Low magnification, transmitted light images of cellular sections are extremely sensitive to movement caused by vibration. If a cellular transmitted image is consistently or sporadically blurred, check the manual method of exposing films described above.

Transmitted light images from thickly prepared thin-sections or mounted peels can be opaque and visually noisy with high levels of diffracted light, such as that resulting from mineral material adhering to peels that have not been demineralized. In such cases anatomical details are often better defined if opaque tracing paper or a frosted glass slide is placed beneath the specimen, but outside the depth of field.

Film types and test films

Monochrome macrophotography can be roughly divided into two categories: carefully illuminated compression and impression fossils require subtle changes of grey scales but cellular sections of anatomically preserved material often require higher contrast images to resolve cellular outlines. Commercially available film such as Ilford Pan F (fine grain) and Kodak 2415 (ultra fine grain) can both be developed in different ways for varying contrast by following the instructions accompanying the film.

Colour slides of fossil material taken in artificial light should always be taken using 'tungsten' film, such as Kodak Ektachrome 64T. If normal daylight film is used the colours are dramatically different from the original with exaggerated yellow tones. If only daylight film is available, blue filters can be placed over the objective lens of the camera or over the light sources. Blue light filters are available in varying intensities and it is a matter of experimentation which shade is necessary for a given material. They are generally easier to use for transmitted light subjects than illuminated compressions and impressions. Difficulties can occur with some systems where a strongly coloured blue filter can affect the accuracy of the exposure meter and/or drastically increase the exposure time.

Preparation techniques can be destructive and it is sometimes necessary to photograph a specimen between steps of a procedure, such as uncovering with needles or etching with acid. In such cases, it is always advisable to carry out a test run of the material under the conditions of lighting and magnification that will be used between stages of preparation. When the results are satisfactory in terms of contrast and sharpness, the material may then be prepared and photographed in steps. If the material is really crucial, a second precaution is to re-photograph the specimen two or three times at slightly different aperture settings, as well as refocusing each time. In this way, one high quality exposure will be guaranteed.

10. Light microscopy of fossil pollen and spores

PETE COXON & GEOFF CLAYTON

Transmitted light microscopy is one of the oldest techniques used for the study of fossil pollen and spores but it is also still the most widely used method for routine identification. This method permits detailed examination of the surface structure and ornamentation of pollen and spores and, provided the specimen is translucent, it also enables internal structures such as an intexine to be clearly seen. Compared with electron microscopy, light microscopy is rapid, inexpensive and requires less complex sample preparation. Reflected light microscopy has also proved useful in the past for studying surface structure and ornamentation, particularly of megaspores, but it has been largely superseded by scanning electron microscopy.

Types of light microscopy

Many sophisticated variants of transmitted light microscopes have been invented, several of which can produce spectacular results for certain types of material. For example, when studying very thin or pale specimens, the 'phase contrast' microscope produces an artificial shadow effect accentuating edges of palynomorphs and especially the outlines of delicate processes which may be virtually invisible using 'normal' light microscopy. 'Nomarski interference microscopy' is even more effective for this type of material, producing enhanced contrast and adjustable background colours for elucidating pollen and spore structure and ornamentation. These and other methods such as infra-red microscopy laser scanning microscopy and fluorescence microscopy are comprehensively reviewed by Scott (1989) and Wood *et al.* (1996). Major microscope manufacturers include Leica, Nikon, Zeiss and Olympus.

For quantitative work, counting is usually carried out with a high quality compound microscope with × 10 eyepieces and using a × 40 and a × 100 (oil immersion) transmitted light objective. The × 400 overall magnification is used for routine counting with the × 1000 reserved for critical determinations. A mechanical stage with a vernier scale is essential for accurate traversing and for locating problematic or particularly interesting palynomorphs. In recent years, the 'England Finder Slide' (see Appendix) has become the most popular method of determining accurate coordinates for specimens on slides, independently of the type of microscope being used.

Detailed observation and photomicrography both necessitate careful adjustment of the microscope to ensure optimum illumination, contrast and depth of focus. The light source of modern microscopes typically comprises a high-power halogen bulb, a field diaphragm and removable filters. Various combinations of filters can be used for colour compensation in order to produce accurate colour rendition with 'daylight' films, or, to deliberately increase or decrease contrast for observation and black & white photography. Before being transmitted through the slide, the light passes through the substage condenser unit and its diaphragm, both of which must be carefully adjusted to give the best results.

Most research microscopes are intended to be used for photomicrography. Details of the photographic system employed vary from manufacturer to manufacturer. In some cases the camera is confocal with the eyepieces so that no additional fine-focusing is required; in others a separate eyepiece must be used to ensure that the photograph is in focus. In recent years, image capture by a video camera attached to the microscope has become a viable alternative to traditional photography, though printouts from most microcomputers and printers are at lower resolution than either black & white or colour photographs. Large numbers of images can be edited and stored using systems such as the Leica Quantimet / LIDA Image Analysis and Archiving System (see Appendix).

Sample preparation

Mounting media include cold-setting resins such as 'Elvacite' (see Appendix), glycerine jelly (although this can cause swelling of miospore exines) and silicone oil (see Appendix). The latter has the distinct advantage that, as well as being optically suitable, it allows three-dimensional pollen grains to be rotated below the coverslip by applying gentle pressure (Moore *et al.* 1991). When dealing with compressed spores and pollen, the palynomorphs tend to lie flat between the slide and the coverslip so that there is no advantage in using silicone oil as a mounting medium. Many workers prefer to count unstained material while others use stains (e.g. a

COXON, P. & CLAYTON, G. 1999. Light microscopy of fossil pollen and spores.
In: JONES, T. P. & ROWE, N. P. (eds) *Fossil Plants and Spores: modern techniques.*
Geological Society, London, 47–51.

2% aqueous safranin solution). Acetolysis of the sample during preparation gives the pollen a light yellow tint.

A relatively modern method used extensively by palynofacies workers and coal petrologists was described by Hillier & Marshall (1988). This technique produces a very thin layer of mounting medium on a slide which is polished rather than covered by a coverslip. The proportion of light reflected from polished surfaces of woody material, 'vitrinite reflectance' can then be measured in addition to the spores and pollen being studied. (see Chapter 16).

Observation

Taxonomic practice based on light microscopy varies considerably according to the stratigraphic age of the material investigated and the nature of the palynomorphs being studied (see Chapter 43). In Quaternary assemblages, every attempt is made to recognize pollen and spores in terms of extant parent plants and actuopalynological terminology is applied. In the Tertiary, considerable difficulties are encountered in assemblages containing both extant and extinct taxa and by the late Cretaceous, morphological classifications are generally used.

The problems encountered by palynologists working on fossil spores and pollen depend, of course, on the state of preservation of the material but are also largely dependent on the age of the material being investigated. In the Lower Palaeozoic and early Devonian, cryptospores and primitive trilete spores are generally small, relatively simple in structure and possess a limited range of surface ornament. Careful observation is required to elucidate details such as the presence of an enclosing membrane or the nature of surface sculpture developed on a very small scale.

From the Middle Devonian to the late Carboniferous, spores are much more diverse in morphology. Monolete miospore taxa are initially very rare in this interval, which is dominated by trilete forms but the former gradually become more common in the Upper Carboniferous. Many forms have two or more exine layers which may be attached on the proximal surface only, or on both proximal and distal surfaces. Other morphological structures include equatorial thickenings (cingulum) and membranous extensions (zona). Towards the end of the Lower Carboniferous, many of the trilete spore taxa had become triangular in shape, rather than circular, with structures developed selectively either at or between the apices.

With regard to suprageneric classification, the distinction between monolete and trilete spores constitutes the fundamental division of the spores but at lower levels several alternative classifications have been proposed (see for example Dettmann 1963 and Neves & Owens 1966). The structures outlined above are of prime importance in these various schemes. Still in Carboniferous times, miospores probably demonstrate maximum

---

Fig. 10.1. (a)–(c) *Convolutispora major* (Kedo) Turnau. Logan Formation (Mississippian = Lower Carboniferous) 'Little Arizona' roadcut, Wayne County, Ohio, USA. An acamerate (single layered) miospore heavily ornamented with irregular ridges. (**a**) Nomarsky interference contrast photomicrograph. The 'false shadow' effect of this technique enhances the outline of the ridges on the distal surface of the spore (scale bar = 30 µm). (**b**) Transmitted white light photomicrograph. The image of the distal surface is superimposed on that of the proximal surface making the geometry of the ornamentation less easy to interpret (scale bar = 30 µm). (**c**) UV fluorescence photomicrograph. The fluorescence of the exine provides a useful but slightly 'blurred' image of the distal ornament (scale bar = 30 µm). (**d**)–(**e**) *Retispora lepidophyta* (Kedo) Playford. 4637 ft, Saudi Aramco well ST8, Saudi Arabia. A reworked miospore of latest Devonian age from a lower Carboniferous shale sample. (**d**) Nomarsky interference contrast photomicrograph showing the reticulate pattern of walls (muri) on the outer exine layer (exoexine). The darker inner exine layer (intexine) can be clearly seen (scale bar = 30 µm). (**e**) Transmitted white light photomicrograph. This 'softer' image shows the same features as in (d) but the reticulate nature of the exoexine is less pronounced. The slightly different plane of focus clearly shows the very narrow raised sinuous labra (lips) which, together with the suturae constitute the trilete mark (scale bar = 30 µm). (**f**) *Pinus* subgenus *Pinus* = *Diploxylon*. Late Middle Pleistocene (Gortian temperate stage), Derrynadivva, County Mayo, Ireland. Nomarsky interference contrast photomicrograph of the distal view of a bisaccate pollen grain, lightly stained during preparation using 1% aqueous safranin. The distal view shows the 2 reticulate sacci (of equal size) with the grain body behind (scale bar = 14 µm). (**g**) *Salix* sp. Late Holocene (c. 3000 years BP), Valencia, County Kerry, Ireland. Nomarsky interference contrast photomicrograph of the equatorial view of a trizonocolpate pollen grain showing two of the colpi separated by a mesocolpium. The reticulum on the mesocolpium has distinct lumina which markedly decrease in size towards the colpus edge (scale bar = 9.4 µm). (**h**) Coryloid cf. *Corylus* type. Late Tertiary (Pliocene), Pollnahallia, Headford, County Galway, Ireland. Nomarsky interference contrast photomicrograph of the polar view of a partially crumpled trizonoporate pollen grain showing three distinct pori with slight thickening of the sexine adjacent to the porus but no distinct annulus. There are many trizonoporate taxa separated on shape, sculpturing and pori structure and many are assigned to 'type' only (scale bar = 9.4 µm).

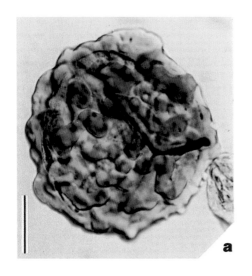

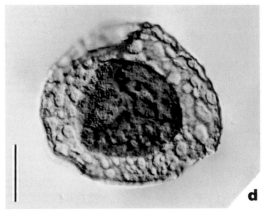

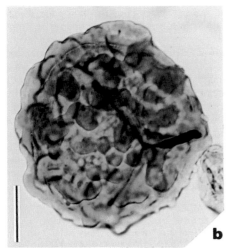

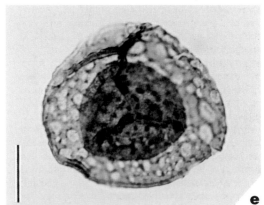

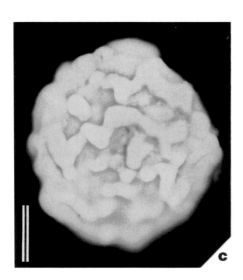

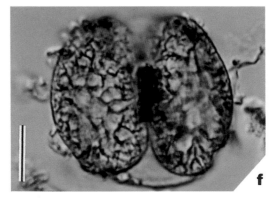

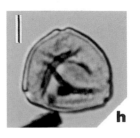

diversity in terms of combinations of structure and surface ornament; some typical forms are illustrated in Fig. 10.1 and described briefly in the caption.

Undisputed saccate pollen are first recognized at the end of the Lower Carboniferous. The early, large monosaccate forms gradually diversify through the Upper Carboniferous with bisaccate forms apparently evolving from them. Saccate pollen rapidly displace spores in most parts of the world with striate bisaccate pollen dominating many Permian and Triassic assemblages. Classification of these pollen depends on whether the grains are trilete or monolete, the number, relative size and attachment of the sacci, and distribution of taeniae (if present). Taxonomic studies of these palynomorphs require slightly different skills to those involved in interpreting highly ornamented spores.

Jurassic and Cretaceous spores are varied in morphology but never surpass the diversity of structure and ornamentation seen in the Upper Devonian and Carboniferous. Saccate pollen are abundant through this interval but are of limited stratigraphic value and consequently are rarely studied in detail.

Typical preservation of pollen and spores from older rocks in many parts of the world involves the palynomorphs having been compressed to the extent that their upper and lower surfaces are more or less in contact with each other, causing difficulties in establishing internal structure and the distribution of surface ornament. Mounting organic residues in silicone oil and rotating individual specimens into more favourable positions for observation is obviously not a viable option with flattened forms and instead, specimens have to be located which have been compressed in non-polar orientations (i.e. with the proximal and distal poles not directly aligned – see Fig. 10.1 (a) and (b)). These 'lateral' and 'oblique compressions' often provide more useful information than the more symmetrical 'polar compressions'. However, most spore and pollen taxa can be accurately identified by experienced palynologists on the basis of their overall appearance and key features, rather than by systematically recognizing all of the morphological characteristics described in the published diagnosis of the species!

Angiosperm pollen first appear in the Early Cretaceous and have a non-laminated endexine and a foot layer, columella layer and tectum as distinct parts of the ektexine. This characteristic structure is shown on Fig. 10.2 and is discussed below.

The resistant outer layer (exine) of the pollen wall of angiosperms and gymnosperms is composed of sporopollenin (Zetzsche 1932) and identification of fossil pollen depends on the preservation of this very stable substance in the exine's structure and morphology (see Fig. 10.2). The patterning of the sexine and parts of the nexine can be distinguished using light microscopy. Spores of pteridophytes and bryophytes also contain sporopollenin but they have a different (often laminated) wall structure which does not contain a columella layer and which is referred to as an exospore (Faegri & Iversen 1975). Pteridophytes have an inner (endosporium) and outer (exospor-

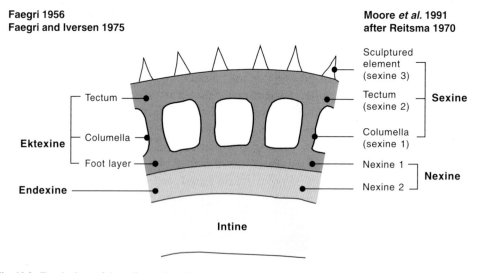

Faegri 1956
Faegri and Iversen 1975

Moore et al. 1991
after Reitsma 1970

Sculptured element (sexine 3)

Tectum

Tectum (sexine 2)   Sexine

Ektexine   Columella

Columella (sexine 1)

Foot layer

Nexine 1

Endexine   Nexine 2   Nexine

Intine

Fig. 10.2. Terminology of the pollen grain exine.

ium) layer that can be recognized and used in identification keys.

The process of pollen/spore identification relies on classifying the complex array of grain shapes (polar and equatorial views), exine apertures (pori or pores and colpi or furrows) and the structure and surface sculpturing of the exine (in angiosperms and some gymnosperms). The morphological complexity has led to a number of terminologies and pollen/spore keys (e.g. Erdtman *et al.* 1963; Faegri & Iversen 1975; Moore *et al.* 1991 – the latter after Reitsma 1970). The terminology used here follows that on Fig. 10.2 from Moore *et al.* 1991.

The shape of pollen and spores can be defined in equatorial and polar views and the use of silicone oil as a mounting medium allows the grain to be viewed in three dimensions on the slide (and also allows obscured grains to be viewed by moving them). The shape classifications most commonly used are described in Moore *et al.* (1991) but it is worth noting that shape varies with a number of factors including depositional and preservational characteristics of the fossil pollen, chemical treatment during pollen preparation and the nature of the mounting medium.

Apertures in the exine (sexine, nexine or both) are classified in two morphological forms: pori (pores which are generally isodiametric) and colpi (furrows which are elongate, length : breadth ratio 2 : 1, with acute ends). Pollen can be classified according to the nature of the aperture(s), their shape, size, number and positioning on the grain's surface and a detailed classification is given by Moore *et al.* (1991). Pteridophyte and bryophyte spores also contain apertures in their walls related to scars left by the division of the original tetrad. Such apertures are distinctive and used diagnostically but they are unrelated to those of angiosperms.

It is possible using a light microscope to view certain aspects of the structure of the exine as well as the sculpturing patterns on the tectum (Faegri & Iversen 1975) although the complexity of patterns (and interference between surface and structural patterns) can be problematic. The pattern types seen in the exine structure (i.e. the columella) and on the outer part of the tectum (sexine 3, Fig. 10.2) are very varied and form an interwoven continuum which is summarized by Moore *et al.* (1991). The use of movement of the focal plane in light microscopy is particularly valuable, allied with a mounting medium allowing rotation of the grain, in distinguishing whether the patterning belongs to the internal structure of the exine or the surface sculpturing (Iversen & Troels-Smith 1950; Erdtman 1956; Faegri & Iversen 1975; Moore *et al.* 1991). The use of phase contrast microscopy can aid in the differentiation of structure and sculpture in pollen grains as it shows differences in refractive index of the material being viewed with denser objects appearing darker. This means that solid sculpturing and structure appears darker than voids or openings which can sometimes be hard to differentiate using bright field illumination.

As the majority of Quaternary taxa are still extant the possibility of using modern reference material (preferably mounted in the same medium as the fossil pollen being counted) exists. Laboratories often have a comparitor microscope (see Appendix) with two stages for direct comparison of modern (type material) and fossil pollen. Similarly detailed catalogues of high quality photographs of modern pollen can be used, e.g. Reille (1992). In addition the WWW contains sites that display images of Quaternary pollen and spores for comparison, e.g. http://www-palecol.plantsci.cam.ac.uk/ (Department of Plant Sciences, University of Cambridge, UK).

11. Light microscopy of cuticles

HANS KERP & MICHAEL KRINGS

The cuticle is a non-cellular layer which covers most aerial parts of higher plants. The cuticle forms a natural cast of the underlying epidermis and clearly reflects its characteristic cell pattern, including stomata (Fig. 11.1e, h), and structures such as hairs (Fig. 11.1f,g), glands (Fig. 11.1c, j) and papillae (Fig. 11.1i). Most species have a unique combination and distribution of cuticular features which can be used for taxonomic studies. This was clearly recognized by the earliest authors who dealt with fossil cuticles (Wessel & Weber 1855; Bornemann 1856). Cuticles also enable the correlation of dispersed organs and are very helpful for reconstructing whole plant taxa (e.g. Harris 1937; Clement-Westerhof 1984). Furthermore, the epidermal morphology can yield important information on the ecology (e.g. Kerp & Barthel 1993; Krings & Kerp 1997a). In recent years cuticles have been increasingly recognized as biosensors of palaeoatmospheric conditions (e.g. Beerling & Chaloner 1994; Kürschner 1996). Last but not least, fossil cuticles can also contribute to our knowledge of growth habits of fossil plants (Krings & Kerp 1997a). Cuticles are often the only source of cellular information of compression fossils.

Cuticles are usually very resistant, their preservation potential being determined chiefly by their primary chemical composition (Tegelaar et al. 1991). Early land plants, gymnosperms and angiosperms normally have well developed and resistant cuticles; only relatively few fossil lycopod, sphenopsid and fern cuticles have been documented.

Material and preparation techniques

Cuticles are found in sediments which have not been affected (too strongly) by oxidation and/or thermal alteration. Some sediments, e.g. the so-called paper shales, are extremely rich in fossil cuticles. Fresh cuticles are usually brown to black in colour. The colour of the material largely depends on its thickness and coalification. Sometimes, cuticles are bleached by natural oxidation. For light-microscopical investigations, cuticles first need to be isolated from the sediment and freed of adhering mineral and plant material such as coalified remnants of tissues. For incident fluorescence microscopy cuticles do not need preparation, although they should be completely dust-free.

The use of freshly collected or freshly split material is strongly recommended because cuticles easily desiccate and oxidize when they are exposed to atmospheric conditions. This is often the case with preparations from older museum specimens. Although cuticles can sometimes be lifted off easily from compressions, usually only small pieces are obtained because untreated cuticles are very brittle. Isolation with chemical methods is preferred. Small selected pieces of rock with single fragments of cuticle, or larger amounts of cuticle-bearing material can be dissolved in appropriate chemicals. The latter method, also known as bulk maceration (Harris 1926), is often more favourable because: (1) larger and more complete specimens can be obtained (Fig. 11.1a, b, c) and (2) this large-scale method often yields organs which are otherwise not

---

Fig. 11.1. All cuticles are from the Upper Stephanian of Central France unless otherwise indicated. Further explanations are given in the text. (**a**) *Pseudomariopteris ribeyronii* (normal bright field). Scale bar = 16.5 mm. (**b**) *Odontopteris minor-zeilleri*, lower pinnule surface (normal bright field). Scale bar = 1.25 mm. (**c**) *Pseudomariopteris paleauii*, pinnule apex (normal bright field). Scale bar = 1.67 mm. (**d**) *Alethopteris zeilleri*, hair base, upper leaf surface (Nomarski interference contrast). Scale bar = 60 µm. (**e**) *Neuropteris cordata* (Nomarski interference contrast). Scale bar = 30 µm. (**f**) *Sphenoneuropteris praedentata* (normal bright field). Scale bar = 330 µm. (**g**) *Sphenoneuropteris praedentata* (normal bright field). Scale bar = 600 µm. (**h**) *Alethopteris zeilleri*, lower leaf surface (Nomarski interference contrast). Scale bar = 25 µm. (**i**) *Lescuropteris genuina* (Nomarski interference contrast). Scale bar = 30 µm. (**j**) *Barthelopteris germarii*, peltate glandular hair (Nomarski interference contrast). Scale bar = 45 µm. (k) *Autunia conferta*. upper pinnule surface, Autunian, Bohemia, Czech Republic (incident UV-illumination / fluorescence). Scale bar = 300 µm. (l) *Peltaspermum retensorium*, upper pinnule surface, Kungurian, Ural Mountains, Russia (incident UV-illumination / fluorescence). Scale bar = 107 µm.

KERP, H. & KRINGS, M. 1999. Light microscopy of cuticles. *In*: JONES, T. P. & ROWE, N. P. (eds) *Fossil Plants and Spores: modern techniques*. Geological Society, London, 52–56.

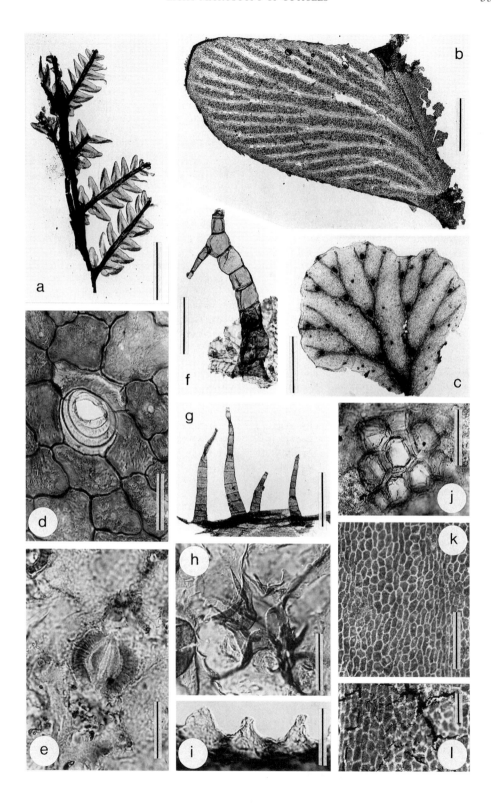

encountered in routine observation such as fructifications.

Each type of sediment requires its own preparation method. Although not usually yielding very well-preserved cuticles, carbonates can be dissolved in 25% hydrochloric acid (HCl). Siliciclastic sediments are dissolved in 45% hydrofluoric acid (HF). Coaly sediments are treated with 30–65% nitric acid (HNO_3) with some potassium chlorate ($KClO_3$). This mixture is known as Schulze's reagent. Some coals can be disaggregated in weaker chemicals.

Siliciclastic sediments are treated with 45% HF until the rock is completely disintegrated. Then cuticles are carefully removed from the acid, either by sieving through a nylon (HF-resistant) sieve, or by picking them out with a fork. The cuticles are then carefully rinsed in distilled water for at least three minutes until the liquid is neutral (pH test). Material obtained in this way is usually still too dark for examination and must first be cleared.

Several maceration methods can be applied, depending on the nature of the material. All of these methods involve oxidation and concentrations of the chemicals and maceration times can vary considerably and must be determined empirically. Maceration should be done very carefully, because too vigorous treatment will result in a loss of material (e.g. thin cuticles), and/or specific cuticular features (e.g. stomatal guard cells). Because bulk samples may especially contain a wide variety of different cuticles, which all react differently during maceration, the reaction has to be interrupted after the first cuticles have slightly changed in colour and can be picked out. Those that are still too dark can be macerated again using the same procedures or weaker maceration agents. The weakest bleaching agents are 5–10% sodium hypochlorite solution (= Eau de Javelle – $NaHClO_2$), and 10–25% hydrogen peroxide (H_2O_2). For more coalified material, the best results are obtained with Schulze's reagent. Some Mesozoic cuticles require only 30% HNO_3 with a few crystals of $KClO_3$ and become translucent within a few minutes, whereas others, including most Palaeozoic cuticles, need to be treated in 65% HNO_3 and $KClO_3$ for up to one week. As soon as the cuticles have slightly changed in colour, the reaction has to be stopped by first decanting the acid and then rinsing the cuticles with sufficient distilled water.

Maceration in Schulze's reagent is the most common procedure but it is also one of the most critical steps in the preparation of fossil cuticles. Larger cuticles frequently fall apart and/or fine details are lost when they are macerated with high concentrations of nitric acid. On the other hand, treatment with low concentrations of HNO_3

normally has little effect. Optimal results are obtained by starting with a low concentration of acid which is increased stepwise by adding concentrated HNO_3. To reduce the effective maceration time in concentrated acid, maceration starts with 20% HNO_3 with a few crystals of $KClO_3$ and each day concentrated HNO_3 (about one third of the total volume) is added until the cuticles start to change in colour. This may take up to five days. Cuticles are then carefully sieved or picked out and are subsequently treated with 5% potassium hydroxide (KOH) or 5% ammonia (NH_4^+/OH^-) for one to five minutes and finally washed in distilled water. The major changes in colour occur during treatment with KOH and rinsing in water.

Coaly sediments should either be treated with KOH (5–10%), H_2O_2 (25–30%), or with Schulze's reagent. Some coals are partly alkali-soluble and KOH will suffice (test with a few drops). Disaggregation of such coals may take up to several days. Cuticles become translucent and are then sieved out and subsequently rinsed with distilled water. This procedure can be followed with H_2O_2.

Most coals need to be treated with Schulze's reagent, which contains only a few(!) crystals of $KClO_3$. Dust fine coal particles occurring in the sample may react very violently and should be removed by sieving. Even then, the reaction is unpredictable and may be very violent. It is recommended to start with a little amount of HNO_3 in a low concentration and watch carefully how the reaction proceeds. If no extreme reaction occurs, it may be safe to proceed by adding more acid and increasing the concentration. However, sometimes the reaction may not start until 10–15 minutes after the acid has been added. If samples react too vigorously (foaming of the liquid and yellow-brown gas given off; spontaneous boiling) the reaction should be stopped immediately by adding 10% KOH. Macerations with Schulze's reagent may take up to one week. The reaction is stopped when the coal is disaggregated, cuticles are released and the acid has become (dark) brown. The acid is then poured off and the cuticles are gently washed in distilled water for at least three minutes until the liquid is neutral (pH test). Although the cuticles may have changed slightly in colour, they may still be relatively dark. During the subsequent treatment with 5–10% KOH (5–10 min) most of the darker material will disappear. The cuticles are then sieved out and washed in gently running water until the water is perfectly clear.

In addition to careful maceration, the handling of very delicate cuticles requires special attention. Cuticles should always be picked out and transferred from one beaker to the other with fine plastic (HF-resistant) or glass tools (other chemicals). For larger cuticles acid-resistant forks are recommended, which have the advantage that cuticles lie more or less flat. For smaller pieces of cuticle plastic or glass rods are to be preferred. The use of forceps and/or tweezers cannot be recommended because the fragile cuticles are easily damaged. During washing and KOH treatment, the cuticles are kept in a fine-mesh nylon sieve in which they lie flat on the bottom. Cleaning cuticles in ultra-sonic generator tanks or centrifuging material is not recommended as very fragile material is easily destroyed.

All chemical preparations should be done using the appropriate utensils (e.g. polyethylene beakers for HF) in adequate fume hoods and taking the necessary safety precautions. Moreover, any new technique should be checked with the departmental laboratory technician and safety officer.

Permanent slides

Glycerine jelly is the preferred mounting medium for fossil cuticles, it has excellent optical pro-perties, can easily be handled and has the great advantage that cuticles can still be manipulated during embedding. Before embedding, cuticles can be stored in glycerine water with a few drops of phenol to avoid fungal growth. Cuticles mounted in Canada balsam or synthetic resins first need to be dehydrated in xylene or ethanol which usually destroy fragile material. Moreover, slides made with these embedding media are often very thick because of their high viscosity and the cuticles not lying flat; Canada balsam may become very dark after some years.

A major problem with glycerine jelly is the formation of air bubbles. Freshly made, and also commercially sold, glycerine jelly usually contains a rather large amount of water and air. To release the entrapped air and also remove excessive water the glycerine jelly is heated for several days in a beaker placed in a water bath until it has become dark yellow. The cuticles themselves should be dehydrated in pure glycerine for at least one day before mounting in the glycerine jelly. For the actual mounting of the cuticles, microscope slides are placed on a precision-controlled warming plate at a temperature of 65–73°C and warm glycerine jelly placed on the slide using a glass rod. The cuticles are placed in the jelly and covered with a suitably sized cover-slip. Larger cuticles may cause a problem as they often do not lie completely flat. Therefore the cover slip needs to be supported; for this purpose small pieces of a broken cover-slip have proved to be better than plasticine, especially as they do not show as prominently on photo-graphs. In order to prevent subsequent desiccation the cover-slip is sealed with colourless nail varnish

after the glycerine jelly has hardened, which may take up to several months for larger and/or thicker slides.

As stated above, one of the advantages of glycerine jelly is that cuticles can still be manipulated during embedding. Cuticles can be spread out on the slide which lies on the heating plate. Furthermore, the upper and lower leaf cuticles often still stick firmly together and need mechanical separation. They can best be separated with fine preparation needles after they have been transferred to the warm glycerine jelly on the slide.

Cuticles can be stained before mounting, but very fragile cuticles are easily damaged during staining. Each staining agent emphasizes different features. The following stains are the most useful: Bismarck brown, methyl green, methylene blue and safranin T; Bismarck brown produces the most natural colours. All these stains are used in a 1% aqueous solution and may take a few minutes, if necessary at 40°C. After staining, the cuticles are rinsed in water and warm glycerine. The effect of staining may be different for various species, even from the same locality.

Microscopy and photography

Normal bright field and Nomarksi interference contrast microscopy and microphotography

Light microscopes with magnifications of × 10–1000 are most commonly used. Larger pieces of cuticle are usually partly out of focus when higher magnifications are used, therefore cuticular details at high magnifications can best be studied in smaller fragments. The use of Nomarski inter-ference contrast is very useful for very thin cuticles as it enhances the relief and makes fine structures visible. Thin cuticles can also be studied in incident normal light as Schönfeld & Storch (1979) and Barthel (1997) demonstrated for *Sphenophyllum* cuticles. This method has the advantage that chemical isolation and further preparation is unnecessary as the slabs are directly placed under the microscope.

Colour slides are made on a normal daylight film using a CB 12 blue filter. Depending on the nature of the material black & white pictures are made either on a low speed (25 ISO) panchromatic (Fig. 11.1e, f, g, i, j) or orthochromatic film (Fig. 11.1d). The latter type of film shows greater contrast but fewer grey tones. For very thin cuticles, a combination of Nomarski interference contrast, a green filter and orthochromatic film may give good results (Fig. 11.1h).

Fluorescence microscopy and microphotography

Fluorescence microscopy can be used for cuticles that have not been appreciably coalified. This method was successfully applied to the study of Tertiary cuticles (e.g. Schaarschmidt 1982), and also for Palaeozoic cuticles (Kerp *et al.* 1990; Naugolnykh & Kerp 1996). Cuticles are studied directly from the compression specimen with a microscope equipped for incident ultra-violet illumination and the necessary filter set. For most cuticles, UV + blue + violet excitation is recommended (cf. Van Gijzel 1979). The material is placed directly under the objectives of the microscope which should have a stage capable of holding macrofossil specimens. Specimens need to be completely dust-free, as dust particles light up very brightly. Optimal results are obtained with magnifications between × 63 and × 250. Lower magnifications often show a very weak fluorescence, whereas the fluorescence is often too strong with higher magnifications resulting in images that are not sharp. Special lenses, not corrected for cover-slips are recommended, but in most cases normal plan-apochromatic or fluorite lenses will give good results for the magnifications indicated above; water-immersion lenses give much brighter images. Fluorescence microscopy has the advantage that no prior chemical preparations are necessary and specimens remain undamaged, which is particularly useful for dealing with type material. Some material does not survive chemical preparations. In some cases cuticles show very minute cracks (Fig. 11.1l) and it is clear that such material would fall apart when the rock is dissolved. In some cases, complete pinnules are obtained by HF treatment, but with Schulze's reagent they fall apart into dust-fine particles. Isolated and entire pinnules can be studied from both sides (e.g. the specimen illustrated in Fig. 11.1k). With the fluorescence microscope larger surfaces can be analysed, including the distribution of stomata and hairs. Such patterns would remain unknown if only small pieces of cuticle were studied using conventional preparation methods. Disadvantages of fluorescence microscopy are the very shallow depth of field and the often limited amount of light available which becomes apparent when specimens are photographed.

Fluorescence colour slides are made on a normal daylight film. When assessing exposure time, the correction factors vary from $1/_3$ to $1/_4$. Nevertheless, with a 100 ISO film, exposure times may still be several minutes. Black and white pictures are taken with orthochromatic film, because panchromatic film gives very little contrast. The use of a low speed (25 ISO) film is to be preferred, although exposure times can be as long as at least 15 minutes (no exposure correction required). Because of the very shallow depth of field, usually only a part of the image is in focus. The brightness increases with higher magnifications, but at the same time the depth of field becomes shallower. Lower magnifications thus require longer exposure times but generally give sharper pictures. Larger numbers of micrographs taken at various focusing levels can be combined into large composite photographs showing the organization of specimens up to several centimetres long (Kerp *et al.* 1990).

Further details on the study of fossil cuticles can be found in Kerp (1990 and literature cited therein) and Krings & Kerp (1997*b*).

We would like to thank everybody who contributed to this paper, either by discussions, notably Prof. Dr Manfred Barthel (Berlin), or by making specimens figured in this paper available for cuticular analysis, especially Dr Jean Langiaux (Gourdon), Dr Gilles Pacaud (Autun) and Dr Zbynek Simûnek (Prague). We gratefully acknowledge financial support by the Deutsche Forschungsgemeinschaft (DFG Ke 584/2-1 and Ke 584/2-2).

12. Scanning electron microscopy of megafossils and mesofossils

MARGARET E. COLLINSON

Scanning electron microscopy (SEM) is a routine technique in palaeobotany for observation and photomicrography. The technique produces high resolution, scientifically informative, three-dimensional images which maximize depth of field. It is particularly well-suited to opaque specimens which are not easily studied by light microscopy (LM). These images are widely accepted as a means of illustrating plant fossils in both non-specialist (Crane *et al.* 1995) and specialist journals. Individual specimens most suitable for SEM study range up to about 1 cm in diameter, a size limited by specimen holders in many machines, but more importantly by the size which it is possible to photograph as a single image (e.g. Fig. 12.1a). Larger objects can also be studied (as indeed they are routinely in forensic work) but this may require access to particular machines and/or tedious production of composite images.

Much material studied by SEM can be categorized as mesofossil, i.e. objects which can be seen by eye but not identified without the aid of a microscope. This category includes many individual organs such as fruits and seeds (Fig. 12.1a,e), megaspores and dispersed sporangia (Fig. 12.1f,i,j). In addition, portions of larger macrofossils are well suited for SEM study. These include cuticles prepared from leaves (Fig. 12.1l,m), wood fragments, portions of peels, cut and etched blocks of permineralized material and replicas (moulds or casts) of portions of impression fossils. Essentially, any suitably sized object can be studied with SEM provided it has clean surfaces, can be dried, and can be attached to a stub without fragmenting or suffering drastic distortion. Decisions about SEM methodology depend largely on evaluating the risk to the specimen and the significance of that risk – study of a unique holotype requires a different approach than study of specimens available by the hundred in a sieved residue.

SEM as a technique in plant palaeobiology

SEM is an essential tool for obtaining the quality illustrations and enabling the detailed observations which are required for descriptive and taxonomic purposes (including for comparisons between fossils and between fossils and modern material) and for the application of these data to systematic, phylogenetic and evolutionary interpretations. SEM study of late Cretaceous fossil flowers has enabled many to be identified in terms of Recent orders and families (Endress & Friis 1994; Eklund *et al.* 1997; Gandolfo *et al.* 1998; Sims *et al.* 1998) greatly improving our understanding of flowering plant evolution. The surface anatomy of digitate cells (Fig. 12.1d) together with the seed shape and the terminal germination plug carrying a micropyle and hilum combined on a central column (Fig. 12.1e) are diagnostic for seeds of the waterlily *Brasenia* which has therefore been shown to range from the early Tertiary to Recent. The surface cell anatomy and details of the micropyle and hilum can only be seen clearly with SEM (Collinson 1990). A combination of SEM with transmission electron microscopy (TEM) is often most informative, for example in studies of pollen (Eklund *et al.* 1997) and megaspores (Batten *et al.* 1998).

Surface details seen only by SEM can also provide evidence of taphonomic processes. Figure 12.1c shows a well-preserved surface of *Stratiotes* with attached 'mucilaginous' cells, whilst Fig. 12.1b shows a specimen where the seed coat has structural modifications (probably due to oxidative decomposition) (Hooker *et al.* 1995). Similarly Fig. 12.1d shows a *Brasenia* seed which has suffered no physical abrasion. Eroded microtopography or scratches indicate transport in an abrasive context (van Bergen *et al.* 1994a). SEM (and TEM) observations of plant fossils may therefore be key elements in monitoring morphological alterations during fossilization. The fossil cuticle of *Ginkgo* (Fig. 12.1m) looks very like that of modern *G. biloba* yet the chemistry is drastically altered. This shows that chemical modifications can occur without alteration to cuticle morphology (Collinson *et al.* 1998).

Features observed by SEM are important for understanding the reproductive biology of ancient plants and their role and interactions in ancient communities. These include evidence for germination (in Fig. 12.1e the cap on the *Brasenia* indicates that this seed had not germinated), presence of bisporangiate sori (Fig. 12.1f as in some *Salvinia* species) and ornamentation on pollen, spore and seed surfaces (Fig. 12.1h,j)

COLLINSON, M. E. 1999. Scanning electron microscopy of megafossils and mesofossils.
In: JONES, T. P. & ROWE, N. P. (eds) *Fossil Plants and Spores: modern techniques*.
Geological Society, London, 57–64.

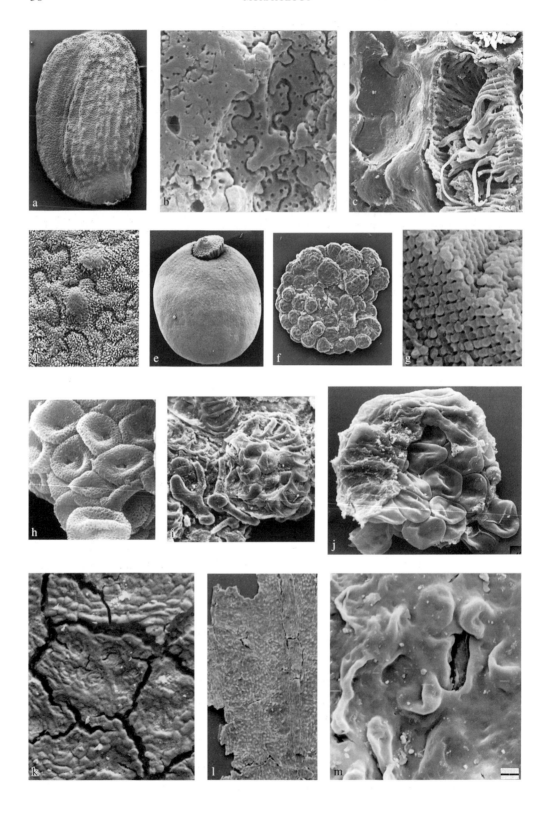

(Collinson 1998; Hemsley *et al.* 1998). Trace fossils of feeding observed by SEM may reveal dispersal and/or predation by animals (Collinson 1990; Hooker & Collinson in press). Contents and composition of coprolites studied by SEM can reveal ancient diets (Collinson 1990; Hooker & Collinson in press). Studies of stomata and substomatal tissues indicate the ecophysiology of early land plants whilst previously unexpected diversity in early land ecosystems is revealed by SEM study of Silurian and Devonian plant mesofossils including sporangia with *in situ* spores (Edwards 1996; Edwards *et al.* 1998).

Fossil charcoal (fusain) is characteristically opaque, black, brittle and inert and hence ideally suited to SEM study. This has revealed the past role of wildfire (Jones 1993) and ancient fire-prone plant communities (Cope 1993) and has utterly transformed our knowledge of early angiosperms, especially flowers, over the last 15 years (Endress & Friis 1994; Crane *et al.* 1995; Friis *et al.* 1995; Herendeen *et al.* 1995; Eklund *et al.* 1997; Gandolfo *et al.* 1998; Sims *et al.* 1998).

Routine SEM study led to the observation of colloidal crystal organization in spore walls (Fig. 12.1g) which has resulted in recognition of self-assembly as a key element in spore wall development (Hemsley *et al.* 1996a). Space limitations prevent a complete account of the applications of SEM in palaeobotany, a subject which was last reviewed by Hill (1990).

Preparation of specimens for standard SEM

The techniques in this section refer to organic specimens. Later parts of the chapter deal with replicas and permineralized or mineralized specimens. Hazard assessments should be made and adhered to for all chemicals and equipment referred to in this chapter.

Cleaning

Specimens will have been obtained according to the researcher's usual methods, such as rock disaggregation using water, hydrogen peroxide (H_2O_2) or hydrofluoric acid (HF); cuticle maceration etc (see Chapter 1; Collinson 1987, 1990, 1995; Kerp 1991; Tiffney 1991; Upchurch 1995; Wellman *et al.* 1996). Be aware that various preparation methods may produce different results, especially in the case of cuticle preparations (Thomas 1974; Kerp 1991; Upchurch 1995; Collinson *et al.* 1998). It is preferable that specimens should not be dried out until the final SEM mounting stage because the risk of breakage increases with number of drying cycles. Specimens which look superficially clean to the naked eye or under the transmitted or reflected light microscope often appear covered in debris when seen under SEM.

If specimens have been coated with varnish or lacquer or have been stored in glycerol or treated with carbowax there may be problems completely removing these materials (Collinson 1987, 1995). Lepage & Basinger (1993, 1994) described the use of a lacquer spray suitable for wet leaves in the field which they demonstrated could be removed to leave completely clean cuticles for SEM. Use of this method is therefore advocated if SEM studies are planned.

Organic specimens should be routinely cleaned by treatment in hydrochloric acid (HCl, use increasing concentrations, 10% to concentrated, if carbonate is believed to be present) followed by HF. Specimens should then be rinsed in HCl (to remove soluble fluorides) and fully neutralized by washing in distilled water. A polypropylene (not nylon or similar material) sieve mesh (meshes 75–115 µm diameter) enables washing directly from HF and speeds up the preparation (NORMESH; Northern Mesh and technical fabrics). A simple sieve can be made by using the lid to fix the mesh directly onto the open neck of a

---

Fig. 12.1. Photomicrographs illustrating the application of SEM in plant palaeobiology. (**a**) Large seed (Eocene *Stratiotes*) as a single image SEM. Scale bar = 1.7 mm. (**b**) Surface detail of Eocene *Stratiotes* seed revealing damage due to oxidative decomposition. Scale bar = 10 µm. (**c**) Surface detail of Eocene *Stratiotes* seed showing no deterioration. Scale bar = 10 µm. (**d**) Surface of sclerotesta, diagnostic of Eocene *Brasenia* and showing pristine preservation with no abrasion. Scale bar = 12.5 µm. (**e**) Seed showing diagnostic germination cap of Eocene *Brasenia*. Scale bar = 250 µm. (**f**) Sorus of a Miocene *Salvinia* species showing bisporangiate organization (larger megasporangia at top). Scale bar = 250 µm. (**g**) Iridescent colloidal crystal organization indicating self-assembly in spore walls (latest Palaeocene *Erlansonisporites*). Scale bar = 0.5 µm. (**h**) Smooth monoporate pollen of *Sparganiaceaepollenites* in an anther. Scale bar = 4.5 µm. (**i**) Part of sporangial cluster of *Acrostichum* showing sterile paraphyses. Scale bar = 32.5 µm. (**j**) Sporangium of *Acrostichum* showing smooth-walled slightly immature spore content. Scale bar = 25 µm. (**k**) Low vacuum SEM image of the surface of a leaf compression fossil, Miocene, China. This enabled study of stomatal parameters on a specimen from which cuticles could not be prepared. Scale bar = 25 µm. (**l**) Flat, uncurled sheet of fossil *Ginkgo* cuticle mounted using negative film. Scale bar = 135 µm. (**m**) Portion of fossil *Ginkgo* cuticle showing striking similarity with modern *Ginkgo* in spite of drastic chemical alteration (also mounted using negative film). Scale bar = 10 µm. For references and further details see Collinson (1990) and Hemsley *et al.* 1996a (g); Collinson *et al.* in press (l,m); van Bergen *et al.* 1994a (a–e).

polypropylene bottle, having cut away the centre of the lid to leave only the screw. It is essential that final rinses be carried out in distilled water and that specimens are transferred to clean containers. Avoid dusty working areas and keep containers covered to prevent entry of airborne particles. Washing on a sieve maximizes the removal of fine debris particles which can ruin the SEM image.

Alternatives to HF cleaning include ultrasonic baths (but these may fragment specimens), prolonged washing and further applications of extraction methods e.g. a second H_2O_2 or nitric acid (HNO_3) treatment. These must be evaluated based upon risk to the specimens and need for cleaning. For cleaning of surfaces prior to replication see the section on replicas.

Fracturing

To study internal anatomy, e.g. of seed coats; wood transverse sections (TS), tangential longitudinal sections (TLS) and radial longitudinal sections (RLS); spore walls (Fig. 12.1g); sporangia; flowers etc. it is preferable to fracture the specimen rather than cut it. Using a single-edged razor blade fracturing can be achieved by pressing onto the specimen and forcing a crack to propagate rather than cutting or pressing the blade right through the material which smears the surfaces. Fracturing or dissection can also be achieved using a scalpel and fine needle (Wellman et al. 1996); freezing under liquid nitrogen and hitting with a hammer (used for lignite rank woods – T. Jones, pers. comm. 1998) or sometimes simply by breaking the specimen by hand (personal observation; Sander & Gee 1990). Alternatively, natural breaks resulting from fossilization or handling can be used (Herendeen 1991; Batten et al. 1998). For comparative studies always use like planes of fracture. Preferably make fractures in water but, if dry, attempt to cover the specimen (e.g. with your free hand) to minimize risk of loss of fragments.

Drying

Experience has shown that specimens are best allowed to dry slowly in air. Selected specimens are picked from water into a clean glass dish using a fine or very fine (00000) sable hair paint brush. Finer brushes can be constructed by trimming off some of the hairs.The drying is more rapid if the excess water droplet is removed with the tip of a rolled piece of tissue (hold the tissue away from the dish to roll it, as most tissues shed fibres easily).

Mounting methods

Stubs

The metal pins or cylinders (stubs) on which specimens are mounted vary in size and shape according to the machine. Some machines can take special large stubs if needed. Do not assume that you can use stubs of one type in a machine designed for others. This may be possible but you may have to buy, or even design, a special adapter. First number stubs on their underside, ideally both with a permanent marker pen (easy to read) and with a needle scratched into the aluminium. Keep a careful catalogue of stubs and specimen details in a dedicated notebook or computer database in which you can also record photograph numbers.

Adhesives

Numerous adhesives are available to attach specimens to SEM stubs. The choice of adhesive depends on the nature of the material, any perceived need to remove material from the stub, the technical requirements of the EM unit and to some extent on personal preference.

I avoid the adhesive carbon pads or discs which are favoured by Wellman et al. (1996). I have found that they do not hold specimens sufficiently (resulting in charging) and that cracks frequently develop in the pad radiating from around the specimen. I also find it hard or impossible to remove small specimens without damage or adherent glue. The same objections apply to double-sided sellotape (in roll or sticky tab form) which also gives very unsuitable backgrounds. Wellman et al. (1996) obviously achieve good results with carbon pads; however, some of the backgrounds have been improved by inking out. Wellman et al. (1996) note that material does not sink into carbon pads (see section on curation) and that specimens 'can be removed relatively easily with little danger of breakage' (p.214).

At the other extreme is the use of an epoxy resin, such as Araldite. This is strong but permanent, and so should never be considered if there is any chance that specimens will need to be removed from the stubs (e.g. to study the opposite surface, to study with LM or TEM, for curatorial or conservation purposes etc.). However, Araldite is often favoured by staff in EM units using high resolution microscopes (including field emission SEM). This is because other adhesives can outgas volatiles under vacuum which deposit on the column or filament, reducing machine performance and image resolution. It is important to discuss your requirements with the EM unit staff.

I currently use Bostik diluted with acetone (c.

50/50 mixture) to a slightly viscous fluid. I first mount a 13 mm diameter coverglass onto the stub using undiluted Bostik. This gives a smooth background. Glue droplets on the coverslip are used for large specimens and films or smears of glue for small specimens. I have also used UHU, which I do not find as satisfactory, and Durofix (no longer available), but any acetone-soluble glue is worth trying.

Bostik and similar glues presumably outgas volatiles under vacuum. I have not noticed problems with machine performance at the range of magnifications that I use routinely ($\times$ 10 to $\times$ 5000, $\times$ 10 000 more rarely). I do leave specimens in the coater usually for at least 15 min with several argon flushes prior to coating and this may help remove volatiles. An additional precaution would be to place mounted stubs in a vacuum desiccator or to leave them for a prolonged period in a coating unit. A very thin smear of Araldite can also be used to glue a coverslip onto an SEM stub and this is to be recommended for study using high resolution machines. A drop of Araldite extending from the glass to the stub may help to reduce charging.

The knack with any adhesive is to obtain the perfect compromise between a sufficiently viscous state that the glue will not 'ride up' around the specimen, whilst also ensuring that the glue is not too dry to prevent adhesion. With acetone (or other solvent-soluble glues) mistakes can be rectified by removing the specimens (see specimen removal below). This is not possible with permanent adhesives. It is not generally possible to describe the ideal state of the adhesive for a given situation. This knowledge is acquired through experience. Furthermore, some days just seem to be bad for stub preparation due, perhaps, to humidity extremes. Long-term storage and contamination of diluted adhesive may also cause problems. Specimens are transferred to the stub using a fine to very fine paint brush dampened very slightly with distilled water, then wiped on lint-free tissue. (A common short cut is to lick the brush but this is not to be recommended and saliva can leave a deposit on the specimen.) I never use tweezers or needles to handle my specimens, although others do so.

Numerous examples of smaller specimens can be mounted on a single stub. This facilitates comparisons and speeds up observations by reducing the number of stub changes and machine pump down time. However, if specimens cannot be removed this can cause problems for curators if stubs have specimens of different taxa. If possible, only place groups of one specimen type on one stub.

Carbon putty (Apiezon carbon putty) can be used to hold items temporarily. This is suitable for robust objects for short single observations, e.g. per-mineralized seeds or small rock specimens con-taining plant fragments. However, the putty may stick to, or leave a stain on, some specimens so it is necessary to test an unimportant specimen or area first.

Silver dag

Colloidal silver dag or silver conducting paint (as an adhesive or as a small 'strip' from specimen to stub) is recommended by some users as a means of reducing charging (electron build-up). It certainly helps with large or porous objects but I only use it as an absolute last resort because it gives an unsuitable background, it is impossible to remove without distributing fine silver particles all over the specimen and it also outgasses volatiles under vacuum.

Negative film

Specimens which curl up on drying (e.g. cuticle sheets Fig. 12.1l,m) or suspensions of smaller objects (e.g. fragments of cuticle, pollen and spores, etc.) can be mounted from a water droplet following Moore et al. (1991) and Collinson et al. (in press). The stub is prepared by attaching, with Araldite, a small square of unexposed, developed negative film, emulsion side uppermost. Do not damage the surface when mounting the film. Allow the Araldite to cure. Pipette a droplet of suspension onto the film or, alternatively, pipette a droplet of distilled water and lift the cuticle sheet into that droplet allowing the cuticle to spread out. Leave the water to evaporate slowly, e.g. 24 h at room temperature (but partially cover the stubs to prevent airborne contamination). Adhesion results on drying of the moistened gelatine film onto which particles or flat cuticle sheets have settled.

Specimen removal

Specimens mounted with solvent soluble glues can be removed from stubs. This is achieved by gently brushing between the specimen and the glue with a fine brush dipped in, or flooded with, the solvent. With care, a single specimen can be removed from a multiple mount. Specimens mounted on carbon pads are removed by Wellman et al. (1996) with fine needles.

Stub storage & curation

Stubs are best stored in a relatively controlled humidity and dust-free environment. A sealed desiccator cabinet is ideal with homemade alter-natives, including bench top desiccators (Collinson 1987, 1995). Small boxes are available designed to store specific types of stubs. These are relatively expensive and again homemade alternatives are sufficient. The essential requirements are that the stubs will stay in the holders, and that the unit holding the stubs will not slip causing the stubs to hit the lid, even if the box is tipped upside down. Tubes for individual stubs (stubs inserted inside the cap and covered by the tube) are ideal for curation in museum collections, for storage amongst other specimens. In this case it is hoped that the control of the museum environment will be sufficient to prevent specimen deterioration. If desiccant is placed in stub tubes or boxes it must be enclosed and immobilized to prevent damage to specimens. Sketches should be made labelling multiple specimens on stubs to ensure that curators and future researchers can locate specimens. If orientation of the sketch is not immediately obvious a distinctive feature (e.g. small object or glue drop) can be added to the stub for orientation purposes.

The shelf life of specimens on SEM stubs is largely unknown and will certainly vary according to the shelf life of the adhesive and the type of specimen (Collinson 1987, 1995). In particular, adhesives such as double-sided sellotape and some solvent-soluble adhesives allow specimens to sink into the adhesive with time (Collinson 1995; Wellman et al. 1996). If specimens can be removed from stubs without damage this may be preferable. On the other hand a future researcher may well need to remount them for SEM observation. Furthermore, some specimens are too delicate to remove safely. Collinson (1995) reported that specimens mounted on stubs with Durofix had been re-examined successfully after 15 years. Specimens on stubs made over 20 years ago and stored in a sealed dessicator cabinet were recently re-examined (personal observation). These included small seeds for comparison with 'Scirpus' lakensis Chandler (see Collinson 1996). Results were the same as those obtained for newly collected and newly mounted specimens although recoating was necessary. It is not helpful to directly compare the new and original SEM photographs because the originals were on 35 mm negatives from a Cambridge S600 whilst the new images were on 120 negatives from a Philips 501B. Wellman et al. (1996, fig. 4) figured SEM images of in situ Devonian spores taken less than five years apart from stubs stored in a sealed box but without environmental control. The specimen was recoated prior to re-examination. They concluded that the ornament (spinose elements with dimensions approx. 0.5–2 µm) on the spores could no longer be recognized as belonging to the species to which the spores were originally assigned. Collinson (in Moore et al. 1991, p.60 and plate 66d–g) re-examined (recoated) stubs with modern pollen grains of Tilia which had been prepared 3 years

before (mounted with negative film). These grains showed very fine scale cracking on the surface (at × 10 000) which it was suggested had arisen due to differential expansion and contraction of the grains and the original coating during storage. The fine surface features (pattern of surface reticulum with lumina from 0.1–1 µm) important for distinction of pollen from different Tilia species, were not affected and all three species could still be readily distinguished. Wellman et al. (1996) documented that the early land plant material (late Silurian to early Devonian) which they studied became extremely fragile when dried, further influencing the likely storage time of specimens on stubs. In this context the photographic negatives or electronic files (see photomicrography) of images attain as high a significance as the specimens themselves, a point also noted by those studying microfossils and pollen (Collinson 1995; Wellman et al., 1996). For advice on storage methods for duplicate specimens see Collinson (1995).

Permineralized and petrified material

If specimens can be dissolved intact from permineralizations treat these according to the preparation methods described above for isolated organic objects. Cut blocks of permineralized material can be polished as if for peeling (see Chapter 13) and then very deeply etched instead of lightly etched. The blocks are then mounted etched surface uppermost (without touching the etched surface) and the exposed cells and tissues can be studied. If the block is large, a rigid permanent adhesive such as Araldite, may be preferable. The specimen block can be attached to the stub and then polished and etched successively. Thick acetate peels can be taken in between for a permanent record. Holmes & Lopez (1986) described a special technique involving dissolving peels which enabled examination of delicate cell walls in phloem and allowed distinction of genuine cell wall sculpturing from that due to flaws in slides and carbonate material (see also Chapter 13). Isolated permineralized and petrified specimens can be viewed by SEM in much the same way as organic material (e.g. Manchester 1988; Crane et al. 1990). Care must always be taken in interpretation of anatomical structures and ornamentation as one is often observing the infill of spaces rather than the original structure, or a complex mixture of both (Kenrick & Edwards 1988; Crane et al. 1990).

Moulds and casts (replicas)

Replicas can be used if it is impossible or undesirable to SEM the specimen, or if only a small part of a large specimen is needed (e.g. one leaf cushion of a *Lepidodendron* stem). Replicas are also appropriate if a positive is required from a negative impression. Successful SEM study is dependent on two parameters: the resolution of the moulding and casting materials, and the cleanliness of the surface which is being replicated. Unwanted organic material (e.g. coaly material on a shale block) can be removed to leave a clean surface for replication by heating the shale to red heat in an open coal fire (Chaloner & Collinson 1975a). Presumably heating in a furnace would also achieve the same effect. Hill (1990) reviewed moulding materials and concluded that Dow Corning silicone rubber 9161 with catalyst 9162 produced the best results amongst the latex and silcone rubbers tested, whilst for resolution of fine structure (e.g. pollen and spore ornamentation) cellulose acetate peels were most effective. The Dow Corning silicone rubber takes up to 3 h to dry so a dam should be built around the specimen to prevent the rubber flowing away. In studies of fine-scale tooth microwear (Collinson & Hooker 1991) we have used a dental moulding material – Coltène President light body polyvinylsiloxane base and catalyst (as is used in human dentistry) – which cures quickly (about 2–10 min depending on conditions). Casts were made using epoxy resin. No separating agents are necessary. For other materials and some safety information see Hamilton Waters (1983). In the case of fossil plants the mould is usually studied directly because this yields a positive replica (external mould) from a negative impression fossil (Hill 1990; Chaloner & Collinson 1975a). As replicas are usually repeatable, any adhesive which is compatible with the material will suffice. Replicas can be photographed easily by light microscopy (e.g. Manchester 1992) but high resolution work (e.g. stomatal structure, pollen and spore ornament) requires SEM observations (Hill 1990).

Coating

Most specimens need to be coated so as to conduct electrons away from the surface and prevent charging. Gold or gold palladium are used commonly but the choice of coating is only really critical in very high resolution work if there is a chance that the coating particles or surface texture may interfere with the image. If there is a possibility that elemental analyses will be used then the specimen should be carbon coated. Generally, carbon coating is not suitable for routine work as it results in noisy images and poor resolution. Sputter coaters can be calibrated to give a known thickness, though again this is usually only appropriate for very high resolution work.

Gold coating has been successfully removed from plant fossils (Manchester & Crane 1983; Manchester 1988; Kenrick & Edwards 1988) by treatment in an aqueous solution of sodium cyanide (Sela & Boyde 1977). An alternative method using amalgamation with mercury (Sela 1977) has not to my knowledge been attempted on plant fossils.

Photomicrography

Film selection is rarely a matter for the user as it will be chosen according to the machine being used. Larger negative sizes (e.g. FP4 120 roll film) are preferable in my experience. Contact sheets are quickly prepared and enable easy comparison of many images. Instant hard copies of images can be obtained by Polaroid film whilst many SEMs now have a 'video print' facility. However, these images are generally of too poor quality for publication. Electronic storage of images is becoming increasingly common. One method is to store images as *.tif (TIFF) files on a floppy disk (a 1.4 MB disk can store three to four images) or optical disk (1000 images per disk). Ultimately images can be transferred to CD-ROM storage (Wellman *et al.* 1996). The *.tif images can be imported into many graphics packages, such as CORELDRAW or POWERPOINT. Laser prints on glossy paper can give images of publication quality (T. Jones, pers. comm. 1998).

SEM images need to have good contrast and to have uninterrupted dark backgrounds around the specimens. This is partly controlled by the adhesive, the smoothness and cleanliness of the mount and also by the machine parameters. New users will need to experiment with the best settings of gain and black levels (brightness and contrast) and should not necessarily accept the settings of the previous machine user or the automatic brightness and contrast (ABC) settings. As a courtesy always check if there is a standard setting for the machine and return it to those settings before you leave.

In addition the KV (electron voltage) and the spot (final aperture) size can drastically alter the image obtained. For example, thin specimens will be affected by beam penetration at higher KVs, and in thin seed coats the surface expression of cell anatomy cannot be seen on some settings (personal observation). At magnifications above 2500 smaller spot sizes are usually needed to improve resolution. Higher KVs maximize the problems of charging, so reduced KV may be necessary even though it can result in less contrast, and noisier less well-resolved images. New SEM users need to obtain appropriate training on the machines from a skilled operator.

Low vacuum (LV SEM) and environmental SEM (ESEM)

If it is necessary or preferable to avoid coating specimens (e.g. type specimens or large specimens) these can be imaged using low vacuum SEM in an 'environmental chamber' (EC). Such a system is attached to an ISI ABT 55 SEM at the Natural History Museum, London, UK and uses a Robinson backscattered electron detector (BSE) with a charge-free anticontamination device (Taylor 1986; Hill 1990). The resolution of this technique is limited to between $\times 1000$ and $\times 500$ magnification depending on the material. The fact that the BSE detector shows atomic contrast means that organic material on an organic-rich matrix can be hard to distinguish. Figure 12.1k shows a portion of a leaf on which stomata and epidermal cell outlines are visible. The cuticles could not be prepared from this leaf and they also did not fluoresce (personal observation) so the LV SEM image offered a means to obtain stomatal parameters, furthermore the leaf is retained intact. (Note that the cracks are original and not caused by the EM). Hill (1990) obtained good quality images with LV SEM, especially from replicas (see above) and charcoal.

True environmental scanning electron microscopy (ESEM) also may not require coating but in addition allows the investigation of wet specimens in their natural state. The samples can be imaged in the presence of water vapour or a variety of other gases. Temperature and pressure in the chamber can be varied (Keddie *et al.* 1996). ESEM is manufactured by Philips Electron Optics and does have potential applications in palaeobotany, for example, if specimen cracking during drying is a problem the ESEM enables imaging of damp specimens. However, because SEM observes surfaces a wet surface will merely provide an image of water, so experience with chamber control would be essential. ESEM uses an adapted and patented secondary electron detector and resolution is therefore comparable with conventional SEM of coated dry specimens and much better than LV SEM for uncoated specimens. I am not aware of any published work with ESEM on palaeobotanical material.

Part Three   Anatomy

13. The acetate peel technique

JEAN GALTIER & TOM L. PHILLIPS

The peel technique, originally developed as a cheap and rapid alternative to the thin section method, revealed another advantage: the possibility of obtaining very close serial sections. The invaluable information thus obtained on tissues systems allows, among others, the development of onto-genetic and biomechanical approaches in fossil plants.

The rapid peel technique (Joy *et al.* 1956) utilizes a preformed sheet of clear cellulose acetate and acetone to embed and remove anatomical sections of permineralized plants. In the process of permineralization the plant tissues and associated detritus were embedded by infiltration and precipitation of mineral matter (Fig. 13.1A). The peel technique simply disembeds or exposes a thin layer of the plant material on the surface by means of chemical removal of the mineral matrix with acids. In turn, the exposed cellular structures are re-embedded in the clear acetate peel, which provides the equivalent of a thin slice through the plant material. There are varied degrees of cell wall preservation and alteration, ranging from almost pristine (Fig. 13.1A, a) to very poor in cases where the residual carbon is lost during later phases of the permineralization process. In these latter cases, the cell boundary may persist (Fig. 13.1A, b) or finally be lost (Fig. 13.1A, c). Transitional forms of preservation may occur within the same fossil plant specimen.

Standard procedure

The following description of the procedure is based on carbonate coal balls, which provide the simplest example with the least restrictive requirements. Specific modifications and warnings are provided for other types of permineralizations.

Preparation of the specimen

Coal balls are customarily cut by lapidary saws with industrial diamonds embedded in the blade edge; the saw blades are cooled by a cutting oil or by water that washes away the removed carbonates. Coal ball slices need to be thoroughly cleaned of cutting oil, usually with a harsh detergent and hot water. The cut surface is smoothed on a lapidary wheel or on a thick glass plate using a paste of abrasive powder (carborundum/silicon carbide) with water. A smooth level surface helps avoid shallow puddles of acetone, which cause wrinkling of the sheet. Thoroughly remove all abrasive and rinse the specimen.

Etching and washing

Place the wet specimen, smooth surface down-wards, in 5% hydrochloric acid (HCl) for about 15 seconds. The bubbles that emerge are carbon dioxide. The specimen may be hand-held in the acid with protective rubber gloves or placed on a few small polyethylene holders on the bottom of the polyethylene container to support the specimen. Avoid holding or touching the surface being etched.

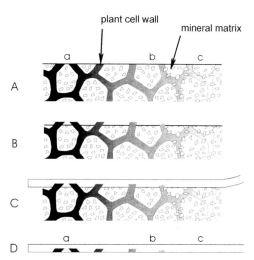

Fig. 13.1. Successive stages in the peel section method applied to a permineralized specimen showing transition from excellent preservation of cell wall (a) to very poor where the residual carbon has been gradually lost (b–c) during later phases of the permineralization. (**A**) The ground surface of the specimen. (**B**) After etching the well preserved organic material projects slightly above the surface whereas the poorer preservation is destroyed. (**C**) The acetate peel is applied to the surface. (**D**) When dry, the peel is removed bringing a thin section of plant cell walls embedded in the cellulose acetate, except in the poorer preservation (c). (Modified from Lacey 1963 and Bateman 1991.)

GALTIER, J. & PHILLIPS, T. L. 1999. The acetate peel technique. *In*: JONES, T. P. & ROWE, N. P. (eds) *Fossil Plants and Spores: modern techniques.* Geological Society, London, 67–70.

The untreated surface of the specimen may be coated with latex paint. Promptly rinse with a gentle stream of tap water for a few seconds and let dry.

Using HCl of a particular concentration permits preliminary tests of the desired etching time. For most calcitic coal balls this averages 15 s with 5% HCl. The etching time for calcareous permineralizations with cold 2–10% HCl may vary from 10 s to several minutes in the longer cases, this is usually indicative of dolomitic cements. Siliceous permineralization may require cold commercial (25–40%) hydrofluoric acid (HF), 30 s to 3 min. Phosphatic and limonitic permineralizations may require 40% HF for 1–2 min followed by 10% HCl, 1–2 min.

Caution: All acids must be used with due caution and HF is an extremely hazardous acid. Use closed polyethylene containers, work in a fume cupboard and wear adequate protective clothing. Be very careful in holding large specimens in acid baths, particularly with HF. The guidelines of the institute's safety officer must be followed when using this acid. When HF is used it is recommended first to immerse the specimen in a solution of sodium carbonate to neutralize the acid before washing with a gentle stream of water or by immersion in a container of water with a gentle stream for up to 30 min.

Drying

Place the specimen, etched-face-up to dry on a surface of pea-sized gravel; this protects the etched surface with very fragile plant cell walls which protrude a few tens of microns above the mineral surface (Fig. 13.1B). Thirty minutes or more may be required for air drying but this may be reduced by gently flooding the surface with acetone or alcohol. If the surface is not perfectly dry a milky opaque area will form on parts of the peel.

Applying the cellulose acetate sheet (Fig. 13.1C)

Use cellulose acetate sheet (see Appendix) 0.05–0.075 mm (0.002–0.003 in.) thick. Cut a piece of sufficient size to extend well beyond the edges of the specimen surface. Place the specimen with the etched surface nearly level and then partially flood about half of the surface with acetone. From the flooded end, quickly and gently roll the acetate sheet with flexed tension, across the surface; the excess acetone should be pushed in front of the sheet as it flattens and excludes air bubbles. If acetone evaporates prior to the sheet covering all the area, add acetone and continue rolling on the peel.

Caution: Acetone is both toxic and flammable, thus it should be used in a well ventilated area, or fume cupboard.

Removing the peel (Fig. 13.1D)

Because the surface is wet with acetone, the peel is dark at first; it changes colour and becomes lighter as it dries; wait at least 30 min (one or two hours is more preferable) to remove the peel by lifting it at one side and gently pulling it off the surface. Use a razor blade if the peel sticks. Peels removed too early tend to curl. The specimen is now ready for repetition of the process after a quick smoothing of its surface (use carborundum 400 to 600-grit paste or paper grade 1000). As many as 20 peels may be made from a 1 mm thickness of petrifaction.

Storing peels

After their rough edges have been trimmed the peels are numbered, placed in labelled envelopes and stored in a dry place. Note that peels are flammable.

Examining, cleaning and mounting peels

The peel section can be examined directly under a dissecting microscope using reflected light, on a white background, with the shiny side up. When greater resolution is required, part of the peel may be cut out and mounted on a microscope slide. Submerge the cut-out peel section, rough surface up, for about 10 min in a 10% solution of HCl to remove adhering calcite. Next place the peel in a container of water to remove the acid; blot dry the peel and place between paper towels and weighted, for 24 hours at 40°C on a warming plate. At this stage, the weight will prevent the edges curling. After immersion of the dried peel section for a few seconds in xylene, it can be mounted in Canada balsam or equivalent mounting media. Note that only Natural balsam remains unaltered by oxidation over long periods of time. (**Caution**: xylene is a carcinogen and must be handled with the appropriate safety precautions.) Large unmounted peels can be covered with a clean glass plate and photographed by reflected light; peels can also be placed directly in the place of film negatives in photographic enlargers for producing diagrams or drawings and used with grid overlays for quantitative analyses.

The method of Joy et al. (1956) has been further described by Lacey (1963), Stewart & Taylor (1965) and Phillips et al. (1976), where more details on slide mounting procedures may be found.

List of materials required: clear cellulose acetate, standard grade 0.075 mm or 0.003 in. thick; Nº 400 Carborundum, large glass plates; polyethylene containers; Natural Canada Balsam (preferable to all synthetic resins); standard glass microscope slides (25 × 75 mm) and cover slips or larger microscope slides (50 × 75 mm).

The liquid peel technique

The modern rapid peel technique is actually an improvement of the liquid peel method introduced by Walton (1928). A cellulose ester solution is poured on the levelled surface of the permineralized specimen. Details on the liquid peel method are given in Darrah (1936), Lacey (1963) and Stewart & Taylor (1965). It is used on permineralizations with exposed irregular surfaces and on flat surfaces, such as those of sporangial masses where sporangia or spore masses have been plucked out by previous peel preparations. Liquid peels are still recommended for obtaining sections or transfers of imperfectly flattened/coarse surfaces such as those of stems or leaves preserved as adpressions. The main limitations of the liquid peel technique are the necessity of fume hood ventilation, long drying time (at least 24 h), variable thickness of the peel and a yellowing of the peel with age.

Plant material suitable for the peel technique

The great success of the acetate peel technique was related to the 1960s boom in the studies of coal ball plants and this method also proved to be very useful with many other types of permineralized plants; examples of these are listed below in decreasing order of relative ease and suitability:

(a) Permineralizations
  1. Calcareous permineralization by deposition of microcrystalline calcite (and dolomite).
     - Plants from fossil peats in Pennsylvanian to Permian coal balls from Europe, Ukraine, China, Canada, USA.
     - Plants from calcareous cobbles, e.g. *Psilophyton* from Gaspé, Canada (Early Devonian).
     - Plants associated with volcanic rocks: e.g. Lower Carboniferous basaltic terrains in Scotland (Pettycur).
     - Plants associated with alluvial and lagoonal sediments: e.g. Berwickshire localities of the Lower Carboniferous of Scotland.
  2. Siliceous permineralization by deposition of colloidal silica forming chalcedony (chert) or microcrystalline quartz.

  - Plants encountered in cherts generally associated with hot springs and volcanic rocks of acidic type: e.g. Lower Devonian of Rhynie; Lower Carboniferous of Esnost (France); Pennsylvanian of Grand-Croix (France).
  - Fossil peat from the Permian and Triassic of the Transantarctic Mountains of Antarctica.
  3. Siliceous to phosphatic permineralization in phosphatic nodules and/or radiolarian cherts in marine sediments, e.g. from the lower-most Carboniferous of Saalfeld (Germany), Montagne Noire (France), New Albany Shale (Kentucky).
     NB Most of these fossils (see (c)1) produce peels of irregular quality.
(b) Fusain *sensu lato*, showing black-blue, brittle cell walls.
   Some material mentioned above ((a)1–2) shows transitions to this type within the same plant fragment (e.g. in calcareous permineralization from Pettycur) and other materials show a mixture of purely fusainized fragments, perhaps of different origins, with calcified or silicified ones (e.g. in coal balls or in Grand-Croix cherts). NB Peels with fusain are generally of poor quality due to a lack of adherence between the acetate and the fusainized cell wall.
(c) Material corresponding to later phases of the permineralization process where cell walls are progressively replaced by minerals.
  1. Incomplete loss of the residual carbon where sometimes cell boundary information alone persists (Fig. 13.1A, b); this applies mainly to siliceous permineralizations already mentioned ((a)2–3) showing the transition of one type to another, e.g. material from Rhynie, Grand-Croix or Montagne Noire.
     NB In this case the peels may be of poor quality (Fig. 13.1D, b) but serial peel sections provide invaluable new information (Edwards 1980; Combourieu & Galtier 1985) when used in combination with traditional thin sectioning. With such material additional information and sharper contrast may also be obtained with photography, using reflected light with the peel still on the surface of the specimen.
  2. When the cell wall is completely replaced by minerals = petrifaction *sensu stricto* (Fig. 13.1A, c) the peel technique does not work (Fig. 13.1D, c); thin sectioning, wafering or polished surfaces are the appropriate techniques (see Chapter 17). This applies to widespread fossil woods of petrified forests from the Permian to the Tertiary.

Applications of the peel technique

Anatomical studies and systematics

Originally developed as an alternative to the thin section method, the rapid peel technique provides anatomical data, which constitute one traditional basis of systematic studies. Anatomical information has also been more recently used in biomechanical analyses of fossil plants (see Chapter 20).

Morphological studies and whole plant reconstructions

An incomparable and unique advantage of the peel technique with regard to thin sectioning (including wafering) is to obtain very close serial sections and of potentially very large areas; this allows 3D reconstructions of small organs (ovules, buds, sporangia) as well as complex organs (cupules) or even branched systems of great length (Holmes 1977) and, finally, reconstruction of the gross morphology of whole plants, such as *Psilophyton dawsonii* (Banks *et al.* 1975).

Rapid selection of material

This applies to coal balls or cherts where plant material is not well exposed on the surface of the specimen. The permineralized block is sectioned through the middle and a peel prepared from one face; a quick examination will provide information on the contents and permit selection of the best specimens. This method has been used with success, using a 'mobile' power saw cooled by water, in the field by J. Holmes for selecting informative coal-balls in Great Britain (Galtier 1997). Less than 10% of coal-balls examined were kept for study but the large collection of peels provided a random sample of information on peat biomass to be used in palaeoecological studies (see below).

Quantitative analysis

The palaeoecological interpretations of coal ball peats pioneered by Phillips *et al.* (1974) (see Chapter 39) are based on the study of large numbers of peel sections – the only method available for obtaining the entire cross-sectional areas of coal balls – which are sometimes of very large size.

Ultrastructural studies

Thick peel sections with their rough surface up, observed under SEM, provide useful information, e.g. on spore and pollen wall ultrastructure (Combourieu & Galtier 1985). Peel sections also have been used in the disappearing peel technique (Holmes & Lopez 1986) for high magnification studies of plant wall structure (see Chapter 22).

14. Embedding techniques: adhesives and resins

TIM P. JONES & NICK P. ROWE

Fossil plants and spores are routinely embedded for morphological, anatomical or biogeochemical studies. A wide variety of different techniques have been developed, many of which are identical or very similar to those used for rocks and minerals (e.g. Humphries 1992). This chapter will briefly outline the underlying principles which palaeo-botanists should consider when devising embedd-ing protocols. Embedding techniques which were developed or adapted primarily for palaeobotanical specimens will be described. We will also describe strategies which can be adopted for the embedding of more problematic palaeobotanical materials, such as highly porous or extremely small macro-fossil remains and spores. In this section we focus on some of the embedding procedures for dealing with macrofossils, for light and reflected light microscope preparations. For accounts dealing with electron microscopy the reader is referred to Chapters 12, 21–24.

The embedding and polishing methods required by a palaeobotanist for anatomical studies, may differ from the strict protocols laid down by the International Organisation of Standardization (ISO, 7404/2 – 1985 (E)) for coal petrographic analysis. This chapter will concentrate mostly on techniques for palaeobotanists, but will briefly outline the 'standard' methodologies. It should be noted that the ISO information is not widely available in libraries. Furthermore, there are limitations con-cerning this literature because you are not permitted to reproduce (photocopy) it because of copyright laws. To us, this situation seems counter-productive in terms of establishing international standards, which should be widely and easily available.

It is important to have a clear objective and research goal in mind before starting any of the actual embedding. With changes in research directions or new ideas, it is often possible to remove rocks or minerals from cured resin, and re-use or re-embed the material; this luxury only applies to some fossil plants and spores. Further-more, contact with chemicals often renders the fossils useless for other biogeochemical studies. Always meticulously follow manufacturer's instructions, and do all 'wet' resin work in a fume cupboard (unless in the field). Even domestically available resins such as Araldite can cause 'skin sensitization', and some such as Spurr's Resin are highly carcinogenic. Always carefully read manufacturers' instructions, and when working with unfamiliar resins always check with your departmental safety officer before use.

Macrofossil remains normally require embedd-ing prior to (i) sectioning for anatomical investi-gation (permineralized material) and (ii) deep surface etching (transfer preparation) for com-pression material. In the former, resins are used to prevent the specimen fragmenting during cutting, grinding and polishing. In the latter, the resin retains organic material, cuticle and the like, while the rest of the mineral surface of the compression fossil is dissolved away in an acid (which does not attack the organic material or the resin). There is an important difference between what we refer to as 'surface embedding' in which specimens are coated with resin to prevent them fragmenting while being trimmed, and 'impregnation embedding' where attempts are made to internally consolidate porous and friable specimens prior to cutting and grinding. The choice of resin depends on the procedure in mind and this is usually a compromise of variables including specimen size and porosity, resin cost/availability and the kind of observation required. When specimens are being embedded or mounted in resin for analyses in specific equipment it is strongly recommended that you contact the operators prior to starting the resin work, and discuss the preparation requirements. Several suppliers of resins, adhesives, etc. are listed in the Appendix.

Types of embedding resins

Cold-setting polyester resin

This is a commonly used, versatile, and relatively safe resin. It consists of two components; an unsaturated polyester resin in styrene monomer, and a catalyst of methyl ethyl ketone peroxide solution in plasticizer. Follow manufacturers' mixing instructions for ratios of resin to catalyst; these are typically in the range 50 : 1. For accuracy of mixing, pour the resin into a pre-marked graduated polythene beaker (once the resin has hardened the polythene beaker walls can be flexed, any residual solid resin removed, and the beaker re-used), and measure the catalyst with a graduated

JONES, T. P. & ROWE, N. P. 1999. Embedding techniques: adhesives and resins. *In*: JONES, T. P. & ROWE, N. P. (eds) *Fossil Plants and Spores: modern techniques.* Geological Society, London, 71–75.

syringe. Once added together, mix thoroughly, but not too vigorously as this can cause an excess of bubbles in the resin. The resin will start to set in a matter of minutes (pot life), thus it is best to prepare the moulds and samples as much as possible prior to mixing. As the resin starts to become more viscous its impregnation and adhesion properties decrease proportionally. Avoid, if possible, making large volumes of resin as the heat this will generate can cause a variety of problems. Although the resin will be hardened within a few hours, leaving the blocks for a few days before polishing will result in a better polish. To obtain an accurate ratio of resin:catalyst it is recommended that volumes not less than 50 ml resin:1 ml catalyst are mixed. Do not discard any excess resin but make 'blank' blocks; these have a range of uses as described later. Fossil plant material can be lighter than the embedding resin, and therefore when the resin is poured, carefully positioned samples can move or even float. This can be avoided by embedding in two stages. First deposit a thin film of resin on the base of the mould to hold the specimen; second, when that has cured and is holding the specimen securely, the mould can be filled (Figure 1, 1A-1D). A final embedded and polished block is shown in Fig. 14.1, 4.

Cold-mounting epoxy resin

These consist of two components, the adhesive and the hardener. One advantage of the epoxy resins over cold-setting polyester resins is that some epoxy resin products are supplied in pairs of tubes or syringes, where equal proportions of adhesive and hardener are used, extremely small amounts can be mixed accurately. Rapid-setting epoxy resins are available with pot lives of only a few minutes; these are useful, for example, where a fossil needs to be orientated precisely in a block, and can be held in position by hand while the resin sets.

Epoxy resins – hot setting

These are often used in rock embedding, but are less useful for plants. The main advantage is when a sample needs to soak in the resin for a prolonged period to obtain good impregnation, i.e. for a number of hours or even days. The resins are set by heating in an oven, with typical curing protocols of 185°C for 15 min or 200°C for 5 min. With especially porous or absorbent fossils (such as fossil charcoal) hot-setting resin can be used in conjunction with vacuum treatment, the idea being that a series of vacuuming/venting cycles will assist the impregnation. In our experience the real

effectiveness of this approach is questionable. However, it has been used very successfully by other workers, for example, in the embedding of calcareous algal plates (see Chapter 53), as well as fossil plant material. If you attempt this method, apply only a thin film to the surface of the fossil because putting a thick coat of resin over the surface acts as a seal, making the vacuuming/venting futile (Fig. 14.1, 2A–B).

Cyanoacrylates

The 'superglues' so beloved by DIY enthusiasts. These are single component adhesives which are catalysed by surface moisture on the specimens. Cyanoacrylates are normally sold as low viscosity liquids, but there is also a gel version available. Used correctly, these adhesives will achieve handling strengths within seconds, but full bond needs 12 to 24 h. Cyanoacrylates can be obtained from domestic suppliers or from the manufacturers. Although many domestic sources sell cyano-acrylates at varying viscosities for different household applications, specific viscosities can be specified from the manufacturer. For void-filling during embedding or wafer/thin section preparation, less viscous cyanoacrylates are necessary. The very thin nature of some cyanoacrylates means that they are easily absorbed into porous fossil material. This characteristic can be advantageously used both in the field and the laboratory (see Chapter 14). Extremely delicate fossils can be 'painted' with adhesive. A 5 ml plastic pot of Superglue should be essential field equipment. Hardened cyanoacrylates can be polished. More specifically, a cyanoacrylate-based product 'Paleobond' for palaeontological applications has been developed particularly for fieldwork and hand specimen preparation.

Composite embedding

Different types of resin will bond to each other. Thus for example, 'blank' blocks can be cheaply and easily made out of cold-setting polyester resin. The polishing face can be ground down with a diamond lap and coarse grit, and holes drilling into the face with a high speed bit. Specimens can then be orientated in the holes using rapid setting epoxy resin or cyanoacrylate adhesives, then the surrounding hole filled with cold-setting polyester or epoxy resins, then ground down and polished.

Other resins

The resins described above will successfully embed the vast majority of plant fossils, but occasionally specialist resins or materials need to be employed.

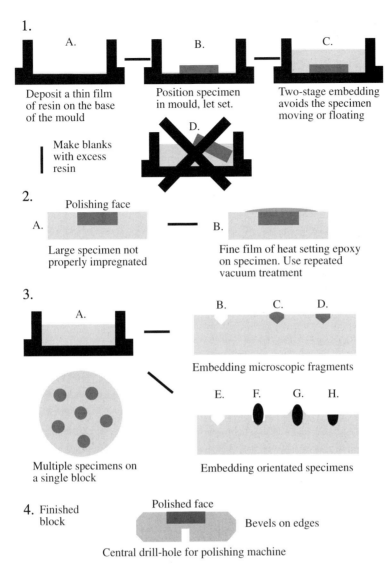

Fig. 14.1. Schematic diagrams of various embedding techniques: (**1A–D**) two-stage embedding to avoid the specimens moving or floating on the resin; (**2A–B**) surface vacuum impregnation; (**3A–D**) embedding particulate fossil matter; (**3A, 3E–H**) embedding small orientated specimens; (**4**) a finished block.

These include, for various uses: UV-curing acrylics, these resins being cured by exposure to ultraviolet light; for transmission electron microscopy (TEM), Spurr's Resin (Schmid 1967; Jones & Chaloner 1991); for fossil charcoal, 2-hydroxyethyl methacrylate (HEMA) resin (Igersheim & Cichocki 1996) and Epon-Araldite mixtures (Marziani & Iannone 1986); for fossil wood, water-soluble epoxy resin Quetol 651 (Abad et al. 1988).

Moulds

Plastic moulds for producing resin blocks can be purchased directly from manufacturers. Although the resin will not adhere to the mould's plastic, after repeated use eventually small amounts of resin do build-up on the mould walls, and eventually the resin blocks will start to stick inside the moulds. The lifetimes of moulds can be greatly increased by spraying a very thin film of silicone mould-release agent to the inside of the mould prior to use. When special shaped moulds are not commercially available, they can be easily made. Make several blocks of the shape and size required out of an easily worked material (e.g., wood). Stick these to the bottom of a plastic tray, then pour latex rubber into the tray covering the blocks to a good depth. Once set this will make an excellent mould, where the resin blocks can easily be removed from the latex.

Embedding plant fossils for quantitative reflected light microscopy

The resin used for embedding plant material for quantitative reflected light microscopy ((ISO, 7404/2 – 1985 (E)) needs to meet the following requirements: no chemical reaction between fossil and resin; setting temperature not to exceed 100°C, and preferably less than 60°C; curing time less than 30 min; good penetration and impregnation, viscosity not exceeding 1 N s m^{-2}; provide a matrix capable of holding the material securely during grinding and polishing; marked reflectance contrast between resin and sample under reflected light; comparable hardness between resin and sample; no large volume changes during hardening. The ISO recommends an epoxy resin of low viscosity, containing diglycidyl ethers and a liquid hardener.

The mould-release agent should have an aromatic content less than 25% V/V. The metal mould used to make the blocks (illustrated in fig 1., ISO, 7404/2 – 1985 (E)) should be placed in a press, and pressure between 14 and 17 Mpa applied for 3 to 5 s several times. The pressure/release cycle will remove trapped air bubbles. The pressure must be maintained for at least 10 min while the block hardens.

Case studies

Embedding of small and very small particles

The following protocol can be used. to embed and polish a small volume of extremely small particles (Fig. 14.1, 3A–D), or small individual fossils (Fig. 14.1, 3A, 3E–H). First make some resin 'blanks', either from cold-setting polyester resin (as mentioned earlier), or some other inexpensive resin. These blanks should be the size of the final block required; typically 40 mm in diameter and 10 mm thick. Grind down to just above the final polished surface with a diamond lap. Once down to this level create a small bevel of 3 mm at 45° around the front edge. Then polish with a grit such as 500 silicon carbide on a glass plate. With a 4 mm high-speed bit, drill a single hole 5 mm deep in the centre of the

back of the block (for the mechanical polisher). On the front of the block, hole(s) are drilled for the fossil material. With a moderate amount of material drill several evenly spaced holes; for a very small amount of material drill a single hole in the centre. The hole(s) should be 3 mm deep at the centre point – equivalent in volume to slightly less than a single drop of resin.

Take a de-greased glass slide, and place 2 drops of cold-setting polyester resin on the surface; spread the drops out with a straight-bladed scalpel. Sprinkle the particulate fossil material over the resin smear. Then with the scalpel blade gather-up the resin/particulate mixture into one corner of the slide, and with the glass slide inclined, allow the (resin + particulates) droplet to fall into the drill-hole on the block's surface. The droplet should completely fill the hole, and just bulge above the surface. Once this has cured it can be ground down to the polishing surface, and polished. When you wish to examine more than just the exposed material, serially repeating the last 3 polishing stages will expose new particulates each time for examination or measurement.

Embedding large plant fossils

Many kinds of plant macrofossils require embedding in resin prior to further examination. For anatomical studies the specimen must be adequately impregnated with set resin so that it does not fragment during, trimming, sectioning and grinding/polishing. Large permineralized specimens with more than several centimetres depth will rarely become thoroughly infiltrated with most resins. The approach of pouring resin around a macrofossil so that the fossil is surrounded by a thick wall of set resin serves little purpose. As soon as a saw blade passes through the resin coating and outer surface of the fossil into the non-impregnated interior, the saw will probably pluck material from the cut face although the outer part of the fossil remains in the mould. Furthermore, cutting blades designed to cut through rocks and minerals are not suitable for cutting through thick layers of plastic which can jam, or worse, during the cutting process. A typical protocol for embedding a plant fossil for sectioning is as follows.

The first stage involves low viscosity embedding; spreading a layer of cyanoacrylate resin over the surface to fill all the cracks and fissures which would cause large parts of the specimen to fragment. This can be highly effective. A further way of improving this first step is to heat the fossil in an oven between 60° to 80°C, place in a cool location and apply the low viscosity cyanoacrylate resin. The cooling effect draws the resin into the specimen. This can be repeated several times with the specimen orientated in various directions so that gravity aids the process as well. The second stage involves surface embedding with a polyester or epoxy resin. This will provide a thicker 'skin' of set resin around the specimen as well as filling larger voids and cracks too large for the first stage low viscosity cyanoacrylate, and will further protect it from fragmenting during trimming/cutting. Some resins can be thinned with an appropriate solvent in the hope that the less viscous resin will more easily enter the specimen, however, this is not highly recommended as the dilution might interfere with the timing and efficiency of the polymerization.

The above stages ensure that the specimen will not fragment during trimming while making an initial cut of a series. Further embedding may then be carried out on cut surfaces to protect against smaller-scale fragmentation within the specimen. Depending on the porosity and tendency to fragment, further applications of low viscosity and possibly also higher viscosity resin can be applied to freshly cut surfaces which can then be ground and polished down.

15. Thin sections and wafering

HAGEN HASS & NICK P. ROWE

Thin sections mounted with thermoplastic cement

Silicified plant fossils are usually studied by peels or thin sections. With the latter method considerable material is lost due to cutting and grinding. Thin sections, however, allow direct observations of three-dimensionally preserved morphological and anatomical structures. Moreover, it is an effective method for material with cell walls that are already partly replaced by silica, and/or thus lack sufficient organic matter for peeling. Thin sections are often epoxy-mounted and not transferable. Only the upper side of the mounted rock slice can be ground down. Thermoplastic mounting media do not have this disadvantage and are therefore preferred, since rock slices mounted in thermoplastic resin can be released when the slide is re-heated (cf. Crepet 1974, p.148). Furthermore, they can be transferred and turned over, so that both sides of the slice can be ground down until the required focusing plane is reached (cf. Remy *et al.* 1994, p.690). This technique is highly suited for anatomical research, including the study of silicified peats comprising small, randomly distributed three-dimensionally preserved plant remains. While thermoplastic cements have been used widely as mounting media, the special turning over technique used at the Palaeobotany laboratory at Munster was developed during several decades of research into the Rhynie Chert.

Material

Material suitable for this technique should be heat resistant, transparent, hard and homogeneous. The size and thickness of thin sections is dependent on these properties. In general, the size of thin sections made with the 'turn over' technique and mounted with thermoplastic resin should not exceed those of standard biological or geological microscope slides (76×26 mm, 48×28 mm respectively). First, the silicate rock is examined to select the appropriate plant remains to be prepared. Then the rock is cut into appropriate blocks and each mounted on microscope slides with thermoplastic cement. By successive cutting and remounting the blocks are then cut into serial sections.

Mounting medium

The recommended mounting medium is 'No. 70C Lakeside Brand' (see appendix). This cement is sold as yellow bars ($15 \times 9 \times 183$ mm) and it is colourless when mounted (refraction index 1.54). The melting point is above 80°C and the cement flows freely at 140°C. According to the manufacturer's instructions the working temperature should be *c.* 140°C. The cement initially starts to boil and ultimately becomes brown when it is overheated at temperatures above 155°C for a longer period. The cement will then also become brittle at elevated temperatures and will lose its adhesive properties. At room temperatures melted cement hardens very quickly, within seconds. Lakeside cement is readily soluble in xylene or acetone.

Some practical experiences with the use of Lakeside cement should be briefly mentioned, since some are contrary to the manufacturer's instructions. Mounting, transferring and turning over thin sections are carried out on an electrical heating plate so that the cement does not harden during processing. The hot sections are handled with tweezers and needles.

Lakeside cement can be applied to the preheated microscope slide by rubbing the end of the solid cement bar over its surface, or by directly melting a chip of Lakeside cement on the slide. The entire slice should be in contact with the slide and the mounting medium should be completely free of air bubbles. The main problems with Lakeside cement are its high viscosity and tendency to form large numbers of air bubbles when microscope slides are coated with cement at the advised temperature of 140°C. Air bubbles are difficult to remove and it is recommended to heat the Lakeside cement at a temperature of *c.* 180°C, i.e. 10°C below the boiling or outgassing temperature. As a result , the viscosity of Lakeside cement is very low and all air bubbles disappear within about one minute. Heating of Lakeside cement to 180°C may be done safely for over 5 min without any noticeable negative effects. Overheated lakeside cement on mounted sections may develop cracks while grinding on a high revolution machine (> 300 rpm). However, such cracks do not develop when the slides are ground by hand or on low revolution machines

Hass, H. & Rowe, N. P. 1999. Thin sections and wafering.
In: Jones, T. P. & Rowe, N. P. (eds) *Fossil Plants and Spores: modern techniques.*
Geological Society, London, 76–81.

(< 300 rpm), not even with extremely thin sections.

In older slides (> 2 years old) large amounts of air bubbles are formed when the slides are heated again for transferring or turning over the sections. The air bubbles already start to form at relatively low temperatures (± 110°C). Whether this is a result of overheating during a prior preparation stage or not, these bubbles do not hinder the removal and transfer of the rock section into fresh mounting medium. Excess fresh cement or remains of older cement can be easily removed by cotton-tipped sticks dipped in xylene or acetone. Lakeside

cement is also soluble in various immersion oils. Before the slides are stored, adhering immersion oil should therefore be removed carefully from uncovered slides.

Thin sections – the basic rock slices

The block is mounted with Lakeside cement and a section is then cut by passing the saw blade close to the glass slide. The blocks can be mounted on the microscope slide at 140°C. Air bubbles can be removed later, when the section is transferred. The

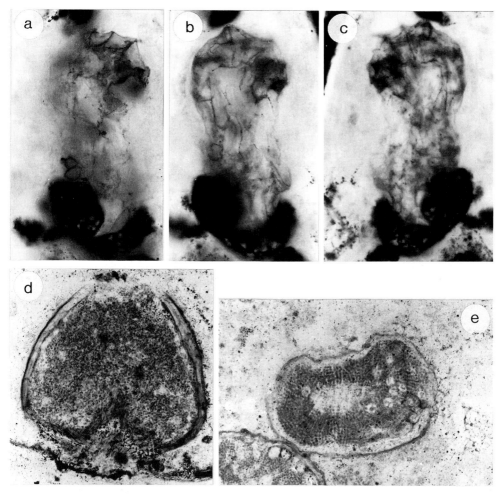

Fig. 15.1. (**a**)–(**c**) Germinating spore of *Aglaophyton major* from the Early Devonian Rhynie Chert; both surfaces of the young gametophyte can be documented by using the turn over technique: (**a**) upper surface; (**b**) median plane; (**c**) lower surface from reverse side; note first development of an apical meristem in the young gametophyte in (a) (a–c, × 300). (**d**)–(**e**) Antheridia of *Lyonophyton rhyniensis*, the presumed gametophyte of *Aglaophyton major*, methodical median sections prepared by using the turn over technique; (**d**) median longitudinal section of a mature antheridium; (**e**) median transverse section of a young antheridium; note the sterile columella in both sections and the filed spermatogenous tissue in (e) (d–e, × 100).

basic section, cut off from the block can be of any thickness but should be thin enough for light-microscopical examination. Sections of Rhynie Chert may vary in thickness between 0.7 and 1.3 mm and still remain transparent.

Thicker sections have the advantage that they often contain more complete parts of plant organs. This allows us to make thin sections of specific structures. Starting with extremely thick sections will lead to the loss of more material because of the degree of grinding necessary, but the final thin section will be of optimal quality and show exactly what is required.

Thin sections – grinding, transferring and turning over

The most interesting structures are selected by microscopical examination and the desired plane of the thin section is then determined. The first step is to grind the section down to just above this level. Abrasive grinding is done with medium carborundum powder (400 grade) on a low-revolution machine (c. 200 rpm) or, more suitable, by hand on a glass plate. The latter method guarantees a better control of the grinding process. After grinding, any adhering carborundum powder is removed by brushing with soap under running water. After being completely air dried in a drying cabinet or on a hotplate at low temperature (below 80°C), the thin section can then be transferred to another slide and turned over.

Lakeside cement is added to a new microscope slide placed on an electric hotplate (c. 180°C, or a few degrees below the boiling temperature). All newly formed air bubbles will disappear in about one minute. The original slide is then heated to the same temperature and the section is gently removed from the slide by pulling it horizontally with a pair of tweezers. Very fragile sections may break when lifted directly from the slide. The section is then transferred to the new slide, turned over and mounted. Since the mounting medium may start to harden during the transfer process, the tweezers may stick to the section. However, they will be easily released when the new slide is heated.

The cement hardens within 10 to 15 min and then the opposite side of the same section may be ground down in a similar way as the reverse side. Continued grinding makes the section thinner, with the selected object lying in the central plane.

Ultimate grinding down to the desired plane has to be done by hand on a glass plate with fine carborundum powder (600 or 800 grade). During this process the thin section should be constantly checked under the microscope.

When the desired focal plane is approached by grinding, one or two final turn overs may be needed. After each turn over, the new surface (the former reverse-side) is still coated with old Lake-side cement. This should be removed with xylene (using cotton-tipped sticks) before further grinding in order to get a better control of the abrasion process. The further the section is ground down, the thinner and more fragile it becomes. The freshly ground surface should not be covered with Lakeside during turning over. If some air bubbles do appear under such a fragile section, it is best transferred to a new microscope slide and mounted again. When the desired focal plane is reached, the slide is ready. Silicified material like that from the Rhynie Chert does not need final polishing.

Covering, observation, and storage

If slides are to be covered with coverslips, the thin section needs to be heated again. A small piece of Lakeside cement is melted directly on its surface and a coverslip is applied under gentle pressure. One advantage of covered Lakeside cement-mounted thin sections is that they do not become sticky. However, the use of coverslips reduces the depth of focus especially with higher magnification (immersion) lenses. When high magnifications are required, the thin section should not be sealed with a coverslip. Uncovered and unpolished thin sections should be studied under oil immersion at all magnifications. Because Lakeside cement is soluble in immersion oil, the oil always needs to be removed carefully (most easily with soap and water) before the slides are stored. Slides still coated with oil tend to adhere to all surfaces as well as each other and the plastic of the slide boxes. Thin sections mounted with Lakeside cement do not show any signs of deterioration after 25 years, neither with regard to optical properties (transparency, homogeneity) nor to the adhesive properties of the embedding medium.

Preparation of wafers

Modern microscopes are frequently equipped with incident light capability and observation under dark field illumination with objectives capable of both transmitted and incident light. Examples include the Olympus BX system with M-plan objectives and the Nikon system with BD-plan objectives. Some anatomically preserved plants are ideally studied from 'wafers' – thin slices of opaque material, polished on both upper and lower surfaces and mounted on glass slides under coverslips. The following method has been developed for the rapid embedding, serial sectioning, 'semi-polishing', and mounting of opaque permineralized sections.

Material

Suitable material for this technique includes any anatomically preserved material which shows good contrast against the background matrix when the cut surface is wetted or viewed after coating with a clear resin. The technique can also be used for tracing three-dimensional patterns through complex compressions, and can be applied to either well indurated specimens or porous friable material requiring significant embedding (Rowe 1992, plate 14, figs 3–4).

Method

Permineralized specimens are painted with one or two coats of polyester resin (see Chapter 16). The saw equipment favoured requires a 'see-saw' arm orientated towards the saw blade with enough 'working room' around the blade for a modified specimen holder and a goniometric platform (universally adjustable and fixable joint) attached to the 'see-saw' arm. An ideal saw is the 'Micro-slice 2' (see appendix) model of micro-saw. Surface-embedded specimens are mounted on standard 76×26 mm microscope slides which are easily mounted and removed from a purpose-built perspex slide holder (Fig. 15.2a,b), and this is fixed to the flat surface of the goniometer. The specimen can then be orientated precisely to the exact position and angle required for the section by tilting and rotating the goniometer (Fig. 15.2b).

Choice of saw blade

The blade thickness of the saw depends on: section interval required, the size of the specimen, the effective cutting depth of the saw blade and the hardness of the material. Specimens with hetero-geneous matrix/fossil material, spaces in the matrix, extremely hard specimens, specimens embedded in thick layers of resin require great care in cutting with thin wafering blades. Preferred blades include low concentration 'Isomet® Diamond Wafering Blades' (see Appendix) for use on hard ceramics produced by 'Buehler UK Ltd'. These vary in thickness and overall diameter from 0.152 mm and 76 mm to 0.63 mm and 178 mm, respectively. Wafering blades are extremely delicate and must be treated carefully.

Embedding

Thin diamond saws designed to cut ceramics are not suitable for cutting plastics and resins. Blades can get trapped in blocks of resin surrounding the specimen and this can easily break the wafering blade beyond repair. The following technique uses

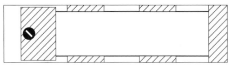

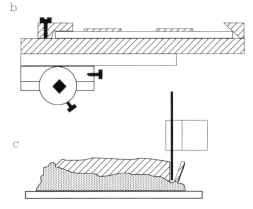

Fig. 15.2. Apparatus for production of serial wafers using 'super glue' technique. (**a**) Plan view of perspex slide-holder with retaining flanges and screw-retaining-arm. (**b**) Side view of holder and glass slide mounted on goniometer (nearside lateral flanges not shown). The goniometer is attached to the 'see-saw' arm of the saw and can be tilted and rotated to orientate the specimen relative to the saw blade. (**c**) Fossil specimen held firmly in silicone rubber 'sealant' on glass slide. The cut wafer is held by the glue after cutting but is then easily removed.

sequential embedding of the fossil material after each slice is cut by injecting super 'glue' (cyano-acrylate adhesive) on to and into the freshly washed and dried cut surface of the block. This approach avoids attempting to slice specimens surrounded by thick layers of resin. Basically the idea is that larger specimens can be cut by thinner blades at smaller intervals while minimizing risk of damage to the wafering blade and specimen.

Mounting

Specimens are mounted on the glass slides with silicone rubber glue (see Appendix). The specimen is partially enveloped in the glue which holds the specimen firmly, but at the same time allows a tiny amount of movement. This allows for effective 'damping' during the cutting process (Fig. 15.2c). Fossils are rarely entirely homogeneous and wafering blades rarely remain perfectly flat and circular after routine use. This mounting therefore absorbs vibrations and bumps caused during cutting, and reduces the risk of damage to the blade and breakage of wafers during cutting.

Sectioning

After surface-embedding the specimen and mounting on the glass slide, the glass slide is mounted on the slide holder by sliding one end beneath the angled flange and securing by rotating the retaining screw via the retaining arm (Fig. 15.2a,b). The silicone rubber glue is pared away from around the area to be cut with a sharp blade, apart from below the specimen. The specimen is then orientated into the required position by moving and angling the goniometric platform and then re-tightening the adjustment screws holding it in position relative to the saw blade. The saw is started at a relatively slow speed, a slow jet of running water is directed onto the wafering blade and the specimen is raised against the blade by slackening the retaining screw locking the see-saw arm. The pressure of the specimen against the blade must be carefully assessed: too much weight and the blade might buckle, too little weight and the specimen may bounce against the blade. Once the speed of the saw has been adjusted so that the cutting is smooth with little or no movement, the cutting is continued until the first slice is completed. When the slice is completed the blade runs against the silicone rubber below, but the cut slice still remains attached and can then be easily trimmed off with a razor (Fig. 15.2c).

The specimen and slide is removed from the holder, rinsed in water and dried under a hairdryer fixed to a stand. When thoroughly dry but still warm, super glue (see Appendix) is applied on to and against the newly cut surface and the specimen moved away from the hairdryer. The block is now allowed to cool, and is orientated so that both gravity and any contraction of cooling air inside the specimen draws the super glue inside the specimen. When the super glue becomes tacky and will no longer be drawn into the specimen, the orientated specimen and slide are again positioned under the hairdryer to accelerate the final drying of the super glue. When the super glue is hardened the second slice can then be cut. The slide is replaced in the slide holder which has remained in the same place relative to the saw blade. The saw can then be advanced to the required distance, depending on the porosity of the specimen and the penetration of the super glue. After the second cut is completed the cycle is repeated. While the specimen is drying, other specimens can be cut on the saw but this means that when a former specimen is re-cut, the cut surface has to be re-aligned with the blade. With

careful manipulation of the tilt and swivel controls of the goniometric platform and careful observation of the parallel cut surface and the blade this actually causes little problem.

Polishing/finishing of wafers

Figure 15.3 summarizes the sequence following the removal of each cut segment from the saw. The cut segment is rinsed in water and then dried under the hairdryer (a). More super glue is applied to the newly cut surface (b). When dry, the lower surface is ground and polished to the desired thickness on a bench-top lap with increasingly fine grade lap disks

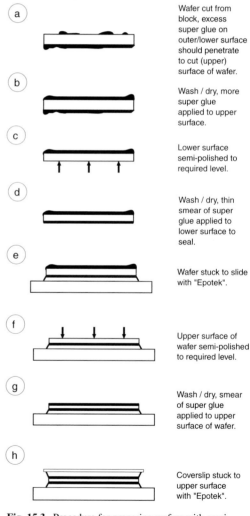

a — Wafer cut from block, excess super glue on outer/lower surface should penetrate to cut (upper) surface of wafer.

b — Wash / dry, more super glue applied to upper surface.

c — Lower surface semi-polished to required level.

d — Wash / dry, thin smear of super glue applied to lower surface to seal.

e — Wafer stuck to slide with "Epotek".

f — Upper surface of wafer semi-polished to required level.

g — Wash / dry, smear of super glue applied to upper surface of wafer.

h — Coverslip stuck to upper surface with "Epotek".

Fig. 15.3. Procedure for preparing wafers with semi-polished surfaces, 'Super glue' and 'Epotek' resin; see text for explanation.

from approximately P400 grade, finishing with P1200 grade (c). Silicon carbide 'Buehler-Met® Metallographic Grinding Papers' (see Appendix) are also supplied by Buehler UK. The 'semi-polished' finish is sufficient if the study of the anatomy largely relies on contrast being enhanced by the refractive index of the resins used in mounting the wafer. After washing and drying again, a very thin smear of super glue is applied to the clean semi-polished surface (d) which prevents air from exiting the wafer into the mounting resin and forming bubbles. When dry, the wafer is mounted (e) onto a glass slide with 'Epotek' (see Appendix) thin-section resin (supplied by 'Inter-tronics', UK). When the resin is completely set, the upper surface of the wafer is ground and then polished to the required level (f), rinsed and dried

and a thin smear of super glue is also applied to this surface (g). When this last layer of super glue is dry, a coverslip is mounted (h) on the specimen with 'Epotek'.

Observation

Both surfaces of the wafer can be observed using dark-field illumination and incident light objectives. The thin layers of super glue used to seal the outer surface of the wafer do not appear to influence the quality of the image up to magnifications of over × 200 and anatomical detail are observable up to × 400. Using these combinations of adhesives and resins, the preparations have remained stable for 7 years to the present time of writing.

16. Polished blocks and reflected light microscopy

TIM P. JONES

This chapter briefly explains the principles and potential of reflected light (RL) microscopy for palaeobotanists, rather than for coal petrologists or organic geochemists. The aim is to study fossil plants using reflected light as a means of observing structural or taphonomic information not seen using other techniques; as well as obtaining numerical data on the fossil's reflectance. I describe a protocol to polish the blocks which can be undertaken in any moderately-equipped polishing/thin-section laboratory; the basic operations of the reflected light microscope are described; and the interpretation of the results is discussed. For a classic text on RL microscopy in coal petrology, readers are referred to Stach et al. (1982) [this has now been partially revised and incorporated into Taylor et al. (1998)]. A recent collection of research papers featuring reflectance – Stout & Boon (1993) – is also strongly recommended. Space restriction prevents mention of all the different makes of RL microscopes; indeed the many different microscope configurations available from individual manufacturers is bewildering. However, it must be borne in mind that whether researchers have available dedicated 'state-of-art' computerized microscopes, or more ad hoc assemblies, the underlying principles remain the same.

Reflected light microscopy consists of the examination of an image produced by reflecting light off a polished surface. The brighter the image the greater amount of light being reflected. Quantitative reflectance requires light filtered to a known wavelength (546 nm is commonly used) being measured by a photometer, and the values obtained being calibrated by comparison with the reflectances from known standards. The main application of quantitative reflectance in organic matter is for maturation studies using the coal maceral vitrinite (Stach et al. 1982). Qualitative studies tend to use unfiltered light, and typically the images are recorded by a camera mounted on the microscope, with information obtained on subjects such as fossil plant anatomy and taphonomy. Some studies utilize both qualitative and quantitative reflected light, an example being temperature formation and taphonomic studies of fossil charcoal. As in embedding, vigorous international protocols exist for polishing the blocks, taking vitrinite reflectances, calibration of the microscope,

the number of readings recommended, and the interpretation of results (ISO 7404/2 and ISO 7404/5).

Polishing blocks for reflected light microscopy

The fossil material should be embedded using the protocols described by Jones & Rowe (Chapter 14). If possible, allow a few days after the resin has hardened before starting the polishing. The procedure used in our laboratory is as follows. The polishing process involves a number of stages, where each stage uses a progressively finer abrasive powder. The first stage entails using a diamond lap to grind down to just above the final polished surface. While diamond lapping, one should constantly check the surface, only apply light to medium pressure, and regularly rotate the block in your hand. Once down to the required level, use the lap to grind off the top edge of the block, creating a small bevel of about 3 mm at 45°. The block must now be ultrasonically cleaned; use distilled water in a clean plastic beaker in the ultrasonic bath – from now on use this beaker only for cleaning at this stage. Carefully check the surface of the block; if the plant material has 'plucked-out' or has exposed open spaces, it may be advisable to surface impregnate the fossil. In this case it is often best to use a low viscosity resin to obtain a better impregnation (see details in Chapter 14).

This should be followed by a grit such as 500 silicon carbide on a glass plate. Always meticulously clean the glass with running water before use, and make a fresh grinding paste. Using moderate downwards pressure, move the block in a figure-of-eight pattern through the paste, stopping at regular intervals to rotate the block in your hand. After 5 min, wash the polishing surface under clean running water to remove the surplus paste. Check that the whole face has a dull matt surface, and there are no scratches remaining from the diamond lap. Checking the surface under a binocular microscope is recommended. Occasionally a grating sensation is felt when grinding – stop immediately, and check the surface of the block. If scratches can be seen on the face some contamination is in the

JONES, T. P. 1999. Polished blocks and reflected light microscopy. In: JONES, T. P. & ROWE, N. P. (eds) Fossil Plants and Spores: modern techniques. Geological Society, London, 82–86.

paste (for example, a fragment of pyrite could have detached from the fossil), and you must start this stage again, carefully cleaning everything and making new grinding paste. Once this stage of the polishing is satisfactory, the block is ultrasonically cleaned (again in a dedicated beaker).

The final two stages are mechanical polishing using 0.3 μm aluminium oxide for the penultimate stage, and 0.05 μm aluminium oxide for the final stage (ISO 7404/5). Use a cloth with a minimum of nap (the fine hairy surface of the cloth). It is recommended to use a lot of pressure on the specimen for these final two stages, as this will minimize relief developing on the polished face. Ultrasonically clean the blocks between the stages (dedicated beaker), and mix the two grinding pastes in dedicated beakers. At the end of the polishing, ultrasonically clean the block. Detailed and precise grinding and polishing protocols for coal petrology are given as appendices A.4.2 and A.4.3 to ISO 7404/5. The method outlined above is essentially the same as the ISOs, and will produce an equivalent quality of polish where specialist coal petrology preparation equipment is not available. A first indication of whether the block is correctly polished is obtained by looking at the surface of the resin; this should be very shiny and reflective like glass, a matt surface indicates a poor polish. The final polished block needs to meet the following criteria (ISO 7404/5):

(1) the surface must be flat and substantially free of relief;
(2) the surface should be substantially free of pitting;
(3) the surface should be substantially free from scratching.

One potential problem with fossil plants, especially well-preserved fossil 'wood' is that the fossil absorbs water from the paste during the grinding and polishing processes. This can result in the fossil swelling proud of the block face; pieces of the fossil can detach from the block; when the specimen dries, the loss of the water results in a negative relief on the block as a result of shrinkage; the embedding resin can even crack as a result of pressure from the swelling wood. A possible solution to this problem is to change the liquid used in the paste to one which is not readily absorbed by the fossil. The choice of liquid depends largely upon your fossil material, and the best option has to be determined by experimentation; possibilities include diesel and glycerol. When cleaning the block between different grades of abrasive use ethanol.

Once you have polished your blocks, they should be examined/measured under the reflected light microscope as soon as possible, as the polished

faces can tarnish or oxidize. For re-examination of material stored over long periods, it is recommended to re-polish with the 0.05 μm aluminium oxide.

Reflected light microscopes

A schematic flow diagram is shown (Fig. 16.1) of the set-up of a reflected light microscope and dedicated computer system (in this case based on Nikon, as used in our laboratory). A stabilized light source provides the light which is reflected off the polished face of the specimen; to allow the light source to stabilize, this should be switched on at least 30 min before calibration. The light is filtered and passes through an aperture or pin-hole. Inside the body of the microscope the light is directed downwards through the objective lens, where it reflects upwards from the polished surface of the specimen. The objective lens is joined to the surface of the specimen by a 'bridge' of immersion oil (non-drying, refractive index 1.518 ± 0.0004 at 23°C). The specimen is moved horizontally by X and Y controls on the microscope stage. The reflected light image is viewed through the eye-piece, and also the light travels upwards into the upper half of the reflected light assembly.

The aperture control unit is joined to the microscope body. Typically with settings over the range: OPEN / 5 / 2 / 1 / 0.5 / 0.2 / 0.1 / SHUT, this controls the spot size being measured by the photometer. Generally I use spot sizes of 0.1 or 0.2 with a × 20 objective lens. A shutter box is attached to the aperture control; these can either be manually or electronically controlled. The photometer measures the amount of light reflected by the selected area on the specimen by converting it into an electric signal. The computer calculates the specimen's reflectance from the photometer's output, the results being electronically stored or printed. Given the sub-standard quality of some dedicated reflected light software graphics, transferring the data into standard 'spreadsheet' software, such as EXCEL, should be considered.

The polished blocks are mounted on to glass slides by means of a piece of sticky, non-toxic, modelling material (plasticene or clay) and a press. The surface of the block must be exactly horizontal (check this by rotating the block). For oil reflectance, place a drop of immersion oil on the surface of the block, and very carefully lower the objective lens into the oil, establishing a 'bridge' between the lens and the specimen. When the image is focused there must still be an oil bridge between the objective and the specimen. If the oil contains air bubbles clean all the oil off the objective lens and the specimen with lens cleaning cloths, and try

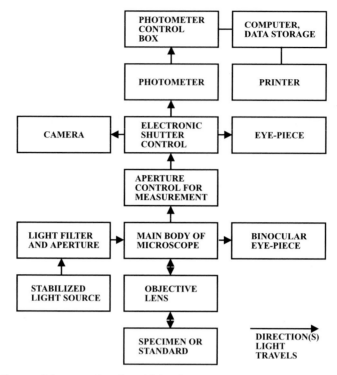

Fig. 16.1. Flow diagram of the set-up of a reflected light microscope and dedicated computer system.

again; the same applies for dust or other contaminants in the oil (these can be seen floating across the image). Always carefully clean the objective lens, standards and specimens after measuring. Although appropriate cleaning agents can be used on the objective lens and standards, never use them on your resin-embedded specimens.

Alignment

Reflected light systems with detachable aperture and shutter controls and photometers must be aligned before use. Every time the system is changed, for example replacing the photometer with the camera, the alignment is lost; of course this does not apply to systems with permanent side-mounted cameras. The light reflected off the specimen positioned exactly under the cross-hairs of the microscope eye-piece must pass through the aperture to the photometer. This is especially important where very small fossil plant fragments or thin cell walls are being measured. If your system does not have a back-projection spot in the field of view, there is a quick and simple method to re-align the system. Place a standard such as YAG under the objective. Despite the fact that the

standards are supposed to be flawless, you will see a number of tiny highly-reflecting flaws in the polished surface, equally a high-reflecting tiny fragment of pyrite in a specimen can be used. Adjust the stage X and Y controls until one of these flaws is exactly under the eye-piece cross-hairs. From now on do not move this standard until the alignment is completed. Fully open the aperture and look through the eye-piece. Sequentially decrease the aperture size down to the measuring aperture size (0.1 or 0.2) on the control unit. As the size of the aperture decreases, using the control box's X and Y adjustment knobs always keep the chosen flaw exactly in the centre of the aperture. Once this has been done you can be confident that the exact position of the cross-hairs in the eye-piece, aligns with the aperture and the light going into the photometer. Remember to move the cross-hairs off the flaw, to a flawless section, when calibrating.

Calibration

The system is calibrated using a series of reflectance standards of known reflectance (ISO 7404/5), with an immersion oil of known refractive index,

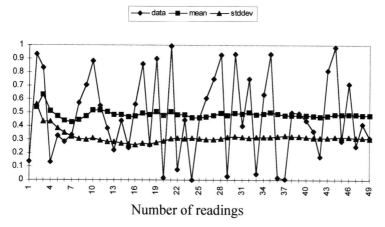

Fig. 16.2. Number of readings against running means and standard deviations for an artificial dataset generated from random numbers between 0 and 1. Even with this wide range of values, the means and standard deviations 'level off' after a relatively small number of readings. For this artificial dataset, after 25 readings the mean reflectance seldom varies by more than ±0.01%.

and filtered light (for example, 1.518 immersion oil at 546 nm). Calibration consists of adjusting the photometer output to zero for zero reflectance, and to a known value for a known reflectance. The reflectance of the specimens is then calculated using similar equations. The zero standard can consist of a hole in a block of resin 5 mm wide and 5 mm deep containing immersion oil (ISO 7407/5), or a non-reflecting 'black body'. This is placed under the objective, and the photometer control adjusted to zero. It is recommended working in a room with very low light levels to minimize 'parasitic' or 'stray light' getting into the photometer.

Place a standard under the objective, and adjust the X and Y controls on the stage until centred on a flawless section inside the inscribed circle of the standard's polished face. Adjust the value of the photometer to a mid-range value. The 'parasitic light' test can be done when calibrating to the standard, use low light levels in the room, but see if there is any photometer value decrease when the room is completely dark. Once calibrated, move the eye-piece cross-hairs to a different, but flawless, section of the standard – the reading on the photometer box should be unchanged. Additional calibration can be done by placing different standards under the calibrated microscope, and seeing if the results obtained exactly match the expected values. The ISO 7404/5 recommends using three well-spaced standards; check the linearity of the multiple calibration standards. The specimen itself can now be placed under the objective and readings taken. Do not change the low light levels in the room while taking readings. Ideally the room temperature

should be maintained at 23°C ± 3°C. Once enough readings of the specimen have been obtained, place the standard back under the objective, and check that the standard is unchanged from the original calibration value.

Taking readings

The ISO 7404/5 1984(E) recommends the following number of readings should be taken: (a) If 98% are less than 0.35%, 100 measurements; (b) 0.35% – 0.7%, at least 500 measurements; greater than 0.7%, at least 1000 measurements (this is clearly impractical unless the system is automated). Results should be presented as mean random reflectance percentage, and standard deviation. In the opinion of this author, a superior method of determining the statistically valid number of readings required for a given sample can be obtained by pre-programming a data spreadsheet with a running mean and running standard deviation. This can prevent the unnecessary reading of many hundreds of measurements for a negligible and statistically invalid improvement in data quality. An example of a plot of a running mean and running standard deviation is shown in Fig. 16.2. Based on a random number generation between 0.1 and 1, it can be seen the running mean very rapidly levels out at 0.5. Vitrinite reflectance data are never shown with more than 2 decimal points (usually the number of decimal points of the nearest standard). Therefore, data are acquired until the running mean does not change by ± 0.01% for a given interval (for example, 25 readings), and this value can then be accepted. This plot was obtained using an

EXCEL version worksheet. The three lines shown on Fig. 16.2 are all plotted against number of readings: (a) diamond symbol = raw numbers; (b) square symbol = running mean; (c) triangular symbol = running standard deviation.

Interpreting quantitative results

Results are usually presented as R_o = mean random reflectance under oil, and σ = standard deviation. The value of R_o need not be shown above 2 decimal points. The results are usually presented as a histogram, with intervals of 0.10% (V-step) or 0.05% (1/2V-step). Vitrinite reflectance is used as a maturation indicator, principally governed by length of time subjected to maximum palaeo-temperature (Murchison et al. 1985). However, the distribution of the values can also provide sedimentological information, for example on the reworking of sediments. It is important to note therefore whether data shows a single peak representing a single vitrinite population, and thus the mean and standard deviation are significant. Readers are recommended to consult Taylor et al. (1998) for a detailed discourse on the interpretation of reflectance results.

17. Opaque petrifaction techniques

PAUL KENRICK

Pyrite (FeS_2) and its oxidation products (e.g. limonite: $2Fe_2O_3.3H_2O$; $FeO(OH).nH_2O$) are a common and important class of minerals involved in plant cellular permineralization. Pyrite is opaque, limonite is semi-opaque, and this optical property has implications for microscopy. Whereas transmission light microscopy of thin sections yields excellent histological detail with silicates and carbonate concretions, this technique is inappropriate for opaque petrifactions. One approach to opaque minerals makes use of optical techniques based on reflectance imaging. An alternative approach involves the selective removal of the mineral and transfer of the organic remains to a suitable, translucent embedding medium. Scanning electron microscopy, particularly the use of atomic number contrast imaging with polished surfaces and topographical imaging with etched surfaces, is an excellent method for investigating details of cell wall structure. This chapter reviews some of the more widely used techniques applied to pyrite and limonite petrifactions.

The pyritization process

Pyritization in fossil plants is intimately connected to the decay process through bacteria-mediated sulphate reduction (Kenrick & Edwards 1988; see also Briggs *et al.* 1996). The critical step is the reduction of dissolved sulphate (SO_4^{2-}) to hydrogen sulphide (H_2S) through anaerobic bacterial respiration (Berner 1984; Canfield & Raiswell 1991). The hydrogen sulphide reacts with fine-grained, detrital iron minerals to produce a monosulphide which is followed by the crystallization of pyrite (FeS_2) in characteristic, minute microspheres (framboids, Berner 1984; Canfield & Raiswell 1991). Pyrite forms during early diagenesis, and data from recent sediments suggest a time frame of days to several years, depending on the nature of the sediment and the availability of resources (Howarth 1979; Love *et al.* 1983).

Within tissues, sulphate reduction and pyrite crystallization occur in naturally occurring or decay-induced lacunae, such as cell lumina, parts of cell walls and intercellular spaces (Fig. 17.1a, c; Kenrick & Edwards 1988). There is no chemical bonding between the organic remains of the plant and the mineral. The extent of decay and pyrite formation in both plants and animals depends upon the taphonomic history of the fossil (Kenrick & Edwards 1988; Canfield & Raiswell 1991; Briggs *et al.* 1996). In plants, organic cell walls often remain intact. Anatomical techniques exploit the ease with which mineral and organics can be separated (Fig. 17.1j), as well as the clear chemical and optical differences between them (Fig. 17.1c). Where there has been more extensive decay, cell walls contain many microcrystalline pyrite inclusions (Fig. 17.1f, g, i). Under these circumstances, techniques that require deep etching yield poor results because dissolution of mineral causes cell walls to disintegrate.

Preservation of tissue systems in the fossil record is linked to chemical and physical differences in cell walls. Tissues with thick, lignified cell walls, such as xylem and sclerenchyma, are more commonly preserved than tissues with thinner non-lignified walls, such as parenchyma and phloem (Fig. 17.1a, e). Furthermore, differential decay can provide information on the distribution of resistant chemicals within cell walls (e.g. lignin, Kenrick & Edwards 1988). Detailed information on wall structure requires high resolution microscopy and high quality polished surfaces.

Oxidation and hydration of pyrite to form limonite (Fig. 17.1b, d) may occur at any time, and some petrifactions contain both minerals. The organic cell wall provides an entry channel for oxidizing chemicals, and microcrystalline pyrite in the vicinity of the wall is usually the first to oxidize. Preservation of histological details is similar in both minerals because the pyrite crystals are pseudomorphed during oxidation to limonite.

Documenting tissue systems and large scale histological features

The most widely used approach involves polished serial thick sections combined with incident light microscopy and dark-field illumination (Matten 1966, 1973; Stein *et al.* 1982). Because the reflectance of limonite is lower than pyrite, the contrast between organics in the cell wall and the mineral-filled cell lumina is less. Better histological details are obtained from limonitic fossils through the complete demineralization of thin sections

KENRICK, P. 1999. Opaque petrifaction techniques. *In*: JONES, T. P. & ROWE, N. P. (eds) *Fossil Plants and Spores: modern techniques.* Geological Society, London, 87–91.

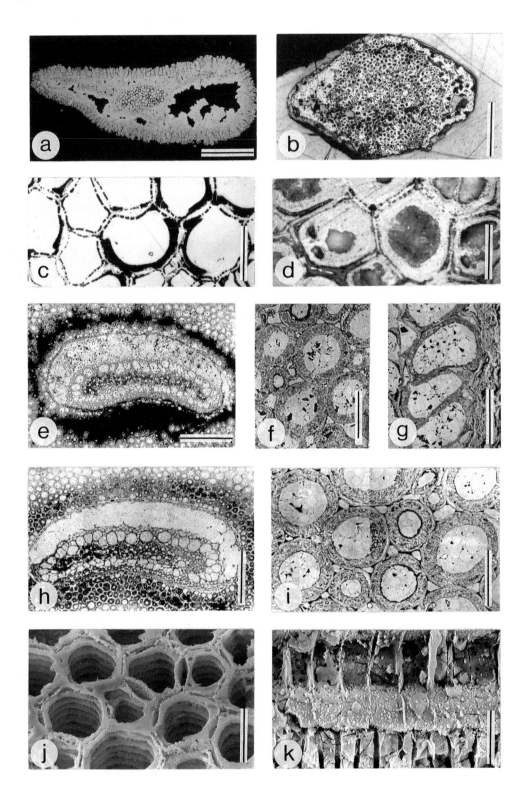

combined with transmission light microscopy (Stein *et al.* 1982). These approaches have the advantage of minimal disruption to tissue systems. The main disadvantage is that the proximity of adjacent sections is limited by the thickness of the saw blade. Also, pyritized specimens are prone to deterioration during storage. An alternative approach uses a modification of the acetate peel technique to remove the opaque mineral, transferring the organic remains of the cell wall to a translucent embedding medium (Chitaley 1985). Transmission light microscopy can then be employed. The peel technique has been used successfully with pyritized fossils, and the main advantage is that adjacent peels (sections) are very closely spaced, providing finer resolution of anatomical change. Also, the elimination of pyrite improves specimen stability during storage. The peel method may yield poor results for cell walls containing many mineral inclusions, and prolonged etching leads to mineral degradation within the source block.

Embedding and sectioning

Specimens are embedded to facilitate handling and to reduce damage during sectioning and polishing. Preliminary heat cleaning to 300°C on a hotplate may be necessary to remove mineral degradation products (e.g. water, sulphuric acid) that can inhibit polymerization of the embedding medium (Stein *et al.* 1982), but this is not recommended as routine because heat treatment can accelerate specimen deterioration. Standard embedding procedures (Chapter 14) are applicable to pyrite and limonite, and a room temperature curing, hard, low viscosity epoxy adhesive (e.g. EPO-TEK 301, see Appendix) or casting resin (e.g. Ward's Liquid Bioplastic, see Appendix) is recommended. Sections of 1–3 mm

thickness are typical and can be cut using a low speed diamond saw (see Appendix) with a thin (*c.* 0.5 mm) blade (Stein *et al.* 1982). Thinner sections can be obtained from a diamond wire saw (e.g. Shute & Edwards 1989, see Appendix).

Re-embedding cut sections

Mineralization within petrifactions is often incomplete. Sections may contain cavities that can cause fracturing or plucking of the mineral during polishing. Even microscopic cracks or pores can lead to extensive surface damage (e.g. Fig. 17.1e: gap surrounding stele). For this reason, re-embedding of cut surfaces is recommended before the use of abrasives (Stein *et al.* 1982). Cut sections are soaked in a low viscosity, catalysed adhesive (e.g. EPO-TEK 301, see Appendix) under reduced pressure (*c.* 10 KPa for 1–2 min) to aid penetration. Air pressure should not be reduced to the level at which volatiles within the adhesive boil. Soaked sections are placed between sheets of aluminium foil sandwiched between glass plates or weighted/clamped glass coverslips to cure. Re-embedding stabilizes the surface and leaves a thin covering layer of adhesive which is removed by careful manual grinding (water lubricant, 400 or 600 grit silicon carbide) on a glass plate. Good results are achieved with a light, even downward pressure on the section and a smooth circular motion across the surface of the glass plate (*c.* 80 rpm).

Low grade polish

Manual grinding of the section on paper-bonded silicon carbide (600 and 1200 grit) lubricated with water produces a rapid, low grade polish. Paper-bonded silicon carbide (see Appendix) is recommended over the more widely used powder form.

Fig. 17.1. Cellular preservation in pyrite and limonite. (**a**) Transverse section of the stem of *Gosslingia breconensis* (Lower Devonian) showing peripheral sterome and central elliptical xylem (pyrite, highly polished, reflected light, bright-field). Scale bar = 0.5 mm. (**b**) Transverse section of the stem of *Minarodendron cathaysiense* (Middle Devonian) showing central terete xylem (limonite, highly polished, reflected light, bright-field). Scale bar = 0.5 mm. (**c**) Transverse section of xylem cells of *Gosslingia breconensis* (pyrite, highly polished, reflected light, bright-field). Scale bar = 24 μm. (**d**) Transverse section of xylem cells of *Minarodendron cathaysiense* (limonite, highly polished, reflected light, bright-field). Scale bar = 38 μm. (**e**) Transverse section of stele of fern rachis (Eocene) (pyrite, highly polished, reflected light, bright-field). Scale bar = 250 μm. (**f**) Transverse section of collenchyma cells of fern rachis (Eocene). Note dispersed microcrystalline pyrite within the organic remains of the cell wall (pyrite, highly polished, reflected light, bright-field). Scale bar = 33 μm. (**g**) Transverse section of xylem cells of fern rachis (Eocene) (pyrite, highly polished, reflected light, bright-field). Scale bar = 33 μm. (**h**) Transverse section of stele of fern rachis (Eocene) (pyrite, light etch, SEM, atomic number contrast). Scale bar = 214 μm. (**i**) Transverse section of collenchyma cells of fern rachis (Eocene). Note dispersed microcrystalline pyrite within the organic remains of the cell wall (pyrite, light etch, SEM, atomic number contrast). Scale bar = 25 μm. (**j**) Oblique sections of the xylem cells of *Gosslingia breconensis* (Lower Devonian) (deep etch of pyritized fossil, SEM topographical image). Scale bar = 30 μm. (**k**) Longitudinal section of a xylem cell of *Gosslingia breconensis* (Lower Devonian) (pyrite, fractured section, SEM topographical image). Scale bar = 15 μm.

Sections are immersed briefly in a sonic bath, or washed thoroughly, between changes of abrasive to avoid contaminating finer grit sizes.

Etching thick sections to enhance contrast

Because of smearing of the mineral during treatment with abrasives or because of low organic content, it may be necessary to etch the polished surface to enhance cell wall contrast. This procedure is not recommended as routine because exposure to acids accelerates the deterioration of minerals. Pyritized fossils are plunged into nitric acid (HNO_3 c. 68%) for between 10 s and 2 min, depending on the nature of the material (Stein et al. 1982). This is followed by immersion in a saturated solution of sodium hydroxide (NaOH) for 1–2 min to neutralize the acid and immersion in hydrochloric acid (HCl) (c. 38%) for approximately 15 s to remove oxidation products. The section is immersed briefly in NaOH solution (c. 10%), briefly re-acidified in HCl (5–10%), and washed carefully for several minutes. Where cell walls contain high quantities of microcrystalline pyrite, etching may have little or no effect.

Etching to enhance contrast is also possible with limonitic fossils, but this is less effective than with pyrite because the reflectance is lower. Commonly used etching reagents include HCl (c. 38%) and oxalic acid (saturated solution) (Stein et al. 1982). Etching times vary greatly depending on the material but typically are between 5–10 min for boiling oxalic acid (Matten 1966) and 2–12 h for HCl at room temperature (Stein et al. 1982). Following etching, sections are neutralized by brief immersion in NaOH solution (c. 10%) and washed thoroughly in water.

Storage and mounting for microscopy

The stability of pyrite under long-term storage varies considerably: some specimens survive indefinitely, whereas oxidation destroys others in weeks. Stability is improved through the exclusion of water and oxygen by storage as permanent slide mounts or in silicon oil (see Appendix) contained in a glass vial. For light microscopy (dark-field), sections are dehydrated through an ethanol series and mounted on glass slides using a permanent mounting medium (e.g. DPX, Euparal, Canada balsam, see Appendix).

Demineralized thin sections for limonite

For limonite, excellent histological results can be obtained through the complete demineralization of thin sections (Stein et al. 1982). Thin sections are made following standard procedures (see Chapter 15; also method in Stein et al. 1982) and are ground to a thickness of 15–25 µm. At this thickness the limonite becomes translucent under bright illumination. Sections are demineralized in HCl (c. 38% for 2–12 h), washed briefly in distilled water (c. 15–30 s), dehydrated through an ethanol series, and mounted in a suitable mounting medium (e.g. DPX, Euparal, Canada balsam, see Appendix). Specimens must not be allowed to air dry because this may result in collapse of the cell walls.

Peel technique

Embedding of larger specimens may not be necessary, but this procedure is essential for small or fragile material. Chitaley (1985) recommended a paraffin wax embedding medium, but epoxy adhesives and casting resins are also suitable (see Chapter 14), providing they do not degrade with exposure to HNO_3. With the exception of the etching reagent, the technique is identical to the standard acetate peel technique (see Chapter 13) developed for calcium and magnesium carbonate permineralizations. Nitric acid (c. 68%) is used for pyrite with an etching time of between 5–15 min depending on the nature of the material (Chitaley 1985). The peel technique is, in principle, applicable to limonite, but long etching times may render it impractical.

Documenting details of cell wall structure

Documenting details of cell wall structure requires high resolution images as well as a critical evaluation of the effects of mineralization (Kenrick & Edwards 1988; Kenrick et al. 1991). A high quality polish combined with reflectance light microscopy (bright-field illumination) or scanning electron microscopy (back scatter electron imaging) is recommended. Both imaging techniques exploit the contrast between the opaque mineral and the organic remains of the cell walls. Under light microscopy, pyrite has a much higher reflectance than organics (Fig. 17.1a, c). Back scatter electrons provide a similar image based on atomic number contrast (compare Fig. 17.1e and h). The iron in pyrite and limonite has a relatively high atomic number and therefore greater reflectance than the carbon-based organics in the cell wall. Both techniques produce excellent results, but scanning electron microscopy provides higher resolution and can be coupled with direct element analysis (e.g. EDAX).

Whereas techniques involving polished sections are two-dimensional, imaging of cell wall morphology in three dimensions is easily achieved through etching or fracturing of the petrifaction, combined with topographical imaging using SEM

(Fig. 17.1j, Grierson 1976; Kenrick & Edwards 1988; Kenrick et al. 1991). Fractured sections are more difficult to interpret than etched sections because there is little control over the plane of fracture and distinguishing minerals from organics is problematic (Fig. 17.1k).

Highly polished thick sections

Standard mineralogical polishing procedures are used, but because of variation among specimens it may be necessary to adjust the number of steps, the polishing time, and the lap speed. The following procedure has been used successfully. Specimens are embedded using an epoxy adhesive (see Chapter 14) in a cylindrical polythene mould (e.g. 15 mm deep, 40 mm diameter). The surface is ground smooth using paper-bonded silicon carbide (600 and 1200 grit) lubricated with water. Highly polished sections are obtained by machine polishing on rotating (c. 80 rpm) cloth laps (e.g. Nylon and Selvyt cloths, see Appendix) using successively finer grades of polish (e.g. 14, 6, 3, 1 µm diamond polish paste, see Appendix). Specimens are polished for c. 5–20 min at each grade and cleaned by brief (30 s) immersion in a sonic bath between grades.

Deep etch

Suitable etching procedures for pyrite were outlined by Grierson (1976) and Stein et al. (1982), and in the section above on etching to enhance contrast. For pyrite, a deep etch with complete surface demineralization takes approximately 30 min in HNO_3 (c. 68%) at room temperature. Suitable etching procedures for limonite are outlined in the section on demineralizing thin sections for limonite (above). Results are less predictable and etching times may be much longer than for pyrite.

Fractured sections

Fractured sections are most easily made from cut thick sections. The specimen is scored with a sharp knife (e.g. scalpel) to encourage it to fracture along a desired plane.

Mounting for SEM and recovering

For atomic number contrast imaging, sections are mounted on aluminium stubs and carbon coated. For topographical imaging, the etched or fractured specimen is mounted on a stub and gold-coated. To remove the gold coat for further etching, the specimen is prised from the stub and immersed for c. 10 min in a 0.1–1.0% solution of sodium or potassium cyanide (Sela & Boyde 1977).

Financial support from the Swedish Natural Sciences Research Council (NFR research grant: B-AA/BU 10728-301) and an NERC research grant (GR3/5069) is gratefully acknowledged. I thank W. E. Stein and H. Kerp for their helpful reviews and Yvonne Arremo for assistance with the illustrations.

18. Lignified and charcoalified fossil wood

ISABEL FIGUEIRAL

Wood is a resistant material which fossilizes by permineralization, petrification, charcoalification, and incorporation into peats and lignites (Creber & Chaloner 1984). Attention is focused here on the techniques used in the study of fossil wood incorporated in Tertiary lignites, archaeological wood and wood that has been charcoalified. The term 'lignified' refers to wood material that was exposed to anaerobic conditions and partially degraded by micro-organisms, possibly for long periods, before final sedimentation and preservation in low grade coal. This type of preservation poses a range of technical difficulties for study. Wood anatomy in lignites is commonly preserved, although earlywood and parenchymatous elements are often crushed (Fig. 18.1). Identification of crushed wood can often only be made on anatomical structures visible in radial section. Charcoal is formed when wood is heated in oxygen-depleted conditions. It is chemically highly inert and not subject to microbial attack. Charcoal is formed commonly under natural conditions during wildfire, and is abundant in the fossil record, archaeological horizons and recent sediments. The following account outlines methods for preparing both lignite and charcoal for microscopy. Those involving embedding and sectioning are time consuming and not suited for routine identifications when hundreds of samples may be required in ecological and stratigraphical studies. In the following account, I outline a method for converting lignified specimens into charcoal, which may then be rapidly examined using reflected light microscopy and/or scanning electron microscopy (SEM).

Traditional methods of preparing lignified and charcoalified wood samples vary, but can be broadly divided into two main approaches: those which include sectioning with a blade or saw followed by observation with transmitted light microscopy; those that involve the preparation of fractured surfaces and observation with reflected light and SEM.

Sectioning and embedding

Simple sectioning and mounting

Most charcoals and many lignites are too brittle or friable for sectioning without some kind of embedding. However, some lignites and archaeological woods are sufficiently consolidated for sectioning without prior embedding.

Lignified woods often require a softening treatment prior to sectioning. If the material is too hard or tough, the blade will either not pass through the specimen at all, or do so irregularly or produce slices that are too thick for transmitted light observation. Softening can be carried out by immersing the specimens in sodium hypochlorite or Foster and Gifford's fluid (36 ml distilled water; 54 ml 95% ethyl alcohol; 10 ml lactic acid, Sanderson 1994). The length of time necessary for this should be empirically tested as over-bleaching might cause the material to macerate and become pulpy. Other softening agents are available and again these should be tested before applying to important material because they may also cause the material to disintegrate.

For routine identifications sections may be hand cut manually using a razor blade. Such sections are rarely good enough for publication-standard photographs but may be a good way of preparing preliminary sections prior to more time-consuming methods. Sections may also be cut using one of a range of microtomes (see Sanderson 1994). Microtome-cut sections will invariably mean clamping the specimen in a stage which might not be practical with fragile specimens. Such specimens can be glued to a wooden block which is then held in the microtome holder. Using this technique, the best sections are mounted on glass slides with Canada balsam (see Appendix) and observed directly, without staining and with transmitted light.

Sections which are blackened and totally opaque must be cleared prior to mounting in Canada balsam. Partial clearing is achieved using sodium hypochlorite solution while total clearing requires staining using general stains such as safranin. The staining process for lignites and archaeological, non-charcoalified material has been described by Schweingruber (1978). After clearing, sections are immersed in a solution of 1% safranin for 3–5 min, then rinsed in water, 50% alcohol and then 96% alcohol until excess stain is removed. The dehydrated sections are then immersed in xylene or toluene before being mounted on glass slides in Canada balsam or synthetic resin. (*Note*: these solvents have been used for many years in this and other laboratories and are often cited in the

FIGUEIRAL, I. 1999. Lignified and charcoalified fossil wood. *In*: JONES, T. P. & ROWE, N. P. (eds) *Fossil Plants and Spores: modern techniques*. Geological Society, London, 92–96.

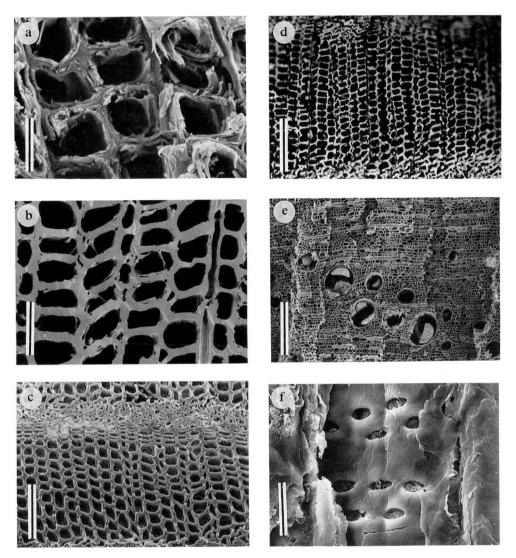

Fig 18.1. (**a**) SEM of lignified conifer wood prior to experimental charring. (scale bar = 23 µm). (**b**) SEM of lignified conifer wood after experimental charring. The surface of the specimen is much 'cleaner' and the fracture surface produced is less irregular than that seen in (b). Miocene, browncoal, Hambach, Germany (scale bar = 40 µm). (**c**) SEM of experimentally charred lignite of conifer wood. The tracheid structure is well preserved except for the early wood which is crushed. Miocene, browncoal, Hambach, Germany (scale bar = 200 µm). (**d**) Reflected light micrograph of experimentally charred lignified conifer wood. The fractured surface is relatively flat and the specimen is clear and in focus (scale bar = 130 µm). (**e**) SEM of experimentally charred angiosperm wood showing organization similar to modern evergreen oak. The heterogeneous organization of the wood has meant that the fracture plane is not flat, but the image is much better than that seen by directly viewing uncharred material (scale bar = 266 µm). (**f**) SEM of experimentally charred lignite. Charring may produce clean surfaces which are readily observed at high magnification to verify small-scale diagnostic characters such as the type of cross-field pits (scale bar = 20 µm).

literature for preparations of this sort. It must be stressed that these solvents are carcinogens and must be used with appropriate laboratory precautions under fume hoods etc. There do exist replacements for xylene and toluene, such as 'Histoclear' (see Appendix) and these should be first tested to see how they perform with these techniques.) With hand-cut or thick microtome sections, it is likely that the section will not lie flat on the slide and it is a good idea to place a weight on the coverslip. Excess resin, squeezed out from under the coverslip, is best trimmed from the slide/coverslip when the resin is no longer fluid but not yet hard.

Embedding/sectioning techniques

Most lignites and some archaeological wood require some form of embedding prior to sectioning. This is particularly the case if large surfaces or features are necessary for study. Embedding non-mineralized wood fossils may be complicated, and there is much scope for modifying standard techniques for a given material.

In the case of particularly friable charcoal fragments, epoxy resin embedding can be carried out using the method described by Smith & Gannon (1973). In this method, charcoal specimens are immersed in acetone for 24 h under a partial vacuum. They are then transferred to a mixture of 1 : 1, resin:acetone, and again placed under a low vacuum for 24 h. The third step involves placing the specimens in a 3 : 1 parts resin:acetone for 24 h in a closed container with silica gel and finally replacing this mixture with 100% epoxy resin. The resin is then left to harden and blocks may be trimmed and prepared for mounting on a microtome. According to Shackley (1981a), if sections are cut using a microtome knife, both this and the block should be lubricated with a mixture of 2 : 1 95% ethyl alcohol and glycerine. Sections should be cut at 8–10 µm before being dried, transferred to a slide, washed with alcohol and covered with Canada balsam or resin.

The method described above may also be used for friable wood fragments, especially when dry. Smith & Gannon (1973) recommend that samples be stained with a 1% aqueous solution of safranin before mounting. and then rinsed with 95% and 100% of alcohol for dehydration, and a final rinse in toluene or toluene substitute.

Less prolonged embedding processes may be used on more consolidated material. Cousins (1975) describes a technique for embedding recent charcoals from volcanic ash sediments using polyethylene glycol, 'Carbowax' (see Appendix). However, the charcoal needs to be softened prior to sectioning. This is carried out by prolonged immersion in 0.5 M sodium hydroxide solution and subsequent washing in near-boiling water, which would undoubtedly destroy many less-consolidated samples. More recently new types of resin have been used for the study of prehistoric charcoal (see Chapter 14). A mixture of epoxy resins was used by Marziani & Iannone (1986), and semi-thin sections obtained with a Reichert ultramicrotome equipped

with a glass knife. Another recent approach concerns microtome sectioning of charcoal specimens embedded in 2-hydroxyethyl methacrylate resin (HEMA), (Igersheim & Cichocki 1996). According to the authors this method simplifies and reduces the embedding process, and can produce high quality sections.

Sectioning

There are basically two approaches to sectioning lignitic wood, archaeological wood and charcoal samples that have been embedded in resin. Relatively soft materials may be sectioned in the same way as modern woods on a microtome. Many types of microtome and blade are available (Sanderson 1994), with probably the most practical being sliding or sledge microtomes. Problems arise when the 'soft' woody material is contaminated with mineral particles that will damage the blade and cause tearing of the section. Specimens should be cleaned thoroughly before embedding, but this might be problematic if the cleaning process causes the material to fall apart. In such cases, the use of disposable steel microtome blades such as 'Histoknife' blades (see Appendix) is recommended. The second approach which is possibly more widely applicable, involves preparation of ground thin sections for observation with transmitted or reflected light. In these cases the specimen is not cut with a blade but with a circular saw with a diamond cutting edge and the section is ground or polished until the preparation is transparent as in geological and mineralogical thin sections (see Chapter 15). Problems have also been found with 'sectioned' surfaces of lignitic material prepared for SEM where cell wall surfaces have a torn and smudged appearance caused by tearing during fracture of the specimen or by the passage of a blade if cut with a knife or razor.

Approaches for preparing fractured surfaces

Charcoal analysis

The following technique has been developed and used routinely for rapid identifications of Quaternary archaeological charcoals.

Specimens are simply fractured by manually snapping or pulling apart the fragment of charcoal between the fingers and along the desired plane for observation; sliding a razor blade along the desired plane may sometimes work but sometimes flattens the three-dimensional surfaces to each side of the blade. Fragments are inevitably irregularly shaped and are placed in a shallow dish, containing dried, clean poppy seeds (*Papaver setigerum*, 0.2–1.0 mm in diameter), which is fixed to a standard glass slide and may be moved around normally on the microscope stage. The poppy seeds offer sufficient support for observation but also allow easy adjustment of the angle and orientation of the specimen for an even plane of focus. Fractured specimens are manipulated using entomological forceps with highly 'flexible' tips. These allow the specimens to be easily picked up and manipulated without being crushed. They may be improvised by inserting small slivers of plastic on to the ends of regular forceps. Specimens are observed with a compound microscope equipped with reflected light with objectives of × 5, × 10, × 20, × 50 and × 80. Low magnification observation requires an especially bright light source and the use of the highest wattage light source possible is recommended. The technique is simple and enables the identification of large sample numbers in a relatively short time (Western 1963; Stieber 1967; Vernet 1973).

Experimental charring of Tertiary lignites for observation with reflected light

Techniques developed for charcoal analysis in the reconstruction of Quaternary vegetation are now also being used in large-scale identifications of Tertiary woods (Figueiral *et al.* 1998). Woods collected from browncoal seams are preserved as both charcoal, resulting from wildfires, as well as lignitic woods. Both naturally and experimentally charred material may be observed and identified under the same conditions and with comparable characteristics.

Fragments of lignitic wood up to about 1 cm^3 are sealed in aluminium foil to exclude oxygen reaching the specimen during heating and each package is labelled with an indelible marker pen. Specimens are placed in a laboratory furnace and heated at 400°C for 20–25 min. The material is then left to cool <u>slowly</u> inside the furnace until the whole apparatus has cooled (up to 10 h) so as to avoid cracks and fragmentation. Specimens may then be removed from the furnace and prepared for observation as outlined above.

Advantages and disadvantages

This technique is considerably less time consuming than techniques required in embedding and sectioning non-mineralized wood material. It involves a minimum of cleaning and sidesteps entirely the use of embedding resins and carefully administered cutting, sawing or grinding/polishing for prepar-ation of sections and ground thin sections. For large-scale, stratigraphic and ecological projects requiring large samples of wood, the use of embedding resins and sectioning might not be practical. With charring and the use of reflected light, large numbers of samples might be processed and identified within a few days. Another advantage is that characteristic or diagnostic features of interest can be located in the material during microscopic observation by sequential manual fracturing the specimen, then screening the freshly broken surfaces under the microscope until the area showing optimal preservation or the desired structure is located. Such an example might include a diagnostic character such as well pre-served cross-field pitting. Sampling for well pre-served or diagnostic parts of a sample embedded in resin might take either luck or a great deal of preparation time. A further advantage of this approach is that charcoalification 'cleans' the fossil wood of fungi and other organic material allowing a much cleaner image of anatomical characters.

One disadvantage of the technique is the narrow depth of focus furnished by standard incident light compound microscope objectives. This is why it is very important to have a good support medium for the charcoal fragments so that specimens can be nudged into an acceptable focus for a given feature. With a little practice this becomes less of a problem.

Another problem is related to the fact that 'unfamiliar' material may be difficult to identify with the resolution available with incident light and the fact that the image at high power contains a lot of scattered and reflected light, particularly if the light intensity is not or cannot be suitably adjusted. Such specimens may be readily verified with the SEM. Charcoal and experimentally charred lignite can be easily mounted on SEM stubs using double-sided tape. We have found that many adhesives such as epoxy resins may expand when setting or in the vacuum of the microscope chamber and charcoal breaks away very readily from the resin when this happens. The most consistently good results come from specimens simply stuck to the stub with double-sided tape which are then gold-coated. If charging becomes a problem, a stripe of conductive paint (e.g. silver dag) may be applied across the specimen and to the stub. When this is necessary it is best to let the paint become tacky before applying to the wood as the liquid will tend to fill the specimen by capillary action.

After charring, the main structural features remain mostly unchanged despite shrinkage and homogenization of cell walls. However, changes do occur in the relative dimensions of the cell walls. According to Schweingruber (1978, p.204) 'The loss of 70–80% of the substances of the wood causes a shrinkage of 7–13% longitudinally and 12–15% radially/tangentially. The cell wall is reduced by $\frac{1}{5}$–$\frac{1}{4}$ of its original thickness'.

Identification references

Identification of Quaternary woods to the levels of family, genus and species is achieved by comparisons with a reference collection of extant species. Reference collections should ideally contain thin sections in all three planes as well as charred reference specimens. Charred reference specimens are produced in the laboratory in the same way as experimentally charred lignites as described above. Comparisons are also made with the many excellent wood atlases of extant plants and reference sources to fossils (Peirce 1936; Beverluis 1943; Kräusel 1949; Greguss 1955, 1959; Jacquiot 1955; Phillips 1966; Jacquiot et al. 1973; Détienne & Jacquet 1983; Schweingruber 1990). Computer databases are also available, such as the OPCN database, the CSIRO family key and the GUESS programme (LaPasha 1986; Wheeler et al. 1986; Ilic 1987; LaPasha & Wheeler 1987). An important reference for the identification of extant hardwoods is to be found in the IAWA list of microscopic features for hardwood identification (IAWA Committee 1989).

19. Fabric analysis and plant anatomy

WILLIAM E. STEIN & CAROL L. HOTTON

The anatomy of living plants and its counterpart in permineralized fossils contains a wealth of ontogenetic, functional and historical information that is often inadequately conveyed by qualitative descriptive terminology. Anatomical terminology depends on the objectives of a given study, ranging from topographic descriptions of cells, tissues or organs, to process interpretations expressing hypotheses about developmental, functional or evolutionary relationships. In many instances, the resolution and effectiveness of comparisons can be substantially improved by quantification. In our work inferring ontogenetic patterns in extinct plants (Stein 1993; Hotton & Stein 1994), for example, quantification is essential to understanding developmental activities of cells in tissues, especially relating individual cell size or shape to physical forces generated during growth within tissues, in addition to other extrinsic or intrinsic factors.

The most common approaches to quantification of biological structure are the so-called 'traditional morphometric' methods (Blackith & Reyment 1971; Sokal & Rohlf 1981; Marcus 1990). Typically, these methods involve collecting a set of measurements, such as distance between homologous locations on the organism, transforming or standardizing the data to account for differences in scale or dimensionality of the variables, and then submitting them to standard multivariate statistical analysis, examining mean differences or variance–covariance structure within and between populations. More recent developments have expanded analysis in several directions. In situations where the entire shape of an organism or one of its parts is of interest, but homologous locations are hard to identify, methods involving outline contours are utilized. In two current approaches, Eigenshape Analysis (Lohmann & Schweitzer 1990) and Fourier Analysis of outlines (Younker & Ehrlich 1977), the objective is often data reduction (Johnson & Wichern 1988) – simplifying complex outline shapes into a set of more simplified variables useful in population comparisons. Also very active in recent years has been 'morphometrics' in a narrower sense (Bookstein 1991) in which data are quantified strictly in terms of coordinates for landmark points specifying relative location on the form as opposed to measuring

distances or other scalar variables. Compared with Traditional Morphometrics, landmark methods have the advantage of inserting the geometry of form directly into the analysis of variance–covariance structure, allowing greater statistical precision in many phases of analysis (Bookstein 1991).

As exciting as these recent developments are in the study of overall animal or plant form, their usefulness at the tissue level is limited where homologous landmarks or outlines cannot be identified. More useful, we believe, is analysis of cell and tissue fabrics, by which we mean the size–shape relationship of a variable number of cells in the context of local and regional cell neighbourhoods within tissues. These kinds of data offer insight into the relative capacity and timing of growth (increase in size) of individual cells and on the physical forces generated internally by growth, or exerted on the tissue as a whole. Although we concentrate on cells in tissues here, the concept can be generalized to include other data having multiple closed contours such as, for example, areolation patterns in leaves. In the past few years, we have developed a method of microcomputer-assisted data collection and analysis of fabric data inspired by geological microfabric analysis (Ramsay & Huber 1983), which we believe is applicable to a wide range of biological problems (Stein 1993; Sorauf & Stein 1993; Hotton & Stein 1994).

Principles

Quantitative analysis of tissue fabric involves measurement of cell or tissue anisotropy, here defined as anisodiametric cell dimensions, or groups of cells with average or minimum distances between them dependent upon direction. Tissue anisotropy can be interpreted as a physical deformation of individual cells (cell strain) or tissues (tissue strain) due to unequally directed forces (stresses) experienced over the course of development or imposed by external agents. By contrast, cell or tissue isotropy may be viewed as reflecting the absence of net directional stresses. Mathematically, the simplest description of strain is the uniform deformation model governed by the affine class of mathematical transformations (Bookstein 1991). Affine transformations have the property

STEIN, W. E. & HOTTON, C. L. 1999. Fabric analysis and plant anatomy. *In*: JONES, T. P. & ROWE, N. P. (eds) *Fossil Plants and Spores: modern techniques*. Geological Society, London, 97–104.

that parallel lines prior to transformation remain so afterwards and, in two dimensions, objects with initially circular outline are deformed (or tilted and projected back onto the plane of the data) into an ellipse. Ellipticity – the ratio of major to minor diameter of the resultant ellipse – measures the strength of the deformation as relative or absolute lengthening of the major axis, shortening of the minor axis, or a combination of both. In structural geology, measurements of deformed objects in a rock sample contribute to the estimation of a general strain ellipse (in two dimensions) or strain ellipsoid (in three dimensions) which are used to infer strength and direction of tectonic forces experienced by rock strata (Ramsay & Huber 1983). In biology, it is often important to consider complex patterns of non-uniform strain (Bookstein 1991), including those that are highly localized on the organism's form and genetically determined. One way to do this is to collect information about multiple objects such as cells, and to analyse ellipticity, orientation, size and location of each relative to the expectations of the general strain ellipse estimated from neighbourhoods of objects at different scales, with criteria for membership in neighbourhoods defined in biologically significant ways.

Data collection

Although many important aspects of plant tissue fabrics are three dimensional, in most anatomical studies one is usually required to reconstruct the geometry from two-dimensional images of sectioned material available, for instance, from peels or ground thin sections (Fig. 19.1a). In fossils, especially, these images are often exceedingly complex and include useful biological information on cell type, shape and size, as well as artefacts of preservation, preparation or observation (Fig. 19.1b). In analysing these images, it is important to maximize the signal to noise ratio. Sophisticated software is currently available for filtering images and 'teaching' recognition of specific kinds of objects. However, in our experience this technology remains vastly inferior to the human brain in interpreting complex images, especially in cases where important architectural features, such as primary wall in fossil plant cells, are not directly

observable. Filtering techniques involving extensive pixel manipulation rapidly degrade the information content of images, and given the usually large number of variables relating to preservation, preparation, lighting and presentation of individual samples, the amount of time required in software development and teaching rapidly becomes prohibitive. In our opinion, it is usually far better to manually interpret and simplify the data presented to an automatic data collector.

In the approach presented here, important aspects of tissue fabrics are captured by analysing cell size and shape in sectional view, ignoring information on wall thickness, differential colour patterns and the like. Outlines of cell boundaries, identified by the inferred location of the compound middle lamella, are drawn by hand on acetate overlays over greatly enlarged photographs. The data collector, consisting of video camera or flat-bed scanner, frame-grabber and software (in our case OPTIMAS, see Appendix, BioScan Inc., Edmond, WA), captures grey-scale video images of the acetate sheets as a $640 \times 480 \times 8$ bit pixel array. Built-in software filters may be used to enhance contrast or otherwise sharpen the difference between lines representing cell boundaries and background. Employing a user-defined threshold in pixel brightness, the software recognizes bounded areas representing individual cells and provides an impressive array of summary information about each one. At this stage of analysis, and following, it is important to recognize the limits of resolution of the data collector and important sources of error. In our studies, estimates of absolute size of cells (such as cell area calibrated to a known linear scale on the image) is often greatly affected by thickness of the lines on the acetate sheet and magnification. However, relative (or rank-order) size is more reliably measured within limits of resolution imposed by the pixel array. Depending upon complexity of the tissue analysed, we have found it feasible to collect data of these types for up to 200–500 cells from a single captured image.

In order to estimate both the general strain ellipse and strain ellipses based on individual cells, we instruct the data collector to collect X,Y coordinates of a number (n) of points ($n = 5$–50, but typically 20) equally spaced around each recognized closed contour, yielding an n-point polygon

---

Fig. 19.1(a,b). *Diichnia kentuckiensis* (USNM 41247) from the Lower Carboniferous of Kentucky, USA (Beck *et al.* 1992). (**a**) Transverse section of stem with attached leaf bases, × 6.3. (**b**) Representative portion of the stele in transverse section, showing a central pith region (P) containing some cells with thick walls, a peripheral region of pith or primary xylem (EX) with thinner cell walls containing a protoxylem strand in at least one instance (arrow a), primary xylem bundles (arrow b) composed of thick-walled protoxylem and metaxylem tracheids, and secondary xylem (2X). Region analysed in Fig. 19.2b–d includes both protoxylem strands (PX) indicated by the arrows, × 33. Scale bars = 20 mm.

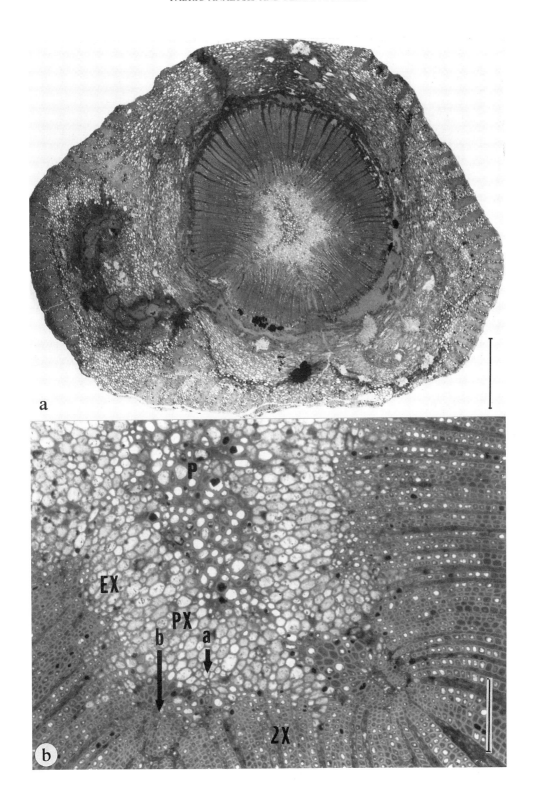

for each cell with sampled points as vertices (see Fig. 19.2a). An ellipse is estimated for each n-point polygon using least squares fitting for conic sections (Erslev 1988). Derived from this are variables relating to ellipticity (Rf_e), area (AR_e), orientation of the major axis (ϕ_e), and location of the centroid (X_e, Y_e) for each ellipse (Fig. 19.2a). Ellipses derived from each n-point polygon can also be used to define neighbourhoods of different kinds, allowing for collection of a set of summary variables. Mean and variance of these variables, as well as ratios between estimates from individual ellipses and neighbourhood means, also provide useful quantitative descriptors (Table 19.1). The following examples illustrate the potential for this kind of information in analysing plant tissues.

Analysis of cell sizes and shapes

Differential timing, enlargement and maturation of primary xylem tracheids, probably under hormonal control (Stein 1993), provides the basis for much of traditional stelar theory (Beck *et al.* 1982) useful in phylogenetic analysis and systematics of major groups of vascular plants (Kenrick & Crane 1997). These processes produce zones of tissue, characterized by cells of different sizes or shapes (Fig. 19.1a–b), that can be located and quantified by variables based on least-squares fitted ellipses of individual cells. Associated with these developmental activities are characteristic tissue patterns, with cells of different sizes or shapes often occurring in distinct zones (Fig. 19.1a). Particularly useful for inferring differing developmental activities underlying maturation of the xylem are averages taken over small neighbourhoods (usually 6–9 cells each), including mean ellipse area for average size of cells (Fig. 19.2b), mean ellipticity for average ratio of major to minor ellipse axis

Table 19.1. *Variables based on ellipses used in fabric analysis of plant tissues*

Single least squares fitted ellipse (Erslev 1988, 1989)
  X,Y coordinates of ellipse centroid
  X,Y coordinates of endpoints for ellipse major and minor axes
  major axis (M) and minor axis (m) lengths
  area of ellipse (AR_e)
  ellipticity ($Rf_e = M/m$)
  angle of ellipse major axis relative to defined reference system (ϕ_e)

Ellipse neighbourhoods
  Definition of neighbourhoods:
    constant distance in all directions from centroid of centre ellipse
    variable distance in all directions scaled to the area of centre ellipse
    constant number of neighbours in order of distance form centre ellipse
    normalized or 'touching' neighbours (Erslev 1988) of centre ellipse
    inclusive (IN) – including centre ellipse in calculation of summary variable
    exclusive (EX) – excluding centre ellipse in calculation of summary variable
  Neighbourhood variables:
    mean area of neighbourhood ellipses ($INmAR$, $EXmAR$)
    variance on area ($INvarAR$, $EXvarAR$)
    mean ellipticity of neighbourhood ellipses ($INmRF$, $EXmRF$)
    variance on ellipticity ($INvarRF$, $EXvarRF$)
    mean resultant length (Davis 1986) ($INvecR$, $EXvecR$)

This is by no means an exhaustive list.

lengths indicating intensity of cell strain (Fig. 19.2c), and mean resultant length of the ellipse major axis (Fig. 19.2d). The last variable, a

---

Fig. 19.2. Characterization of cells in tissues as fields of least-squares fitted ellipses and neighbourhoods. (a) Method of analysis. Cells are imaged by microcomputer from hand-drawn acetate overlays over greatly enlarged photographs. Relative X,Y coordinates are extracted for 20 equally spaced points around the contour of each cell (20-point polygon). From this, a best-fit ellipse is estimated by least squares (Erslev 1988). Each cell ellipse may be characterized by area (AR_e), ellipticity ($RF_e = M/m$) and orientation of the ellipse major axis (ϕ_e). Neighbourhoods for each ellipse are defined in several ways and summary measures are calculated (Table 19.1). (b)–(d) Transverse section through a portion of the pith, primary xylem and secondary xylem of *Diichnia kentuckiensis* illustrated in Fig. 19.1b (these images rotated 90° counterclockwise), centre of the stem toward the upper-left. A total of 426 cells were analysed on a $640 \times 480 \times 8$ bit pixel array. Inclusive neighbourhoods (each cell plus 6 nearest neighbours) are placed in integer classes according to values of a specified variable, indicated by four-level shading ranging in order of intensity from black (class 1 – smallest values) to white (class 4 – largest values). (b) Classification based on $INmAR$; protoxylem and secondary xylem may be distinguished from metaxylem based on size. (c) Classification based on $INmRF$; peripheral pith or metaxylem is characterized by relatively high mean ellipticity (shading classes 2–4), indicating strain in a radial direction. Some cell neighbourhoods near the protoxylem strands show the highest mean ellipticity (class 4, arrows) probably as a result of combining a general tissue strain with more localized strain associated with each protoxylem strand. (d) Classification based on $INvecR$; neighbourhoods of highest alignment of ellipse major axes among cells in neighbourhoods correspond in part to the region of highest mean ellipticity observed in (c).

standardized scalar measure based on a vector resultant of unit length directional vectors reflecting ϕ_e, ranges from 0 (random orientation) to 1 (completely parallel orientation), and provides a measure of agreement among cell ellipses as estimators of a uniform strain in the tissue (for derivation, see Davis 1986, pp.314–321). Observing the least-squares fitted ellipse derived from each 20-point contour also allows visual interpre-

tation of non-uniform strain experienced by tissues during growth. Particularly conspicuous here are the tracheids elongated radially around each protoxylem strand (Fig. 19.2c, arrows). A more regional pattern of tracheid deformation also occurs in the metaxylem, especially near the periphery of the primary xylem (Fig. 19.2d), perhaps reflecting the fact that the centre of the stele is essentially incompressible, and that expansion of these cells in

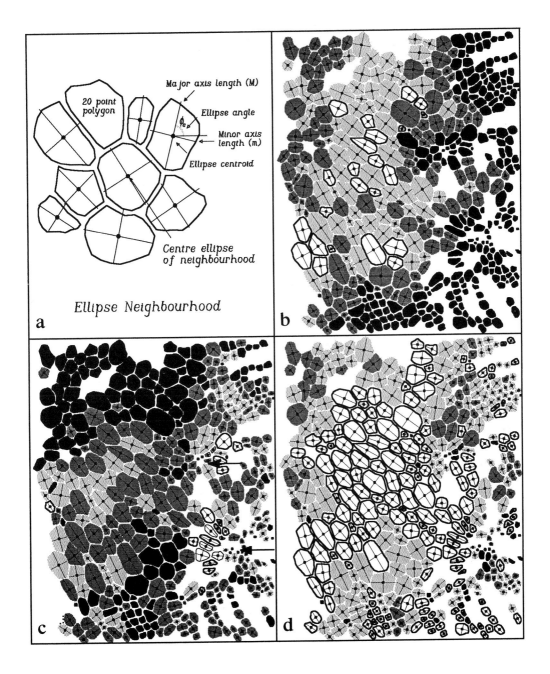

a radial direction meets with least resistance. In order to identify patterns of size and shape in different tissues, or to follow developmental trajectories, morphospaces (e.g. Raup 1966) based on measured variables may also be constructed (Fig. 19.3).

Analysis of strain

In studying ontogenetic changes in tissues, it is also useful to estimate a general strain ellipse for different tissue regions. It is clear that mean ellipticity will overestimate general tissue strain by an amount inversely related to mean resultant length of the ellipses (compare Figs. 19.2c–d), so a more direct approach is desirable. In one study (Hotton & Stein 1994), we employed a technique derived from structural geology called Fry analysis (Fry 1979; Ramsay & Huber 1983; Erslev 1988). Fry analysis involves successively placing the centroid of each cell in a region of interest at the centre of a coordinate system and plotting the centroids of all neighbours. The result is a scatter

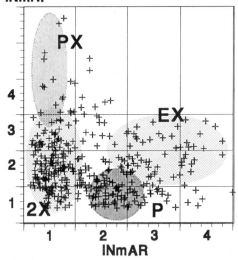

Fig. 19.3. Morphospace plot of variables shown in Fig. 19.2b–d for neighbourhoods of cells; inclusive mean area, *INmAR*; inclusive mean ellipticity, *INmRF*. Measurements in these plots are relative and scaled so that membership in the discrete classes of Fig. 19.2b–d can be compared directly with the distribution of points; internal grid represents boundaries of the classes. Different regions can be identified with specific tissues, including protoxylem (PX), radially elongate peripheral pith or primary xylem (EX), secondary xylem (2X) and central pith (P); approximate limits of morphospace regions for each tissue are indicated by shading drawn by eye.

diagram in which a central void represents minimum cell packing, and is surrounded by a relatively high density ring of points representing the locations of near neighbours. Ellipticity of the ring provides a measurement of overall tissue strain. Erslev (1988, 1989) has proposed improvements of the Fry method designed to increase precision in characterizing the ring, including normalized Fry analysis where inter-centroid distances in the plots are divided by the sum of cell ellipse radii in the same direction, and enhanced normalized Fry analysis where only the centroids of 'touching' cells are plotted, as defined by a tunable variable ('selection factor') that compares inter-centroid distances with the size of each ellipse. Software for performing all of these analyses is commercially available (INSTRAIN – see Appendix under Rockware).

Shown here (Fig. 19.4a–c) are normalized Fry plots of sectors of the morphospace defined by the variables used in the previous example (Fig. 19.3), primarily occupied by different tissues. Plotting individual cells whose neighbourhoods exhibit the smallest mean area, mostly secondary xylem (2X), we observe a nearly circular ring of scatter (Fig. 19.4a), indicating no preferred direction of minimum or maximum cell ellipse centroid spacing. The tissue thus appears isotropous, and little or no strain may be inferred. By contrast, in the tissue region observed at the periphery of the primary xylem comprising neighbourhoods with relatively large and radially elongate cells (EX), a distinctly elliptical ring of scatter is observed (Fig. 19.4b). Tissue anisotropy estimated from ellipticity of the normalized Fry ellipse in the diagram is approximately 1.5–1.8, thus providing a quantitative estimate of the relative difference in cell expansion in the radial versus tangential directions in the tissue as a whole during development. In cell neighbourhoods exhibiting relatively large size and low mean ellipticity, including mostly central pith (P), but also some cells at the boundary between primary and secondary xylem (Fig. 19.2b–c), tissue isotropy is again found (Fig. 19.4c).

Importance of fabric analysis

The quantitative techniques of fabric analysis described above offer increased precision in the description of morphology of fossil and living plants at the cellular and tissue level. From this, we can reconstruct individual ontogenies (Hotton & Stein 1994), and evaluate how developmental systems in plants evolve (Stein 1993, 1998). Our work has shown that similar patterns of cell size and shape, recognizable in otherwise differing tissues, reflect common underlying developmental processes. Two examples can be cited here; for

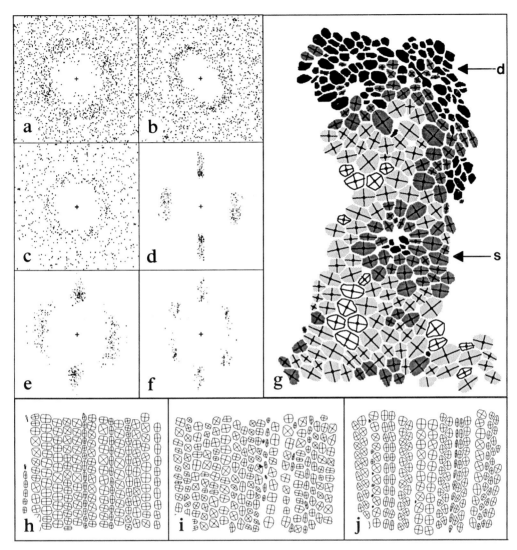

Fig. 19.4a–j. Analysis of tissue fabrics. (**a**)–(**c**) Normalized Fry plots analysing centre-to-centre distances between cells comprising sub-samples identified by the discrete classifications of inclusive mean area (*INmAR*), and inclusive mean ellipticity (*INmRF*) in Fig. 19.3. Plots are in the same orientation as Figs 19.2b–d, so ellipse directions can be directly compared. (**a**) Cells in class 1 for *INmAR*, representing tracheids of the secondary xylem (2X) plus cells of the two protoxylem strands (PX). (**b**) Cells in classes 2–4 for *INmAR* and classes 2–4 for *INmRF*, identifying a region of elongate cells near the periphery of the peripheral pith or primary xylem (EX). (**c**) Cells in classes 2–4 for *INmAR* and class 1 for *INmRF*, representing mostly cells of the central pith region (P). (**d**)–(**f**) Enhanced normalized Fry plots showing Fry resonance of secondary xylem in different plants analysed in transverse section; tracheids in radial files running from top to bottom. (**d**) Modern pine, showing high degree of order in both radial and tangential directions; selection factor = 1.16. (**e**) *Callixylon* sp. from the Upper Devonian of New York showing generally less order both within and between radial files of tracheids; selection factor = 1.30. (**f**) Late Carboniferous *Medullosa*, showing six preferred directions reflecting regular offset of tracheids in adjacent radial files; selection factor = 1.16. (**g**) *Triloboxylon* from the Middle Devonian of Virginia (Stein 1993); primary xylem rib in transverse section showing a relatively 'shallow' protoxylem strand near the centre of the stele, arrow s, and two relatively 'deeper' protoxylem strands near the rib tip, arrow d. Shading reflects a four-part classification of cell neighbourhoods based on AR_e, as in Fig. 19.2b. (**h**)–(**j**) Twenty-point cell polygons and least-squares fitted ellipses of regions of secondary xylem analysed in (**d**)–(**f**). (**h**) *Pinus ponderosa*, commercially prepared slide. (**i**) *Callixylon* sp., Genundewa limestone (Frasnian), New York, SUNY-Binghamton collections. (**j**) *Medullosa* sp., University of Illinois peel.

more detail, see Hotton & Stein (1994). The first, previously termed the black hole effect, involves small-scale patterns of radially elongate cells often surrounding small isodiametric cells, observed in protoxylem (Figs 19.1b, 19.2c, arrows; 19.4g, arrows), as well as sclereid nests of cortical and pith tissues. We infer that this pattern is a consequence of relatively early maturation of the central-most cells causing localized radial strain on the living, and still expanding, surrounding cells of the tissue. Developmental or evolutionary changes in timing of this process relative to the general rate of cell expansion also have co-ordinated effects on average cell sizes and ellipticities, termed protoxylem depth (Stein 1993) in stelar architecture (Fig. 19.4g, arrows).

A second phenomenon, which we term Fry resonance, is the clustering of cell centroids within local regions of the Fry plot (Figs 19.4d–f). This pattern sometimes reflects physical causes, such as hexagonal close-packing of similar size objects, but is of greater interest when it reflects cells derived from cell lineages, such as from the vascular cambium (Figs 19.4h–j). For example, in the secondary xylem of modern pine (Figs. 19.4d, h), cell locations are highly clustered in a radial direction reflecting successive equally spaced tracheids in radial files, but locations are also clustered to a degree in the tangential direction. This pattern in pine appears to reflect a significant structural constraint in spacing, perhaps involving co-ordination in division of cambial initials in adjacent radial cell files, and contrasts with the apparently less constrained pattern in the Devonian progymnosperm *Callixylon* (Figs. 19.4e, i). Another pattern is observed in the late Carboniferous seed plant *Medullosa* (Figs. 19.4f, j), where clustered offset of cells in adjacent radial files is conspicuous. In the latter instance, it remains to be determined whether the offset reflects a genetically constrained division pattern in the vascular cambium, or instead is due to physical packing adjustments in cell locations during maturation of the tissue. However, these examples clearly point to the importance of going beyond tissue-specific descriptions of form to the identification of universal tissue patterns and, from that, to the inference of universal underlying causal factors.

20. Biomechanical analysis

THOMAS SPECK & NICK P. ROWE

The size, shape and overall posture of plants are important characteristics for identifying the growth forms of fossil plants and inferring the structural complexity of their ecosystems. A number of studies have employed biomechanical methods to investigate stem structure, branching morphologies and crown architectures of fossil plants and to estimate quantitatively their maximum height (Niklas 1977, 1990, 1992, 1994, 1997; Raven 1984; Niklas & Kerchner 1984; Speck & Vogellehner 1988a,b, 1992a,b, 1994; Mosbrugger 1990; Speck 1994a,b; Vincent & Jeronimidis 1992; Rowe et al. 1993; Speck & Rowe 1994; Mosbrugger & Roth 1996; Rowe & Speck 1997; 1998; Spatz et al. 1998). Interest has focused particularly on the critical buckling length: the maximum height an upright column can reach before it fails due to global buckling caused by its own weight, and this approach has been widely applied to fossil plant stems (Mosbrugger 1990; Niklas 1990, 1992, 1994; Speck & Vogellehner 1992b, 1994; Speck 1994a).

This chapter outlines a method for empirically investigating growth forms of fossil plants by recalculating and comparing the biomechanical properties of stem segments from different ontogenetic stages. A necessary step in demonstrating how this is achieved is to show briefly how growth forms among living plants can be characterized by patterns of mechanical data from ontogenetic stages.

Characterization of living growth forms

Mechanical properties of plant stems may change during ontogeny and it is the trends in these changes that we use to characterize different growth forms (Speck 1994b; Speck & Rowe 1998). Growth forms of woody plants can be distinguished by plotting experimentally measured values of flexural stiffness (EI) and structural Young's modulus (E_{struct}) against axial second moment of area (I) (Fig. 20.1a–f). Bending tests are carried out on fresh living material using a mechanical bending apparatus or an Instron testing machine. Flexural stiffness quantifies the ability of a support member, in this case a plant stem, to resist bending forces. It

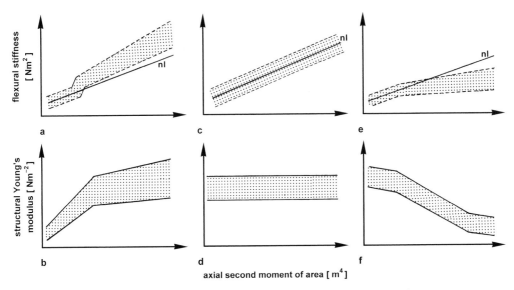

Fig. 20.1. Variation in flexural stiffness (nl: neutral line) and structural Young's modulus during ontogeny among different growth forms (double logarithmic plots against axial second moment of area). (**a–b**) 'self-supporting tree', (**c–d**) 'semi-self-supporting plant', (**e–f**) 'non-self-supporting liana'.

SPECK, T. & ROWE, N. P. 1999. Biomechanical analysis.
In: JONES, T. P. & ROWE, N. P. (eds) *Fossil Plants and Spores: modern techniques.*
Geological Society, London, 105–109.

is calculated as the product of the axial second moment of area and the structural Young's modulus of the stem. The axial second moment of area is a geometrical parameter that describes the cross-sectional size and shape of stems and tissues in relation to the neutral plane and direction of bending. It also reflects the overall size of a plant stem, and among plants with secondary growth, it can be used as a proxy for stem diameter and thus stem size. Structural Young's modulus is a parameter describing the material properties of a stem in bending. The prefix 'structural' is used to emphasize the fact that it represents a mean value of an inhomogeneous composite material. It is calculated by dividing the flexural stiffness of a tested stem by the mean axial second moment of area. In plots of flexural stiffness against the axial second moment of area (Fig. 20.1a, c, e) a 'neutral line' is calculated by extrapolating the value of structural Young's modulus from the youngest ontogenetic stage (E_{OS1}) for higher values of axial second moment of area, i.e. older ontogenetic stages (neutral line = $E_{OS1} \times I$). This neutral line is used to observe how flexural stiffness changes during ontogeny. If stem growth involved proportional and uniform increase of all stem tissues, the percentage contribution of each stem tissue towards the axial second moment of area would remain constant. Furthermore, if the Young's modulus of each stem tissue also remained constant during ontogeny, values of structural Young's modulus for the whole stem at different ontogenetic levels would remain constant and values of flexural stiffness would lie along the neutral line. The trends of flexural stiffness relative to the neutral line have been used to identify three kinds of growth forms among extant woody plants (Fig. 20.1a, c, e)

1. *Self-supporting woody plants (shrubs and trees)*
   The structural Young's modulus increases significantly during ontogeny and values of flexural stiffness for older ontogenetic stages are clearly above the neutral line (Fig. 20.1a–b). The contribution of strengthening tissues (wood) towards axial second moment of area increases during ontogeny.
2. *Semi-self-supporting (leaning) plants ('Spreiz-klimmer')*
   Structural Young's modulus and the contribution of each stem tissue to axial second moment of area do not change significantly during ontogeny. Values of flexural stiffness do not show a distinct increase nor decrease relative to the neutral line (Fig. 20.1c–d).
3. *Non-self-supporting woody plants (lianas)*
   Structural Young's modulus drops significantly during ontogeny and values of flexural stiffness for older ontogenetic stages are clearly below

the neutral line (Fig. 20.1e–f). The contribution of strengthening tissues towards the axial second moment of area is drastically reduced during ontogeny, whereas the contribution of bending flexible tissues increases.

Not surprisingly, detailed analyses of a wide variety of self-supporters, semi-self-supporters and lianas, indicate that each class can be further subdivided according to subtly differing but nevertheless mechanically distinguishable patterns during development. This suggests that the approach might be applied to investigate many more ecologically significant types of growth than the three categories outlined above (Speck & Rowe 1998).

Characterization of fossil plant growth forms

Because fossil plants are nearly always found as disarticulated units, it is extremely difficult to construct convincing hypotheses of overall size, posture and growth habit. The experimental findings from living plants have therefore been used to derive a method for inferring self-supporting, semi-self-supporting and non-self-supporting growth forms from isolated fossils. Mechanical properties of fossil material cannot, of course, be tested experimentally and so have to be recalculated from the compositions and arrangements of stem tissues. A range of ontogenetic stages (stem diameters) is required for a given fossil species. These have to be anatomically preserved and show the relative proportions and geometries of different stem tissues that can be measured quantitatively. The method then involves back calculation of the bending mechanical properties of the stem for each ontogenetic stage. This is followed by a comparison of the pattern of changes in mechanical properties between ontogenetic stages of the fossil with those observed among living growth forms.

Method for recalculating mechanical properties of fossil stems

The recalculation of flexural stiffness and structural Young's modulus of fossil plant stems involves the following basic steps (full details of the procedure can be obtained from the following references: Speck & Vogellehner 1988a; Speck 1994a; Speck & Rowe 1994).

(1) Transverse sections of available permineralized axes are arranged into ontogenetic stages. These are normally based on stem diameter and/or readily identifiable developmental

stages of the stem such as onset and development of wood and bark, evidence of leaf shedding, leaf trace occlusion and so on.

(2) Geometric models of the actual tissue distributions within each transverse section are constructed (Fig. 20.2). The overall outline and tissues of the stem are modelled as centrisymmetrical structures, which approximate most closely the organization present in the fossil (Speck *et al.* 1990). This involves the measurement of all geometrical parameters necessary for the calculation of the axial second moment of area of each tissue for each transverse section. These include, among others, radial thicknesses of tissues, distances from the centre and angles of isolated tissues such as leaf trace bundles or fibre bundles from the centre. If more than one type of tissue occurs in a 'ring' of tissue, such as xylem and rays in wood, the relative proportions of each are calculated as alternating wedges and the appropriate tangential measurements are made on the specimen and included in the geometric description of the model. If one or more of the tissue areas are lobed or have an irregular outline, the shape is approximated as closely as possible with an appropriate geometrical formula describing the outline as a lobed or 'star-shaped' outline using polar coordinates (Speck *et al.* 1990); in such cases, the model outline is approximated from measurements made on the fossil of the number and mean distance of the lobes and intervening 'bays' of tissue respectively from the centre of the stem. The geometrical data are combined into centrisymmetric models of each entire stem section by calculating averages for many of the measurements and using further combinations of polar coordinates to describe each tissue geometry for each specimen (Speck *et al.* 1990). Using analytically-derived formulae describing each tissue distribution for each ontogenetic stage it is then possible to calculate the cross-sectional area (A_{ges}) and axial second moment of area (I_{ges}) of the entire stem and of each stem tissue (A_i, I_i) (for full accounts of the relevant formulae see: Speck & Vogellehner 1988a,b; Speck *et al.* 1990; Niklas 1992; Rowe *et al.* 1993; Speck & Rowe 1994).

(3) After quantifying the geometrical arrangement of each stem tissue for each transverse section, the structural characteristics of all cell types for

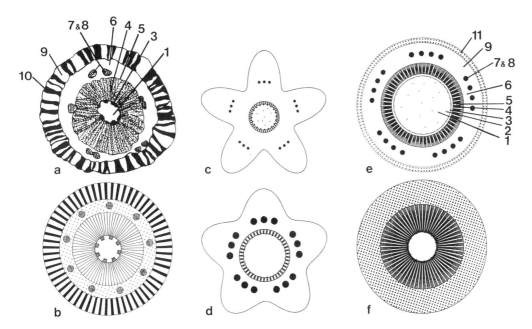

Fig. 20.2. Compound centrisymmetrical models of transverse sections of fossil stems. (**a–b**) *Lyginopteris oldhamia*: (**a**) transverse section of actual stem (radius 9.1 mm); (**b**) compound model used for recalculation of mechanical parameters (from Speck *et al.* 1990). (**c–f**) *Pitus dayi*, compound models of ontogenetic stages of increasing age (from Speck & Rowe 1994). (1) pith, (2) tracheid bundles in the pith, (3) primary xylem bundles, (4) secondary tracheids and (5) ray parenchyma of wood, (6) inner parenchymatous cortex (incl. phloem and vascular cambium), (7) tracheids and (8) rays of petiole traces, (9) parenchymatous and (10) sclerenchymatous outer cortex, (11) periderm.

each tissue have to be measured. Mechanical characteristics of a given modern plant tissue such as parenchyma or wood can vary from plant to plant as a result of different cellular morphologies. Therefore, measurements are made of cell lumen diameters, cell-wall thickness and cell length and observations are made of the tapering and cell-wall ornamentation and pitting from transverse and longitudinal sections; these morphological characteristics and measurements can then be used to search for the closest matching extant tissue (Speck et al. 1996).

(4) After morphological characterization, each fossil tissue has to be correlated with the most similar extant tissue type for which exist experimental mechanical data. It is assumed that the chemical constituents of the cell walls and the degree of hydration characterizing the fossil tissues in life were the same as in extant plants. In order to estimate more precisely the Young's modulus of a fossil tissue quantitatively, the Young's modulus of the most similar living tissue is recalculated for a material constructed entirely of cell wall (E_{pc}). By using the ratio of cell wall area (A_{cw}) to total cell area (A_{tc}) from transverse sections of the corresponding fossil tissue, the Young's modulus of the fossil tissue (E_t) can then be recalculated:

$$E_t = E_{pc} \times (A_{cw}/A_{tc}) \qquad (1)$$

(5) If fossil plant stems are considered as composite materials, the flexural stiffness (EI_{ges}) of each stem cross-section can be calculated from the total number of tissues m (equation 2). Because each tissue type has been modelled individually, the relative contribution of each stem tissue towards the flexural stiffness of the whole stem ($EI_{i,rel}$) can also be calculated (equation 3). Finally, the structural Young's modulus (E_{struct}) of each stem segment can be calculated (equation 4). In the equations below, $E_{t,i}$ and I_i are the Young's modulus and the axial second moment of area respectively of the i-th tissue.

$$EI_{ges} = \sum_{i=1}^{m} E_{t,i} \times I_i \qquad (2)$$

$$EI_{i,rel} = \frac{E_{t,i} \times I_i}{\sum_{i=1}^{m} E_{t,i} \times I_i} \qquad (3)$$

$$E_{struct} = EI_{ges} / I_{ges} \qquad (4)$$

These calculations are carried out for the full range of available transverse sections. It is then possible to demonstrate the patterns of change in bending mechanical properties between different ontogenetic stages, and to compare these with those based on living plants to infer the growth form of the fossil. This has now been carried out for a variety of woody Palaeozoic species including: Diaphorodendron vasculare, Lyginopteris oldhamia, Calamopitys sp. and Pitus dayi (Speck & Vogellehner 1992a; Rowe et al. 1993; Speck 1994a; Speck & Rowe 1994; Rowe & Speck 1998). In addition to analysing overall growth form, the contribution of the different stem tissues to flexural stiffness has also been recalculated for these plants and for a number of small-bodied early Devonian land plants. Contribution of specific tissues to flexural stiffness is of wide interest for determining the importance of individual tissues to the mechanical stability of the stem. This calculation has been used to determine the importance, or not, of early vascular systems and hypodermal steromes for support among early land plants (Speck & Vogellehner 1988a,b, 1992b, 1994), and for determining the mechanical roles of wood, leaf traces and outer cortex of Carboniferous lycopsids and seed plants.

The approach outlined above only deals with mechanical parameters related to bending and structural Young's modulus. Some first results from living plants suggest that torsional stiffness and torsional (shear) modulus can also show discrete variations during ontogeny and may also be used to discern different growth forms. The recalculation for fossil plants could be carried out with a comparable method as that described for bending.

In this approach the identification and use of 'ontogenetic' stages is particularly suited to permineralized plant axes that are rarely interconnected. After constructing the hypothesized ontogenetic sequence, isolated transverse sections of the same species can contribute to a sample from all parts of a hypothetical plant stem system. These kinds of isolated data from separate fragments have been termed 'general data' in such studies (Rowe & Speck 1998). Occasionally, extensively preserved permineralized fossils may provide the opportunity to study transverse sections at known intervals along a stem or axis (Rowe et al. 1993). This kind of dataset, termed 'positional data', may provide more fine-tuned information on adaptive growth and responses of branches and stems to the local environment. Positional data are also necessary for determining mechanical patterns and growth forms among plants for which it is difficult to adequately construct a series of ontogenetic stages. This refers particularly to small-bodied herbaceous plants or pseudoherbaceous plants that lack significant secondary growth and whose axial diameters may not necessarily reflect age or position on the plant

(Rowe & Speck 1998). However, long permineralized stem segments that are sufficiently preserved to allow measurements are extremely rare (Rowe *et al.* 1993).

Problem areas

There are two main areas of problems when using this ontogenetic approach for recalculating mechanical properties of fossil plants (Rowe & Speck 1998). The first concerns the difficulties of dealing with disarticulated plant fossils. Proof of conspecificity might be difficult between ontogenetic stages. Sometimes, different 'species' (in the sense of different biological species) may be included in an analysis to enlarge the range of sufficiently well-preserved stem segments and the study may then represent a kind of 'generic' synthesis (Spatz *et al.* 1998). The interpretation of such data is therefore rather different from that based on parts believed to represent a single biological species. Entire ontogenetic stages might be unmeasurable or missing from the fossil record (Speck & Rowe 1994). This will also have implications on the interpretation of the mechanical signal, but we argue that an incomplete signal can still be informative for inferring a growth form. In the example of *Pitus dayi*, the young branch segments yielded a clear self-supporting signal despite the fact that the rest of the putative arborescent plant was absent (Speck & Rowe 1994; Rowe & Speck 1998).

Among fossil plants it is usually impossible to distinguish between stem segments that represent different growth phases or modules of a plant species (e.g. independent seedlings or saplings from young distal twigs of a mature plant). Studies from a range of extant angiospermous growth forms indicate that young growth phases, whether of distal or regenerative shoots of mature plants or of seedlings or saplings often show similar stem anatomies and similar mechanical properties (Speck & Rowe 1998). However, this remains to be seen for plants with widely differing body plans

and developmental systems seen in many extinct groups. Large-bodied plants with secondary growth show an obvious sequence of ontogenetic stages related to stem diameter. In many small-bodied plants secondary growth is limited or absent and ontogenetic sequences are difficult to identify. Overall size of the stem might not be a good indicator of stage of development because stem size might vary according to internal primary growth rhythms (Rowe & Speck 1997, 1998).

The second problem area is that mechanical properties of fossil tissues cannot be determined experimentally, but must be assigned after quantitative comparisons with living plant tissues. Entire stem cross-sections are rarely preserved, and are often altered in overall shape. Typically, only parts of a transverse section will show preservation of all stem tissues. In these cases, the original stem shape and tissue pattern must be estimated analytically from segments of a single transverse section or several neighbouring sections (Speck *et al.* 1990; Speck & Rowe 1994). Wall thickness of fossil cells is sometimes difficult to measure and this is especially true for 'soft tissues' such as parenchyma, phloem and sometimes also for bark (Speck & Rowe 1994). Correlation of fossil tissues with those of mechanically tested living plants can therefore be difficult. It is often the case that an appropriate 'match' for a fossil tissue cannot be found simply because an appropriate living tissue has not yet been tested or because no closely corresponding tissue type exists in living species (Speck 1994*a*; Speck & Rowe 1994). As a result, the actual mechanical values of each tissue and each ontogenetic stage cannot be ultimately established. However, it is the relative changes in mechanical properties between ontogenetic stages that yield the pattern characterizing growth forms. For this reason we are wary of directly comparing the recalculated mechanical values of fossil stems with data from living plants, but are much more confident in comparing the patterns of mechanical values resulting from ontogenetic change and their significance for inferring the growth form of the fossil.

Part Four   Ultrastructure

21. The ultrastructure of fossil cuticle

THOMAS N. TAYLOR

The cuticle is a continuous extracellular membrane that covers the outer surface of the aerial parts of plants and, as such, is a partially effective barrier in retaining water and high concentrations of solutes within the tissue and in inhibiting the penetration of pathogens. As a result of the protective role that the cuticle plays, the chemical and physical properties of this unique membrane have been investigated extensively (see, for example, Cutler et al. (1982) and references therein). In living plants the cuticular membrane (CM) consists of the outer wall of epidermal cells that contains a continuous layer of lipid materials composed of insoluble cutins that form the framework and soluble waxes deposited on the surface (Holloway 1982). The CM is a heterogeneous layer with each of the component parts characterized by their position and chemical composition. A composite CM would include an outer layer of epicuticular wax (Fig. 21.1a) beneath which is the cuticle proper composed of cutin and cuticular wax secreted onto the external surface of the outer epidermal cell walls. Beneath the cuticle proper may be multiple layers (Fig. 21.1b) that form the majority of the CM and which extend into the spaces between adjacent epidermal cells. It is important to note that in living plants the presence or absence, thickness, chemical composition and structural organization of the CM is highly variable and characterizing the cuticle depends on the species, organ and stage of development. Based on transmission electron microscopy (TEM), Holloway (1982) has characterized the fine structure of six basic types of cuticular membrane structure.

Because of the relatively resistant chemical composition of plant cuticles they are often well preserved and can be traced back to the Lower Devonian where they are associated with plant parts preserved as compressions. Other cuticle specimens are fossilized as fragments and can be released from the rock matrix by various maceration techniques generally involving acid treatment. Since many plants possess distinctive epidermal cell patterns and appendages (Fig. 21.1d), the epidermal anatomy of a taxon is faithfully reproduced as a cast in the cuticle. Because of the high fossilization potential of cuticles and the occurrence of distinctive features, cuticle analysis has played an important role in

many areas of palaeobotany ranging from the correlation of dispersed organs in plant reconstruction to the determination of various palaeoecological (Kerp & Barthel 1993) and climatic factors (Kerp 1991). Initially most cuticular analyses were based on transmitted light microscopy, but in recent years these studies have increasingly relied on a combination of techniques including scanning electron microscopy (SEM).

Cuticle extraction and preparation

Compressions represent one way in which plant parts may be fossilized. In some instances the thin carbonaceous film of the compression also contains the cuticle membrane. One method used to remove pieces of cuticle from the compressed fossil involves applying several coats of clear finger nail varnish or other collodion to the surface of the leaf and then removing the transfer. A modification of this technique involves digesting the rock matrix in the appropriate acid if the transfer cannot be peeled from the surface (Dilcher 1974). Other compressions such as Eocene angiosperm leaves are represented by cuticular envelopes that can be gently teased intact from the rock matrix with dissecting needles, washed and, if necessary, stained with safranin to enhance details. Other fossil cuticles, such as paper coals, are relatively easy to prepare. These deposits consist almost entirely of plant cuticles and typically can be removed from the bedding surfaces often without chemical maceration. Relatively large pieces of paper coal can be immersed in an aqueous solution of 5% potassium hydroxide (KOH) for 48 h followed by rinsing for 5 days in a gentle stream of water (DiMichele et al. 1984). The cuticles can be separated from any adhering matrix by adding a 32% solution of hydrogen peroxide (H_2O_2) for 24 h followed by rinsing in repeated changes of water. Some fossil cuticles are very difficult to separate from the rock matrix. In these instances small samples can sometimes be scraped from the surface and cleaned with dilute ammonia (30%) or KOH (5%) (Archangelsky et al. 1986). In other studies 40% nitric acid (HNO_3) followed by 5% ammonium hydroxide was used to treat the cuticles once they were removed from the matrix (Archangelsky

TAYLOR, T. N. 1999. The ultrastructure of fossil cuticle. *In*: JONES, T. P. & ROWE, N. P. (eds) *Fossil Plants and Spores: modern techniques*. Geological Society, London, 113–115.

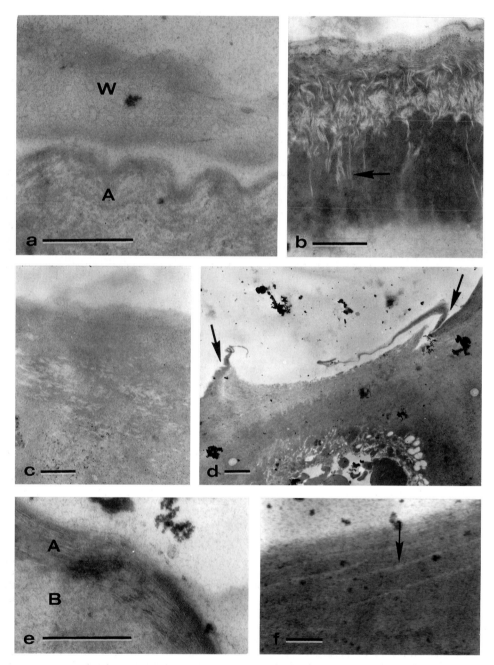

Fig. 21.1. Fossil cuticle. (**a**) Section showing epicuticular wax (W) and sinuous nature of lamellae in lower epidermis cuticle (A) (*Tarphyderma* – Cretaceous), scale bar = 0.5 μm. (**b**) Cuticle showing heterogeneous organization including radial channels (arrow). (*Tarphyderma* – Cretaceous), scale bar = 0.5 μm. (**c**) Upper cuticle of *Tarphyderma* (Cretaceous) showing diffuse nature of outer layer, scale bar = 0.5 μm. (**d**) Section of trichome base (between arrows). Note stratification of varying layers in cuticle (*Ticoa* – Cretaceous), scale bar = 1.0 μm. (**e**) Section of lower epidermis cuticle showing lamellae (A – layer) and homogeneous B zone (*Tarphyderma* – Cretaceous), scale bar = 0.5 μm. (**f**) Lamellae (arrow) in cuticle component (*Ticoa* – Cretaceous), scale bar = 0.5 μm.

& Del Fueyo 1989). Since the cuticle fragments sometimes contain adhering minerals, it is important to carefully wash the samples in distilled water, sometimes treating with hydrofluoric acid (HF) to remove silica grains (Maheshwari & Bajpai 1996). Prior to embedding cuticles in epoxy for TEM it is critical that all samples be carefully examined with a dissecting microscope for mineral particles. This is especially important since such particles will destroy the edge of the knife used to make ultrathin sections.

Preparing the cuticle of living plants for TEM is especially difficult since the cuticle membrane is relatively impervious, and thus it is not easy to impregnate with resins for ultramicrotomy (Holloway 1982). For some extant plant cuticles extended periods of time are required for complete impregnation of the CM especially for thick specimens, and this can only be determined using several embedding schedules (Krüger et al. 1996). Impregnation time does not appear to be a major problem for fossil cuticles based on the limited number of studies that have been undertaken to date (Archangelsky et al. 1986). For example, very satisfactory results have been obtained by pre-staining 1% osmium tetroxide for 120 min followed by dehydration in a graded series (25%, 40%, 60%, 75%, 85%, 95%) of alcohol for 20 minutes each, and then two 20 min changes in absolute alcohol and two 20 min changes in 100% acetone. Following the dehydration series the cuticles were placed in a 3:1 acetone and Spurr mixture and rotated for 5 h, then a 1 : 1 mixture of acetone and Spurr for 10 h and a 1 : 3 acetone and Spurr mixture for 10 h. Cuticles were then placed in 100% Spurr resin in flat aluminium dishes in a vacuum oven for 12 h and polymerized at 60°C at 380 mm Hg. Appropriate specimens were subsequently cut from the plastic and mounted on flat blocks of Spurr with Elmer's Wonderglue. Sections were cut on an ultramicrotome in the interference colours of silver to pale gold. Sections were then collected on Formvar-coated copper grids, and stained with 1.5% $KMnO_4$ for 10–30 min followed by 2% uranyl acetate (5–10 min) or lead citrate for 1–5 min. It is important to underscore that various stain schedules were employed so as to achieve maximum contrast. Transmission electron microscopy of biological and geological materials necessitates the use of various hazardous chemicals (e.g. osmium tetroxide, Spurr resin). Extreme caution should be used at all times and investigators should be familiar with the appropriate procedures

and regulations involved in the handling, storage and disposal of such materials.

Interpretation

Cuticle ultrastructure in extant plants has been important in analysing the cuticular membrane as it relates to water permeability, in particular cuticle layer structure/function relationships (Krüger et al. 1996). Studies of the fine structure of fossil cuticles have been directed at determining the degree of cuticle preservation (Fig. 21.1c), organization of structural components (Fig. 21.1e), as a character in interpreting the physical environment in which the plant lived (Archangelsky et al. 1995), and the interpretation of complex features that require increased resolution. In addition, cuticle ultrastructure may be important as a taxonomic feature (Barale & Baldoni 1993; Maheshwari & Bajpai 1996). From the limited number of ultrastructural studies of fossil cuticles undertaken to date it appears that most of the features that appear in extant plant cuticles also can be found in the fossils (Taylor et al. 1989). For example, one type of Cretaceous cuticle was highly stratified at the fine structural level, with several layers containing well-defined zones, some with lamellae (Fig. 21.1f) (Archangelsky et al. 1986). In another study, cuticle fine structure provided the necessary resolution needed to interpret the organization of the stomatal complex and thus offer a more accurate assessment of the structure/function relationships as they relate to the CM of this fossil plant (Archangelsky & Taylor 1986; Archangelsky et al. 1995). Fine structural studies of cuticles also provide the opportunity to detect delicate structures in fossils such as evidence of infection pegs formed in response to fungal attack (Archer & Cole 1986). In living plants, surface waxes and components of the cuticle also function as signals between the plant and other organisms. Certain structural features that can be correlated with similar features in extant plant cuticles offer a variety of possibilities for investigating plant/animal/fungal interactions on cuticles (Kerstiens 1996). Despite the relatively small number of studies dealing with the fine structure of fossil cuticles to date, the use of cuticle ultrastructure in palaeobotany may also provide an indirect method of determining how cuticles have evolved. This offers a potential means of indirectly investigating the biochemical aspects of the origin and evolution of cutin synthesis in plants.

22. Plant cell walls

TIM P. JONES & NICK P. ROWE

This chapter will consider methods used for microscopical and ultrastructural study of fossil plant cell walls, in particular fossil wood and charcoal. The study of the fine structure of fossil cell walls has been used in a variety of contexts. These include detailed comparative studies of wall structure, stratification, ornamentation and pitting among different plant groups (Schmid 1967; Smoot & Taylor 1978, 1984; Kenrick et al. 1991; Kenrick & Crane 1991) and taphonomic studies on cell wall biodegradation and breakdown with peatification (Cohen et al. 1987), and the effects of charcoalification (McGinnes et al. 1971). An important aspect of this chapter is the identification of artefacts and real features in the cell walls.

Transmission and reflected light microscopy

Transmission light microscopy of thin sections is routinely used for the study of plant cell walls (see preparation techniques of Chapters 13, 15 and 22). For rock sections, Humphries (1992), defines the thickness of 'standard' thin sections at 30 µm, and ultrathin sections at 10 µm. Standard sections are usually more than adequate for younger material, for example Recent peats (Cohen et al. 1987), which could even require staining. For material which has undergone more coalification, progressively thinner sections are required (Stach et al. 1975). Some materials (e.g. charcoal) and some minerals (e.g. pyrite) will be effectively opaque even as ultrathin sections. Despite the significantly higher resolution of electron microscopy, transmission light microscopy is more than adequate for uses such as the identification of basic cell wall anatomical features (such as wall pitting), as well as assessing the state of preservation.

The examination of plant cell walls under reflected light can reveal information not seen using other microscopical techniques. Material should be embedded and polished using the techniques outlined in Chapter 14. Quantitative reflectance shows that the well-characterized changes in cell wall ultrastructure seen by scanning electron microscopy (SEM) (e.g. Figs 22.1a–d) are accompanied by an increase in cell wall reflectance, along with the same progression from stratification to homogenization to cell wall breakdown (e.g. Figures 22.1f–i).

Scanning electron microscopy (SEM)

Scanning electron microscopy is widely used in the study of fossil wood (Figs 22.1a, e and charcoal cell walls (Figs 22.1b–d). In addition to examining comparative wood ultrastructure, SEM is important in the study of biodegradation (Levy 1987; Brett & Waldron 1990), and charcoalification. At the ultrastructural level, the principal effect of charcoalification is to eliminate all cell wall stratification (i.e. S1 and S2 layering). Charcoalified cell walls are homogenized (Jones 1993). This homogenization was first described by McGinnes et al. (1971) for modern charcoal using SEM, and is now routinely used for fossil charcoal identification.

Non-indurated fossil wood

SEM studies of fossil wood often require longitudinal, radial and transverse sections. Orientated sections are produced either by cutting or fracturing the wood. The recommended method for cutting fossil wood is to use a brand new razor blade, but in our experience this most often results in 'smeared' sections, however sharp the blade. Even cuts made with ultra-sharp, TEM glass knives often smear the cell walls, and such sections might not be usable either for routine identification, or publication-standard photographs. Dry fossil wood is often quite brittle, and the fracture-faces may be quite clean under SEM. An alternative and rapid method of obtaining 'clean' surfaces which does not involve embedding is to shatter a specimen which has been frozen in liquid nitrogen. The specimen is immersed in liquid nitrogen for a couple of minutes, and shattered using a small hammer. The specimen must be completely frozen before shattering otherwise it will be crushed. The main problem with this technique is that orientation of the fracture surfaces cannot be controlled.

Another method, applicable to both modern and well-preserved fossil wood, to obtain cleanly fractured/exposed cell walls while retaining cell wall stratification, is low (heating) temperature treatment; i.e. hot enough to discolour the wood,

JONES, T. P & ROWE, N. P. 1999. Plant cell walls. *In*: JONES, T. P. & ROWE, N. P. (eds) *Fossil Plants and Spores: modern techniques*. Geological Society, London, 116–120.

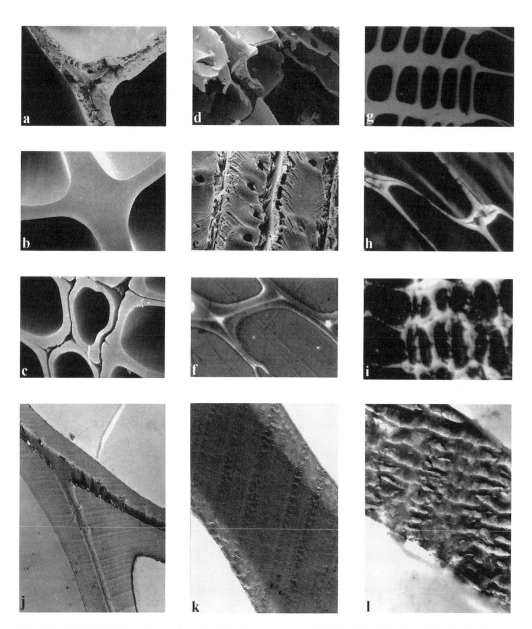

Fig. 22.1. (**a**) SEM of living *Pinus sylvestris*, following exposure to 190°C for 1 h, cell wall stratification is still visible, scale ×1400. (**b**) SEM of living *P. sylvestris*, following exposure to 260°C for 1 h, showing cell wall homogenization, scale ×1900. (**c**) SEM of living *P. sylvestris*, following exposure to 440°C for 1 h, showing cell wall cracking, scale ×850. (**d**) SEM of living *P. sylvestris*, following exposure to 600°C for 1 h, showing cell wall disintegration, scale ×850. (**e**) SEM of Miocene fossil wood, showing cell wall desiccation, scale ×1000. (**f**) Reflected light (RL) micrograph of living *P. sylvestris*, following exposure to 210°C for 1 h, showing cell wall stratification, scale ×900. (**g**) RL micrograph of living *P. sylvestris*, following exposure to 250°C for 1 h, showing cell wall homogenization, scale ×800. (**h**) RL micrograph of living *P. sylvestris*, following exposure to 370°C for 1 h, showing cell wall cracking. scale ×800. (**i**) RL micrograph of living *P. sylvestris*, following exposure to 600°C for 1 h, showing cell wall disintegration, scale ×850. (**j**) TEM of living *P. sylvestris*, following exposure to 200°C for 1 h, showing cell wall stratification, scale ×4000. (**k**) TEM of living *P. sylvestris*, following exposure to 260°C for 1 h, showing cell wall (artefact) stratification, scale ×8000. (**l**) TEM of Cretaceous charcoal, scale ×8000.

but not so hot as to convert it to charcoal. For example the cell walls of a fragment of *Pinus sylvestris* which was heated at 190°C for 1 h are illustrated in Fig. 22.1a; the wood turned dark brown, but manually fractured easily and cleanly, and the cell wall stratification was retained.

Fossil charcoal

Fossil charcoal is highly suited for SEM examination. It can be broken easily with clean, sharp fractures (see Chapter 18). For large specimens (if expendable), mounting with epoxy resin, rather than sticky tabs, is preferred because bonding is more secure, and the coated epoxy surface between the specimen and the stub minimizes problems with charging under the beam. Other workers (for example archaeobotanists) preferentially use sticky tabs because their specimens frequently break off the stub if attached with epoxy resin – see Chapter 18). A small dab of silver DAG will further prevent problems with charging. We recommend storage of all prepared SEM stubs in a dessicator prior to use. Stubs containing many specimens, or a single large specimen, can take a long time to vacuum down because they contain large volumes of absorbed gases. It is more efficient to load this type of material into the SEM well in advance of examination (i.e. leave under vacuum overnight).

Transmission electron microscopy

Transmission electron microscopy (TEM) has rarely been successfully applied to the study of fossil wood, but ultrastructural details can be obtained even from Palaeozoic material (Schmid 1967). Schmid documented compound middle lamella, intercellular spaces and S_1 and S_2 layers of cell walls in unusually well-preserved 'fusinized' *Callixylon* from the Lower Mississippian Brea Sandstone, USA.

More recently Jones (1993) and Jones & Chaloner (1991) used TEM in a series of experiments on fossil wood and charcoal, and Recent and laboratory-manufactured charcoal. The embedding and microtoming used was an adaptation of Schmid's (1967) technique. Samples of approximately 1 mm^3 were soaked in propylene oxide, a link reagent for Spurr's resin, for 24 h. This was then replaced by a mixture of 50% Spurr's resin/50% propylene oxide and gently rotated (agitated) for 48 h. Using fine-nosed tweezers, the samples were then transferred to 100% Spurr's resin and gently rotated for a further 24 h. This last stage was repeated and the samples were transferred into individual beem capsules (small plastic containers with snap-shut lids) and polymerized at 70°C for 12 h. Ultrathin sections were cut on a microtome using a glass knife. The material did not require staining.

Inconsistent results from the sectioning proved to be a major problem in the application of this technique. Modern wood and Miocene fossil wood embedded and sectioned relatively easily, with cell wall ultrastructure clearly seen (Fig. 22.1J). Modern charcoal proved easy to embed, but more difficult to section, with knife 'juddering' a constant problem. Modern charcoal also displayed 'artificial' stratifications in the cell walls, presumably from differential quality of resin impregnation (see Chapter 23 for TEM artefacts which have been erroneously interpreted as plant ultrastructure) (Fig. 22.1k, modern charcoal). Fossil charcoal was very difficult to microtome, with very poor quality sections being obtained. The micrograph in Fig. 22.1l, of Cretaceous charcoal (fusain) was the best result obtained after many attempts. Fossil charcoal also showed artificial (resin-impregnation) stratifications in the cell walls (?) and evidence of extreme knife 'juddering'. Furthermore, the sections proved to be extremely fragile under the electron beam. Better results might be obtained by using a diamond knife, but since the fossil material contained some pyrite (destroying a number of glass knives) this was not attempted.

Disappearing peel technique

A number of problems are connected with methods of viewing fine structure of fossil plant cell walls from organically preserved permineralized material. A systematic investigation of fossil plant cell walls by John Holmes in the early 1980s documented several types and causes of artefacts, as well as differences in image quality, generated by light, scanning and transmission electron microscopy. Here follows a brief synthesis of these findings. Further details on the problems and techniques surrounding high magnification analysis of fossil plant cell walls, in particular those involving acid etching and peel techniques, can be found in Holmes & Lopez (1986).

The standard peel technique basically consists of two steps. First, the mineral matrix surrounding the cell walls is etched using an appropriate acid. Second, the protruding cell walls are embedded in acetone-softened, cellulose acetate sheet, which on removal from the rock matrix, retains the embedded plant cell walls (see Chapter 13). This technique is effective for low magnification histology, but may cause artefacts in high magnification applications.

Problems associated with high magnification applications of the peel technique

Effervescence from acid etching can cause severe damage to cell walls. This is particularly destructive to walls that are orientated parallel to the rock surface (typical of longitudinal sections), as well as thinner cell walls of tissues such as parenchyma and phloem. Significant damage is caused using standard etching-strength acids of 1–6%. Furthermore, cell wall fragments are released creating artefacts under high magnification light microscopy. This is a major problem for interpreting fine-scale structures such as pores and wall thickenings. A second disadvantage with the standard peel technique is that organic wall material may be indirectly bonded to the acetate sheet via an intervening layer of minerals. Subsequent demineralization of the peel will therefore remove a lot of organic material, in particular longitudinally orientated walls. A third problem is related to powdery residues (calcite for carbonate coal balls) formed during etching (300–500 μm thick). These can be partly removed by demineralization, but significant amounts can remain because they penetrate deeper into the acetate sheet.

Problems and artefacts seen during observation

With the SEM it is often difficult to distinguish small-scale morphological features from non-organic material and objects adhering to the organic structures. The potential inorganic artefacts may include mineral matrix remaining in the peel as well as the powdery calcite precipitated during etching. With TEM, orientation and interpretion of small fragments of cell wall at high magnification is a problem. Standard etching or deep etching creates further difficulties because large expanses of cell wall easily fragment, or are destroyed by effervescence. Furthermore, the preparation of ultrathin sections is hampered by the presence of mineral material in the peel that blunts the knife.

The standard peel technique therefore poses a number of problems for detailed, high resolution observations. There is a basic dilemma underlying the protocol. We generally want to remove as much mineral material as possible from the organic cell walls, but further treatment with acids also destroys the cell walls. The disappearing peel technique provides (i) a way of etching specimens with minimal damage to cell walls; (ii) a medium for supporting the etched cell walls and removing all the acetate peel along with ingrained mineral material and powder precipitate, etc; (iii) a method of mounting the specimen for light microscopy and

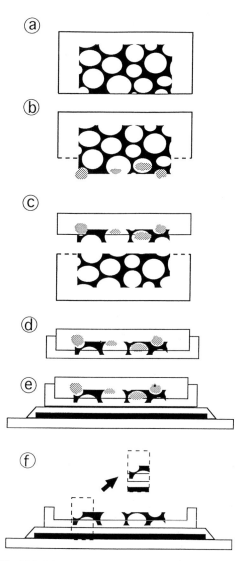

Fig. 22.2. Disappearing peel technique. (**a**) Block of matrix with permineralized plant tissue, the lower surface has been ground flat to the required level. (**b**) Low concentration acid etch (0.05% HCl – for carbonate coal ball). (**c**) application of cellulose acetate peel and acetone and removal of peel. The cell wall material has embedded into the peel as well as clumps of calcite precipitate (stippled). (**d**) The peel is pressed onto a thin layer of Araldite so that protruding organic material is embedded in liquid Araldite. (**e**) The Araldite and peel is cemented to the specimen holder. The lower surface of the peel is embedded in liquid Araldite. (**f**) After removal of the cellulose acetate in acetone and demineralization of the calcite precipitate in 0.05% HCl, the wall material can be observed directly by light microscopy and/or SEM and TEM. Sections can be cut away and embedded for TEM (after Holmes & Lopez 1986).

SEM, and/or further embedding for TEM on a specially made holder-slide.

Preparation of improved peels

Organic plant cell walls remain significantly more intact after being etched in much lower concentrations of acid. For European carbonate coal balls, concentrations of 0.1 to 0.01% hydrochloric acid (HCl) ensured that longitudinal cell wall surfaces parallel to the block surface were relatively undamaged. The quality of the organic cell walls in the peel also depends on the depth of the acid-etch, the preparation of the block surface prior to etching, the diameter of the cells of particular tissues, and wall thickness. The optimum etch depth is around one-third to one-half of the cell diameter, and deeper etches will only increase the probability of damage to the cell walls. The depth of etch depends on the mineral matrix and should be adjusted to meet different materials: 30–60 s in 0.05% HCl produces an etch of approximately 1.0 μm depth for Late Carboniferous, non-dolomitic, British coal balls. Etches are performed with the block orientated so that loose material will sink or float away from the surface. Holmes & Lopez (1986, p.794) list three variations of peels etched with low concentration acid. The first involves slow, low-concentration acid-etches for depths to approximately half the cell diameter of the tissue targeted. The second, termed a 'rip-peel', can be made immediately after the peel just described. A cellulose acetate sheet and acetone are applied to the recently peeled surface without prior grinding or etching. This type of peel makes use of the fact that the previous peel has left behind cell wall material which was lying on the surface of the matrix and would otherwise be destroyed by effervescence if etched again. A third type of peel involves grinding with fine carborundum powder on a lap and then aluminium silicate powder on a felt pad until the matrix surface shines. The surface is then etched with low concentration acid to obtain an etch of 1 μm. Both the second and third types of peel preparation were found to be particularly useful for obtaining large areas of plane surfaces of longitudinally aligned cell wall (Holmes & Lopez 1986).

Preparation of holder

A piece of cellulose acetate sheet is cut to a size just smaller than a glass slide. A thin layer of acetone is applied to the glass and the acetate sheet is pressed into the slide and allowed to dry. The sheet is then covered with a thin layer of 'Araldite' which is spread just beyond the acetate on to the glass and left to harden (Fig. 22.2e). Sealing the acetate sheet within the Araldite is an important step, as later the whole slide mount is immersed in an acetone bath.

Preparation and embedding of peel

A peel is prepared using low concentration acid etching and careful preparation of the block surface to optimize the cell wall material according to one of the three methods described above (Fig. 22.2a–c). Following the removal of the peel from the rock, a thin layer of Araldite is spread over the side containing the organic matter (Fig. 22.2d). This is heated to 55°C to make the Araldite quite fluid and is then firmly pressed onto the pre-prepared Araldite surface of the holder and allowed to set (Fig. 22.2e). The slide is then placed in an acetone bath (with stirrer) for 15 min to dissolve completely the acetate sheet of the peel, but leaving the organic material lodged in the Araldite (Fig. 22.2e).

The organic material is then demineralized gently in 0.05% HCl for 1–2 h to remove any remaining calcite residue, avoiding breakage of cell walls. The specimen can now be observed with the light microscope equipped with oil immersion lenses. The oil may be placed directly on the specimen surface and can be wiped off afterwards.

After light microscopy, specific parts of the preparation can be cut away on the basal acetate sheet of the holder (this was protected from the acetone bath by the surrounding Araldite) and separated from the slide (Fig. 22.2f). These can then be mounted on the appropriate stubs for SEM or embedded in blocks for further sectioning for the TEM. One of the advantages of this technique is that the preparation may be viewed at high magnification using different types of microscopy to verify or double check for potential artefacts. One of the main problems is that on application of the cellulose acetate sheet to the fossil /matrix surface, the softened cellulose acetate forms a mould of all features (organic and inorganic) of the prepared surface. These are moulded again and persist in the final Araldite surface after the dried peel is pressed against the softened Araldite. Such surfaces may then cause difficulties in interpretation when observed with the SEM.

23. Megaspore ultrastructure

ALAN R. HEMSLEY & IAN J. GLASSPOOL

Megaspores are a common subject for ultra-structural analysis since they are large enough to handle as individuals and exhibit great diversity of surface morphology and internal wall structure. These features appear to provide useful data in the interpretation of phylogeny among heterosporous plants. Since the first investigations of fossil megaspores by Pettitt (1966), a considerable fund of data has been accrued. Techniques have changed little over this time, advances having been made in instrumentation and imaging systems.

Ultrastructure by scanning electron microscopy (SEM)

The use of SEM to examine ultrastructure is not as widespread as that of transmission electron microscopy (TEM) principally because resolution by SEM, usually of fractured walls, is not as good as that obtained by TEM. However, SEM imaging provides important information about the three-dimensional structure of a wall which might otherwise only be obtained by comparison of serial sections, a prospect that is unlikely even given the softest of fossil megaspore walls. Wherever possible, TEM analysis of wall structure should be complemented by comparable SEM images to facilitate interpretation (see Fig. 23.1e, f). The production of stereo-pairs is recommended (e.g. W. A. Taylor 1990). Walls for SEM investigation should be freshly fractured using a razor blade as ready-fractured fragments may have been abraded. Although nitric acid and Schulze's solution (Traverse 1988) are of use in cleaning megaspores, the oxidative reactions alter the chemistry of the sporopollenin resulting in loss of cohesion (Hemsley *et al.* 1996*b*) and possible alteration to ultrastructure.

Preparation from SEM

There is no need to remove the gold/palladium or carbon coating that results from SEM analysis, indeed, when using spore fragments, this can be of use in indicating the original outer surface. It may, however, be necessary to remove traces of mineral residue (silicates) in hydrofluoric acid (HF) before commencing embedding. This does not remove

pyrite which may damage diamond knives and will certainly destroy glass knives. Due to the size of megaspores, and the sometimes impervious layers within the wall, if not already fractured, it is wise to cut specimens in half using a razor blade to allow full penetration of the resin. This also results in two blocks for sectioning which may be valuable insurance and ensures that the spores do not contain air bubbles which could cause problems during embedding and sectioning. It also reduces the size of the individual specimens resulting in easier sectioning. Pipette on 95% amyl acetate or methanol to loosen whole megaspores or mega-spore fragments from the SEM stub. Transfer these directly to acetone or ethanol (100%) in glass tubes with lids using a mounted bristle or needle.

Embedding

Use a fume hood when preparing resin. Resin should be a pale straw colour following mixing according to the instructions (for the 'hard mix') given by Spurr (1969). If it is rusty or orange in colour, polymerize and dispose. Always test-polymerize a little of the resin intended for final embedding before consigning the spores (within it) to the oven. Again, if the resulting test block is dark, mix fresh resin and repeat the test. Resin can be mixed from the required components beforehand and stored for up to two months at –20°C without noticeable autopolymerization. If using frozen resin, remove from the freezer at least 1 h before use to reach room temperature. Do not remove the lid when cold, nor use at less than room temperature since condensation of water vapour may occur, resulting in poor embedding. Other resins have been tried with some success (e.g. Kempf 1971), but it is important to match resin and specimen hardness as closely as possible to minimize the production of artefacts. Trial and error is often the best method of ascertaining hardness, but generally, the darker the spore, the harder the required resin.

Standard embedding procedures involving gradual dehydration sequences and intermediates are unnecessary for fossil material. Rinse each specimen twice in solvent (acetone) to remove traces of amyl acetate and transfer to HPLC grade, extra dry solvent (a couple of millimetres depth is

HEMSLEY, A. R. & GLASSPOOL, I. J. 1999. Megaspore ultrastructure. *In*: JONES, T. P. & ROWE, N. P. (eds) *Fossil Plants and Spores: modern techniques.* Geological Society, London, 121–125.

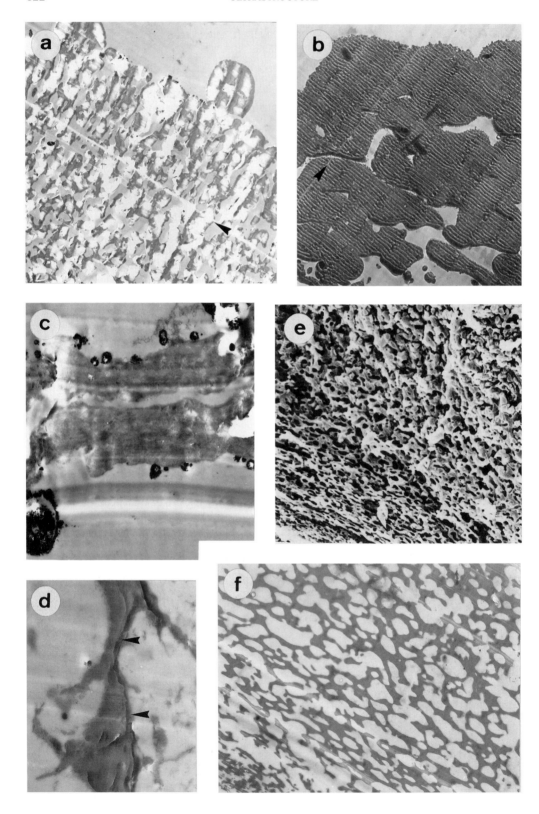

usually sufficient). Tumble in a rotator. Replace with fresh solvent after 12 h and add an equal quantity of Spurr's resin. Wear gloves as the resin is carcinogenic. Tumble gently for 12 h and replace the solvent and resin with fresh 100% resin. Tumble for a further 12 h. Repeat twice further. Use flat latex embedding moulds to polymerize the resin. Fill each segment of the mould to the level with fresh resin. Using a cocktail stick or similar implement, catch each spore or fragment on the tip (easier than it sounds due to the viscosity of the resin) and submerge it in the fresh resin within the mould, preferably to one end. Ensure it is free of air bubbles. Top up each mould with a few drops of resin such that the meniscus is convex. This allows for shrinkage during polymerization and results in a stronger block. Polymerize the resin in an oven set to 70°C and preferably under vacuum. Remove and cool between 8 and 15 h later. Polymerize all waste resin and implements prior to disposal.

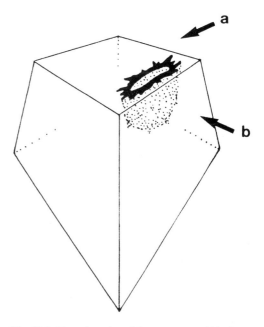

Fig. 23.2. The orientation of the megaspore within the resin block in relation to the direction of cut is important. Here, the megaspore sank to the base of the mould during polymerization and thus rests parallel to one face of the block. Cutting in the direction of the arrow labelled '**a**' is preferable to that of '**b**' but requires more frequent realigning of the glass knife.

Preparing blocks

Blocks should be removed from the mould and labelled immediately. Blocks may be stored indefinitely in the dark. Their preparation involves trimming around the specimen to facilitate cutting with the ultramicrotome. Using a fine saw, remove the end of the block, cutting around 1 mm above the specimen. Trim the sides in a similar manner at an angle away from the specimen (see Fig. 23.2). Spurr resin dust is harmful by inhalation and should be removed by hand-held vacuum cleaner during trimming. Gloves should be worn. If the specimen has sunk during polymerization to the lower face of the block (which is sometimes an advantage), trim the upper surface away to within 1 mm of the specimen. If not, trim away both faces to within 1 mm, again at an angle. Aim for a flat-topped, four-sided pyramid with the specimen in the centre or to one edge (Fig. 23.2). Some advocate producing a trapezoid block face outline, but this would appear to make little difference in practice when using this resin. Using a new, one-sided razor blade, continue to pare down the faces of the pyramid to within $\frac{1}{2}$ mm or less of the specimen.

Be patient and take off only thin slices as attempts at thick slices may shatter the block. Trim the top of the pyramid down as close as possible to the specimen, keeping it flat. The block is now ready for sectioning.

Sectioning

Details of ultramicrotomy rely, at least in part, on the machine one is using and whether one wishes to employ glass or diamond knives. In general, always ensure that the block face (with the specimen just beneath) is vertical and that the block is as securely

Fig. 23.1. (**a**) Section of Carboniferous lycopsid megaspore wall illustrating severe damage resulting from chatter. Linear knife scores (arrow) indicate that the knife itself is damaged and should have been replaced, ×1500. (**b**) A similar section showing chatter at a smaller scale. This form is generally caused by the production of too thick a section but may also reflect a severe discrepancy between resin and specimen hardness. Again, arrow indicates a knife score, ×2000. (**c**) Severe damage to a Devonian progymnosperm megaspore resulting from the all-too-visible pyrite, ×1500. (**d**) Edge effects (arrows) in a Carboniferous fern megaspore wall resulting from initial impact of the knife edge with the specimen, ×7500. (**e**), (**f**) Comparable SEM and TEM images of the same Carboniferous lycopsid megaspore wall emphasizing the importance of relating both types of image to achieve an accurate interpretation of structure, (e) ×1300, (f) ×4000.

clamped as possible. Knives must also be tightly clamped. Most megaspores are to some degree compressed and most will also have settled with an orientation roughly parallel to the original lower surface of the block during polymerization. Orientation of the specimen in relation to the cutting edge of the knife is important. Usually it is best to prevent the knife encountering large widths of specimen simultaneously. It is therefore advisable to avoid parallel orientation of specimen and knife edge (Fig. 23.2b). Orientation of the specimen perpendicular to the knife edge works well (Fig. 23.2a), but the knife (if glass) will wear rapidly where it intercepts most of the specimen. Ideally, one should aim for an angle of approach between these two extremes, but this is difficult when the specimen has sunk to the base of the mould. When trimming the block face on the microtome, do not be tempted to take thick slices to reach the specimen as the resin is brittle and the block face may shatter. It is better to remove numerous thin slices. One should be able to detect the specimen within the trimmed sections once sufficient resin has been removed, indeed, remove at least 30 μm (60 μm for large megaspores) of specimen otherwise tangential wall sections may be obtained.

As with microtomy of modern materials, it is advisable to aim for silver/gold sections (as seen by surface interference colour), following release of resin tension using chloroform vapour applied from a soaked cotton bud (avoid contact of chloroform with the water meniscus and the block). However, where material is brittle, blue sections are more likely to retain the specimen, rather than it fragmenting into the supporting water and leaving just an outline in the resin section. Resins with differing refractive indices will show different colours at corresponding thicknesses.

Catching sections floating on the water meniscus is not easy. Washing grids before use in glacial acetic acid may improve section adherence. Some advocate submerging the TEM grid beneath the water meniscus in the 'boat' and bringing it up underneath the floating sections, lifting them off of the meniscus from below. Others place the grid onto the floating specimens, lifting it off again quickly with the sections (hopefully) stuck to the lower surface. Whichever method is used, it is best to use formvar-coated grids as these provide better support for the large expanse of specimen within the section, the weakest part. Small mesh grids help support specimens but may obscure areas of detail, perhaps even the entire wall. Always catch the sections on the coated surface of the grid and try to ensure that they are close to the centre as peripheral sections may be obscured by the grid carrier within the microscope. Store grids in a grid holder or on sheets of dust-free filter paper in covered petri dishes.

Staining

Stains may show features not otherwise apparent, but can also produce artefacts (e.g. $KMnO_4$, Bell 1988; Reynolds 1963). Whether wall layering determined by staining is a real rather than diagenetic feature is debatable, but if the requirement is to demonstrate differences in composition of fossil sporopollenin (by whatever cause) then staining is beneficial. Lead citrate (as a 5% solution applied to specimens for 10 min) appears most effective. This may be prepared from 1.33 g $Pb(NO_3)_2$, 1.76 g $Na_3(C_6H_5O_7).2H_2O$ and 30 ml distilled water in a flask, shaking for 1 min, followed by intermittent shaking for 8 min. Then add 1 M NaOH (8 ml), diluted with 50 ml of water and invert repeatedly to mix. Grids may be treated by placing them coated face-down on a single drop of stain. These can then be washed in a drop of distilled water and dried by touching the edge with a filter paper.

Observation and artefacts

The exact method of specimen observation depends upon the instrument to be used. However, some general guidelines apply. Treat grids with care, handling only with forceps and leaving uncovered for the minimum of time. Once grids are in the microscope, always be careful with the beam intensity as this can damage the material. Once a specimen is punctured, it may tear through the specimen and the resin sliver will begin to roll up. Exposing an area of resin without specimen to the beam for a few minutes will serve to 'cure' the resin and render it more resistant to damage, although this technique can be more damaging where large mesh grids are employed.

A range of artefacts are common when cutting large expanses of specimen. We illustrate some of these for reference (Figs 23.1a–f). The most common artefacts are forms of knife chatter that result from an over-used glass knife, lack of corresponding hardness of specimen and resin, unsatisfactory speed of cut or a poorly clamped specimen or blade. Generally these can be alleviated by a fresh knife, harder resin, and slower cut respectively. Figure 23.1a illustrates extreme knife chatter resulting in a banded effect (loss of specimen) perpendicular to the direction of cut (clearly ascertained by the diagonal knife mark (arrow). Figure 23.1b shows minor knife chatter which is common where sections are too thick. Again, chatter marks are perpendicular to the line of cut (arrow). Figure 23.1c depicts severe damage resulting from the presence of pyrite, in this case on the spore surface. Note the holes associated with the pyrite particles and the severe (horizontal) knife marks resulting from damage to the knife edge. Scuffing is also apparent, giving a mottled effect to the specimen. Fig. 23.1d shows a common artefact that occurs where the knife contacts the edge of the specimen (which scuffs for a short distance), leaving an apparent edge feature. This artefact can be avoided by cutting along, rather than against a megaspore wall.

24. The ultrastructure of fossil pollen and spores

THOMAS N. TAYLOR

The application of transmission electron microscopy (TEM) to palaeopalynology can be traced
back to 1959 when Ehrlich & Hall demonstrated
that pollen of Eocene age was sufficiently well
preserved to provide meaningful information about
the organization of the wall at the ultrastructural
level. Pettitt (1966) provided a broad survey of
fossil plant spores and demonstrated the importance
of ultrastructural information in palaeobotany. In
association with scanning electron microscopy
(SEM) (Fig. 24.1a), it is now possible not only to
observe the minute details on the surface of ancient
pollen grains and spores, but also to examine the
structural framework underlying this ornament
(Hibbert 1967; Taylor 1968). Today, electron
microscopy is a relatively routine research tool in
many areas of palaeobotany and palynology. The
combination of these imaging systems has provided
a wealth of new information about the systematics,
development and biology of fossil pollen and
spores. All of these data have contributed important
characters that have been especially useful in the
elucidation of land plant phylogenies.

Pollen and spore samples

In situ *grains*

The best source of material for ultrastructural
studies of pollen grains and spores comes from *in
situ* specimens (e.g. T. N. Taylor 1990; Balme
1995). Pollen grains and spores can be macerated
from the structure in which they were produced
(sporangium) using dilute acids. One technique
involves the construction of a small wax wall
around the sporangium. As grains are released they
can be recovered with a micropipette. There are
several advantages of using *in situ* grains over those
that are dispersed in the rock or sediments. One is
the large number of grains that are available for
study, thus providing the opportunity to examine
natural variability (size, shape, ornament, presence
or absence of certain structures) within a known
population of pollen and spores. In many instances
the systematic affinities of these grains are known,
making it possible to evaluate ultrastructural
information within a broader taxonomic and
phylogenetic framework. *In situ* specimens within a
cone for example, may also offer the opportunity to

compare different stages of development in the
formation of the wall or surface ornament that
probably could not be distinguished in dispersed
grains. Finally, the large population of grains of
known biological affinity makes it possible to
utilize a variety of techniques in order to extract the
maximum amount of ultrastructural information.
For example, techniques have been developed so
that a single grain may be examined in light,
scanning and transmission electron microscopy
(e.g. Doyle *et al.* 1975; Daghlian 1983). This
approach also provides a method of examining
structural features of the same grain in different
imaging modes, a procedure that is sometimes
critical in interpreting structure/function relationships.

Dispersed grains

Pollen and spores that are dispersed in sediments
also provide the opportunity to obtain useful
information within a biological context. For
example, dispersed pollen tetrads from the late
Barremian–early Aptian show ultrastructural
features that resemble those in extant pollen of the
Winteraceae and thus provide the opportunity to
suggest affinities (Doyle *et al.* 1990). Another
approach was used by Pocock & Vasanthy (1988)
who utilized fine structural characters in dispersed
pollen as a basis for suggesting that Upper Triassic
grains may have affinities with angiosperms. This
approach is especially important in calibrating
where in geological time particular groups might
have originated based on the occurrence of pollen
and spores.

Dispersed grains are extracted by crushing the
sediment in distilled water with a mortar and pestle
and then centrifuging using ZnCl heavy liquid
solution to separate the organic residue by flotation
(Brenner 1963). The organics including the pollen
grains, are then pipetted off and a few drops of 10%
hydrochloric acid (HCl) added. The sample is then
washed several times with distilled water,
centrifuged, and hydrofluoric acid (HF) added to
remove clay particles. After repeated washings the
sample is oxidized for 2–3 min with a 5.25%
solution of sodium hypochlorite, washed again, and
then treated with 10% ammonium hydroxide
(NH_4OH) for three minutes (Walker & Walker

Taylor, T. N. 1999. The ultrastructure of fossil pollen and spores. *In*: JONES, T. P. & ROWE, N. P. (eds)
Fossil Plants and Spores: modern techniques. Geological Society, London, 126–131.

126

1984). After the grains are washed they may be stained and embedded according to the same schedule used for *in situ* grains.

Choice of protocols

Of importance is the need to detail the precise protocols and techniques used in studying the fine structure of fossil pollen and spores (Taylor *et al.* 1996). This is especially significant since the developmental stage of the grain, the nature of the preservation process, and any subsequent dia- genesis (Fig. 24.2a) of the specimens can influence the appearance of the spore or pollen grain wall at the ultrastructural level. All of these modifications may influence the ability of the pollen or spore wall to take up different stains, and in some instance to reveal delicate structures such as lamellae. For example, within a large population of grains there is a high probability that some may have been preserved at slightly different stages of wall development (Fig. 24.1c). As a result it is necessary to examine sections of varying thickness which have been treated with different concentrations and combinations of stains for varying periods of time. This is important so as to be certain that delicate structures are not masked because of thick sections or the excessive accumulation of stains. In addition, serial sections of several grains should be prepared to ensure that differences can be distinguished between developmental and diagenetic effects (Fig. 24.2a). Moreover, the use of serial sections may prove valuable in identifying certain structures that only occur in specific regions of the grain (i.e. wall components in the region of apertures). Unfortunately, there are numerous descriptions of the ultrastructure of pollen and spores that are based on a single section stained for a fixed period of time. In far too many instances no details are provided regarding the preparation protocols. As a result erroneous conclusions may be reached that, in turn, are incorporated into phylogenetic studies. For example, the presence or absence of various sporoderm components has been used to distin- guish major groups of seed plants. Structures, such as lamellae (Fig. 24.1c) and other 'layers' that are present only during specific stages of wall develop- ment, would be missed if only a single grain is sectioned (Taylor & Rothwell 1982; Taylor & Alvin 1984). Moreover, artefacts caused by excessive stain precipitation may be interpreted as a distinct component of the pollen or spore wall (Fig. 24.1b), or diagnostic structures would not be observed because of excessive stains. Interpre- tations based on only a few sections in which there is little control of stain protocols may lead to inaccurate conclusions regarding precisely how the wall may have formed ontogenetically, and relying on only a few sections of a single grain can also result in missing certain small structural details or germination sites. There can be no single, universal stain protocol since not all grains are preserved at the same stage of development and under the exact same set of preservation variables. Thus it is incumbent upon investigators to use a variety of stain concentrations plotted against time in stain, and that these protocols are carefully recorded in the methods section of the paper.

Embedding and orientation

In addition to the necessity of sectioning numerous grains, each pollen grain or spore must also be properly orientated prior to preparing ultrathin sections (Fig. 24.1d). There are several methods that can be used to accomplish this. One is to embed specimens in thin wafers of mounting medium so it is possible to see and orientate the grain for sectioning. The most commonly used embedding materials for fossil grains are Epon- Araldite or Spurr's low viscosity resin (the manufacturer provides instructions on how to prepare for various hardness levels; see Appendix for 'EM suppliers, USA'). In instances where grains or spores are large they may be embedded directly in resin in a shallow aluminium (4.0 cm) pan. Embedding fossil grains may also be accomplished by adding the grains to a drop of resin between two Teflon-coated standard microscope slides and then selecting the desired grain by viewing the wafer in transmitted light. Another procedure that is used for small grains or strew samples involves pipetting grains onto cellulose filters under suction and then coating both sides of the filter in agar. These filters can then be dehydrated and gradually infiltrated with resin in shallow pans (Osborn *et al.* 1991). Still another method involves positioning grains in small blocks of agar which can be treated in 4% paraformaldehyde and 2% osmium tetroxide, dehydrated in a graded ethanol series, and subse- quently transferred to propylene oxide and embedded in Epon-Araldite (Lugardon & Delcambre 1994). All of these procedures make it possible to cut a small block containing a grain from the resin wafer and cement it with super glue to a styrene rod which will fit into the ultramicro- tome chuck. This procedure ensures that sections will be in a desired orientation. The proper orientation of sections is especially important since oblique sections, especially of compressed grains (Fig. 24.1f), may result in an inaccurate assessment of the structure of the grain and thickness of the wall. A case in point concerns the endoreticulations that extend a short distance in from the inner saccus

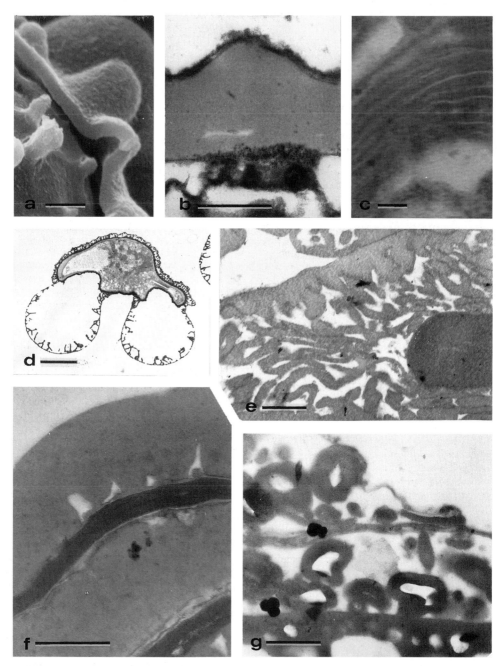

Fig. 24.1. Fossil pollen and spore ultrastructure. (**a**) Fractured surface of Carboniferous pollen grain showing organization of sporoderm (scale bar = 2.0 µm). (**b**) Section of Carboniferous spore with excess stain deposition on outer surface (top) (scale bar = 0.5 µm). (**c**) Detail of sporoderm showing delicate lamellae separated by white lines (scale bar = 2.0 µm). (**d**) Section of complete saccate pollen grain showing endoreticulations arising from the inner surface of the sacci (scale bar = 10 µm). (**e**) Section of saccus showing protosaccate condition (scale bar = 1.0 µm). (**f**) Cretaceous pollen grain wall showing lighter and darker regions as a result of differential staining (scale bar = 0.5 µm). (**g**) Tapetal membranes (T) and orbicules (O) on surface of fossil pollen grain (scale bar = 0.5 µm).

wall of eusaccate pollen grains (Fig. 24.1d). Although protosaccate grains may appear superficially similar to eusaccate types, their sacci contain slender threads that extend from the inner saccus wall to the outer surface of the corpus (Fig. 24.1e). In an oblique section through the endoreticulations, it is possible to mistake a eusaccate type for a protosaccate grain (Osborn & Taylor 1993). The ability to differentiate these two grain types is useful in deciphering sporoderm development, perhaps the evolution of the saccus, and as a potentially important character in phylogenetic reconstructions.

Stains and ultramicrotomy

There are a variety of approaches that have been used for staining ultrathin sections of fossil grains. Some investigators fix grains in glutaraldehyde and post-fix in osmium tetroxide before embedding. Most investigators, however, stain after ultrathin sections have been cut. The most common stains used for fine structural studies of fossil pollen and spores are 2% uranyl acetate, 2% aqueous potassium permanganate, and 0.25% lead citrate.

Although glass knives have been used to prepare ultrathin sections of fossil pollen and spores, a diamond cutting edge is far superior, especially when sections are prepared in the silver–gold range that is necessary to resolve especially delicate structures of the wall (Taylor & Grauvogel-Stamm 1995). Once ultrathin sections are cut, they can be collected on 1×2 mm slot grids dried onto formvar support films (Rowley & Moran 1975). For larger grains, support films may not be necessary. It is at this stage that sections can be post-stained depending upon the stain schedule used. In addition to using a large number of grains, multiple stain schedules should also be employed in which sections are stained for varying times and in different stain concentrations. For example, for seed fern pollen 2% aqueous potassium permanganate for 30 min, and post-fixing in 2% aqueous uranal acetate for 1 h in the dark provided the best results (Taylor & Rothwell 1982). While a time-consuming procedure, it is necessary to experiment with different stain concentrations for varying periods of time to achieve the maximum amount of information from the sections.

In a few studies where ultrathin sections were prepared, stains were not used (e.g. Hemsley et al. 1994b). While it is possible to see the pollen or spore wall in these preparations, in general the results are unsatisfactory and provide no opportunity to resolve delicate wall layers of the sporoderm (Hemsley & Scott 1991).

Terminology

There is a large and sometimes complex terminology associated with the study of pollen grains and spores that has continued to increase with the utilization of electron microscopy. The recent standardization of pollen and spore terms has been an important advancement (Punt et al. 1994), and will need to continue to incorporate new sporoderm features and stages in wall development that form the basis of ultrastructural studies.

Sources of additional ultrastructural information

While the principal thrust of pollen and spore fine-structural studies has been concerned with features of the pollen or spore wall, there is also a potential wealth of ultrastructural information on the surface of the grain and within the lumen. When grains are gently macerated from sporangia and pollen sacs in ethylenediamine tetraacetic acid (EDTA) it may be possible to examine the tapetal membranes that were formed in association with the process of microsporogenesis. Acids of this type are especially useful since they are not effervescent and thus bubbles do not break up delicate structures. Tapetal membrane systems sometimes adhere to the surface of the grain and when grains are prepared with these structures in mind, important ultrastructural information can be obtained about microsporogenesis. When found in association with immature pollen grains, tapetal membranes (Fig. 24.1g) provide an independent method of determining stages in pollen wall ontogeny (Taylor 1976). For example, in the case of the Mesozoic pollen type Classopollis, the presence of tapetal membranes in association with orbicules demonstrates the developmental pattern involved in synthesizing the final ornament to the pollen wall surface (Taylor & Alvin 1984).

Orbicules or ubisch bodies are also an important source of fine-structural information. They are known as early as the Devonian (Gensel 1980), and in extant plants are generally associated with a secretory or parietal tapetum system (T. N. Taylor 1990). These small, sometimes hollow structures often possess the same ornamentation as that on the grain surface (Fig. 24.1g), indicating that in some plants the final ornamentation is a product of tapetal activities. The opportunity to examine membranes and orbicules on fossil spores and pollen will become an increasingly important and new source of developmental and evolutionary information, since the secretory pattern is believed to be the primitive type based on microsporogenesis in living plants (Pacini et al. 1985). Fossil evidence

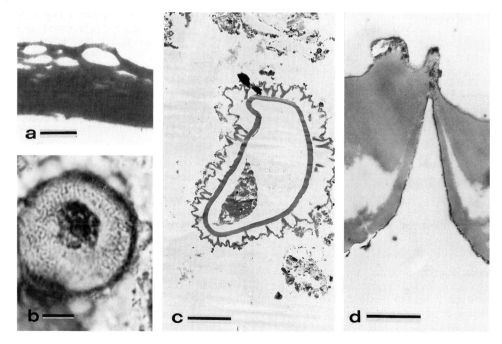

Fig. 24.2. Fossil pollen and spore ultrastructure. (**a**) Section of Devonian spore showing separation of wall layers (scale bar = 0.5 μm). (**b**) Transmitted light photomicrograph showing cell contents (scale bar = 5 μm). (**c**) Section of grain illustrated in (b), showing wall and cell contents (scale bar = 5.0 μm). (**d**) Wall of Cretaceous spore showing unusual sporoderm ultrastructure (scale bar = 2.0 μm).

documenting the type of microsporogenesis makes it possible to test this hypothesis.

Although some fossil pollen grains and spores contain cytoplasmic, and perhaps nuclear residue, the frequency of these occurrences remains low (e.g. Millay & Eggert 1974; Brack-Hanes & Vaughn 1978). As a result there has been relatively little attention directed at the fine structure of these structures. In one study the contents of the lumen of Carboniferous age pteridophyte spores were examined at the fine-structural level (Fig. 24.2b,c) (Taylor & Millay 1977). The material appeared to correspond to the cytoplasmic organization seen in the development of some extant endosporal gametophytes (Taylor & Millay 1977). One of the most exciting demonstrations of the importance of fine-structural studies of fossil plant remains is the report of grana stacks, starch deposits, nuclei and plasmodesmata in a Miocene leaf (Niklas *et al.* 1978). While these types of preservation are rare, they do demonstrate that very delicate structures capable of yielding significant information about the biology and evolution of fossil plants can be recovered and compared with similar structures in living plants.

Interpretation

Because of the complexities of the pollen and spore walls and the absence of low magnifications in transmission electron microscopy, it is sometimes necessary to make montages of grain micrographs. While this requires multiple micrographs that must be assembled into 'single' view, such composite micrographs provide the opportunity to interpret features such as germination sites, harmomegathic structures, and differences in wall structure within the context of the entire grain.

The ultrastructure of fossil pollen grains and spores provides heretofore unavailable information about the biology and evolution of past biotas. While there are standard techniques available for fossil pollen and spore studies, the investigator must devise appropriate modifications of these techniques to fit the questions that are being asked and the nature of the preservation. Only in this way will it be possible to extract the maximum amount of information from the specimens. As in the case of living materials that are studied at the ultrastructural level, it is the preparation procedure that is most important to the success of the investigation. In spite of the fact that we know relatively little about the way in which plant parts are fossilized, the evidence available to date indicates that very delicate biological structures are preserved and can be a valuable source of information. Electron microscopy provides the opportunity to ask new questions about pollen and spores and to extend the resolution of inquiry to the subcellular level.

Part Five   Geochemistry

25. Collection and storage of fossil plant remains for organic geochemical analyses

PIM F. VAN BERGEN

This chapter is a general guide to the collection, storage and initial preparation of plant fossils for studies using geochemical techniques. To date, a large number of chemical methods, including elemental analysis, spectroscopy, chemolysis, pyrolysis, lipid analysis and stable carbon isotope analysis on both bulk organic carbon, as well as on individual organic compounds, have been applied to a diversity of fossil plants. These include fossil remains such as algae, leaves, wood, periderm, propagules, spores and pollen. The main aspects determining the collection and subsequent storage of material depend on which technique(s) will be used and the exact palaeobotanical or geological question(s) that are to be addressed. The four main general objectives for which geochemical techniques have been used in the study of fossil plants are:

1. determining the 'original' chemical composition of fossil plant tissues/structures;
2. studying chemical transformations which can be related to the palaeoenvironment and/or depositional setting;
3. obtaining an insight into the level of thermal maturity of fossil material;
4. determining chemosystematic relationships.

There is no single protocol for the collection and storage of plant fossils and subsequent geochemical analyses. This chapter will provide general guidelines as to how to obtain organic geochemical information from fossil plants, starting from collecting in the field, storage in the laboratory, through to general considerations related to the overall chemical approach (Fig. 25.1). However, it should be emphasized that, whenever possible, detailed information should be obtained from experts in the relevant field(s) of research prior to sampling.

Collecting

General considerations

In principle, there are no direct restrictions as to the physical and chemical state of plant fossils suitable for geochemical analyses. Fossil plant material obtained from non-weathered sediments and sites unexposed to rooting of modern plants will normally provide the most reliable chemical results of the fossil. Recent weathering and biodegradation often cause significant chemical alterations of fossils. Furthermore, when sampling for chemo-systematic purposes, collecting from sediments which have had relatively little overburden, and thus little diagenetic alteration, will substantially enhance the possibility of survival of taxa-specific compounds (van Bergen *et al.* 1995). In general, the collection of material can be divided into:

1. fossils for bulk parameter analyses or for the study of water and solvent insoluble material (i.e. for elemental analysis, spectroscopy, pyrolysis, chemolysis);
2. material for the examination of water and/or solvent soluble constituents, such as pigments and lipids.

At weathered and exposed sites it is recommended to sample primarily for analyses of bulk and insoluble material because the soluble organic fraction in such samples is often significantly modified.

Sample size

With respect to sample quantity, most geochemical methods require relatively small amounts of material, ranging from grams to sub-milligrams. For example, analyses of soluble compounds from plant fossils may require several grams. The amounts for elemental analysis, chemolytic and spectroscopic methods range from 1 to several hundred milligrams dependent on the organic matter contents. Certain pyrolysis methods will need as little as 0.05 mg of organic matter (equivalent to approximately 2 large megaspores) to yield meaningful results. Where possible, the collection of larger amounts of material is recommended, thus allowing study by a combination of chemical techniques.

Sample handling

When collecting material physical contact between bare skin and fossil remains should be avoided because of the risk of contamination (e.g. 'skin

VAN BERGEN, P. F. 1999. Collection and storage of fossil plant remains for organic geochemical analyses.
In: JONES, T. P. & ROWE, N. P. (eds) *Fossil Plants and Spores: modern techniques.*
Geological Society, London, 135–138.

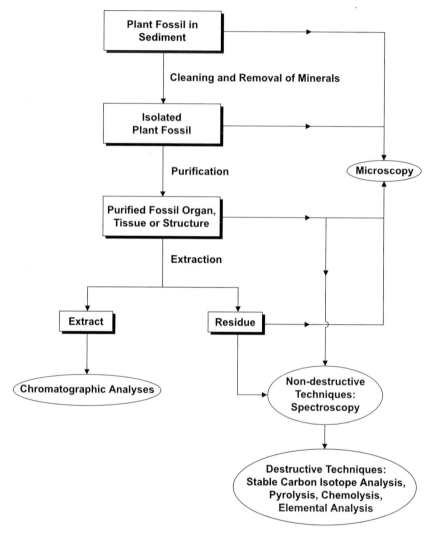

Fig. 25.1. A schematic analytical protocol for the study of fossil plant remains.

lipids', DNA). Small specimens, can be manipulated carefully with a range of tools from tweezers
to a small trowel. If larger specimens are handled
by hand, the surface of the specimen/material
should be removed or cleaned prior to geochemical
analyses. Collecting specimens for studies of labile
chemical compounds may need special equipment
and materials such as inert gases (argon and
nitrogen) or organic solvents (methanol and
dichloromethane), to prevent rapid chemical
deterioration, such as oxidation of lipids and
nucleic acids. With this latter type of sampling,
physical contact between bare skin and fossil
remains should be avoided at all cost. Cool boxes
with dry ice (solid CO_2) can be used to transport

these chemically labile samples from the field to
the laboratory.

Packaging

For both types of sampling, an accepted method is
to wrap the material in aluminium foil and store in
special plastic bags with a low plasticizer content.
However, aluminium foil should be avoided when
collecting material from acidic environments, such
as peats, or containing substantial amounts of
minerals that may form acids (e.g. pyrite) as this
may dissolve the foil. In these latter cases the
material can be placed directly into the special
plastic bags providing the material is transferred

immediately after return to the laboratory. The use of common packaging material based on organic materials (e.g. ordinary plastic bags, paper, tissues, newspaper) for wrapping samples must be avoided as contamination can result from plasticizers, ink, cellulose, lignin or plastic particles. If the material is going to be stored prior to analyses, collecting blocks consisting of the plant remains *in situ* in the matrix should be considered.

Storage

The storage of fossil plant remains for geochemical analyses depends on which technique(s) will be used, and to what extent the material/specimen will be isolated and purified (Fig. 25.1). If the matrix contains chemically labile minerals which may affect the organic composition, the specimens should be isolated (see below).

In general, samples should be dried to prevent fungal and algal growth as these can significantly affect chemical results. If samples are collected from sites exposed to sea water, these should be rinsed using double-distilled water to remove salts. The drying process can be either air-dried, oven-dried or freeze-dried, depending on the material and subsequent techniques. Drying may cause substantial cracking of the material, affecting, for example, conventional or scanning electron microscopic (SEM) examinations. Thus if microscopy is planned one should consider subdividing the material or, if only limited amounts are available, it is best to first examine the material using microscopy, followed by the chemical techniques. In most cases the dried fossils used for bulk and insoluble material analyses should be stored dry, preferably in air-tight glass vials or jars, away from heat, and in the dark to minimize oxidation. Replacing the air surrounding the specimens with an inert gas such as N_2 is recommended. Alternatively, the dried material can be vacuum sealed and stored in a freezer. For some smaller specimens containing substantial amounts of sulphur and/or pyrite, storing under organic solvents, such as methanol, acetone or dichloromethane, in a refrigerator to retard oxidation may be considered. Fossils collected for water and/or solvent soluble analyses should be stored directly in a freezer to minimize chemical degradation. Only as a last option should the fossils be stored in glass under liquids, such as water, glycerol, etc. The problem of contamination by fungi and/or algae can be overcome by the use of fungicides such as thymol. Although thymol can be removed by solvent extraction, it normally impregnates the entire fossil which will consequently affect the chemical results. Furthermore, upon drying some

fungicides crystallize out on the surface of the specimen affecting observation by microscopy.

Preparation for chemical analyses

Isolation from matrix

Figure 25.1 shows a schematic analytical protocol for the study of fossil plant remains after the initial collection. The first step is to isolate the specimen, e.g. whole or part of organs, such as leaves, or specific plant structures such as cuticles, from the mineral matrix. This is preferably undertaken by physical/mechanical, rather than chemical means, in order to avoid possible chemical alteration. The physical removal of minerals can be facilitated by ultrasonication in liquid, normally using water or organic solvents. However, for the majority of plant fossils, chemical maceration is required to release the specimen(s) from the sediments in which they are found. The use of dilute hydrogen peroxide (H_2O_2) has shown no obvious effects on the chemical composition of the fossil (van Bergen *et al.* 1995). Similarly, with respect to the commonly used hydrochloric/hydrofluoric acid (HCl/HF) maceration, it is generally believed that this treatment, including the heat induced during the maceration, has no significant chemical effects. However, it should be noted that specimens from relatively immature sediments, still containing polysaccharide moieties, such as cellulose, may undergo some chemical alterations upon HCl treatment (Klok *et al.* 1984). Oxidizing reagents such as nitric acid (HNO_3) should NOT be used as they dramatically alter the chemical composition beyond recognition (Hemsley *et al.* 1996b).

Purification and extraction

If required, the sample can be further purified by removing any attached organic material not belonging to the specimen under study. For example, sclerotic tissues should be separated from translucent ones because both are often composed of different chemical constituents (i.e. sclerotic material contains aromatic moieties, translucent structures often contain aliphatic constituents). In particular, coalified material adhering to plant structures, such as cuticles, greatly affects the chemical signal obtained and in such cases physical rather than chemical methods should be employed. At this stage it has to be decided whether or not to powder the fossil plant material. Powdering is recommended as it will increase chemical homogeneity of the sample. However, in the case of very small samples or specimens (e.g. parts of very thin cuticles, megaspores) one might consider leaving the material intact in order to facilitate sample handing. When the investigations do not involve studying the solvent-soluble fractions, the material should be extracted using organic solvents; this is to avoid any possible contamination, such as plasticizers or skin lipids, introduced during sample collecting and preparation. Solvent extraction can be undertaken by either soxhlet extraction or ultrasonication.

Use of geochemical techniques

In order to obtain a thorough chemical understanding of the selected material, one should aim to use a combination of different chemical techniques on the same specimen(s). In addition, it is always very instructive to subject specimens to microscopic examinations before and after chemical analyses, as this may assist chemical interpretations (Boon et al. 1989; Collinson et al. 1994; van der Heijden & Boon 1994; van Bergen 1994; van Bergen et al. 1995). Only chemical analyses of solvent insoluble material are possible on specimens which are to be examined first by microscopy (mainly light microscopy (LM) and SEM). This is because the material has to be cleaned, mostly by solvent extraction, after the necessary handling for microscopy. Most non-carbon dags can also be removed by solvent extraction. However, although not ideal, it should be noted that SEM specimens coated with anything other than carbon, and attached by adhesives, other than carbon-containing dags, can still be analysed by some chemical techniques such as pyrolysis and chemolysis, and still yield meaningful data (van Bergen, Collinson & de Leeuw, unpublished data).

The collection of sufficient material permits the sample to be sub-sampled and can provide enough material for a range of different chemical methods. In the case of limited or small samples, one should first use non-destructive techniques, such as solid state ^{13}C nuclear magnetic resonance (NMR) spectroscopy, and then the destructive techniques such as elemental analysis, chemolysis and pyrolysis. However, as mentioned earlier the amount of material will often be the determining factor with respect to the choice of destructive technique.

26. Carbon stable isotope analysis of fossil plants

HERVÉ BOCHERENS & ANDRÉ MARIOTTI

Discrimination against ^{13}C in favour of ^{12}C during photosynthesis in modern terrestrial plants leads to characteristic differences between the carbon isotope composition of plant tissues and that of the source atmospheric CO_2 (Nier & Gulbransen 1939; Evans et al. 1986; Ehleringer 1991). Carbon isotopic compositions of plant tissues are primarily determined by the photosynthetic systems adopted by the plants (C_3, C_4 or crassulacean acid metabolism (CAM)), but are also correlated with environmental factors such as temperature, light intensity, water stress and salinity (e.g. review in Tieszen 1991), and may also to some extent reflect the isotopic composition of atmospheric CO_2 (Marino & McElroy 1991). Fossil plants usually have carbon isotope values which reflect those of the living tissues (Nambudiri et al. 1978; Rigby et al. 1981; Bocherens et al. 1994; see DeNiro & Hastorf 1985; T. P. Jones 1994 for possible exceptions), and carbon isotopic signatures measured on fossil plants have been used to determine photosynthetic types (Nambudiri et al. 1978; Throughton et al. 1974), water and salinity stress (Bocherens et al. 1994), and level and isotopic composition of CO_2 in ancient atmospheres (Toolin & Eastoe 1993; van de Water et al. 1994; White et al. 1994; Xiahong & Epstein 1995).

Until recently, measurements of carbon isotopes in organic matter were performed manually in sealed quartz tubes in muffle furnace (see Swerhone et al. 1991; Girardin & Mariotti 1991 for full description of this technique), but automated commercial units coupling an elemental analyser with an isotope ratio mass spectrometer are now available. This technique greatly reduces total sample preparation time without loss of analytical precision (Barrie & Prosser 1996; Brand 1996). The latter technique will be described in this chapter.

Principles of the automated carbon isotopic measurement

The automated carbon isotopic measurement starts with the combustion of the sample in an elemental analyser, followed by purification of the evolved CO_2, and subsequent determination of the carbon isotope ratios, in an automated sequence that can analyse around 50 to 200 samples in a row. Carbon isotopic abundances are expressed as $\delta^{13}C$ values: $\delta^{13}C = (^{13}R_{sample}/^{13}R_{standard} -1) \times 1000‰$, where ^{13}R stands for the ratio $^{13}C/^{12}C$, standard being PDB (marine carbonate: belemnite from the Pee Dee Formation) (Craig 1953).

The measurements of carbon isotope ratios are currently performed using two methods: (1) a dual inlet system, and (2) a continuous helium flow system. A dual inlet system consists of trapping and subsequently cryogenically purifying the CO_2 evolved from the combustion of the sample. The evolved CO_2 is then introduced into the mass spectrometer by a dual inlet system, which allows simultaneous analysis of the sample and reference gas several times. A continuous helium flow system analyses the sample gas once, and then compares this against the reference gas. The advantages and limitations of both systems will be discussed later.

Sample preparation

Grinding may be important in homogenizing samples. This may be achieved by a piston-action ball technique described by Rondon & Thomas (1994). Before isotope analysis, the fossil plant samples may need to be pretreated in order to remove possible carbon containing contaminants. Inorganic carbonates are removed by acidification. A gentle process is recommended in order to prevent partial acid hydrolysis of plant organic matter that may alter the carbon isotope ratios. Ground samples are soaked in a 0.001 M hydrochloric acid (HCl) (pH = 3) solution. After agitation over 30 min, the pH is checked. If pH becomes less than 3, drops of 0.5 M HCl are added until pH reaches 3 again, while the solution is agitated over 30 min. The pH is continuously checked. This procedure is repeated until the pH stabilizes at 3. At this stage the sample is totally decarbonated.

Absorption of humic acids may have occured in fossil plant materials. Removal of this contaminant can be performed using 1 M sodium hydroxide (NaOH), for durations ranging from three hours (Gröcke 1997) to one day (DeNiro & Hastorf 1985). The effects of this kind of treatment are variable according to the origin of the samples, and

BOCHERENS, H. & MARIOTTI, A. 1999. Carbon stable isotope analysis of fossil plants. In: JONES, T. P. & ROWE, N. P. (eds) Fossil Plants and Spores: modern techniques. Geological Society, London, 139–142.

this step of pretreatment may be used according to the results of comparison tests between the isotopic compositions of treated and untreated fractions of the same specimens (Gröcke 1997). Sulphurous compounds can have a detrimental effect on the mass spectrometer and should be removed by standard chemical procedures, such as nitric acid (HNO_3) treatment (Gröcke 1997), before carbon isotopic analysis.

Samples are weighted in tin capsules ($h = 5$ mm; $\varnothing = 4$ mm), which have been cleaned twice in carbon tetrachloride and acetone in order to reduce carbon traces and to decrease the blank values. The filled capsules are positioned in an autosampler (sampler drum for 49 samples). One available configuration allows unattended fully automatic analysis of up to 196 samples in one batch (three special sample drums for 49 samples each). Within each batch of samples, it is important to insert an

internal standard with a homogeneous and well-determined carbon isotopic composition. CE Instruments provides high purity chemicals for internal calibration, for example cyclohexanone, atropine, phenantrene and acetanilide. These products have been checked for isotopic homogeneity, with good reproducibility (Girardin & Mariotti 1991). Our experience shows that for routine measurements, a large quantity of one product can be used, after extensive homogenization, such as tyrosine from Merck®. Calibration of the elemental analyser is achieved using the standard, tyrosine, ranging in weight from 0.4 to 3 mg. The yields of CO_2 generated by the combustion of the laboratory standard are useful for interpreting isotopic results where large variations in carbon content are expected. Three to four empty tin capsules should be analysed for each box, in order to correct the measured carbon amount values

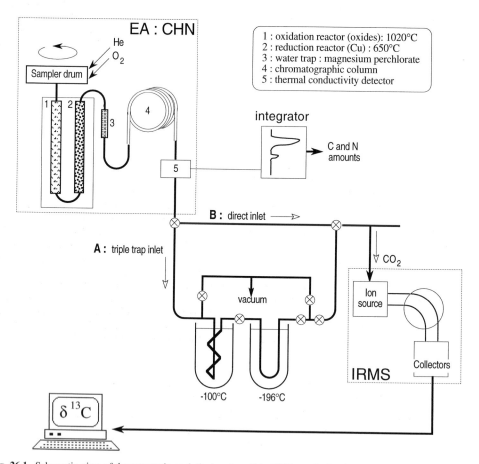

Fig. 26.1. Schematic view of the automatic analytical system. EA: CHN stands for elemental analyser, IRMS for isotopic ratio mass spectrometer. Between these two points are illustrated the alternative routes of CO_2 through (A) interface of trapping and (B) direct inlet in continuous flow.

Table 26.1. *$\delta^{13}C$ values (mean and two standard deviations) of well homogenized samples, with different chemical natures and C/N ratios, analysed with an elemental analyser coupled with a dual inlet isotope ratio mass spectrometer*

Sample	C/N ratio	Number of analyses	mean $\delta^{13}C$	standard deviation (two sd)
Graphite	pure C	32	−23.29	0.070
Graphite + NH_4^+	3 to 54	25	−23.39	0.042
Cyclohexanone	2.6	55	−26.03	0.036
Tyrosine	7.7	24	−23.27	0.074
Atropine	14.6	12	−29.39	0.090
Phenanthrene	pure C	9	−24.10	0.122
Acetanilide	6.8	9	−30.23	0.098
Egg albumine	3.6	22	−17.21	0.114

Data from Girardin & Mariotti (1991)

from the background value. Fossil plant samples typically contain 15 to 40% C, but variation in carbon content of fossil plants is highly dependent on the maturation level of the sample. Thus 1 mg of sample contains 150 to 400 µg C and the weight of sample to be analysed will depend on the analytical system. A preliminary determination of the carbon content may be necessary using a decoupled elemental analyser in order to determine the optimal weight of the sample for stable isotope analysis.

Once a series of samples with standards is loaded, gas preparation by the elemental analyser proceeds as follows (Girardin & Mariotti 1991; Fig. 26.1). The samples are purged of air by a flow of helium in the sampler drum, then the capsule falls from the sampler drum into the combustion furnace [1 on Fig. 26.1] containing the oxidation reactor set at 1020°C, where flash combustion takes place due to the simultaneous injection of 10 ml pure oxygen (99.999%, CO + CO_2 <1 ppm) in the carrier gas (99.999% He, 80 ml min^{-1}). The exothermal oxidation of the tin capsule increases the temperature to *c.* 1800°C ensuring complete oxidation. After combustion, the evolved gas is taken by the helium flow into the second furnace [2], containing reduced copper, set at 650°C, where nitrogen oxides are reduced into molecular nitrogen (N_2)

and excess oxygen is retained. In this reactor, silver wool traps sulphur and halogens while a tube containing magnesium perchlorate ($Mg(ClO_4)_2$) [3] traps water. The chromatographic column [4] separates CO_2 from N_2 and these are successively measured by a thermal conductivity detector. The carbon and nitrogen abundance is then calculated by comparison with the corresponding areas obtained for known amounts of standard tyrosine in the same analytical conditions [5].

Isotopic analysis

In the case of the dual inlet analytical system (A in Fig. 26.1), CO_2 is trapped with liquid nitrogen while N_2 and He are evacuated. The trap is then heated and the CO_2 is then introduced into the dual inlet system. The pressure is automatically regulated by bellows in order to match the pressure of sample against the standard gas. The external analytical precision, which quantifies errors accumulated over the whole analytical process (as opposed to the internal precision which evaluates mass spectrometer performance), for homogenized samples presenting different chemical compositions ranges from 0.04 to 0.12‰ (Girardin & Mariotti 1991; Table 26.1). If the sample is too small and contains less than *c.* 200 µg C, the cold

Table 26.2. *$\delta^{13}C$ values (mean and two standard deviations) of well homogenized samples, with different chemical natures and C/N ratios, analysed with an elemental analyser coupled with a continuous flow isotope ratio mass spectrometer*

Sample	C/N ratio	Number of analyses	mean $\delta^{13}C$	standard deviation (two sd)
Cyclohexanone	2.6	12	−25.98	0.176
Tyrosine	7.7	39	−23.04	0.184
Alanine	2.6	19	−23.60	0.262

Table 26.3. *Compared characteristics of dual inlet and continuous flux isotope systems*

Isotopic analytical system	dual inlet	continuous flow
external analytical precision (‰)	±0.1	±0.3
range [µg C]	200–2000	30–300
duration of one analysis (min)	20–30	<5
remarks	liquid nitrogen tank	

finger is automatically activated and the whole CO_2 is introduced in the mass spectrometer. This process increases the standard error of the measurement due to the possible trapping of impurities.

In the case of the continuous flow system (B in Fig. 26.1), the isotopic analysis takes place during a predetermined time sequence, which includes the passage of whole CO_2 but excludes N_2. The external analytical precision ranges from 0.18 to 0.26 (Table 26.2), but it is improved if the amount of CO_2 from all the samples in a series falls within a narrow range of values.

The comparison of both techniques shows their advantages and limits (Table 26.3). Comparison of a dual inlet system with a single inlet system has been presented by Knight *et al.* (1994). The dual inlet system is slower than continuous flow, but presents a better analytical precision due to the introduction of a constant fraction of the sample gas. The continuous flow system is faster and does not require a bulky liquid nitrogen tank that has to be filled regularly, but analytical precision may be worse than for the dual inlet system. This drawback can be reduced by preparing homogeneous series of samples of approximately equal carbon content.

We wish to thank G. Bardoux, C. Girardin and M. Grably for their invaluable insight on the technical part of the analytical process. D. Gröcke helped improve this chapter with useful comments.

27. Pyrolysis and chemolysis of fossil plant remains: applications to palaeobotany

PIM F. VAN BERGEN

The bulk of plant remains preserved as organic fossils in the geosphere is macromolecular in nature. This complex chemical composition substantially restricts the techniques that can be used to obtain insight into the molecular composition of these materials. Two methods which can provide detailed molecular information are chemolysis and pyrolysis. Pyrolysis can be used for an effective initial screening of the chemical composition of the fossil material (e.g. Collinson *et al.* 1994; Stout & Boon 1994; van Bergen *et al.* 1995), subsequently using chemolytic techniques to obtain additional insight into more specific chemical building blocks (e.g. Logan & Thomas, 1987; van Bergen 1994; Gelin *et al.* 1997 and references cited therein). From a palaeobotanical point of view these methods can provide information on the taphonomic processes, which may have affected the fossils, the maturity of the material and the systematic significance of certain compounds.

Both methods are destructive and are based on the cleavage of chemical bonds in solid organic materials (e.g. plastics, polyesters, biopolymers, humic materials, kerogens). In chemolysis techniques, specific chemical reagents such as CuO, RuO_4, HI, NiB, LiI, etc. are used. In pyrolysis, thermal energy in an inert atmosphere, or *in vacuo*, is used to yield structurally significant fragments (Fig. 27.1). The choice of chemical reagent in chemolysis is mainly dependent on the type of chemical bonds to be cleaved, thus allowing the targeting of very specific structural moieties. In contrast, pyrolysis is a relatively 'non-specific' method in terms of the types of linkages that are broken, as this is dependent on the thermo-stability of bonds. Pyrolysis is particularly powerful if the organic substances are intractable to 'wet-chemical' techniques and/or when nothing is known about the specific moieties present. Only a very small amount of the actual pyrolysis products are detected and identified (Larter & Horsfield 1993). However, comparisons with other more quantitative methods, such as solid state ^{13}C nuclear magnetic resonance, have revealed that in most cases the pyrolysis products released are representative of the overall macromolecular structure (Larter & Horsfield 1993).

Pyrolysis methods

The variety of pyrolysis methods available to the plant palaeobiologist can be roughly divided into

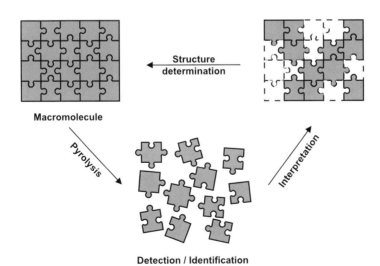

Fig. 27.1. Schematic representation of pyrolysis (modified after an idea by Dr J. S. Sinninghe Damsté).

VAN BERGEN, P. F. 1999. Pyrolysis and chemolysis of fossil plant remains: applications to palaeobotany. *In*: JONES, T. P. & ROWE, N. P. (eds) *Fossil Plants and Spores: modern techniques*. Geological Society, London, 143–148.

off-line and on-line configurations. These are based on whether the pyrolysis products formed are first collected and studied at a later stage (off-line), or analysed directly (on-line) using separation (e.g. gas chromatography, liquid chromatography) and identification techniques (i.e. infrared spectroscopy, mass spectrometry).

Off-line pyrolysis

Off-line pyrolysis configurations include open and closed systems. In open systems the sample is placed in a furnace under a continuous flow of N_2 or He and the compounds released upon thermal decomposition are cold-trapped. In closed systems, the material is sealed in tubes under vacuum, N_2 or with water (hydrous pyrolysis) and heated. After heating, the products formed within the tube are washed out using solvents or 'thermally' extracted out of the residue. The main advantages with off-line configurations are that (i) the actual pyrolysis products are obtained and (ii) the products released can be quantified if an internal standard has been added. Obtaining pyrolysis products has the advantage that they can be further separated and analysed using various other chemical techniques, for example, stable carbon isotope analysis ($\delta^{13}C$ values) of the products can be used to provide palaeoclimatic signals. Quantification of the products provides information regarding the level of chemical transformation that the plant fossil has undergone which, in turn, can be related to, for example, the maturity of the specimen. From a palaeobotanical point of view, one minor disadvantage with off-line devices is that relatively large amounts of material are needed (50–100 mg or more). To date, few studies have been published using off-line pyrolysis of morphologically well-defined plant fossils (e.g. Behar & Hatcher 1995).

On-line pyrolysis

On-line pyrolysis configurations have been widely used to study plant fossils such as algae, wood, leaves, cuticles, periderm, seeds, fruits, spores and pollen (e.g. Boon et al. 1989; Collinson et al. 1994; Hatcher et al. 1994; van Bergen et al. 1995). This type of pyrolysis includes Rock Eval pyrolysis and the more frequently used flash pyrolysis (i.e. Curie-point, filament and laser pyrolysis) and temperature-resolved pyrolysis. Rock Eval pyrolysis is a method which yields basic elemental data (C, H, O) but provides no detailed structural information on the building blocks of the material. In the other on-line systems, the products released upon flash pyrolysis and temperature-resolved pyrolysis can be immediately swept into a gas chromatograph (GC) or analysed directly by a mass spectrometer

(MS). With most flash pyrolysis devices, used in combination with a GC, the sample is either placed on a platinum ribbon or inside quartz tubes within a resistively heated coil (filament devices), or applied on a Curie-point wire (Curie-point devices). In configurations where the pyrolysis device is directly coupled to a MS, the sample can be introduced in a number of different ways, including attachment to a Curie-point wire or on the filament of a thermo-heated probe (Boon 1992 and references cited therein). The main advantages of the flash and temperature-resolved pyrolysis are (i) the ability to perform rapid chemical fingerprinting of complex insoluble mixtures and (ii) the use of only microgram quantities (less than 0.05 mg) of, what are often limited, chemically recalcitrant organic samples. An additional advantage of the pyrolysis-GC configurations is the ability to separate different compounds having similar molecular formulae, thus providing detailed information on the molecular composition of the fossil material. Pyrolysis-MS is particularly useful for the detection of larger dimeric, trimeric and oligomeric products (Boon 1992). This latter method is one of the most informative pyrolysis techniques to investigate polysaccharides, such as cellulose and hemicellulose, and as such, is very useful for investigating many aspects of fossil plants.

Pyrolysis methylation

Within the field of pyrolysis, a major problem is the formation of functionalized polar products that are difficult to detect. This can be overcome by using pyrolysis with on-line methylation, which in recent years has gained substantially in popularity (McKinney et al. 1995 and references cited therein). This method enhances compound separation/ detection and the chromatography of functionalized polar products. Furthermore, it may provide additional information on characteristic molecular building blocks. However, this method is not a pyrolysis technique per se but rather a thermally assisted chemolysis technique. For additional information about various pyrolysis techniques and their general applications and limitations, the reader is referred to review papers by Irwin (1993 and references cited therein), Boon (1992), Larter & Horsfield (1993) and Saiz-Jimenez (1994).

Chemolysis methods

The main advantage of chemolytic analyses is that very specific molecular building blocks can be targeted through the use of certain chemical reagents. Chemolysis is often used in conjunction with pyrolysis as the latter can reveal different structural moieties that can be subsequently studied using appropriate reagents; dependent on the structural moieties present different reagents will be needed. Commonly used chemolytic methods involve treatments using a base and/or acid. Base treatments are used primarily to release ester-linked moieties, whereas acid treatments break peptide bonds. For the cleavage of chemically more stable linkages such as ethers and carbon carbon bonds, other reagents are used such as CuO, RuO_4, HI, HNO_3 and $KMnO_4$ (see 'choice of chemolysis reagent').

Preparation of fossil materials

In order to study fossil plants using pyrolysis or chemolysis, the specimens have to be isolated from the sediment and freed of adherent minerals and other organic tissues (for additional information regarding the general collection, storage and preparation of fossil plant material for geochemical techniques, see Chapter 25). It is then necessary to decide whether to powder the material. Powdering is generally to be recommended as it will increase the homogeneity of the sample and enhances the extraction of compounds soluble in organic solvents. Powdered samples are used preferentially in most pyrolysis (i.e. temperature-resolved systems using probes) and chemolysis techniques. In the case of very small samples or specimens (i.e. megaspores, parts of very thin cuticles) one might consider leaving the material intact in order to facilitate sample handling especially for pyrolysis. Chemolysis, off-line and most on-line pyrolysis techniques can deal with intact samples.

Solvent extraction

If the material has not been collected specifically for geochemical studies, it is recommended that specimens are extracted using organic solvents (e.g. dichloromethane, methanol, hexane) to remove possible organic contaminants such as lipids derived from contact with skin and plasticizers from plastic bags and wrapping. Moreover, abundant soluble compounds can affect the pyrolysis, in particular the flash pyrolysis of insoluble macromolecular material present in the fossils. If unextracted, the presence of soluble compounds can be determined by on-line temperature-resolved pyrolysis–mass spectrometry or sequential/fractionated pyrolysis using a filament pyrolysis device.

Choice of pyrolysis times and temperatures

Appropriate pyrolysis temperatures and pyrolysis times depend on the material under study, the pyrolysis technique used and the type of infor-

mation to be obtained. In principle, higher pyrolysis temperatures and longer times will increase fragmentation and therefore the yield of either smaller pyrolysis products and/or moieties which are more cross-linked in the macromolecular matrix. Increased temperature settings with on-line flash pyrolysis–gas chromatography systems can drastically affect the distribution patterns of homologous series of released pyrolysis products (Irwin, 1993). In off-line systems, longer pyrolysis times may also result in the enhanced formation of secondary and/or recombination products.

For off-line systems virtually any temperature (mostly between 200°C and 500°C) and any time (mostly between 1 h and 72 h) may be chosen. The on-line temperature-resolved mass spectrometry systems do not use a fixed temperature but thermally desorb from c. 200°C to 800°C within a time span of approximately 20 s. The most commonly used temperatures with on-line flash pyrolysis systems are 358°C, 610°C and 770°C with pyrolysis times of either 5, 10 or 20 s. These temperatures primarily result from the fact that most of the initial work on fossil plant remains used Curie-point devices which are temperature constrained by the Curie-points of the ferromagnetic wires. However, a range of pyrolysis temperatures can be employed using Curie-point devices from 358°C to 1128°C (Irwin 1993). In filament flash pyrolysis devices, the temperature is continuously variable up to 1200°C. As a general rule, higher pyrolysis temperatures and longer pyrolysis times are used for more recalcitrant, i.e. geologically mature specimens.

Choice of chemolysis reagent

In contrast to pyrolysis which, in principle, can be used on any kind of organic plant fossil, chemolysis relies on specific reagents which will only cleave particular types of chemical bonds. The choice of reagent greatly depends on the building blocks present in the fossil plant material. It is beyond the scope of this paper to describe in detail all the procedures of the different chemolytic methods which are primarily in the realm of organic chemistry. In addition, procedures are frequently adapted and often vary between laboratories (cf. Gelin et al. 1997).

Basic chemolytic methods often involve treatments using a base (e.g. sodium hydroxide (NaOH), potassium hydroxide (KOH)) and/or acid (e.g. hydrochloric acid (HCl), sulphuric acid (H_2SO_4)). Base treatments are primarily used to release ester-linked moieties (e.g. present in cuticles and periderm), whereas HCl is used to break peptide bonds. In the chemolytic hydrolysis of monosaccharides from polysaccharides H_2SO_4 is employed. The cleavage of very stable chemical linkages, such as ethers and carbon–carbon bonds, needs other reagents depending upon the building blocks. For example, cupric oxide (CuO) oxidation is used for the cleavage of ether bonds in lignin but can also be used to obtain insight into biopolyesters (cutin) in cuticles. Ruthenium tetraoxide (RuO$_4$) oxidation degrades double bonds, ether and ester linkages in aliphatic materials such as those present in cuticles and algae. Another method to study ether-linked moieties in cuticles and algae is the use of hydrogen iodide (HI) treatment. Alternative chemolytic oxidation procedures which have been used to study fossil plant material include nitric acid and permanganate oxidation.

General palaeobotanical applications using pyrolysis and chemolysis

To date, studies of fossil plant remains using these destructive methods have mainly concerned (i) characterizing and understanding the chemical transformation of organic material present in the fossil(s) and (ii) determining whether differences observed are of chemosystematic significance. Apart from revealing information regarding the level of maturity the characterization may also provide additional insight into taphonomic and preservational processes that affected the plant fossils before and during fossilization.

Chemical transformations

To date, pyrolysis and chemolysis studies of chemical transformations have mainly concentrated on fossil wood and other sclerified plant tissues and have assisted in providing detailed insights into peatification and coalification processes (e.g. Hatcher et al. 1994; van Bergen et al. 1994c). In modern equivalents of such fossilized tissues, the main chemical constituent is ligno-cellulose, a complex of lignin and structural polysaccharides (cellulose and hemicellulose). On fossilization these complexes are often chemically modified (e.g. Hatcher et al. 1994) with polysaccharides usually the first to be degraded (i.e. first the hemicelluloses and later the cellulose). The relative amounts of polysaccharide products are often used as a means of determining the state of preservation of the fossil. For example, the presence of cellulose markers in Miocene seed coats is evidence for high quality chemical preservation (van Bergen et al. 1995). The use of pyrolysis–MS in combination with chemical ionization (CI) is one of the most informative pyrolysis techniques to investigate specimens containing polysaccharide. Chemolytic analysis of polysaccharides most frequently

involves the use of H$_2$SO$_4$. Lignin-derived products, (methoxy)phenols, also undergo chemical transformations providing insight into the maturity of the fossil. Initially, the methoxyphenols are demethylated leading to formation of OH groups which upon increasing maturity are also lost leading to the formation of simple phenols (e.g. Hatcher et al. 1994). However, one has to bear in mind that the chemical composition of the fossil greatly depends on the biomacromolecules which were present in the specimen prior to fossilization. The degree of chemical transformation of the lignin moiety may also influence, to a large extent, the level of chemosystematic information inferred from the pyrolysis and chemolysis results (see below).

Chemosystematics

Up to now, pyrolysis data, and some chemolysis results, have been studied from a wide range of fossil structures with respect to chemosystematics,

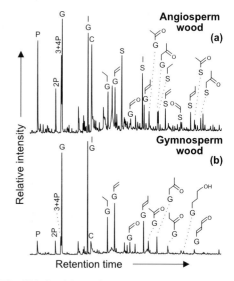

Fig. 27.2. Partial gas chromatograms of on-line filament (pyrolysis temp. 610°C) pyrolysates of Miocene (**a**) angiosperm wood and (**b**) gymnosperm wood from the Hambach open-cast mine, Germany. Key: P = phenol; 2P = 2-methylphenol; 3 + 4P = coeluting 3-methyl- and 4-methylphenol; G = 2-methoxyphenol; S = 2,6-dimethoxyphenol; C = 1,2-benzenediol (catechol). Side chains of the G and S components are attached at carbon position 4 of the ring. The vertical axis indicates the relative amounts of the various products released whereas the horizontal axis refers to the time which it takes for a compound to elute from the capillary column; this depends primarily on the boiling point of compounds, products with higher boiling points have a longer retention time.

e.g. wood, sclerotic tissue layers of propagules, cuticles and spores (van Bergen & de Leeuw 1993; van Bergen et al. 1994d, 1995 and references cited therein; van Bergen 1994).

Most sclerotic and woody plant structures contain lignin. In modern plants there are three distinct types of lignin. Gymnosperms are characterized by 2-methoxyphenols (guaiacyl; G Fig. 27.2), whereas angiosperms contain 2-methoxyphenols as well as 2,6-dimethoxyphenols (syringyl; S Fig. 27.2a; e.g. Saiz-Jimenez & de Leeuw 1986 and references cited therein). Among angiosperms, monocotyledons and legumes also contain, apart from G and S units, p-hydroxyphenol moieties. These products can also be detected in pyrolysates and chemolysis data of fossil specimens dependent on the age, maturity, and original chemical composition of the material. However, during fossilization, the characteristic lignin markers are often transformed or selectively degraded (e.g. Hatcher et al. 1994). In particular, syringyl units are preferentially lost/modified over guaiacyl moieties, with guaiacyl moieties being transformed to 1,2-benzenediols (C; Fig. 27.2a, b). Interpretations of fossil lignin and the systematic affinity of the sample must be made with caution: the presence of only guaiacyl moieties might not necessarily indicate gymnospermous affinity but could also represent modified lignin from angiospermous material (cf. testae of the angiosperm water lilies *Brasenia* and *Sabrenia* in van Bergen et al. 1994c).

Another group of plant fossils studied using pyrolysis includes leaf and stem cuticles which yield mainly aliphatic products (alkanes, alkenes, etc.). Most flash pyrolysates of pure fossil cuticular structures are characterized by homologous series of n-alkanes and n-alk-1-enes and in many cases 2-alkanones and 2-alkenones (cf. Fig. 27.3; cf. Tegelaar et al. 1991; van Bergen et al. 1994d). These products in fossils are generally ascribed to the macromolecule cutan although a contribution to some of these products from modified 'cutin-derived' material can, as yet, not be excluded (Tegelaar et al. 1991, 1993). The distribution pattern of characteristic alkane/alkene pairs, in particular those of longer chain (C > 20) homologues, in combination with the alkanones, can be used to provide chemotaxonomic information (cf. pyrolysates of testae of fossil *Potamogeton* and *Limnocarpus*; both in the Potamogetonaceae, Fig. 27.3). However, prior to drawing unambiguous conclusions from these distributions a few aspects have to be considered. The main aspect of significance within this context is the maturity of the specimens. Many of the pyrolysates from older cuticles (Carboniferous and Devonian; van Bergen et al. 1994d; Lyons et al. 1995; Ewbank et al. 1997) show distribution patterns maximizing around

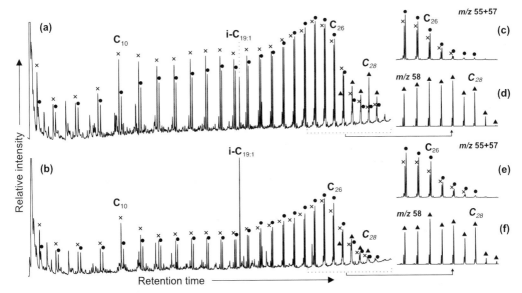

Fig. 27.3. Gas chromatograms of on-line Curie-point (pyrolysis temp. 610°C) pyrolysates of Upper Eocene cuticular propagule layers (testae; van Bergen 1994) of (**a**) *Potamogeton* and (**b**) *Limnocarpus* showing similar characteristic distribution patterns in the alkane/alk-1-ene (c and e; note decrease after C_{26}) and alkan-2-ones (d and f; note decrease after C_{26} and C_{28}). Key: x = n-alk-1-enes; ● = n-alkanes; ▲ = n-alkan-2-ones. C_{10} refers to decane and dec-1-ene, i-$C_{19:1}$ to prist-1-ene and C_{28} to octacosan-2-one.

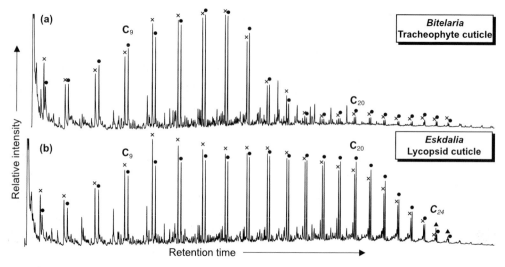

Fig. 27.4. Gas chromatograms of on-line Curie-point (pyrolysis temp. 770°C) pyrolysates of (**a**) axis cuticle of the tracheophyte *Bitelaria* (Lower Devonian; Johnson & Gensel 1992) and (**b**) stem cuticle of the lycopsid *Eskdalia* (Lower Carboniferous; Collinson *et al.* 1994) showing presence of longer chain alkanes, alkenes and alkan-2-ones (C > 20) in material which has been subjected to very little overburden (Fig. 27.2b). Key: x = *n*-alk-1-enes; ● = *n*-alkanes; ▲ = *n*-alkan-2-ones. C_9 refers to nonane and non-1-ene. C_{24} refers to tetracosan-2-one.

relatively short-chain alkanes and alk-1-enes (10 to 14 carbon atoms; cf. Fig. 27.4a). Such patterns with a maximum at these short-chain homologues are not necessarily of direct chemosystematic significance. This is because increasing maturation is known to lead to an increase in cross-linking within organic materials and thus would lead, in the case of such aliphatic structures, to the formation of more shorter products. Analyses using higher pyrolysis temperatures and/or longer pyrolysis times, which may be necessary to examine mature specimens, will also skew the distribution towards shorter-chain products (Irwin 1993). Hence, in order to obtain data of chemosystematic value one will have to compare specimens with the same level of maturity, and preferably as immature as possible

(cf. the stem cuticle of the Lower Carboniferous *Eskdalia* which had undergone little overburden Fig. 27.4b). Another point worthy of note is that the distribution patterns often show enhanced relative abundances of the C_{10} (Fig. 27.4) and C_{14} alk-1-enes. These are of no chemosystematic significance but solely due to rearrangements occurring during the pyrolysis of linear long-chain carbon chains.

Prof. J. W. de Leeuw and Dr M. E. Collinson are thanked for valuable discussions. NERC grants GST/02/536 and GR3/9578 and the use of the NERC Mass spectrometry facilities, University of Bristol (FG6/36/01) are gratefully acknowledged. Prof. P. G. Gensel kindly provided the *Bitelaria* specimens and Dr I. Figueiral kindly provided the Miocene Browncoal material.

28. Solid-state ^{13}C nuclear magnetic resonance of fossil plants and spores

PATRICK G. HATCHER, VICKY H. PAN & GARY E. MACIEL

Prior to the early 1970s, nuclear magnetic resonance (NMR) spectroscopy was limited to studies of compounds in solution and was generally not suitable for the study of insoluble fossil plants and spores. The technique basically uses the fact that a sample placed within a magnetic field absorbs radio-frequency signals and the frequency of absorption (resonance) is related to the chemical structure surrounding the nucleus being investigated for the compounds of interest. While there exist a large number of elements with NMR-sensitive nuclei, one of the more common nuclei has been ^{13}C. Traditionally, only samples soluble in appropriate solvents could provide useful structural information. The development of cross-polarization (CP) (Pines et al. 1972) and magic-angle spinning (MAS) (Schaefer & Stejskal 1976 and references therein) opened the door to studies of generally insoluble materials, and one of the first applications of this new technique was for the characterization of coal (Bartuska et al. 1977). Since that time, solid-state ^{13}C NMR has evolved greatly, and modern applications exploit the versatility that solid-state NMR offers towards defining the chemical structures of solid materials. It has now become a routine method where one simply places a powdered sample into a sample holder that spins at the magic angle (54.7° to the vertical magnetic field of a very powerful cryogenic magnet), inserts the spinner into a probe that inserts into the bore of the magnet, and obtains a spectrum within a matter of hours by accumulating digitized data from a repeated series of radio-frequency pulses and acquisitions. Fourier transformation of the accumulated data provides a one-dimensional spectrum reflecting the various spectral features of the sample. In addition to the traditional one-dimensional NMR spectrum of fossil plants and spores, spin relaxation studies offer the ability to extract structural information related to molecular mobility of the solid samples, and spectral editing approaches allow extraction of structural details such as molecular connectivities. While the versatility of solid-state ^{13}C NMR technique offers a wide range of valuable tools for structural determination with its varied experiments, the traditional one-dimensional CPMAS spectrum has been the most used in examinations of fossil plants

and spores. Recently, a significant amount of attention has been directed at establishing whether the traditional CPMAS technique provides a quantitative representation of the structural components within coal and related materials. The consensus is that some discrimination of carbon types can occur if the relevant spin dynamics issues are not well characterized, or if experimental parameters are not appropriately set, or if the samples themselves contain substances that prevent attainment of the desired experimental performance. The purpose of this chapter is to discuss the varied experiments available for structural analysis, and the applications of solid-state ^{13}C NMR for studies of fossil plants and spores.

Analytical techniques and requirements

The CPMAS experiment provides for both high resolution and high sensitivity for examining the solid-state NMR of dilute spins such as ^{13}C and ^{15}N (Schaefer & Stejskal 1976), and ^{13}C NMR is decidedly the most useful NMR nucleus for studies of fossil plants and spores. Briefly, a typical analysis involves filling a MAS rotor with sample and placing the rotor in the coil of the spectrometer (the rotor axis is orientated at 54.7° to the magnetic field direction). The rotor is activated by a gas jet to spin at an appropriate speed (usually 3–10 kHz), and the spectrometer pulse sequence and data acquisition are started. In the Fourier transform approach, the desired pulse sequence is repeated and the data acquired from each repetition are added until suitable signal-to-noise is achieved. The pulse sequence used is based on proton spin polarization in the sample and induces the build-up of the ^{13}C signal by exchanging magnetization with the protons. Thus, the signal one observes for carbon is influenced directly by the surrounding protons and is primarily dependent on the relaxation behaviour of protons rather than carbons.

There are some critical requirements, requiring careful attention, for certain experimental parameters in performing a CPMAS ^{13}C NMR experiment. The two most critical parameters are the CP contact time (T_{CP}) and recycle delay time (T_{PD}). The recycle delay is the dead time needed between repetitions of the pulse sequence, which

HATCHER, P. G., PAN, V. H. & MACIEL, G. E. 1999. Solid-state ^{13}C nuclear magnetic resonance of fossil plants and spores. In: JONES, T. P. & ROWE, N. P. (eds) Fossil Plants and Spores: modern techniques. Geological Society, London, 149–155.

allows the re-establishment of spin equilibrium of the protons. This usually requires about four times the proton spin-lattice relaxation time constant, T_{1H}. In general, for a variety of solids, such as coal, humic and fulvic acid and fossil plants, T_{1H} values are in the range of 0.1 to 0.3 s and recycle delays of about 1 s are usually sufficient. The choice of T_{CP} is influenced by the cross-polarization time constant, T_{CH} (the time constant for the exponential build up of carbon magnetization through exchange with the magnetization of protons) and the proton rotating-frame spin-lattice relaxation time, T_{1H} (the time constant for the exponential decay of spin-locked proton magnetization). An intelligent choice of T_{CP} is critical because sufficient time must be given for build-up of signal through T_{CH}, while avoiding relaxation of the protons according to T_{1H}. Appropriate values for T_{CP} can be determined by variable contact time experiments. A variable contact time (VCT) study simply involves obtaining a series of standard CPMAS experiments with various value of T_{CP}. A qualitatively suitable T_{CP} can be directly obtained from the VCT study by finding the T_{CP} that provides the maximum intensity for the main carbon resonances of interest in the sample. A suitable analysis of VCT data yields values of T_{CH} and T_{1H}, from which one can 'correct' observed intensities to convert them into quantitatively significant numbers.

Problems occur in a *single* CPMAS experiment (not a VCT sequence) when the various carbon resonances do not have a common 'optimum' T_{CP} and one must choose a single T_{CP} to represent the spectrum. Another problem can arise from a situation in which T_{1H} is so small that the full build-up of ^{13}C magnetization by cross-polarization is never achieved; in this case, an essential requirement for a simple intensity interpretation, that $T_{1H} \gg T_{CH}$, is not met. In this instance, a single CPMAS experiment fails to provide spectra that are quantitative representations of the carbon resonances in the sample. Such situations can often arise if the sample contains significant quantities of paramagnetic materials such as Fe^{3+} or contains an abundance of free radicals (usually in samples of high maturity). Another problem, which can affect T_{CH} more so than T_{1H}, is a lack of sufficient protons in a sample to efficiently transfer magnetization to the carbons. Such conditions are encountered in samples of high maturity, where condensed rings systems give rise to small proton concentrations and the removal of the protons from close proximity to carbons for efficient transfer of magnetization.

To overcome the inherent problems with CPMAS discussed above, one can employ an experiment that is commonly referred to as a direct polarization (DPMAS) or Bloch decay experiment. In DPMAS, the observed nuclei (e.g. ^{13}C) are polarized by ^{13}C spin-lattice relaxation and this is combined with magic angle spinning and high-power proton decoupling. In the direct polarization experiment, the observable ^{13}C magnetization is recovered between pulses directly via ^{13}C spin-lattice relaxation, that is, by the exchange of energy between the 'lattice' and the ^{13}C nuclear spins. This process can be very slow for many solids, with carbon spin-lattice relaxation time constants, T_{1C}, typically of the order of seconds to minutes. Also, the DPMAS experiment is performed without cross-polarization, so one loses the CP-enhancement factor (roughly 4). Consequently, the DPMAS experiment suffers from signal-to-noise problems relative to the CPMAS experiment. DPMAS experiments require very long experiment times, not only because of the long recycle delay time (4 to 5 times T_{1C}) but also because a larger number of acquisitions are needed for achieving an adequate signal-to-noise. The advantage of the DPMAS experiment is that it does not depend on the CP dynamics and, with an appropriate choice of recycle delay time, one avoids intensity distortions. Thus, DPMAS spectra can be quantitative straight-forwardly. With the development of large-volume (>2 cm^3) MAS systems, by Zhang & Maciel (1989), to improve the signal-to-noise ratio in DPMAS experiments, it is possible to obtain high-resolution ^{13}C DPMAS spectra in solids in acceptable experiment times. DPMAS has the added problem of signals from the rotor caps or sample holders. Fluorinated Kel-F, the plastic used for these caps, has a very low H content and cross-polarizes slowly; hence no CPMAS signals are observed. However, DPMAS spectra do show the carbons from the Kel-F.

The ^{1}H–^{13}C dipolar-dephasing experiment (Alemany *et al.* 1983; Hatcher 1988 and references therein) is another very useful experiment for fossil plants and spores. In the dipolar-dephasing experiment, after the protons are spin-locked and cross-polarization induced, as in the conventional CPMAS experiment, a variable dephasing time, is inserted, during which the high-power proton decoupler is turned off. During this period, carbon magnetization becomes influenced (dephased) by strong dipolar interactions between ^{13}C and ^{1}H spins. Carbons directly bonded to protons dephase much more rapidly than those without directly bonded protons; i.e. ^{13}C signals of carbons having attached protons decrease at much faster rates than those of non-proton-bearing carbons. The dipolar interaction is also affected by the motion of the spins or structural moieties. For very mobile molecules and spin systems, the carbon magnetization dephases much slower than for carbons of immobile molecules and spins systems. The ^{13}C magnetization of methyl carbons, even though proton-bearing, dephases at a rate similar to those of non-proton-bearing carbons, because rapid rotation reduces the effect of the ^{1}H–^{13}C dipolar interaction (Hatcher 1988). By carrying out the dipolar-dephasing experiment on a solid sample, one can study the fraction of carbon that is proton-bearing or non-proton-bearing in the system and such measurements are useful for assessing the average degree of protonation for aromatic systems (Hatcher *et al.* 1989).

In recent years, the trend has been to obtain all NMR spectra, including CPMAS ^{13}C NMR spectra, on spectrometers of higher field strengths (>300 MHz for protons). In general, one gets the impression that higher static field strengths in NMR will enhance sensitivity and/or resolution. However, this may not always be true for some geo-organic solids. It has been pointed out by Maciel (see Snape *et al.* 1989) that ^{13}C CPMAS NMR studies of coals are best done on spectrometers with ^{1}H frequencies between about 60 and 120 MHz.

The spinning speed employed in a MAS experiment must be at least comparable in Hz to the largest chemical shift anisotropy (CSA), if the spinning sidebands generated by MAS modulation of the chemical shift are to be substantially attenuated (Maricq & Waugh 1979). If MAS speeds are less than the size of the CSA, large spinning sidebands appear in the spectra, and these may overlap with 'centreband' resonances of interest, making it difficult to interpret the CPMAS spectra. Also, the intensities of the resonances are redistributed partially into the sidebands, causing a decrease in the centreband resonance signals of primary interest and an overall decrease in signal-to-noise ratio of the CPMAS spectra. The size of the CSA in Hz is linearly proportional to the strength of magnetic field. Therefore, at high magnetic fields, a faster sample-spinning rate would be needed to remove spinning sidebands (SSB) in the spectrum. For CPMAS ^{13}C NMR at 2.3 Tesla (a ^{1}H frequency of 100 MHz), the minimum acceptable MAS speed is about 4.7 kHz to obtain spectra of coals without troublesome SSB. In order to increase the spinning rate, the rotor diameter must be reduced and this reduces the size of the sample that can be examined. For example, a rotor of 9 mm diameter is able to spin at 6 kHz, but one must reduce the rotor diameter to about 4 mm to be able to spin at 15 khz. It was found that the signal-to-noise ratio for the spectrum of humic materials obtained at 7 Tesla with a 4 mm spinner was reduced, compared to the spectrum obtained at 2.3 Tesla with a 7 mm spinner; this reduction is due to the smaller volume of the 4 mm spinner(Fründ

& Lüdemann 1994). The effect of the smaller sample volume could not be compensated by the intrinsic sensitivity enhancement of the higher field. The best way to increase sensitivity for ^{13}C CPMAS experiments on geo-organic solids on low field spectrometers (1.4 to 2.8 T) is to increase the sample size by using a large-volume spinner (Zhang & Maciel 1989).

Besides this effective reduction in signal-to-noise ratio at higher fields due to sample size reduction, there is a serious additional limitation with the use of high MAS speed to reduce the SSB problem. This limitation is an interference with the CP process (Stejskal *et al.* 1977; Sardashti & Maciel 1987) caused by modulation and partial averaging of the ^{1}H–^{13}C dipolar and ^{1}H–^{1}H interactions needed for efficient CP. The result is that the apparent ^{13}C aromaticities obtained by CPMAS spectroscopy can be lower than those obtained from spectra obtained by use of CP without MAS (Solum *et al.* 1989). Therefore, even if one is able to spin fast enough to avoid the sideband problem in a ^{13}C CPMAS spectrum using 200–300 MHz spectrometers, one has to either expect the loss of some portion of aromatic intensity or use a modulated CP scheme that alleviates the problem.

In a high-spinning-speed CPMAS experiment, the Hartmann–Hahn matching profile breaks down into a series of narrow matching bands separated by the spinning speed, which leads to difficultly in establishing and maintaining an efficient matching condition. The modulated CP methods – variable-amplitude CP (VACP) (Peersen *et al.* 1993) and ramped-amplitude CP (RAMP-CP) (Metz *et al.* 1994) – have been development to solve the problem with the interference of high-speed MAS with CP efficiency by restoring flat matching profiles at high spinning speeds. In conventional CP, a constant-amplitude proton-spin-lock pulse is used, while in VACP a train of shorter proton-spin-lock pulses with different amplitudes and constant phase is used. In RAMP-CP, a ramped-amplitude of proton-spin-lock pulse (H channel) or a ramped-amplitude of carbon field strength (X channel) is used. This variable or (ramped) amplitude effectively creates a series of different Hartmann-Hahn conditions that eliminate amplitude mismatches of the two spin-lock fields, and results in flat matching curves over a wide range of spinning speeds, with little or no loss of signal intensity as compared to conventional CP.

In another approach to overcoming the problems of fast MAS in high-field spectrometers, some laboratories have resorted to use of slower spinning rates, but employing a technique called 'total spinning sidebands suppression (TOSS)' (Dixon 1982) to experimentally remove sidebands.

However, this approach involves a multiple-pulse sequence that needs to be executed to 'perfection' to avoid introduction of artefacts in the spectra and requires signals with large T_{2C} values. Even if the introduction of artefacts is prevented, one always observes an intensity loss for resonances having large CSAs (e.g. aromatic and/or a carboxyl carbons), because TOSS does not efficiently transfer signal intensity from sidebands back to the centrebands. As an example of this effect, Fig. 28.1 shows the ^{13}C NMR spectra of a humic acid obtained with CPMAS on a 100 MHz spectrometer using (**a**) 2.8 kHz MAS, with CPMAS on a 300 MHz spectrometer using (**b**) 3.6 kHz MAS, and with CPMAS-TOSS on a 300 MHz spectrometer using (**c**) 3.6 kHz MAS. As one can see, the

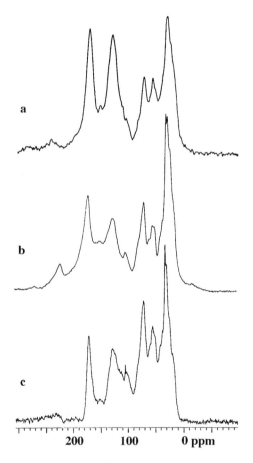

Fig. 28.1. Solid-State ^{13}C NMR spectra of a humic acid isolated from a soil (Nittany Ridge, PA) and obtained under the following conditions: (**a**) CPMAS at 2.3 T (100 Mhz) with a spinning speed of 2.8 kHz; (**b**) CPMAS at 7 T (300 MHz) with 3.6 kHz spinning; and (**c**) CPMAS-TOSS at 7 T with 3.6 kHz spinning.

humic acid spectrum in Fig. 28.1b suffers from serious SSB overlap and loss of aromatic intensity, when compared to Fig. 28.1a obtained at low field with a slower spinning rate. The humic acid spectrum obtained with CPMAS-TOSS (Fig. 28.1c) also suffers serious loss of aromatic intensity. The lower signal-to-noise ratio for the CPMAS-TOSS spectrum (Fig. 28.1c) is due primarily to a lower number of scans.

To summarize, the use of higher-field NMR spectrometers for ^{13}C CPMAS studies requires either (a) a low-spinning speed and a relatively complex experiment (TOSS) or (b) a fast spinning speed with modulated CP in order to obtain a simple spectrum without sideband overlap. Even so, in approach (a) some significant signal distortions can occur and this can limit the quantitative interpretations of such spectra, and in approach (b) one suffers from a small sample size. The simplest way to obtain CPMAS spectra of geo-organic solids is by use of a lower-field spectrometer, where sideband-suppression is not needed, especially for quantitative studies. Perhaps the best and most quantitative method for obtaining solid-state ^{13}C NMR spectra is the DPMAS approach, where problems with the CP method are avoided. This requires use of high-volume spinners and patience.

Applications to fossil plants and spores

The traditional CPMAS ^{13}C NMR approach has been used as a characterization tool for a variety of fossil plants, plant-derived substances, and spores (Wilson 1987). Thus, fossilized samples of wood, bark, resin, leaves, seeds and spores have all been examined with this technique. Representative spectra of these substances are shown in Fig. 28.2 to provide the reader with a visual description of the structural features. The spectral information derives from peaks relating to aliphatic carbon bonded to other aliphatic carbons (0–50 ppm), aliphatic carbon bonded to oxygen and nitrogen atoms (50–110 ppm), aromatic carbons bonded to hydrogen and other aromatic or aliphatic cabons (100–140 ppm), aromatic carbons bonded to oxygen atoms (140–160 ppm), carboxyl or amide carbons (160–190 ppm), and aldehyde/ketone carbons (190–220 ppm). Assuming the spectra were obtained properly, the relative intensities of the regions relate to relative contributions the various structures make to the average structure of the sample. Most spectra contain additional signals that must be viewed as artefacts. These are related to the spinning sidebands generated by insufficient spinning speeds. Such artefacts become more problematic with spectra obtained at high field, as discussed above.

Perhaps the most studied of fossil plant remains

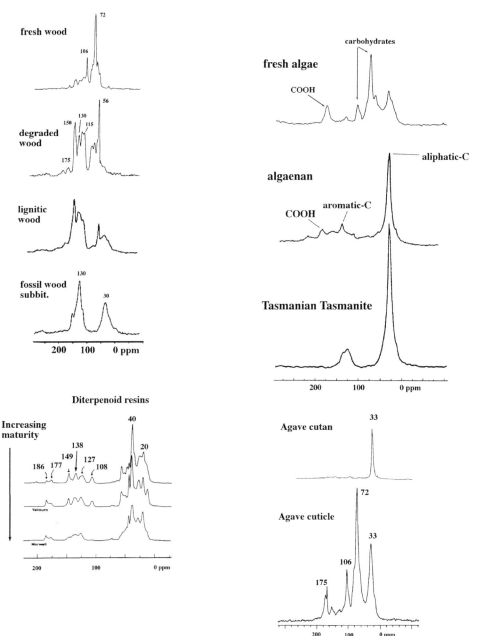

Fig. 28.2. Various CPMAS ^{13}C NMR spectra of modern and fossil wood of increasing maturity, fossil diterpenoid resins of increasing maturity, fresh algae, isolated algaenan, fossil algae (Tasmanian Tasmanite), fresh isolated cuticle from *Agave americana*, and isolated cutan from the Agave.

has been fossil wood, because sufficient material for analysis can always be obtained from coal seams and associated deposits. In a series of papers, Hatcher and co-workers (Hatcher *et al.* 1994 and references therein) examined the transformations of wood from the peat stage to coal of bituminous rank to extract details of the coalification process. They combined the traditional CPMAS ^{13}C NMR with dipolar dephasing (spectral editing) and pyrolysis/gas chromatography/mass spectrometry to acertain that fossil wood undergoes a series of structural changes involving specific reactions transforming lignin in the wood to the vitreous black substance comprising fossil wood. The most notable of changes, which can be readily observed in Fig. 28.2, are (1) selective loss of cellulosic materials (peaks at 72 and 106 ppm) to concentrate lignin as a residue (peaks at 56, 115, 130 and 150 ppm), (2) transformation of lignin to dihydric and eventually monohydric phenolic structures (peaks at 130 and 150 ppm) with preservation of the 3-carbon side chain as aliphatic structures (0–50 ppm), and (3) eventual loss of phenolic character to produce a substance composed primarily of aromatic (peak at 130 ppm) and aliphatic structures (peak at 30 ppm). The outer seed coats of fossil seeds (van Bergen et al. 1994a) and coal-ball entrained stems from a Medullosan seed fern (Hatcher et al. 1982) show similar structural details related to coalification of lignin-derived components.

The fossil plant material that has been next most frequently studied by NMR, is fossil resin. The spectra shown in Fig. 28.2 clearly show a difference compared to fossil wood in that the dominant signals are aliphatic carbons (0–50 ppm) related to the terpenoid structure. Lambert & Frye (1982) presented the first CPMAS ^{13}C NMR spectra of fossil resin of the diterpenoid skeleton and noted that, aside from the intense signals for aliphatic carbons, some less abundant signals in the region of 100–150 ppm can be attributed to olefinic carbons whose changes with increasing maturation involve the dimunition of peaks at 108 and 149 ppm and changes in the complex envelope of aliphatic peaks. Later, Cunningham et al. (1983), Wilson et al. (1984), Simoneit et al. (1986) and Lambert et al. (1985) noted similar changes. Employing spectral editing and pyrolysis/gas chromatography/mass spectrometry, Clifford & Hatcher (1995) suggested that these spectral changes reflect condensation and cyclization reactions involving the side-chain carbons of the diterpenoid structures. Other fossil resins have been shown to have a different skeleton – that of a sesquiterpenoid structure. The NMR spectra of these are also dominated by aliphatic signals but differ in that the aliphatic signals are not as clearly resolved and the olefinic carbons (100–150 ppm) are not resolved either (Crelling et al. 1991).

Solid-state ^{13}C NMR has been used to examine leaf material from fresh and degraded plants (Tegelaar et al. 1989; Benner et al. 1990; Kögel-Knabner et al. 1994). It is clear that, in fresh leaves, carbohydrates are the dominant biopolymers, as spectra are dominated by signals in the range of 60–110 ppm. In degraded leaves and isolated cuticles, the spectra change significantly, with the changes dependent on the nature of the biopolymers isolated within the cuticles. Most plant cuticles are composed of a biopolymer related to aliphatic polyesters (Holloway 1984) and the NMR spectra (Fig. 28.2) reflect this by showing mostly aliphatic carbons (Tegelaar et al. 1989). In spruce, the isolated cuticle gives a spectrum dominated by cellulosic materials and lignin, and the chemically resistant component of this cuticle is related more to lignin than aliphatic polyesters (Kögel-Knabner et al. 1994). As plant leaf material undergoes diagenesis, the carbohydrate components are degraded selectively and the more resistant lignin- and polyester-derived components are selectively enriched. Further diagenesis probably transforms both of these, but perhaps enriches the residues in the most resistant biopolymers. Nip et al. (1986) suggest that the biopolymers from leaf materials most likely to be fossilized in coal are the most resistant ones they have named 'cutan'. The NMR spectra (Fig. 28.2) and pyrolysis data for these have indicated structures related more to polyethylene than polyesters. Recent NMR studies of the cutan from Agave americana show that additional peaks in the range of 100 to 170 ppm define a structure that is not polyethylene-like but is composed of an aromatic core to which long-chain fatty acids are linked with ester bonds (McKinney et al. 1996). NMR studies of fossil cuticles (Nip et al. 1989; van Bergen et al. 1994d; Lyons et al. 1995; Hemsley et al. 1996b) indicate that aliphatic carbons are the dominant spectral features. These are likely derived from cutan biopolymers (Nip et al. 1986). The small aromatic component of most spectra of fossil cuticles is likely derived from the aromatic core described by McKinney et al.(1996).

Pollen and fossil pollen have been the subject of intense study and solid-state ^{13}C NMR spectroscopy has made some significant contributions to understanding the structure of these materials (Hemsley et al. 1996b and references therein; Hayatsu et al. 1988; Guilford et al. 1988). Modern spores appear to have many features that are common to modern plant materials, namely the high carbohydrate contents. This is apparent from NMR spectra of pollen and isolated sporopollenin (Guilford et al. 1988; Hemsley et al. 1996b). However, the isolated sporopollenin contains additional signals in both the aliphatic and aromatic regions of the spectra and large differences can be noted in sporopollenins from different extant plants (Hemsley et al. 1996b), implying that compositional differences could be used as phylogenic indicators. Fossil sporopollenins, however, show NMR spectra containing aliphatic and aromatic signals with little spectral resolution and a general dominance of aliphatic signals (Hemsley *et al.* 1996*b*). It is important to mention here that the dominance of aliphatic over aromatic carbons in spectra of fossil sporopollenin may be due to the fact that most published spectra were obtained at high field and required the TOSS sideband suppression method. As previously noted, some significant loss of aromatic signals can occur with this method, so the observed dominance of aliphatic over aromatic signals may be artefactual in spectra of sporopollenins presented by Hemsley *et al.* (1996*b*).

Fossil algae have been difficult to study by NMR techniques because sufficient material for such analyses is difficult to obtain. One must rely on accumulations of unialgal residues from ancient rocks, and these are not common. Extant algae are more easily examined by NMR and numerous studies have employed this technique to examine whole cells as well as isolated resistant biopolymers contained therein (Zelibor *et al.* 1988; Derenne *et al.* 1992). Whole cells contain mostly carbohydrates and proteins and their spectra reflect this (Fig. 28.2). The resistant biopolymer 'algaenan' which eventually becomes fossil algae is dominated by aliphatic carbons (0–50 ppm, Fig. 28.2). Minor peaks are observed for ether (50 ppm), carboxyl (175 ppm) and aromatic carbons (100–160 ppm), indicating perhaps a structure composed of aliphatic fatty acids that are linked via ester and ether bonds (Blokker *et al.* 1997). NMR spectra of fossil *Tasmanites* (Fig. 28.2), which are fossil cysts of algae (Hemsley *et al.* 1996*b*; Wilson *et al.* 1988), are dominated by aliphatic signals (0–50 ppm), with little aromatic carbon contributions to the spectra. Extant algaenan contains signals for oxygenated components which disappear in the fossil algae, indicating that maturation effectively removes these functional groups to produce structures that are very paraffinic and are likely to be good precursors to oil during maturation (Collinson *et al.* 1994).

Concluding remarks

While we cannot present an extensive review of the applications of solid-state ^{13}C NMR studies of fossil plants and spores within the constraints of space in this chapter, we hope that sufficient information and examples give the reader the sense that the NMR techniques offer an attractive means of characterizing these materials. The sample limitations (usually >50 mg) and need for caution in selection of appropriate experimental parameters provide some limitations. However, nearly all techniques have these. It is the use of NMR as a complementary analytical method in studies of fossil plants and spores that will provide the most meaningful information.

29. Isolation, identification and authentication of DNA sequences derived from fossil material

EDWARD M. GOLENBERG

When using fossil samples in DNA analyses, the scope of the research project, rather than the researcher, will define the composition, age and mode of preservation of the study material. Each of these factors will affect the probability or possibility of preservation of DNA. Sources from which successful DNA extractions have been reported include amber inclusions (Cano *et al.* 1992; DeSalle *et al.* 1992; Poinar *et al.* 1993), plant compression fossils (Golenberg *et al.* 1990; Soltis *et al.* 1992), mammalian midden plant material (Rogers & Bendich 1985), dried herbarium materials (Rogers & Bendich 1985) and archaeological remains including air dried (Helentjaris 1988), charred (Helentjaris 1988; Horai *et al.* 1991; Brown *et al.* 1994), and even water-logged samples (Lawlor *et al.* 1991). It should be noted that for each of these materials there are also many anecdotal reports of failure to retrieve authentic DNA from individual ancient samples (Sidow *et al.* 1991; Bailey *et al.* 1996; Höss *et al.* 1996*a, b*; Poinar *et al.* 1996; Austin *et al.* 1997; Yang *et al.* 1997*b*), which may indicate that research projects should begin with multiple samples to ensure success. While there is no linear relation between age of the sample and the fragment size of preserved DNA or even the probability of preservation (Pääbo 1989; Hagelberg & Clegg 1991; Kelman & Moran 1996), younger samples that were rapidly dried will be expected to yield more consistent results than will extremely ancient hydrated samples. Additionally, most of the work to date dealing with ancient DNA has concentrated on animal samples, and therefore much of our experience of the characteristics of preserved DNA comes from such material. Yet, in animal tissue, most of the degradation of DNA occurs relatively rapidly post-mortem and is the result of digestion by enzymes released by autolysis or epifaunal bacteria. As cell death in plants does not occur as rapidly following tissue separation (abscission, seed dispersal, limb breakage) and internal bacterial growth is not as extensive in plants, initial DNA degradation rates should be slower in plant tissues. Ultimately, the taphonomy of the material will determine the long term preservation.

In this chapter, I will present the general approaches for DNA extraction from preserved plant material. I will discuss the special considerations entailed in ancient DNA work, and will present approaches to the testing of authenticity of putative ancient DNA sequences.

Experimental design and extraction techniques

DNA extraction techniques from fossil, sub-fossil, and herbarium samples follow common protocols used on modern, fresh material (see Sytsma 1994), but are modified to compensate for the three major concerns encountered when searching for ancient DNA, contamination, inhibition, and minute amounts of degraded DNA. Controls against contamination of an ancient sample from any outside source, whether ancient, modern, or synthetic are of paramount importance. Whenever possible, all tools and materials used in the extraction process should be disposable. Those instruments that are reused must be soaked in a 0.5% sodium hypochlorite solution for several hours, rinsed thoroughly in distilled water, and then exposed to short-wavelength UV light for thirty minutes. Solutions should be aliquotted into small volumes sufficient for only five to ten extractions to limit the extent of accidental carry-over. If possible, a blind sample design following Yang *et al.* (1997*a*) should be used. With this design, samples are provided to the researcher for DNA extraction and initial sequence analysis without identification except by sample number. If possible, multiple samples from the same source should be included in to test later for repeatability of results. Thus, the identity of the samples, and even of the replicates, are unknown to the researchers extracting and analysing the DNA. Correct identification of replicate samples by sequence identity supports the integrity of the data, and argues against semi-random, chimeric reconstruction of the data from fragments. As will be discussed in more detail below, correct identification of samples to a species or genus level in comparison with published sequences and based on standard phylogenetic analyses supports the authenticity of the ancient source of the data. When a blind sampling design

GOLENBERG, E. M. 1999. Isolation, identification and authentication of DNA sequences derived from fossil material. *In*: JONES, T. P. & ROWE, N. P. (eds) *Fossil Plants and Spores: modern techniques*. Geological Society, London, 156–160.

cannot be executed because of the obvious physical identity of the sample, all extraction and amplification procedures should be undertaken along with unrelated specimens so that contamination from a modern congener or from a related ancient sample can be ruled out (Cooper *et al.* 1996).

Complete isolation of ancient DNA extraction procedures in dedicated rooms along with dedicated clothing and equipment (Handt *et al.* 1994a) can be helpful in reducing contamination and is considered by some to be mandatory for working with ancient DNA. However, as most contamination derives from initial contamination of the sample tissue itself due to prior handling, improper storage, or internal fungal or bacterial growth, or from contamination of reagents during DNA amplification from previous reactions, a dedicated ancient DNA laboratory is neither necessary or sufficient to ensure the integrity of the samples and the results.

DNA extraction techniques from fossil or preserved material have been reviewed by Rogers (1994) and Yang *et al.* (1997*b*). While their conclusions are based on extractions from soft and hard animal tissue, the general observation of Yang *et al.* (1997b) that no single extraction technique is universally superior, also applies to plant material. In general, while a resin-based approach, in which DNA adheres to silica resin beads, and proteins, lipids, polysaccharides are washed away, tends to produce cleaner DNA extracts, the yield is generally lower than that from detergent/enzyme digestion and alcohol precipitation. Additionally, the size of DNA fragments will affect the yield in both the precipitation and resin extractions, although precipitation yield, especially with a co-precipitant, will be robust over a greater range of DNA fragment sizes than will specific wash solutions with the resin. Accordingly, this chapter will describe in detail the detergent-based precipitation extraction which we commonly use, and refer the reader to the above-mentioned papers and the references therein for other approaches. I also refer the reader to a plant extraction solution/protocol (DNAzol ES) by Molecular Research Center which has proved superior on some but not all extractions from pack-rat midden plant material (Golenberg & Nixon, unpublished).

All work areas must be cleaned with a 0.5% sodium hypochlorite solution before working with the samples. Fossil samples may be surface sterilized by dipping in a 0.5% sodium hypochlorite solution followed by thorough rinsing in sterile water, although if non-bacterial or fungal species-specific genes are to be studied this is not absolutely essential. The organic material is then removed from the substrate and ground in the presence of the extraction buffer. It is preferable to

grind the tissue directly in disposable microfuge tubes with disposable plastic pestles to reduce the possibility of outside contamination or carry-over. This may be done by hand or with a hand drill attached to the pestle. When disposable supplies are either not available or when the material is too hard to grind with the plastic pestles, porcelain mortar and pestles may be used but they must be cleaned using the sodium hypochlorite/UV treatment described above. The extraction buffer contains 2% CTAB, 1.4 M NaCl, 20 mM EDTA (pH 8.0), 100 mM Tris HCl (pH 8.00), 1% PVP (MW = 40 000), 4 mM DEDTCA and 5 mM ascorbic acid (Bickel & Golenberg unpublished). This is a modification of the extraction buffer reported in Golenberg (1993) with the addition of the two antioxidants DEDTCA and ascorbic acid. The final volume of extraction buffer is brought to 0.7 ml, and the sample is incubated at 65°C for at least one hour. The sample is then centrifuged at $10\,000 \times g$ for 10 min to pellet the solid debris and the supernatant is transferred to a clean tube. The supernatant is then extracted once by adding an equal volume of phenol:chloroform:isoamyl alcohol (25 : 24 : 1 by volume), and mixing by inverting the tube several times. Care must be taken as the warm extraction solution will cause the organic solution to evaporate which can increase the pressure in the tube, causing it to pop open. The tube is then centrifuged at room temperature for five minutes at $10\,000 \times g$ to separate the aqueous and organic layers, and the aqueous layer is transferred to a clean tube. Under most conditions the aqueous layer will be on the top, however, under some salt conditions, the layers may be reversed. The researcher is well advised to identify the layers before discarding what is thought to be the organic waste solution. (This may be done by adding a few drops of phenol to the suspected organic solution. If the phenol goes into solution, the tube indeed contains the organic layer. If the phenol separates, the tube contains the aqueous layer.) A second extraction is done using chloroform:isoamyl alcohol (24 : 1) by again inverting the tube several times, centrifuging, and transferring the aqueous layer to a clean tube. DNA-free glycogen (1 µl of a 1 mg ml^{-1} solution) is added to serve as a carrier molecule during precipitation. One volume of isopropanol is added, and the samples are mixed by inversion. The DNA is precipitated overnight by incubating at –20°C. The DNA/glycogen is pelleted by centrifuging at room temperature at $10\,000 \times g$ for 30 min. The supernatant should be removed and discarded. The pellet is washed twice by adding 1 ml of 70% ethanol, centrifuging the tube, and removing the supernatant. Extreme care must be taken at this point so that the pellet is not dislodged and accidentally discarded with the wash. The pellets are then air dried or briefly dried (5 min) under vacuum and resuspended in 100 µl 1/10 X TE (1 mM Tris HCl, 0.01 mM EDTA, pH 8.0) buffer.

It is not uncommon for the pellet to be highly discoloured by a brown residue. Another indication of unwanted co-precipitants is the presence of a blue fluorescing compound under UV light when a sample of the extraction is size-characterized by electrophoresis in an agarose gel. These compounds may interfere with enzymatic amplification. A variety of post-extraction purification approaches are possible. The reconstituted DNA solution may be passed over a silica-based resin column (Qiagen – see Appendix under 'DNA products'), or mixed with a resin slurry (Promega Wizard purification systems or Bio 101 GENEClean systems, see appendix 'DNA products'). Co-precipitants are washed off the column or removed while still in solution. The DNA is subsequently released by changing the wash solutions.

Another approach is to precipitate the DNA with CTAB by adding a 1/10 volume of 5% CTAB and incubating on ice for 20 min. The CTAB/DNA is pelleted by centrifugation at 4°C and $3000 \times g$. The supernatant is removed, and the CTAB is redissolved by the addition of 70% ethanol and 200 mM sodium acetate (pH 6.0). This solution is centrifuged at $10\,000 \times g$ for 20 min. This extraction of the CTAB is repeated two additional times, followed by a 70% ethanol wash to remove the salts. The DNA pellet is dried and reconstituted in 1/10 TE (Murray & Thompson 1990). It should be noted that these techniques do not remove all co-precipitants and can result in loss of DNA. The researcher is advised to ascertain the necessity of these secondary purification procedures by testing whether DNA amplification is actually inhibited.

PCR amplification and DNA sequencing

Ancient DNA presents specific problems for amplification of genes, due primarily to the presence of inhibitors and fragmentation of the template DNA (Golenberg 1991, 1993). These limitations, plus low DNA concentration levels, primer incompatibility, sub-optimal temperature and/or time settings, can often lead to negative amplification results. While negative results are consistent with the absence of endogenous DNA, they are by no means proof of the absence of DNA. Therefore, careful trouble-shooting is warranted before an extraction is counted as being devoid of DNA. Inhibition can be tested by aliquotting a volume of the test extraction normally used in PCR into a positive control reaction. The absence of an amplified product in comparison with the presence in an 'undoped' positive control will identify strong

inhibitory effects. Partial inhibition may result in a reduced product. Alternatively, highly fragmented DNA will act as a sink for dNTPs and enzyme in a polymerization reaction when overlapping fragments act as primers which are extended. This polymerization then partially reconstructs degraded templates, but in so doing competes with the targeted PCR for substrates. This reduces the efficiency of the intended PCR and results in lower specific product yield (Golenberg et al. 1996;Nixon & Golenberg unpublished). When the degraded DNA is the intended template, the combination of competition due to template reconstruction, the low initial amounts of complete template, and any inhibitory effect will result in no detectable PCR products. Strong or partial inhibition may be overcome by secondary purification of the product as discussed above or by serial dilutions of the template (Golenberg 1991, 1993). Inefficiency or absence of product due to fragmented template DNA can be overcome by a preliminary reconstruction polymerization reaction without primers followed by a specific PCR. Alternatively, a nested PCR in which an initial reaction is completed and an aliquot is used as the template in a secondary reaction which uses primers that are flanked by the primers in the first reaction (Golenberg et al. 1996; Yang et al. 1997b).

Actual amplification should follow standard procedures. Using a two-step nested approach as introduced above, a 25 µl reaction may be set up using 12.5 pmoles of flanking forward and reverse primers, 0.2 mmoles dNTP, 1.25 units Taq polymerase, 2.5 µl of the manufacturers-supplied 10× reaction buffer and 2 µl of the DNA extraction. $MgCl_2$ concentration must be empirically determined for each reaction, although 3 mM is a standard starting point. Annealing temperature and incubation times for denaturation, annealing and extension will vary depending on the thermal cycling machine, target sequence length and primers. Although theoretically a DNA polymerase with some $3'–5'$ exonuclease activity would be advantageous for long amplifications or reconstructions, we have not been able to demonstrate any advantage over the use of the standard Taq polymerase (Nixon & Golenberg unpublished). Disposable aerosol barrier pipette tips should be used to prevent cross-contamination. Similarly, all reagents should be aliquotted into small volumes so that any solution contamination can be checked and easily rectified. After all of the reagents except for the enzyme and the template DNA have been mixed, the reaction solutions, on ice, should be exposed to short wave UV light to encourage the formation of pyrimidine dimers in any double-stranded DNA that may be in solution. This will hinder amplification of potentially contaminating

DNA. To avoid unnecessary exposure to outside contamination, the primary reactions are not examined by agarose electrophoresis until after the secondary or nested PCR is set up or completed.

In the nested PCR, two primers, a forward and a reverse, are designed to be 3′ to the original forward and reverse primers. These are used with 1 µl of the primary reaction as the template. To ensure ample product for final sequencing, a 50 µl reaction is set up. Temperatures and times must be adjusted for the new primers and the increased reaction volume. Following secondary amplification, a 5 µl aliquot may be run on an agarose horizontal gel and stained with ethidium bromide to characterize the presence and size of any PCR products.

Unless an overriding reason for cloning exists, PCR products should be sequenced directly. Cloning samples individual molecules from the population of amplified products. These individual molecules may reflect polymerization errors, recombined fragments (Pääbo 1990; Handt et al. 1994b; Golenberg et al. 1996), or external contamination (Handt et al. 1994b; Krings et al. 1997). Each clone gives equal weight to individual errors in the polymerization process, and the ultimate understanding of the sources of sequence variation will be dependent upon the extent and strategy of clone sampling. The total exclusion of some clones and acceptance of others due to an a priori expectation of what the authentic sequence can or cannot be (Handt et al. 1994b; Krings et al. 1997), is an understandable and logical, though biased approach. Indeed, this criterion is also used whether one is using cloning or direct sequencing of ancient or modern DNA. Products that are of the wrong size or are clearly the wrong gene are routinely labelled as PCR artefacts and recorded as spurious results. Acceptance of clones, on the other hand, is more problematic and open to interpretation. For example, arguing that the majority represented sequence is authentic and minority represented sequences are incidental contaminants ignores the fact that amounts of a given product may be more a function of the extent of contamination, the difference in number of templates and the specific sequences complementary to primers than of the actual authenticity. Direct sequencing of PCR products exploits the understanding that individual amplification errors will be semi-random in a sequence and will occur in low frequency in the final products unless the error is engendered in the initial amplification cycles in reactions with few original template molecules. This will also be true of chimeric molecules generated by 'jumping PCR' (Pääbo et al. 1990). Thus, most polymerase errors will be detectable, if at all, as weak background noise. This can easily be tested by sequencing the products of two independent amplifications. The exceptions which prove the rule are amplifications of base pair substitution alleles in heterozygous individuals in which alternative bases appear in equal intensities at the segregating sites. This 'majority rule' sequence does not in itself necessarily prove the authenticity of the sequence for the reasons just stated, but it does obviate the necessity of choosing among sampled sequences. While it is argued that cloning should be used to establish the diversity of sequences present when direct sequencing produces ambiguous results because of the heterogeneity of the PCR product, it may be more prudent to reject such compromised samples.

Direct sequencing of PCR fragments has become simple and routine with the availability of many commercial kits and the more common availability of fluorescent dye automated sequencing. It is essential to work with PCR products having only single bands. If multiple bands occur when characterizing PCR products on an agarose gel, either the entire reaction solution should be run on an agarose gel and the desired band cut out and isolated from the co-amplified bands, or reaction conditions, usually reduced $MgCl_2$ concentrations and/or higher annealing temperatures, should be modified to achieve the desired, single product band. Residual primers, dNTPs, and 'primer–dimers' (short amplified fragments resulting from primers annealing among themselves) must be removed or inactivated before sequencing. A number of resin-based purification kits designed specifically to treat PCR reactions are available, such as Wizard PCR Preps (Promega, see Appendix under 'DNA products') or QIAquick Spin PCR Purification Kit (Qiagen, see Appendix under 'DNA products'). These kits are based on DNA size-specific binding and are optimal over a range of PCR product sizes. If your product is outside the optimal range, either too big or too small, the PCR reaction may be treated by shrimp alkaline phosphatase and exonuclease I (Amersham, see Appendix under 'DNA products') which dephosphorylate the free nucleotides and digest the single stranded primers in solution, respectively. This treatment will not remove 'primer–dimers', so if these occur in high concentration they must either be removed by gel isolation or by reaction condition modification.

Cycle sequencing can then be performed on 200 fmoles of PCR product (13.2 ng/100 bp) or less (especially when the fragment size is less than 150 bp) using commercially available kits such as Thermal Sequenase (Amersham, see Appendix under 'DNA products'). This approach may use dye terminators for running on ABI-like auto-sequencing machines, fluorescine-labelled primers for running on ALF Pharmacia-like machines, or radioactively end-labelled primers for manual sequencing. End primers used in the amplification steps may be used for sequencing. If you intend to use fluorescine-labelled primers for sequencing, these may be ordered and used in the initial PCR reactions, thereby saving the expense of ordering separate sequencing primers.

Sample verification

Authentication of DNA sequences remains the most important and contentious aspect of work on ancient and fossil DNA. As discussed above at numerous points in the experimental procedure and design, controls must be incorporated throughout all stages of fossil DNA extraction and amplification. These controls identify possible sources of contamination or increase the confidence of the researcher in the robustness of the data. Accordingly, negative DNA extractions (extractions without fossil material) should be processed along with actual samples to assay for contamination in common extraction solutions. Blind sampling to test for repetitive results in actual duplicate samples and unique results in different samples allows for independent confirmation within a single laboratory, identification of cross-sample contamination, and prevents biased data sifting for desirable results. Additionally, many researchers use the difficulty of amplification as a test for authenticity of ancient DNA, with low yield or limited size of amplifiable fragment as criteria for authenticity of the ancient source of the DNA (DeSalle 1994; Höss *et al*. 1994). While these results are consistent with ancient DNA amplification, they are neither necessary nor sufficient indicators of the actual source of the template DNA. A criterion of duplication of results in independent laboratories has also been suggested as a criterion for authentication (Handt *et al*. 1994*b*). While this again is certainly desirable, it is often impractical if the fossil is minute and is completely destroyed in the extraction process. Independent replication also does not rule out common contamination of the sample prior to division among laboratories, and does not rule out independent contamination of a common allele as

can easily occur if laboratories work on similar model systems or human DNA. The most desirable test would be independent replication based on different samples from the same species obtained from different sources. Lastly, if techniques are not identical, the lack of success in one laboratory does not necessarily negate the veracity of results in a second laboratory (Hänni *et al*. 1994).

The only non-arbitrary tests of authenticity are phylogenetic or coalescent analyses. Phylogenetic analyses of the query sequence, especially if it is still only identified to the active researcher by sample number and not by species, can indicate general association of a sequence with other previously published sequences, which is usually sufficient to identify the source of the sequence to the family or lower taxonomic level. If, after identification of the sample, the placement of the sequence on the gene tree is consistent with the *a priori* phylogenetic expectation, then the antiquity of the source of the sequence is supported. Some caution must be taken when the query sequences are from extremely ancient samples, as branch lengths will be expected to be short and bifurcation points may be low in the tree resulting in a high probability of incorrect placement of the purported fossil branch (Golenberg 1994, unpublished). In such cases, short branch lengths may be taken as some support of the authenticity of the sequence. At the opposite extreme, when samples are thought to be either contemporaneous or nearly so, coalescent theory may indicate whether sequence differentiation is within the expected range. With these approaches in mind, it is extremely important to remember that the null hypothesis being tested is that the sequence is authentic. Hence, when the phylogenetic grouping is clearly spurious or the sequence differentiation is too large to belong to the reference population, the null hypothesis may be rejected and the samples may be considered to be contaminated. If, however, the expectations are met, that is, the sequence groups within the expected taxonomic range, then the authenticity of the sequence is supported but certainly not proven. Nonetheless, this approach is consistently used to identify mistaken assertions of ancient DNA, and is implicitly used in all reports of sequences from modern samples and so must remain the only ultimate test of authenticity.

30. Mineralogical and geochemical analyses

BEN J. WILLIAMSON & TIM P. JONES

Mineralogical and geochemical analyses are being increasingly used in palaeontological applications such as taphonomy, diagenetic alteration, fossil plant and palaeoenvironmental biogeochemistry. This chapter describes some of the most commonly available techniques that can be applied to fossil plants and spores. We describe the basic principles, suitability and amounts of material required, sample preparation, data output and evaluation.

Mineralogical analysis

X-ray diffraction (XRD)

This is a routine technique for the identification of crystalline materials in geological samples. An application of XRD in palaeobotany is the precise determination of the mineralogy of permineralized plants. A beam of X-rays of known wavelength strikes the sample and is diffracted at angles dependent on the structure of the mineral. The diffraction pattern is output as a series of 'lines' on photographic film or as an array of peaks on systems with electronic detectors. The positions of the peaks can be measured in $°2\theta$ (the diffraction angle) and converted to d spacings (the 'interplanar' spacing) using the Bragg equation:

$$\lambda = 2d \; Sin \; \theta$$

where λ = X-ray wavelength and θ = glancing angle of diffracted beam. The peak positions can be compared with an existing computer database of XRD patterns of mineral standards such as the Powder Diffraction File (International Centre for Diffraction Data, 12 Campus Boulevard, Newtown Square, PA 19073-3273, USA). There are two basic types of analyses: photographic techniques which require less than 0.01 g of powdered sample, and electronic systems which require c. 0.1 g. Samples are usually powdered in an agate or steel pestle and mortar. For samples consisting of a mixture of minerals, the proportions of each can be calculated from the relative peak intensities. This is, however, a complex technique requiring careful calibration, against standards with known compositions, and absorption corrections (see Cressey & Schofield 1996).

Recommended reading: Bish & Post (1989).

Cathodoluminescence (CL)

This is the visible, infra-red and ultraviolet light emitted by certain materials when irradiated with electrons. It is caused by the presence of certain trace elements (mainly Mn^{2+} and REE^{3+}) and/or defects in the crystal structure. It should be noted that the presence of >1 to 1.5 wt% Fe will prevent CL in most minerals. The main uses of CL are the identification of growth zones in individual crystals and different generations of minerals. In the study of fossil plants it can be used, for example, to identify original textures, the effects of diagenesis, such as phases of cellular infilling (Moshier & Kirkland 1993), or to distinguish between detrital quartz and silicified plant material (Ruppert et al. 1991). CL may be studied by either using a transmitted light microscope fitted with a CL attachment or by using an SEM with a CL detector. Small fragments of fossil plant material can be viewed either unprepared, embedded in polished epoxy or polyester resin blocks, or as polished sections. The choice of resin is important as some, such as Canada Balsam and Lakeside 70, will break down under the electron beam. All resins luminesce and this can be problematic when examining highly porous samples where the CL from the embedding resin can obscure the CL from the sample. Larger areas of resin on the surface of the block can be masked using non-luminescing paint or foil.

Recommended reading: Marshall (1988).

Geochemical analysis

Electron probe microanalysis (EPMA)

The application of EPMA in the scanning electron microscope (SEM) with electron probe microanalysis is a relatively easy to use, non-destructive technique for the quantitative chemical analysis of geological materials. It can either be used for spot analysis at a single point (usually 1 to 40 μm in diameter) or to produce X-ray element maps of an area by measuring the relative abundance of individual elements at a series of points in a grid square. Almost all the elements of the Periodic Table can be analysed, except those with low atomic number (H, Li and Be), although the analysis of B, C, N and O is not routine. There are

WILLIAMSON, B. J. & JONES, T. P. 1999. Mineralogical and geochemical analyses. *In*: JONES, T. P. & ROWE, N. P. (eds) *Fossil Plants and Spores: modern techniques.* Geological Society, London, 161–164.

two main types of microprobe systems in common use: ED (energy dispersive) and WD (wavelength dispersive), the latter giving better detection limits, usually <500 ppm. Samples are prepared as polished sections or in polished resin blocks, such as those used in quantitative reflectance light microscopy, but which must be carbon-coated. The sections or resin blocks are loaded into the sample vacuum chamber and viewed under high magnification to select points for analysis. A beam of electrons is fired at the sample surface which results in the production of X-rays with energies and wavelengths specific to the elements present. The instrument is calibrated by analysing standards of known compositions. A computer corrects for matrix effects, which depend on the type of material being analysed (see Reed 1996), and to calculate element abundances. The data are output as a print-out or computer file. Many modern microprobes can also produce distribution maps of different elements (X-ray maps) in small (usually <1 mm^2) areas of the sample. This could, for example, be used to differentiate between organic and inorganic materials, or to elucidate variations in the chemical compositions of different phases of permineralization. X-ray maps of the distribution of Ca, S, Fe and C in Lower Carboniferous *Lyginorachis* sp. are shown in Fig. 30.1A to D.

Recommended reading: Morgan (1985) and Reed (1996).

Analytical transmission electron microscopy (TEM)

This method works on a similar principle to SEM-EPMA, the difference being that the analysis is undertaken in a transmission electron microscope. Samples which can be analysed using this technique include ultra-thin TEM sections of embedded specimens, or ultra-small particulate matter. An important aspect of this analytical technique is its ability to derive chemical and crystallographic data from extremely small samples, and pinpoint the location of specific elements within samples on a 0.01 μm scale. Specimens can be embedded in resin (typically Spurr's Resin), ultramicrotomed, and mounted on a coated or uncoated TEM grid as outlined in Chapter 23. For ultra-small particulate matter, a 100 mesh titanium or nickel TEM grid is coated with pioloform which provides a supportive substrate. The particles are suspended in pure water, sonicated to discourage 'clumping', and a 1 μl aliquot is transferred onto the grid and allowed to air-dry (BéruBé *et al.* 1997). Gauging the concentration of the particulate matter in suspension to get an acceptable distribution on the grid is dependent upon the samples, and requires some

trial and error. Data are presented in two basic forms, either as a quantitative X-ray spectrum for a single point (which can be converted to concentrations), or as element maps for specific areas.

Recommended reading: Morgan (1985).

Inductively coupled plasma–atomic emission spectrometry (ICP–AES)

This is among the most commonly used techniques for the rapid quantitative measurement of major elements and a wide variety of trace elements. An example of its application is the analysis of the inorganic components of coals to elucidate geological and geochemical processes during coalification (Goodarzi & Swaine 1994; Vogt 1994). Typically, the sample is powdered, homogenized and *c.* 100 mg is accurately weighed out for major element analysis and *c.* 1 g for trace elements analysis. Trace elements are commonly defined as those forming <0.1 wt% of the sample. For major element determinations, the powder may be fused with lithium metaborate then dissolved in nitric acid whereas for trace elements the powder is usually dissolved in a combination of high purity acids. The sample solution is nebulized (sprayed) into a high temperature argon plasma where it is vaporized and ionized to yield radiation characteristic of the elements present and with radiation intensities proportional to element concentrations. The intensity of the radiation from each element is measured and the signal is converted into concentration by comparison with a calibration curve. Detection limits are often less than 0.005 wt% in the sample and analytical errors characteristically vary from 2% to 5%. Almost all elements of the Periodic Table can be measured although for some elements, other techniques may be more appropriate. For the determination of Si as a major element, for example, X-ray fluorescence (XRF) is more appropriate as it offers better precision.

Recommended reading: Thompson & Walsh (1983).

Inductively coupled plasma–mass spectrometry (ICP–MS)

This is increasingly used for the rapid quantitative measurement of a wide range of elements at ultra-low levels. In a standard procedure, samples are introduced as a solution and are ionized in an argon plasma in much the same way as for ICP–AES, but ions are measured rather than photons. Detection limits are very low (sub ppb or ng/ml in solution). Most elements in the Periodic Table can be

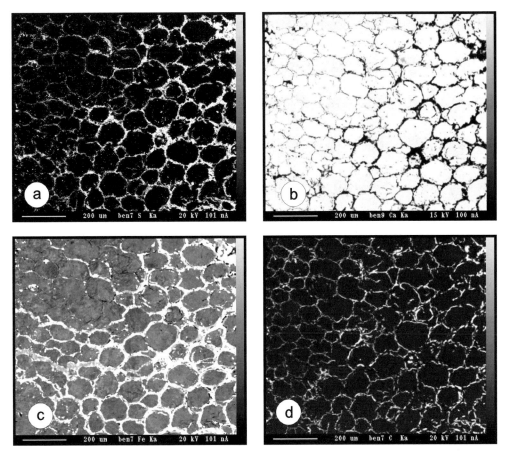

Fig. 30.1. (a–d) X-ray element maps for S, Ca, Fe and C for Lower Carboniferous permineralized *Lyginorachis* sp. The maps show a continuous grey scale from black to white representing low to high counts, respectively. S appears to be concentrated within the permineralized cell walls only. The grey tone of the infilling in the Fe map indicates some Fe is present in the mineral in the cellular spaces, with the element being relatively concentrated in the sites of the cell walls. Ca is found in the sites of the cellular spaces. Since the specimen is a carbonate permineralization, the C probably represents a concentration of original organic C in the cell walls; the signal from C in the infilling carbonate has been swamped by the signals from associated heavier elements (Ca, Mg, etc).

measured although ICP–MS is not generally appropriate for major element determinations which should be carried out using a technique such as ICP–AES or XRF.

Semi-quantitative point analysis of solid samples is possible by ablating a 10 to 100 µm diameter (by variable depth) hole in the surface of the sample using a high-intensity laser beam, although this technique is still under development. Samples are prepared as thick (>100 µm) polished sections or in resin blocks. For the study of permineralized plants, point analysis may be more appropriate than whole sample analysis as many fossil plants contain inclusions of extraneous material such as quartz grains which will affect the results of the whole

sample analysis. The detection limits for laser ablation ICP–MS are usually between 10 ppb and 1 ppm in the solid, depending on the amount of sample ablated.

An application of ICP–MS in the study of fossil plants is in whole coal trace element analysis (Totland *et al.* 1993). Two basic preparation techniques, both designed to remove the organic carbon, are: (1) ashing and (2) microwave digestion (Igarashi *et al.* 1991) of the sample in a solution of nitric and hydrofluoric acids. Ashing involves burning off the organic carbon in a furnace leaving a residue (ash), which can then be dissolved in acid and processed through the ICP–MS; although this can lead to some loss of trace elements. Microwave digestion is best undertaken using pressure relief type PTFE digestion vessels on a rotating carousel (Nakashima *et al.* 1988). The objective is the complete oxidation of the organic material and therefore the times and acid strengths largely depend on sample type and amount.

Recommended reading: Jarvis *et al.* (1992).

Atomic absorption spectroscopy (AAS)

This is often used as a complementary technique to ICP–AES as it is more appropriate for the determination of alkali metals and certain trace elements (e.g. Igarashi *et al.* 1991). It is, however, not used routinely for major element quantification as most instruments can only measure one element at a time. Samples are dissolved using procedures similar to those for ICP–AES. The solution is nebulized into a flame or vaporized in a graphite furnace to produce an atomic vapour. Radiant energy characteristic of the element being analysed is directed through the vapour and the amount of energy absorbed is measured, this being proportional to element concentration. Detection limits in solution vary from 1 ppb to >100 ppm for flame AAS. Furnace procedures are generally much more sensitive but are prone to matrix effects. The choice of method should be discussed with experienced laboratory staff. The more refractory elements (e.g. As, REE, S, Th, U) may be better determined by other methods such as ICP–AES or Instrumental Neutron Activation Analysis (INAA).

Recommended reading: Slavin (1978).

Data evaluation

Geochemical data are usually output in the form of a list of weight percent oxides or weight percent elements. These can be converted using the equation:

$$\text{wt\% element} = (\text{wt\% oxide/mol.wt oxide}) \times \text{at.wt element.}$$

Trace element concentrations are usually reported in parts per million (ppm) or micrograms per gram ($\mu g\ g^{-1}$), which are equivalent. To convert wt% element to ppm multiply by 10 000. The best method for applying such conversions and for studying the data is to input or import it into a 'spread sheet' computer program with a graphing facility and statistical routines. A wide variety of graphs can be plotted, such as variation diagrams, 'spider diagrams' etc. (Rollinson 1993). Discuss your results with an experienced operator, paying especial attention to any elements which are subject to interference or are present at concentrations outside the calibration range.

When making any interpretation as to the likely causes of a particular pattern or trend in the data, the possible effects of analytical and other errors must be considered. There are a wide variety of sources of error in quantitative analysis, the most common being contamination of sample, incomplete sample dissolution, interferences between elements, and problems with machine calibration. Contamination can be avoided by the careful use and thorough cleaning of apparatus during sample preparation, mainly during the grinding and polishing processes. Interference between elements is a potential problem in almost all forms of chemical analysis. Possible interferences should be checked for all elements being determined using published tables or through discussion with experienced laboratory staff. The accuracy of almost any geochemical analysis depends on the standards used for calibration. These should have compositions as close to that of the sample as possible, to minimize 'matrix' effects, and should have accurately known element abundances. The best way to check instrument performance and dissolution procedures is to analyse regularly multiple sets of the same sample and reference materials of known composition. Some indication of analytical error should be recorded with the data, ideally as error bars on individual data points in a geochemical diagram. When reporting your methodology, the 'precision', 'accuracy' and 'detection limits' of each set of analyses needs to be quoted. Precision, is 'a measure of the reproducibility of the method and is determined by making replicate measurements on the same sample'; accuracy is 'an estimate of how close our measured value is to the true value – it is normally done by reference to recommended values for international geochemical reference standards'; detection limit is 'the lowest concentration which can be "seen" by a particular method and is a function of the level of background noise' (Rollinson 1993).

31. Spore colour measurement

JOHN E. A. MARSHALL & BARBARA L. YULE

Fossil spores (and pollen) are made of organic matter which thermally matures during burial with the progressive loss of H and O relative to C. This chemical change is apparent in the physical properties of the spores, such as the reflectivity of cut and polished surfaces and most obviously as colour change. Spore walls are initially 'transparent' but turn through yellow to orange and then brown and black with increasing burial. The characterization of this colour change is important as it reveals the thermal maturity of the fossil material. Such information is of obvious importance in evaluating the potential of hydrocarbon source rocks and their burial history. Colour information should always be provided during documentation of fossil plants, spores and pollen. Its significance is that morphological features in the fossils (i.e. reduction in spore diameter) are dependent not just on taphonomic processes but also on their thermal history.

Sample preparation

Sample preparation for spore colour determination is identical to standard palynological processing (e.g. Wood et al. 1996; Chapter 4, 31) except that neither oxidation nor significant heating must be employed. General practice is for the removal of carbonate in hydrochloric acid (HCl) followed by decant washing to remove any soluble calcium. The sample is then demineralized in hydrofluoric acid (HF), decant washed and sieved at an appropriate mesh size (generally 10, 20 or 30 µm) for the required palynomorphs. The demineralization in HF forms precipitates of a variety of neoformed fluorides which only have limited solubility in cold mineral acids. Consequently their removal is difficult. Their solubility is increased in hot HCl but its use clearly involves a heating step. However, if kept to a short duration, such heating has a negligible effect on the palynomorphs. Therefore long treatments, for example in water baths, should be avoided. A good method is to very briefly (seconds) boil the sample in 50 ml of approximately 15% HCl (25 ml of sample plus 25 ml of 28% HCl), followed by an immediate dilution into approximately 500 ml of water and immediate sieving. Such short-term heating does not alter the colour of the palynomorphs. This observation is supported by heating experiments with modern spore material (Gutjahr 1966) showing that at temperatures of about 100°C, significant change only occurs after hours and takes some 60 hours to reach equilibrium. This method also enables sieving of solutions which, before dilution, would dissolve the nylon filament sieve mesh. The rapid dilution, promoting the reprecipitation of neoformed fluorides, does so at such small crystallite sizes that they easily pass through the smallest mesh sizes employed.

Although oxidation is clearly inappropriate for samples destined for thermal maturity determinations, it is often essential to remove amorphous organic matter (AOM) which otherwise greatly dilutes the palynomorph and phytoclast content. A popular method has been to use very long oxidations in Schulze solution followed by potassium hydroxide (KOH) or, more recently (R. A. Jones 1994), microwave digestion in nitric acid (HNO$_3$). Such techniques change both the chemistry and colour of the spore walls. A much more appropriate, and indeed efficient, technique for AOM removal is the use of a tunable ultrasonic probe (e.g. Wood et al. 1996). Unlike an ultrasonic bath, where the samples are placed in a tank of water and energized by external transducers, the probe is immersed in the sample. The probe can also be tuned to maximize energy output and have its power regulated for most effective use. Such an ultrasonic probe works by causing localized cold boiling (cavitation). Micro-scale increases in temperature and pressure of up to 4800°C and 10^8 Pa (Lickiss & McGrath 1996) occur but the heat generated is rapidly dissipated through the entire sample. This cavitation results in rapid fragmentation of the AOM, so that it can be selectively removed by sieving. It has been suggested (Jones & Ellin 1998) that the use of such an ultrasonic probe during oxidation damages palynomorphs. This is not the case for AOM removal in water, provided that its use is controlled. As with oxidation techniques the process is essentially destructive and the procedure is one of controlling the system to limit damage. The ultrasonic operates by preferentially fragmenting the weakest components within an assemblage. Hence, with a sample rich in AOM, the palynomorphs are essentially unaffected, provided that energization time is minimized. Normally about

MARSHALL, J. E. A. & YULE. B. L. 1999. Spore colour measurement. *In*: JONES, T. P. & ROWE, N. P. (eds) *Fossil Plants and Spores: modern techniques.* Geological Society, London, 165–168.

165

10–15 s is appropriate, depending on the amount and robustness of the AOM. Following ultrasonic treatment the sample can be checked for damage by examining the sieved fines for broken palynomorph fragments. However, if a sample without AOM is sonicated, damage to the palynomorphs can occur. This has been determined by measuring the changing proportion of proximate to chorate dinoflagellate cysts within a single sample during successive repeat ultrasonic treatments. However, such damage occurs over minutes rather than the seconds employed for routine ultrasonic treatment and is hence not a cause for concern.

Spore selection

It is most important when determining spore colour to select a consistent and representative palynomorph group. General examination of a single assemblage will readily reveal palynomorphs with varying morphology which have different colour exines. Typically, the more complex spores and pollen will have darker colours. Often this is influenced by wall thickness, but it can reflect compositional differences between the wall layers with many intexines being both darker in transmitted light and with higher reflectivities in reflected light. In addition, simple spores can often have quite dark walls, a characteristic which appears to be inherent from their exine structure. It should also be noted that the colour range observed within a sample is strongly dependent on thermal maturation level (Marshall 1991) with oil-mature (averaging orange colour) samples showing the greatest variation. A general pragmatic approach is to select a palynomorph group which in low maturity samples shows limited colour difference. Such palynomorph groups would be simple single-layered sac-like spores such as *Leiotriletes* and *Calamospora* (Palaeozoic) and *Deltoidospora* (Mesozoic). These also have the advantage of being geologically long ranging. Other groups with long geological histories are bisaccate pollen, but these can prove difficult to determine as the sacci are often thinned and pitted. The best approach in this instance is to use the central body (corpus) of the pollen grains. Other groups, most suited to Mesozoic studies are ubiquitous forms such as *Classopollis/Corollina* and the exoexines of *Callialasporites*.

Diagenetic effects

Spore colour can be influenced by depositional sedimentary environment. Primarily this takes the form of paler and reduced hue colours in palynomorphs from AOM-rich sediments. For example, the same species of spore collected from adjacent samples at the same locality can have a spore colour reduced by 1 to 2 points if from AOM-rich facies. As such, this colour suppression is identical in cause and result to the suppression of vitrinite reflectivity in the same environments (Senftle *et al.* 1993). Although bitumen impregnation has been advocated as the cause of such reflectivity reduction, this cannot be the case as suppression of both colour and reflectivity occurs within immature young sediments. It is understood here, to result from the influence of the primary depositional environment. If either phytoclasts or palynomorphs are deposited within an environment where the organic matter is hydrogen rich and will ultimately become AOM, they alter diagenetically to take on some of the chemical characteristics of the bulk of the organic matter. The contrast is a burial environment rich in land plant debris which has a quite different chemistry and hence a different diagenetic environment. Hence, when determining spore colour within AOM facies, it must be recognized that colour suppression will occur (by up to 20%) in comparison to equivalent phytoclast-rich kerogen assemblages.

Other diagenetic effects are manifest from palynomorphs in AOM-rich facies. In general, the walls will be less well preserved and the clarity of sculptural detail reduced. In addition to a general degradation, palynomorphs can also show direct evidence of damage from diagenetic mineral growth such as the presence of pyrite (framboids and cubes) which are ubiquitous and well documented. Palynomorphs can also show damage from other minerals, usually as negative pseudomorphs (i.e. holes showing the external mineral form). Unlike pyrite these minerals (e.g. gypsum, calcite) are normally removed during diagenesis or laboratory processing. Although less common, these can be equally instructive as to diagenetic and depositional environment, good examples being the 60°/120° negative pseudo-morph impressions which result from dolomitiz-ation.

Visual spore colour scales

There is no universally accepted spore colour scale or correlation with vitrinite reflectivity. A number of colour scales have been proposed (Fig. 31.1) which have been adopted with varying degrees of success. Amongst these the most popular are the TAI scale of Staplin, the SCI of the Robertson Group and the pollen/spore colour standard (SCS) of Pearson. The TAI (Thermal Alteration Index) scale is based on 5 points (summarized in Staplin 1982) with intermediates making it an 8-point scale. It has been based on a limited number of sets of picked standard 'palynomorphs' selected by

Spore Colour	SCI	TAI	SCS	G	R_v
Colourless - pale yellow	1			175	0.2
			1		
Pale yellow - lemon yellow	2	1.5			
			2		
Lemon yellow	3				0.3
		2.2	3	172	
Golden yellow	4				0.4
			4		
Yellow orange	5	2.4			0.5
			5		
Orange	6				0.6
			6	150	
		2.6			0.7
Orange brown	7			100	
		2.8	7	75	0.8
					0.9
Dark brown	8	3.0		50	1.0
			8		
Dark brown - black	9	3.5	9	10	2.0
Black	10	4.0	10		3.0

Fig. 31.1. Approximate correlation of various spore colour scales. The named spore colours are provided for reference. All these correlations should considered as guidance only. The parameter G (green) is calibrated to vitrinite reflectivity. SCS has been calibrated primarily by using microspectrophotometry. SCI, spore colour index; TAI, thermal alteration index; SCS, spore color standard; G, green light from image analysis; R_v, vitrinite reflectivity.

Staplin. As such these are not easily accessible as primary standards. However, it has been adopted by a number of oil (Exxon) and service companies (Geochem).

The SCI (Spore Colour Index of the Robertson Group; Fisher *et al*. 1980; Collins 1990) is perhaps the most widely used spore colour scale and certainly the most refined. It is based on a series of 19 single-grain palynomorph mounts determined by a single operator. It is a 1–10 scale with the addition of half-unit steps. It has also undergone modification and recalibration at its upper limit. Standards are commercially available but again are generally beyond the reach of the casual user.

The spore colour standard of Pearson (1982, 1984) uses a series of Munsell colour standard papers to define a 10-point scale. Such an approach has been criticized (Collins 1990) as such colours are not comparable to those of palynomorphs viewed in transmitted light. However, as a scale it is widely available, having been reproduced within the limits of colour printing (Plate I in Traverse 1988). Clearly for a casual user, this scale, with reservation, represents a readily accessible standard which will suffice for general spore colour des-

cription. As such its application would introduce a welcome increase in precision of spore colour description to palaeobotanical description. As regards the calibration to vitrinite reflectivity, the most successful and widely applied thermal maturity measure, it is recognized that spores and pollen being different in composition to vitrinite will behave kinetically differently during varied burial and thermal histories. Thus any vitrinite calibration should be regarded as a general equivalent and invaluable cross-check on thermal maturity level but never inter-convertible.

Quantitative spore colour measurement

There have been a number of approaches to the quantified measurement of palynomorph colour. Early attempts (Gutjahr 1966; Grayson 1975) measured absorbance or its reciprocal, transmittance, at a single wavelength fixed with a band-pass filter and acquired with relatively simple light measuring systems. Results were quoted relative to 100% transmittance or absorbance. The advent of commercial computer-controlled microspectro-photometers (manufactured by Zeiss & Leitz) saw a number of further attempts to quantify colour (Lo 1988; Van Gijzel 1990). However, the most significant advances have been made by scanning the complete spectra. These results are best presented using the international colour system (C.I.E., Commission Internationale de l'Eclairage) of chromaticity co-ordinates and luminance (Marshall 1991; Milton 1993). The C.I.E. co-ordinates define a colour solid within which a maturity pathway can be determined. As such these colour systems are complex and not readily convertible to a single quantified and reproducible system as has proved so successful with the vitrinite scale. However, what they do provide is a quantified colour measurement. This shows how spore colours change with burial/increased temperature and enable rigorous comparison of visual spore colour scales. The principal conclusions from such determinations are:

(1) during pre-hydrocarbon generation burial, a regular and progressive series of yellow spore colours occurs;

(2) at about the main point of hydrocarbon generation a rapid (with respect to depth/increased temperature) series of colour changes occur with the spores moving through a series of orange colours to brown/black;

(3) at this break in colour change, the range of colour within the same spore type (including distinction to species level) in single samples is very great, encompassing yellow to brown;

(4) once beyond this colour break these brown

black colours are relatively insensitive to further burial/increased temperature;

(5) measurement of a set of SCI standards and the pollen/spore colour standard of Pearson both show significant deviations from the quantitatively defined average spore colour trend. The standard spores have generally been picked as richer colours. These standards should be regarded as approximations to a real thermal maturity colour series.

These results emphasize that spore colour scales are strongly non-linear and thus limited in their application for burial history modelling where they compare unfavourably to vitrinite which is linear over the main interval of interest. They are, however, excellent in marking the onset of hydrocarbon generation.

A simplified quantitative colour measurement system

The measurement of colour with microspectro-photometers involves very specialist and, in consequence, expensive equipment (generally in excess of £100 k), which is unavailable to all but the most serious users. However, one quantitative colour measuring system which is widely available is that inherent in the software of most modern image analysis systems. As such, it relies on computer transformations of electronically acquired images with conversion of the pixels from the CTV to RGB (red–green–blue) colour co-ordinates. These define a colour solid similar to the C.I.E. system. However, such conversions are probably not uniform between systems and it is certainly not clear as to how these conversions are achieved and how they relate to the C.I.E. system. As such they lack the precision and reproducibility of micro-spectrophotometers but provide a valuable proxy quantitative colour measurement. Such image analysis equipment is readily available in most laboratories with the advantage of relatively low cost quantified colour measurement. A number of palynomorph (Yule *et al.* 1995, 1998) and microfossil (Helson *et al.*1995) colour studies have been made using such instruments. Results from such a system (*Optimas*, Fig. 31.1) show that the simple measurement of G (green) provides a good relatively linear single colour parameter.

Barbara Yule thanks British Gas for financial support.

32. Bulk geochemistry as a guide to provenance and diagenesis

RICHARD M. BATEMAN

Bulk geochemical analyses have long held a pivotal role in hard-rock geology (e.g. Potts 1994; Gill 1996). Their application to sedimentary rocks has been more sporadic, though examples exist from several disciplines, including oil exploration, limestone diagenesis/metamorphism (e.g. Rock & Waterhouse 1986), sedimentary provenance, soil science and archaeological provenance (e.g. Farrington & Bateman 1992). Palaeozoological applications have been few and palaeobotanical applications still fewer (Bateman 1995).

Here, I make an unashamedly subjective plea for the far wider application of bulk geochemical analyses to palaeobotanical problems, using two examples from Scotland: (1) A concerted attempt to unravel the stratigraphy, diagenesis and provenance of a complex series of volcanigenic horizons bearing petrified Dinantian plants at Oxroad Bay, East Lothian, Scotland (Bateman & Scott 1990); (2) a far smaller data-matrix elucidating the diagenesis of marine horizons bearing Middle Jurassic plants at Bearreraig Bay, Skye, Scotland (Bateman & Morton 1994; Bateman *et al.* 1999; unpublished data). As befits an advocacy of a grossly underused technique, the chapter focuses more on applications and interpretations than precise methodologies; the data-gathering phase of the analysis is best performed by experts in specialist laboratories.

Preferred techniques

Like most methods of chemical analysis, geochemical techniques designed to determine the bulk composition of rocks – notably X-ray fluorescence spectrometry (XRF), inductively coupled plasma–atomic emission spectrometry (ICP–AES) and inductively coupled plasma–mass spectrometry (ICP–MS) – have become far more sophisticated over the last 20 years as a result of technological advances (Potts 1994; Gill 1996). In particular, increased automation of the laboratory analytical phase has resulted in: (1) the ability to obtain data for most of the desired variables from a single analytical run, accelerating the process and reducing operator time; (2) decreasing minimum sizes of rock samples necessary to acquire such data; and (3) potentially decreased costs. The vast majority of palaeontologists lack direct access to

such expensive equipment, and hence must contract out analyses to well appointed geochemical laboratories. However, at the time of writing the British Geological Survey charge *c.* £50 per sample for sample preparation, XRF analysis for the ten major oxides, plus acid digestion carbonate assay (see below, and Chapter 30). Thus, either substantial research grants or informal arrangements with sympathetic laboratories are required for in-depth studies.

Elements investigated are categorized according to their overall relative abundance in the Earth's crust. The ten most common rock-forming elements (listed in Table 32.1) are generally reported as percentage oxides (less the various volatile components aggregated as 'loss-on-ignition'), whereas the remainder are less common (typically <0.1% and hence termed trace elements) and reported as parts per million element. The

Table 32.1. *ICP–AES data for the ten common rock-forming elements (as weight % oxides) from horizon P8 of the Middle Jurassic petrified plant-bearing sequence at Bearreraig Bay, Skye*

Oxide	Sediment	Concretion	Change (%)
H_2O	1.51	0.61	NA
LOI	17.7	32.3	NA
CO_2	26.4	61.8	NA
CaO	16.67	35.52	+510
MgO	1.51	1.14	+81
FeO	4.10	2.03	+19
Na_2O	0.68	0.31	+9
K_2O	1.75	0.67	−8
P_2O_5	0.64	0.38	+42
MnO	0.22	0.12	+31
Al_2O_3	7.16	2.88	−4
TiO_2	0.58	0.23	−5
SiO_2	46.20	19.31	0 (fixed)

LOI, loss-on-ignition; NA, not applicable.
Relatively unconsolidated sediment is compared with enclosed diagenetically generated concretionary nodules. SiO_2 is used as a notional constant in order to estimate the relative degrees of concentration of other oxides in the plant-bearing nodules, and CO_2 is given as $CaCO_3$ equivalent by acid digestion (R. M. Bateman & N. Morton unpublished data).

BATEMAN, R. 1999. Bulk geochemistry as a guide to provenance and diagenesis.
In: JONES, T. P. & ROWE, N. P. (eds) *Fossil Plants and Spores: modern techniques.*
Geological Society, London, 169–173.

main elements of life (H, C, N, O) and the inert gases cannot be screened successfully by bulk geochemical methods. If needed, they must be assayed by separate, targeted techniques (e.g. Avery & Bascomb 1974). For palaeobotanists, the most important of these compounds is carbonate content, given the importance of $CaCO_3$ as a common petrifying agent. Also, elements used in the pre-analytical vitrification process cannot be determined, hence the preferred use of $LiBO_2$ as a fusion medium; Li and B are low atomic number elements of modest concentration and limited interest.

XRF, ICP–AES and ICP–MS differ primarily in the minimum sample size that can be accommodated, sensitivity and lower detection limits for specific elements, and most importantly their ability to quantify elements of low and high atomic numbers plus the halides. XRF requires relatively large samples and cannot determine elements of atomic number ≤ 8 or S, but can detect the halides F and Cl. The ICP methods offer better overall sensitivity using smaller samples. ICP–AES can detect Li, Be, B and S, but not F or Cl. ICP–MS offers even lower detection limits, can in addition yield data on C plus all halides, and is especially effective for rare earths and transitional elements of high atomic numbers.

Laboratory procedures and data acquisition

The techniques employed by Bateman & Scott (1990) epitomise a typically broad-brush approach to sedimentary geochemical data acquisition, based on procedures recommended during the late 1980s by the Soil Survey of England and Wales. Approximately 10 g samples were excised from apparently unweathered central zones of selected slabs cut from petrifaction-bearing sedimentary blocks and fine ground (<0.5 mm) in agate mills (note that larger samples and finer grinding may be desirable). Free-water contents of the entire samples were determined by heating the sample powder in nickel crucibles at 105°C for 28 h (Bascomb in Avery & Bascomb 1974). The dehydrated samples were then sub-sampled for three treatments: loss-on-ignition, carbonate content and automated ICP–AES analysis.

Loss-on-ignition was determined by heating sample powders in ceramic crucibles at 900°C for 18 h, thereby expelling from the rock volatile components such as bound water, CO_2 (including that bound up in carbonates) and all organic matter. Carbonate content was assessed by exposing 0.5–2 g sub-samples to 3N HCl and measuring the volume of CO_2 evolved, using the Bascomb (1961)

calcimeter and the procedure and formula of Bascomb in Avery & Bascomb (1974):

$$CaCO_3 \text{ equivalent } (\%) = V \times P \times K/W \times T,$$

where V = volume of CO_2 evolved (cm^{-3}), P = atmospheric pressure (mm Hg), K = constant (0.1604), W = weight of oven-dried powdered rock sample used, and T = room temperature (K).

Sample powders for ICP–AES analysis were fused with $LiBO_2$ in platinum crucibles, and the vitrified products were dissolved in 6% HNO_3 (e.g. Dahlqvist & Knoll 1978). The resulting solutions were passed through an automated ICP spectrometer, generating data for all ten elements listed in Table 32.1 (as wt % oxides, with Fe given as FeO), a restricted range of less common transition elements (e.g. Cd, Co, Cr, Cu, Mo, Ni, Pb, Zn), and in some cases several additional trace elements (both as ppm).

Non-algorithmic comparison

The primary advantage of bulk geochemical analysis is that it generates with relative ease, and from almost any rock sample, a large number of fully quantified variables (e.g. Bateman & Scott 1990, tables 3–6), most suffering relatively low statistical errors.

In studies involving few samples, obvious patterns can be extracted from the data by eye. For example, Table 32.1 presents geochemical data for two rock samples from Bearreraig Bay, Skye (R. M. Bateman & N. Morton, unpublished data). Here, fragmented but exquisitely petrified Jurassic plants and abundant marine invertebrates are concentrated within small (<10 cm maximum dimension) calcareous nodules. These concretions occur in several horizons of less consolidated calcareous siltstones and sandstones deposited c. 10 km beyond the palaeo-shoreline (Morton 1990; Bateman & Morton 1994; Bateman et al. 1999).

Table 32.1 compares data for a nodule containing petrified plant megafossils from one of the richer horizons with the immediately adjacent, less consolidated sediment that preserves only plant microfossils (Morton 1990). The primary objective was to determine which elements had migrated during diagenesis to form the nodules (and thus preserve the plants) and in what relative proportions. This was achieved by assuming that SiO_2, a component of many of the more diagenetically resistant minerals (most notably the sole constituent of quartz), had not migrated and thus should be a constant proportion of both the nodules and surrounding sediment. Although not wholly reliable, this assumption is didactically useful. The observed ratio of matrix SiO_2 to nodule SiO_2 (2.39) was then used to calculate expected percentages of the other major element oxides in the diagenetic nodules, and the percentage divergence in the nodule from the expected value was noted.

Any strongly negative divergences would indicate violation of the key assumption that SiO_2 had not migrated, but in fact only three small negative deviations are evident in Table 32.1 (the largest is minus 8% for K_2O). Small positive deviations can similarly be discarded as falling within the presumed margin of error of the method, but several oxides show significant concentration in the nodules; there are slight increases in Fe, P and Mn, a near-doubling in Mg, and a five-fold increase in Ca. The greatly increased CO_2 content of the nodules suggests that much of the dissolved, migrating Ca crystallized out as $CaCO_3$, an interpretation that is supported by the examination of petrological thin-sections and explains the presence of high quality calcareous petrifactions.

Another example of non-statistical interpretation is provided in Fig. 32.1, which summarizes an attempt to provenance a loose block (LB/D166, collected from the foreshore of Oxroad Bay in 1965 by K. L. Alvin) that contains the petrified type material of the early rhizomorphic lycopsid *Oxroadia gracilis*. This task was challenging, as re-examination of the locality in the 1980s revealed eight plant-bearing localities in the Bay (A–H) and no less than an estimated 31 individual plant-bearing horizons (Bateman & Rothwell 1990; Bateman & Scott 1990). However, extensive geochemical analyses of these horizons demonstrated that significant (>10 ppm) molybdenum (Mo) concentrations were confined to the upper horizons of a single complex exposure, D (Fig. 32.1). A Mo profile through this exposure revealed that the crucial loose block (Mo = 22 ppm) is likely to have originated from horizons D2.15 (20 ppm), D2.17 (26 ppm) or D2.26 (25 ppm), thus illustrating a rather unconventional application for a decidedly obscure element. Complementary petrological studies revealed greatest affinity with horizons D2.12, D2.15 and D2.21. Thus, the only overlap between geochemical and petrological similarity is horizon D2.15, strongly suggesting that this was the source of the crucial block.

Algorithmic comparison

However, there are more effective ways than univariate comparison of exploiting the large quantitative databases generated from bulk rock geochemistry. Figure 32.2 presents a computer-generated multivariate ordination, using only the ten commonest elements, for 19 *in situ* plant-bearing horizons sampled at Oxroad Bay plus three unprovenanced loose blocks (LB) bearing especi-

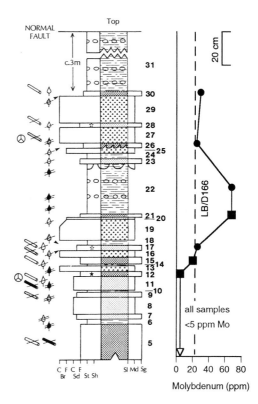

Fig. 32.1. Lithological log for the upper half of the sedimentologically complex Exposure D at Oxroad Bay, East Lothian, which contains 16 horizons bearing calcareously petrified plants. The molybdenum (Mo) content of each possible source horizon is plotted for comparison with the Mo content of a palaeobotanically valuable plant-bearing loose block of unknown source horizon collected from the adjacent foreshore (dashed vertical line at 22 ppm). The results are most consistent with an origin of the block from *in situ* horizons 2.15, 2.17 or 2.26, a correlation narrowed to horizon 2.15 following thin-section studies (only horizons shown as squares possessed the correct petrographic characteristics).

ally important petrified plants, including the aforementioned *Oxroadia*. Ordinations are excellent tools for visually summarizing complex multi-dimensional relationships of samples in two dimensions that encompass much of the variation, and for simultaneously identifying those variables that are most diagnostic of specific sample groupings (e.g. Digby & Kempton 1987).

Here, the chosen ordination technique was principal coordinates analysis (PCO: e.g. Gower & Digby 1981) applied to percentage oxide data that were standardized to unit variance before being subjected to Gower's (1971) similarity coefficient.

The coefficients were also used to generate a minimum spanning tree (MST: Gower & Ross 1969), an unrooted tree that links samples of greatest overall similarity by bonds of contrasting strengths. All multivariate analyses were conducted in *Genstat* (see Appendix) (Payne *et al.* 1993).

The results can be used to explain diagenesis and plant preservation, and to provenance the three loose blocks (Bateman & Scott 1990). Axis 1 of Fig. 32.2 accounts for a remarkable 65% of the total variance, and reveals an inverse relationship between Al, Ti, Si and K that are relatively abundant on the left of the plot and Ca, LOI (dominantly CO_2) and Mn that are relatively abundant on the right. The much weaker Axis 2 (15%) largely reflects a downward relative increase in Mg. In fact, this plot reveals two mutually perpendicular diagenetic trends. The first trend represents induration via enhancement in dolomitic minerals [$CaMg(CO_3)_2$] of petrifaction-bearing horizons by local ionic migration, accurately reflecting the Ca/Ca + Mg ratio of *c.* 0.6 inherent in the volcanic tuffs that dominate the fossil landscape. The second trend apparently represents biogenic precipitation, in transient contemporaneous lakes, of calcite ($CaCO_3$). This was selectively extracted from the lake waters by algae, yielding higher grade plant preservation with a much larger Ca/Ca + Mg ratio of 0.94–0.97. Relative degrees of overall calcification are well illustrated by the superimposed CO_3 isopleths.

The minimum spanning tree on Fig. 32.2 is especially useful for assessing the degree of success in attempting to geochemically 'fingerprint', and thus provenance, the three loose blocks (open circles). The *Oxroadia*-bearing LB/D166 is embedded deeply in the calcitic group and shows greatest similarity to horizons D2.15 and D2.17, eliminating the stratigraphically higher option of D2.26 identified from Mo content (Fig. 32.1). Block LB/C084, rich in *Protocalamites*, has a convincing link to the only petrifaction-bearing horizon of Exposure C (C2c). However, the relatively poorly preserved *Bilignea* stem from loose block LB/B013 can only be tentatively assigned to the petrographically similar Exposure B, also having roughly equal geochemical similarities to Exposure E and a mineralized vein from Exposure C (C2v).

Thus, this attempt at geochemical fingerprinting of key loose blocks is judged a qualified success. Most other analogous provenance problems should

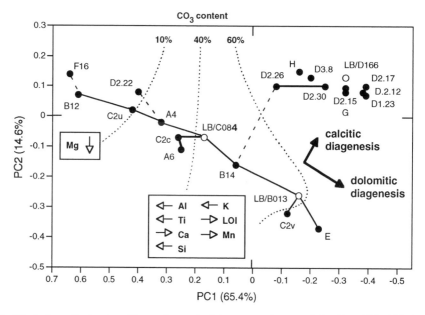

Fig. 32.2. Principal coordinates plot with superimposed minimum spanning tree, derived from ICP–AES data for the ten commonest rock-forming oxides in 19 plant-bearing horizons (spots) and three loose blocks (circles) from Oxroad Bay. Relative contributions of elements to the first two axes, and their directions of increase along the vectors, are indicated, as are approximate isopleths for carbonate content. Plot is based on fig. 18 and table 8 of Bateman & Scott (1990), though with Axis 1 reversed to allow diagenesis to increase in intensity from left to right. Minimum spanning tree links are differentiated into strong (>98% similarity; thick line), moderate (95–98% similarity; thin line) and weak (<95% similarity; dashed line); all links within the tightly-knit top-right group exceed 98% similarity.

be easier to solve, as very few fossiliferous localities are as stratigraphically complex as Oxroad Bay. As well as loose blocks, the technique is equally applicable to key museum specimens where the source locality is known (and remains accessible) but the precise horizon of origin is not (either because it was never recorded or the label has been lost). A geochemical survey of the locality should in most cases reveal the source horizon.

However, it is important to note that this geochemical provenancing technique cannot, as has been suggested by others, be applied to bivariate plots such as those depicting the relative abundances of two isotopes of a single element. Given only two variables, the risk of an accidental coincidence of the unknown sample(s) with specific potential source rocks is too great. The strength of the bulk geochemical approach is the large number of variables that are encompassed in the two-dimensional plot; this greatly reduces the risk of 'accidental' *ad hoc* similarities. Of course, the rigour of the multivariate analysis is increased if isotope data are added to the bulk geochemical data.

An attempt by Bateman & Scott (1990, fig. 16) to use ICP–AES data to interpret a third aspect of the Oxroad Bay locality was less successful. An additional data-matrix of 23 samples of plant-free volcanic tuffs sampling the full geographic and stratigraphic spectrum of deposits at the locality was ordinated in an attempt to determine the relative stratigraphic positions of the plant-bearing horizons, which are extremely difficult to determine due to severe faulting and folding associated with extensive syn-depositional volcanism (even the same horizon can be difficult to correlate among different exposures). The hope was that magmatic composition would have changed during the volcanic activity, but in practice all tuff samples indicated a constant local magmatic composition. Geochemical composition varied only according to the dominant particle sizes of individual tuffs, which in turn reflected the relative proportions of magmatic and non-magmatic material.

Summary

Inductively coupled plasma spectrometry (ICP) and X-ray fluorescence spectrometry (XRF) are rapid, automated methods of quantifying the bulk geochemistry of powdered, artificially vitrified rocks. Most elements of the Periodic Table can be quantified, though those of low or high atomic numbers, halides, and inert gases are problematic. Even a basic analysis of the ten major rock-forming elements plus LOI and carbonate assay is sufficient to 'fingerprint' a rock sample, yielding a dataset that can be fed directly into a multivariate ordination to compare and classify sediments (bivariate plots of geochemical data or isotopic ratios are inadequate for such studies, due to the much greater probability of encountering *ad hoc* similarities among samples unrelated by shared processes of formation).

The three main potential palaeobotanical applications of ICP/XRF data illustrated here are: (1) stratigraphical correlation within and among fossil-bearing horizons, particularly across structurally complex geological terrains (ideally in combination with field mapping and/or geophysical studies); (2) determining modes of preservation and depositional environments of fossils (ideally in combination with petrological thin-section and/or microprobe studies); (3) correlating *ex situ* fossils with potential source horizons, either because the fossils have been naturally eroded from the exposure to generate loose blocks or because information on the provenance of specimens is lost or inadequate (ideally in combination with petrological thin-section and/or microfossil studies). Bulk geochemical analyses merit much greater attention from palaeobotanists than they have received to date, given their flexibility and broad applicability.

Part Six   Conservation, Databases and Protocols

33. The plant fossil record on the internet

MICHAEL C. BOULTER

The Plant Fossil Record (PFR) database project began in 1990 with the Frankfurt Declaration. This set out the scope of the project and the agreed Field headings for each record; the consequent details are described by Lhotak & Boulter (1995). As well as this descriptive database the July 1997 version at the web site http://ibs.uel.ac.uk/ibs/ contains many other facilities of use to palaeontologists and evolutionary biologists. This article refers to the September 1997 version of the website. Its content is changed regularly and new technology enables the structure to be modernized at least twice a year, so what you see at the PFR site after reading this may be different to what is described here. At the Home Page you select 'Taxonomy' or 'Presentations'. Each contains the same items which are arranged under these different headings.

Descriptions

The taxonomic, bibliographic and morphological details of all fossil genera included in the Index Nominum Genericorum, together with the type's stratigraphic age are included in the descriptive part of the PFR database. All these details have been checked and revised against the nomenclatural details catalogued by Andrews (1970), Blazer (1975) and Watt (1982), and the stratigraphical names have been quantified according to Harland *et al.*'s (1989) time scale. Other details, including morphological accounts, have been added for some genera by named authorities, a process which will continue if this database is to become the authoritative standard.

Internet links are established from the PFR database to gophers at the Smithsonian Institution, the Peabody Museum and Berkeley. Examples of further descriptive data have been scanned from the Jansonius & Hills (1976) pollen and spore index cards, and copied from a CD-ROM modern angiosperm family database (Watson & Dallwitz 1994) which gives drawings of the taxa as well.

Fossil species of modern angiosperm genera have been added by Brown (1992) and can be found in the database against the plant genera searched from Brummitt's (1992) index.

Occurrences

A database of published plant fossil occurrences, with the location (latitude and longitude), geological age in millions of years (Ma) and the authority, has been compiled directly from the published literature. The original published details are copied verbatim, even if they are known to be incorrect: individuals can download their own selections from the database and make their own interpretations. When an institution can take responsibility for adding new data, those data and earlier records can be tagged with specialist's comments (respecting the rules of nomenclature). The sources are from a freely available magnetic palynological database called Taxon v.3.1 (see Appendix), and the plant megafossil data from magnetic files at Vienna (Eder-Kovar 1990) and Saint Petersbourg (Budantsev, pers. comm.). The latitude and longitude coordinates (as accurate as the source publication allows) and the age in Ma (published stage names are converted to numbers after Harland *et al.* 1990). Boulter *et al.* (1996) have collected most of the published literature of megafossils of Aceraceae and these are also included. This is the best group to use when testing the future potential of the system and, of course, such compendia from other plant groups must be compiled for further work. It is a time-consuming task but it can lead to analysis of the data, an all-to-rare process in palaeobotany.

Data entry

New data of fossil plant descriptions and occurrences can be added to the database, at the International Organization of Palaeobotany (IOP) office, once they are published in the accountable scientific press. They should be sent by post or as a Microsoft Excel file with columns listing details of genus, species, author, date, journal, stratigraphic age, latitude, longitude.

Data output

Palaeogeographic maps by Smith *et al.* (1994) at roughly 10 Ma intervals through the last 150 Ma can be selected on the internet (http://ibs.uel.ac.uk/ibs)

BOULTER, M. C. 1999. The plant fossil record on the internet. *In*: JONES, T. P. & ROWE, N. P. (eds) *Fossil Plants and Spores: modern techniques*. Geological Society, London, 177–178.

to show the distributions of the occurrences in the database, and then also these data can be downloaded as lists.

Other palaeontological presentations

The *Fossil Record 2* database of the times of first and last appearances of fossil animal and plant families (Benton 1993) is also available at the internet site. Java programs enable users to plot rate of -origin and -extinction curves for the families they select. Occurrence curves show the change in the number of records through geological time. Distortions from unreliable and otherwise dirty data can be smoothed at different levels by a program using fuzzy theory.

The major breakthroughs (paradigm shifts)

All linked names can be retrieved together

In these and other palaeontological databases internet links are being established to synonyms, priority names, organs and other information of nomenclatural relevance such as whole-plant information. Lumpers and splitters are most extremely represented in palaeobotany by supporters of the 'Names in Current Use' proposals and by proponents of Hughes' (1994) 'Biorecords' respectively. At the same internet site there are also links to several modern-genera databases (such as Brummitt 1992; Watson & Dallwitz 1994).

Different hierarchical models can be compared simultaneously

The two sets of hierarchies in evolutionary biology, the ecological series from global biogeography to local ecology, and the different levels from genes to species to higher taxa, are data rapidly becoming available from a single search command on the internet. This enables information to be selected and to be used to investigate patterns of macroevolution (Eldredge 1996) from many disciplinary outlooks as well as from a pluralist perspective. Brummitt's (1992) list of modern vascular plant genera gives a hierarchical display of all the families in the vascular plant record recognized by Cleal (1993) and Collinson *et al.* (1993).

Theories of biogeographical migration can be tested

Theories of vicariant biogeography (Nelson & Rosen 1981) and the distribution patterns of genera, families etc. through space and time are easy to test on the system (within the limits of the information in the database). Internet users can select taxa of

their choice and plot them on palaeogeographic maps. The Global Plotter facility at the same home page enables these data to be compared with the world distribution of all families of modern flowering plants presented by Thorne (1992). If your machine can run Java (Netscape 3 on Windows 95) you can query the database and compare the mapped distributions to Thorne's observations of any modern family you select.

Incomplete and unreliable data can be cautiously considered

Individual users have the opportunity to check the data from the original publication, to update taxonomic, geographical and stratigraphical features and even to remove records from the dataset to be used personally for presentation or analysis. A properly financed administration would be able to curate and monitor these kinds of comments from specialists and other users. As in our understanding of all natural systems there are many sources of error and many incomplete records and the fossil record itself has many innate weaknesses. For example, global rock volume varies between particular stratigraphic intervals, and scientific attention has concentrated on particular global regions and stratigraphic intervals. Applications of Fourier analysis and fuzzy theory are available to smooth some of the curves and data can be checked by a program (at the same site) offering rarefaction procedures.

Theories of evolutionary changes can be tested

The database can be used to test hypotheses of evolutionary rate and other patterns. New concepts communicating relationships between taxa, such as virtual systems, can be built, such as cladograms and phylogenetic trees (Brummitt 1996). From the databases we have available, and from their analysis by statistical and mathematical procedures, we are finding patterns of evolutionary change and ecological/geographical association that make interesting comparisons to earlier work, mainly from the Chicago school's work on data from marine invertebrates of the Palaeozoic.

So, for example (once again if you can run Java at your internetted pc) you can select a set of families (whose stratigraphic range is in our database of Benton 1993) and plot the times of their origins, extinctions and occurrences.

This presentation on the internet is largely the work of Helen Fisher, David Gee and Dilshat Hewzulla and I thank them for their energies and creativity. The editors of this volume are also to be applauded.

34. Taxonomic and nomenclatural alternatives

BILL G. CHALONER

Fossil plants and spores present a series of problems in the processes of naming and classifying. Most fossil plants represent only parts of an original whole plant, and the bulk of the names applied to them are based only on such parts. As a result we have names such as *Alethopteris* (applicable to certain Carboniferous pteridosperm leaves), *Laurocarpum* (a name based on Tertiary fossil seeds) and *Lagenicula* (a name for certain Carboniferous dispersed megaspores).

Classifying organisms (systematics or taxonomy) is theoretically quite a distinct process from that of applying names to them (nomenclature). Yet in reality, for fossil plants especially, the procedures of naming and classifying are closely interrelated (Collinson 1986). The problems which ensue in dealing with fossil plants have been very fully reviewed in a series of papers edited by Spicer & Thomas (1986), and as a single coherent presentation by Meyen (1987). A more recent and comprehensive review is given by Traverse (1996), although he concentrates on fossil spore systematics rather than that of larger fossil plant organs (macrofossils).

While most authors dealing with fossil plants (palaeobotany) and spores (palynology) have used the binomial nomenclature universally adopted for all living organisms, some have opted out of this convention, feeling that it is inappropriate for fossil plants. Even some of those who use binomial nomenclature have elected not to use the higher (suprageneric) levels of plant taxonomy, and have placed their fossil names in a hierarchy of groups created expressly for fossil material. Some of these 'alternative taxonomies' will be briefly considered in this chapter.

Codes of nomenclature

The requirements for scientific names of organisms to be generally accepted are set out in several 'codes' drawn up and agreed to internationally. The naming of fossil plants is governed by the International Code of Botanical Nomenclature – the 'ICBN' – (Greuter *et al.* 1994), which has been revised every five or six years, for the last few decades. Other codes exist which govern the naming of animals and of bacteria. A good account of the working of all these codes, with a comparison between them, is given in Jeffrey (1989). There is considerable support at the present time for the concept that these several codes could be reconciled under a single set of international rules for the scientific names of all organisms, the 'BioCode' (see Hawksworth *et al.* 1994, and the Draft BioCode, Hawksworth 1996). However, there is also a considerable body of botanical and zoological systematists who vigorously oppose such a merger. At the present time, and certainly into the near future, the naming of fossil plants will be governed by the existing provisions made in the ICBN. That nomenclature code deals, of course, not only with the names of plant genera and species, but with the names applied to the higher taxa within the systematic hierarchy (families, orders, classes and divisions) and to this extent reaches into the realm of taxonomy.

The essential requirements for the names of fossil plants (including spores) to be 'legitimate' (in its technical sense of conforming to the ICBN and so being generally acceptable to the palaeobotanical community) may be briefly summarized here. Fundamental to the Code is 'priority' – the concept that the first validly published name applied to a taxon (genus, species) is the correct name, and has priority over later names (synonyms) for the same kind of organism. The ICBN also has a series of 'starting dates', prior to which competing names will not be recognized. These 'starting dates' for the application of the priority rule are different for different organisms; for fossil plants the date is 31 December, 1820 (see Greuter *et al.* 1994, Art 13.1 f). The name must be accompanied by a description, technically a 'diagnosis', which spells out the difference of the new taxon from those most similar to it.

A further important feature of the ICBN is the concept of typification; that each name (of a species, genus and up to the level of family) has a type, a specimen on which the application of the name is ultimately based. This can be important if there is any dispute about the concept and limits of a given name, for both living and fossil organisms. The type designated by the original author is referred to as the holotype. If a holotype specimen was not designated by the original author, a later worker may designate a 'lectotype' from among the specimens on which the species was based by the

CHALONER, W. G. 1999. Taxonomic and nomenclatural alternatives. *In*: JONES, T. P. & ROWE, N. P. (eds) *Fossil Plants and Spores: modern techniques*. Geological Society, London, 179–183.

author. If all of the original material has been lost, a 'neotype' may be designated, from among specimens believed to represent the species. An important innovation in the application of the type concept was brought into the most recent edition of the ICBN (Greuter *et al.* 1994) in the form of the 'epitype'. This is 'a specimen or illustration selected to serve as an interpretative type when the holotype, lectotype or previously designated neotype...is demonstrably ambiguous'. This gives an opportunity for a later author to tighten up the application of a name based on a poorly chosen (or perhaps poorly preserved !) holotype.

There has been some confusion about the concept of a 'type', especially among those who see it as claiming in some way to be 'representative' of the whole taxon, which of course it could not be. The type is merely a specimen to which the name is irrevocably attached; no single specimen can define the concept of a taxon, which is determined by the perceived range of the entire population to which the name is thought to be applicable. For fossil plant species (but not living ones) an illustration is also required by the Code, at least for names published after 1912. This would normally (but not necessarily) be of the holotype of the name of that species. These are just some of the requirements for legitimacy of a fossil plant or spore name; for a fuller consideration of the complexities of applying the ICBN to fossil plants and spores, a good account is given in Traverse (1996).

Nomenclatural problems with fossil plants

The ICBN recognizes that because the vast majority of fossil plant names are based on single organs, the application of those names has some fundamental differences from the way in which we handle those based on extant (living) plants. In the usage of the ICBN, a taxon is either 'fossil' if the type of its name is a fossil, or 'non-fossil' if the type of its name is a herbarium or preserved specimen of an extant plant. A core problem relating to fossil names based on detached parts is spelt out in Art. 3.3 of the ICBN (Greuter *et al.* 1994): 'Because of the fragmentary nature of the specimens on which the species of some fossil plants are based, the genera to which they are assigned are not assignable to a family, although they may be referable to a taxon of higher rank. Such genera are known as form-genera'. It is important to note that this statement applies only to 'some fossil plants'. That article in the ICBN does not of course mean that all genera based on 'fragments' are therefore form-genera. Indeed, the great majority of Tertiary angiosperm fossil leaves are assigned to genera which are still extant (i.e. 'non-fossil' genera).

The ICBN cites several examples of form-genera, one of which is *Dadoxylon*, a genus based on structurally preserved wood. The anatomy of this 'wood genus' shows much in common with that of the living conifer *Araucaria*; but wood produced by certain Carboniferous Cordaitales (probable ancestors of the conifers) and some Mesozoic true conifers would, if found on its own, be properly assigned to *Dadoxylon*. The genus *Dadoxylon* accordingly represents a category of fossil wood which was produced by plants belonging to more than one order (at least Cordaitales and Coniferales). Indeed it is 'not assignable to a family', and what is more, in this case and some others, we know that such a form-genus comprises members of more than one family. The acknowledgement of the 'unnatural' nature of form-genera in that sense is implicit in their recognition in the ICBN.

However, many genera of fossils, usually based on just a single category of plant organ, can none the less be assigned to a single family, either of living plants (a non-fossil family) or an extinct family based solely on fossils. A number of structurally distinctive genera of fossil spores can reasonably be attributed to a family, if for example they have been found inside the relevant fructification. For example, the genus *Lagenicula* (a megaspore obtained from the cones of some members of the Lepidodendraceae) can be assigned to that family (see Fig. 34.1). It is still, however, a name characterized in terms of spore morphology alone, and the name *Lagenicula* should not be used for the cone from which spores of that type were extracted. Figure 34.1 illustrates how the time-ranges of related organ genera give a further unique character to these taxa, which has no counterpart in non-fossil genera. It might be thought that if members of two organ genera are found joined together in a single fossil specimen (in so-called 'organic connection') then they should be regarded as synonyms. But the likelihood is very great that the two genera will not have the same range in geological time. The organs on which they are based are characterized by a different spectrum of features, which surely evolved independently. As shown in Fig. 34.1, within the Pennsylvanian megaspores conformable with *Lagenicula rugosa* are known to occur inside the cones of *Flemingites russellianus*. However, megaspores with the morphology which characterizes the genus *Lagenicula* extend over a longer time span than the record of cones conforming to the definition of *Flemingites*. This situation reinforces the need for maintaining separate taxa for detached organs of fossil plants.

Turning to fossil genera which can be assigned to 'non-fossil' (i.e. living) families, the generic name

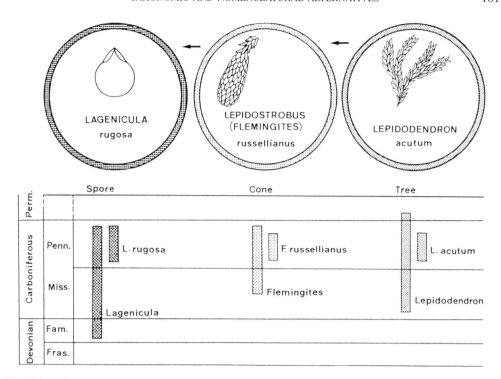

Fig. 34.1. A diagram to show the difficulty in handling names of fossil plants which are known to occur in connection at one horizon. The three species shown above are known to occur in 'organic connection' in the Pennsylvanian – the megaspore within the cones, and the cone attached to the leafy shoots of *Lepidodendron acutum*. However, other species of all three genera are known to occur outside the stratigraphic range of those three species. *Lepidodendron(sensu lato)* is known throughout the Carboniferous and into the Lower Permian. Megaspores conformable with the genus *Lagenicula* are known in the Upper Devonian. Despite this connection between the three species, the three genera therefore cannot be treated as synonyms. The abbreviated terms at left refer to the Permian, Pennsylvanian and Mississippian, and within the Devonian, to the Famennian and Frasnian stages (from Chaloner 1986).

Laurocarpum is based on the endocarp of certain fossil seeds preserved with three-dimensional detail in pyrite in the Eocene London Clay. The genus was described by Reid & Chandler (1933) and they were satisfied that the seeds on which it was based showed characters which made it appropriate to attribute them to the living family, the Lauraceae. Genera such as *Laurocarpum* and *Lagenicula* have long been referred to as 'organ-genera'; that is, the genus is typified by a single type of organ, and only organs of that generic character can be placed in them. However, nomenclaturally they are treated in just the same way as 'non-fossil genera'. They are assignable to all the higher categories of the taxonomic hierarchy, from the family on up; and all the members of such an organ-genus are believed to be attributable to the same family (in contrast to a form-genus, as indicated above). For that reason, the ICBN makes no distinction between such organ genera and living, non-fossil genera, and makes no

explicit reference to them. But the distinction between organ genus and non-fossil genus is worth retaining in those terms, as a fossil lauraceous leaf could not be placed in *Laurocarpum*, since it does not conform to the generic concept of that genus. In other words, the fossil leaf cannot show the features which characterize the type of *Laurocarpum*, which is a seed. This is a fundamental distinction between an organ-genus and a genus of living plants, where the name applies to all parts of the plant, indeed to the whole plant.

In summary, there are at least four ways in which fossil plant genera are fundamentally different from those based on living plants.

1. Different organs of what was a single plant species will of necessity, if found detached from one another, be assigned to different genera. This is an inevitable product of taxa being based on fragmentary fossils.

2. All the species of a living plant genus necessarily belong to the same family. With fossil form-genera, this need not be so. The genus of Palaeozoic fern-like fronds, *Pecopteris*, is based on a multi-pinnate frond with pinnate venation. Some species (e.g. *Pecopteris arborescens* (Schloth.) Brongniart) belong to the living fern order the Marattiales, while *P. feminaeformis* belongs to the extinct fern order the Zygopteridales.

3. All living plants can normally be assigned at all levels in the hierarchy of our taxonomy – that is to a family, an order, a class and a division within the plant kingdom. Because of the very limited range of characters shown by some fragmentary fossils, this may not be the case for them. Certain genera have been based on plant fragments which can only be assigned to perhaps an order, but clearly conform to the character of more than one family within the order. (*Dadoxylon* cited above is a case in point.)

4. The preservation state of a fossil plant may determine the genus to which it can be assigned. There is no comparable situation for living plant taxa. The spore-bearing cones of the Carboniferous arborescent lycopod *Sigillaria* are known in two different states: permineralized (so showing much internal anatomical detail), and as compression fossils, showing the external form of the cone. These two preservation states each reveal a different range of characters, and so are defined in different terms. The permineralized form is assigned to the genus *Mazocarpon,* while the compression state is placed in *Sigillariostrobus*. There is ample evidence that these two genera overlap conceptually (Chaloner 1953), but they are not synonyms in a nomenclatural sense. Since the two genera are defined on a different spectrum of characters, there is a high probability that they have somewhat different ranges in time, as those character combinations evolved independently.

Alternative taxonomies

A number of authors faced with the problems of applying binomial nomenclature to plant fossils have offered ways of bypassing the procedures stipulated in the ICBN. Early in the history of palynology, Raistrick & Simpson (1933), for example, did not attempt to use names for their Carboniferous miospores, but referred to them by a system of letters and numbers. Interestingly, they designated the major categories of spores with a letter, and sub-numbered each type of spore within one of the letter groups. In effect, they were designating genera with letters and species with numbers! This was just an early instance of what have since come to be called parataxa; the application of designations particularly to parts of fossil organisms, or the traces of organisms. This term is now widely used for any system of naming and classifying in which the normal systems of the Botanical and Zoological Codes cannot be followed. Obvious examples among animal fossils are ichnotaxa, 'trace fossils' of organisms, ranging from footprints to bites out of fossil leaves. Many authors apply binomial nomenclature to such traces, but despite their binomial form such names constitute parataxa in that they refer not to organisms but to the trace of the organism. One such taxon, based on a burrow or a bite from a leaf, may not be the work of a single kind of causal organism, and so cannot be classified in the sense that the fossil animal itself normally can. Some authors (e.g. Meyen 1987; Hawksworth 1994) would include fossil plant form-genera in the category of parataxa. Meyen makes the distinction between such parataxa of fossil plants, and 'eutaxa' – that is, taxa comparable to those based on living organisms, which can be assigned at all levels in the taxonomic hierarchy. Other authors restrict the term parataxa to nomenclatural units which expressly avoid any resemblance to orthodox binomial nomenclature.

Meyen (1987) goes on to elaborate the idea that certain parataxa can be seen as 'satellites' to certain eutaxa, even though they are not themselves eutaxa. For example, the Mesozoic conifer form-genus *Brachyphyllum* is based on leafy shoots, different species of which are known to be attributable to two coniferalean families, the Araucariaceae (non-fossil family) and the Cheirolepidiaceae (fossil family based on an organ-genus). *Brachyphyllum* can then be regarded as a satellite genus to the Coniferales (Pinales *sensu* Meyen), although it cannot be assigned to a single family.

One of the most radical of these departures from orthodoxy was the procedure proposed by Hughes (1989). This was the culmination and refinement of a series of schemes for designating parataxa of fossil spores, which attempted to avoid some of the shortcomings of type-based binomials. He was also strongly opposed to using non-fossil ('living') generic names for Mesozoic fossils, as he believed this obscured the evidence for evolutionary change that the fossil record contains. For example, he rejected (Hughes 1986) the application of the generic name *Ginkgo* to Mesozoic leaves 'resembling those of living *Ginkgo biloba*'. He designated his taxonomic units 'palaeotaxa', which were a modified form of the entities which he had earlier called 'biorecords'. The name of each palaeotaxon would be compounded from three parts specifying the 'paleobiogroup' to which it belonged (e.g. 'Angiopoll', from angiosperm pollen), a 'time slot' within which it occurred (e.g. the Aptian stage of the Cretaceous) and a morphologically based descriptor (e.g. 'monobac'), referring in this case to the baculate exine sculpture. The total trinomial consisting of palaeobiogroup-time slot-paleotaxon would constitute the complete name. Hughes aimed particularly to prevent each clearly defined parataxonomic unit becoming blurred by specimens being assigned to it which were remote in time and space from the original record. He believed that in many cases this would result in so extending its meaning and range that it would become valueless. He argued that by developing a more finely tuned system of designation, a more refined time correlation based on palynology could be achieved. At present, it is only possible to say that his system will be vindicated if it is seen to stand the test of time.

A very different and less controversial approach to a palynological system of parataxa was set up by R. Potonié as a framework for grouping fossil spore binomials (genera and species) on the basis of their morphology. It was intended as a series of pigeon-holes for fossil spores of all ages, which would ignore what was known of the real affinity of some of them, so that they could all be ordered on a common scheme. This was his Morphographic System, set up jointly with his student Kremp (Potonié & Kremp 1954) and refined in a series of papers over the ensuing twenty years. Spores were placed in a nested series of categories analogous to a taxonomic hierarchy but with a terminology borrowed from military units; the core unit was a Turma, with above it an Anteturma and below it, the Subturma, Infraturma, Subinfraturma and so on. These morphographic units were completely 'artificial' in the sense that, for example, they brought together megaspores and microspores of unrelated plants, on the basis of their structural similarity. But they represented a framework within which any newly described fossil spore could be assigned a position close to structurally similar forms. This classification is widely used particularly for Palaeozoic and some Mesozoic spores, but becomes less relevant in arranging younger spore taxa, many of which may be assigned to living families and even genera as in Tertiary spore assemblages.

Spicer (1986) advocates opting out of conventional nomenclature entirely, in dealing with Cretaceous and Tertiary angiosperm leaf impressions. He argues that there is 'a strong case for alternative, parallel non-Linnean taxonomic systems that allow for more flexible specimen groupings. ....They should provide a temporary "holding pattern" for specimens and an experimental "scratch pad" for testing artificial or natural relationships'. This plea for a wider use of parataxa may find sympathetic support in other areas of palaeobotany.

35. Curation in museum collections

CEDRIC H. SHUTE & TIFFANY S. FOSTER

The procedures outlined here refer to practices in the Palaeobotany Section of the Natural History Museum, London (NHM), but provide a model reflecting general practices elsewhere.

What happens to your specimen if you donate it to the museum?

The museum would have accepted your donation using a variety of criteria which can be applied effectively only by an experienced curator who is familiar with the collection concerned. At the NHM ultimate responsibility for the acceptance of material rests with the Trustees; the only legal obligation is to accept holotype specimens if they are offered.

The following are examples of criteria for accepting specimens other than primary types: specimens from a locality not previously represented, or poorly represented, in the collection; specimens from a precise stratigraphic horizon from a locality which might already be in the collection, but where the horizon is vague; particularly fine examples of species already in the collections; species new to the collections; specimens showing unusual preservation; specimens cited previously in a publication; specimens about to be cited.

You will sign a 'Transfer of Title' form which gives the museum legal ownership of your donation. The specimen(s) is then recorded and indexed as being your donation, and will include your personal details and data about the specimen. This information is kept centrally in the Palaeontology Department and is, at present, hand recorded. You will get an official acknowledgement of your donation. The specimen is checked for any special conservation requirements and action taken if necessary. The next step is to enter information about the specimen/s in an electronic database specific to palaeobotany. This information includes, amongst others, the collector/presenter, along with the scientific name given to the specimen, stratigraphic details, locality information, lithology, and remarks on the type of preservation and any particular conservation carried out. If the specimen has been featured in a publication the details are recorded. The specimen is given a unique registration number in the database.

The registration number is hand written on a ticket and glued either to the specimen, or to a container if required. The 'ordinary' hand specimen is stored in a suitably sized white cardboard tray made from acid-free cardboard. A small label with selected data is printed out from the database and kept with the specimen or container. An appropriate home in the collections is now found for the specimen and the location within the collections recorded in the above-mentioned database.

Conservation

The primary purpose of curation is to keep well documented specimens, in good condition, sensibly arranged and readily accessible for study. Conservation of specimens has, therefore, a major role in, and is an inseparable part of, curation. It would be disappointing, to say the least, for a researcher to discover a label and pile of fragmentary remains, particularly if the fragments represent all that is left of a figured, or even worse, a type specimen.

The Palaeontology Building at The Natural History Museum in London is air-conditioned to control humidity and temperature levels. Ideally, different preservational states should be stored in different conditions according to their conservation requirements. For example, specimens with a high pyrite (FeS_2) content need to be kept at around 30% relative humidity while Pleistocene bones, for example, need to be kept at around 50–60% relative humidity. Temperatures should be maintained between 16–18°C and the specimens should be protected from light. The specimen storage units consist of drawers and shelving with doors 'sealing' the units. Doors should be shut after use as they act as a buffer between the conditions in the drawers and the surrounding areas, and most importantly, help keep conditions within the drawers as stable as possible.

Despite the above, additional care often has to be taken with specimens preserved in pyrite. A combination of carbon and pyrite seems to be particularly conducive to pyritic decay as discussed by Howie (1979). The breakdown of FeS_2 (iron sulphide) under conditions of increased humidity to various hydrated iron sulphates results in expansion of the pyrite and the production of sulphuric acid

SHUTE, C. H. & FOSTER, T. S. 1999. Curation in museum collections. *In*: JONES, T. P. & ROWE, N. P. (eds) *Fossil Plants and Spores: modern techniques.* Geological Society, London, 184–186.

(Bang 1994; Newman 1998). The equation is

$$FeS_2 + O_2 + H_2O \rightarrow FeSO_4.H_2O + H_2SO_4.H_2O.$$

Pyritic preservations of plants often have a carbon + pyrite combination that requires special attention in order to prevent decay. If the specimen already shows signs of pyrite decay (a fine white or yellow crystal growth), it is treated in the Palaeontology Conservation Unit. First the specimen is placed in a controlled environment to slow the decay process. The controlled environment is usually an airtight polyethylene or polypropylene container, which also contains a silica gel desiccant equilibrated to buffer the relative humidity to the specified level of 30%. The containers we use are from the 'Snapware' range of 'Stewart containers' (see Appendix) produced by the Stewart Company. Specimens are visible through the sides of the container. If the container needs to be opened, a record is kept of each occasion and includes the length of time open, or for how long the specimen was taken out. The next step of treatment is then determined. It may not be necessary to treat the specimen further and it will be stored in the collections in the controlled environment of the Stewart container and monitored closely. However, in some cases chemical treatment may be required. There are two methods of chemical treatment and both utilize hazardous chemicals which must only be used in a suitable workplace environment. One treatment involves exposing the specimen to ammonia gas which reacts with the sulphuric acid and with the hydrated iron sulphates, giving a general unbalanced equation of

$$FeSO_4.H_2O + H_2SO_4.H_2O + NH_3 \rightarrow$$
$$(NH_4)_2SO_4 + Fe(OH)_2 + H_2O.$$

The neutralized decay products are mechanically removed by brushing, scraping, airbrading or grinding with dental burrs, depending on the fragility of the specimen. The other involves the use of a neutralizing, chelating agent (see Glossary; ethanolamine thioglycollate) which removes the decay products chemically by neutralizing the sulphuric acid (the ethanolamine) and removing the iron from the oxidized pyrite (the thioglycollate). Whatever treatment is given, the specimen must then be stored in the specified environment and monitored.

Certain localities are well known for 'producing' pyritic plant specimens which require special care – the Eocene London Clay Formation is an example, discussed in detail by Collinson (1983). Specimens from the London Clay are kept in Silicone Fluid (Dow Corning 200/350cs grade) in lidded glass tubes so as to exclude all air and moisture. As an adjunct to this, Plastazote (see Appendix) (a dense foam plastic) is used to line the drawers which store the tubes so that they do not fall over when the drawer is opened or shut. Plastazote can be readily cut to the drawer size and suitable sized holes for the tubes made with a corkborer. If a pyritic specimen is not from a known 'special care locality' and shows no obvious signs of decay then no special care is undertaken, but specimen will be monitored. If subsequently the specimen shows signs of decay it will be specially treated as outlined above.

Specimens in a fragile matrix might need consolidating and the matrix, but not the specimen, may be coated with 'Butvar' (see Appendix) (polyvinyl butyryl). The plant specimen itself should not be coated as it can obscure fine detail, but collectors are often tempted to varnish a specimen to enhance the contrast with the matrix. Broken specimens can be joined together with a chemically reversible adhesive such as 'Butvar' or 'Paraloid B72' (see Appendix). Collinson (1987) gives more detailed discussion on the special problems of conserving palaeobotanical material. Wellman *et al.* (1996) discuss the particular problems associated with the storage of material on scanning electron microscope (SEM) stubs.

The database

Details of the specimen are recorded in an electronic database which replaced hand written ledgers in 1990. This database is an in-house modified version of a PIC-based commercial system, PACE-UX Runtime System Rev 2.1.3 (see Appendix) from Ampersand Systems Ltd, and contains 314 fields and sub-fields which can be interrelated. One of the sets of fields relates specimens and preparations made from them and vice versa.

The registration number

The first field in the database is the registration number consisting of a letter prefix and a number which will be unique to the specimen. In the Palaeobotany Section the prefix is V. If the specimen is subdivided the following applies: part/counterpart – the suffix 'a' for the part and 'b' for the counterpart. Preparations are given a $ sign suffix followed by a number. Individual plants – on a slab of shale, for instance – are numbered (1), (2) etc. Thus, a registration number V.99999b (4) $5 indicates that it is the fifth preparation from the counterpart of a fourth designated specimen from a specimen with the base number 99999. For an example of this usage in a publication see Rowe (1992). Registration numbers can be given to authors prior to the submission of a manuscript for publication.

All this effort is to create a permanent curatorial link between a specimen and any associated fragments related to that specimen; modern investigation can frequently result in an original specimen which now consists of many deliberately organized pieces (deliberate as opposed to a specimen in many pieces because of neglect). Shute (1986) discusses the complexities of the terminologies and designation of type material, and exactly what the term 'specimen' might mean with reference to palaeobotanical material.

An appropriate home

The fossil plant collection at the NHM, London consists of approximately 250 000 specimens which include some 30 000 microscope slides. Specimens are arranged according to their geological age, locality and botanical classification.

The base unit we use in the arrangement of the collection is stratigraphical. The collection ranges the geological column from the Proterozoic to the Sub-Recent and appropriate subdivisions are used for the Periods and Epochs. As examples, the Devonian is subdivided merely into Lower, Middle, Upper, whereas the Tertiary is much more stratigraphically subdivided.

Within the major stratigraphic units the collection is separated into material from the British Isles and material from elsewhere (for the sake of brevity, in practise we refer to British and Foreign collections and these terms are used throughout the remainder of this article). So, for instance, the British Jurassic is followed physically in the collections by the Foreign Jurassic.

For the Foreign collection there is a systematic arrangement of the countries of the world, and this arrangement is followed in any of the stratigraphic divisions of the collections outlined above. Obviously, dependent on our acquisitions or the availability of material of a given age from a country, there will be gaps in the collections. The arrangement skips any gap and goes on to the next country on our list.

Within the stratigraphic divisions and countries contained in the collection the next arrangement is one involving the hierarchy of Botanical Systematics – the classification of the plant Kingdom. Without delving deeply into this, the end result means that in, say, a collection from the Eocene of a particular country the plants could be ordered from algae to angiosperms. If a collection is from a single locality and Horizon and is considered sufficiently large it is kept together, but still in its appropriate place in the collection layout, and arranged in its botanical classification. Examples of this in our collection can be found, for instance, in the British Lower Carboniferous where material from the Drybrook Sandstone of Gloucestershire is distinguished, and in the Foreign Oligocene where plants from Florissant, Colorado are similarly treated.

The end result from all the above is that, for example, a conifer from the Oligocene of Austria would finish up numbered, recorded and placed appropriately in the collection. Importantly it can readily be found again! The computer database contains the location of the specimen in the collection, but apart from this a card index is maintained of genera and species and the same cards contain information on localities of these species and where they can be found in the collection. A question which could well be asked of us might be: what fossil plants have you got from Turkey? Because of the frequency of such questions another card index was built and is maintained which lists all the countries from around the world from which we have material, any stratigraphic divisions of that country, and where in the collections they can be found. Whilst all the above concerns a major collection of plant fossils, Shute & Cleal (1987) deal with aspects perhaps more pertinent to smaller collections.

We should like to thank William Lindsay of the Palaeontology Department for his advice on conservation practice.

Part Seven Sedimentology, Taphonomy and Stratigraphy

36. Experimental sedimentology

GARY J. NICHOLS

Fossil plant and spore material is found in the stratigraphic record preserved in sedimentary rocks. In order to provide a palaeoenvironmental context for these fossils, an analysis needs to be made of the physical and chemical conditions under which the sediment was deposited. This is a standard procedure of facies analysis which is used to interpret sediments and sedimentary rocks in terms of the environment of deposition (Walker & James 1992; Reading 1996).

An important part of facies analysis is a consideration of the processes of sedimentation. It is often possible to constrain such parameters as water depth and current velocity and use this information to quantify the physical conditions at the time of deposition. Quantification of palaeo-hydraulic conditions is possible because a wealth of data has been collected over several decades based on laboratory experiments (e.g. Harms *et al.* 1975). These experiments have almost exclusively involved the behaviour of siliciclastic sand and mud in flume tanks and wave tanks. Such material typically has a density between two and three times that of water, and most sand grade material has a specific gravity close to that of quartz (2.65 g cm^{-3}). The fluid dynamic properties of particles in a flow are mainly dependent on the contrast between the density of the clasts and the transporting medium although the shape of some materials (e.g. mica grains) is also a factor. The settling rate of clasts is governed by Stoke's Law and is dependent on both mass and volume. The force required to move a particle in a flow is related to its mass rather than its size according to Bernoulli's Equation (Allen 1985). Consequently, any particles which are significantly less dense than 'normal' clastic material, such as fossil plant material, will behave differently and their distribution in sediments cannot be predicted using relationships determined for sand and mud.

Experimental sedimentology studies involving material which is of low density, including particles with initial densities less than that of water, have been carried out on pyroclastic material (Whitham 1986). Pumice fragments may have a lower bulk density than water because they form as a rapidly-cooled 'froth' of molten rock which incorporates gas bubbles as it solidifies. Pumice may initially float, but sinks as it becomes waterlogged. The rate at which waterlogging occurs depends on the rate at which gas is replaced by water through inter-connected pores within the fragment. Large pumice clasts may float for months or years before becoming waterlogged and sinking (Whitham 1986).

Hydrodynamic properties of plant material

Fresh plant tissue floats on water under most circumstances, so any wood, leaves, flowers, spores, seeds, pollen, etc. will initially be carried on the surface of flowing water and remain buoyant in standing water. Plant tissue of all types sinks once it becomes waterlogged. The rate at which waterlogging occurs will be determined by the permeability of the surface of the material and the ease with which water percolates into the pore spaces within the tissue to displace gas. Highly porous tissues, such as palm tree stems, absorb water quickly and therefore sink rapidly, whereas some seeds, for example, may have coatings which are relatively impermeable. A further factor is the shape of the plant debris: leaves have a large surface area and may be partially supported by surface tension, especially in calm water. Agitation of the water tends to increase the rate of waterlogging by repeatedly immersing material floating on the surface. The rate of waterlogging may vary from a few hours to many years. Any consideration of the behaviour of plant material in water must therefore take into account the fact that the particles will have started off buoyant and can only have been deposited and become part of a stratigraphic succession once the material has become waterlogged.

Experimental sedimentology of plant material

The behaviour of plant material under different conditions of transport and deposition has been considered by a number of authors (Spicer 1981; 1989*b*; Collinson 1983*a*; Ferguson 1985; Hill & Gibson 1986; Christophel & Greenwood 1988), but in most cases work has concentrated on observations of material in natural streams and

NICHOLS, G. J. 1999. Experimental sedimentology. *In*: JONES, T. P. & ROWE, N. P. (eds) *Fossil Plants and Spores: modern techniques*. Geological Society, London, 189–193.

lakes. Spicer (1981, 1989*b*) and Ferguson (1985) carried out laboratory and field experiments on the settling rate of different types of leaf and Cope (1985) performed some experiments on the settling of charcoal. Holmes (1994) presents a review of experiments on the behaviour of palynomorphs under different flow conditions in laboratory flume tanks and under field conditions, including the studies of Brush & Brush (1972). In this chapter only experiments involving macroscopic material are considered and the reader is referred to Holmes (1994) and Brush & Brush (1972) for details of experimental procedures appropriate for palynomorphs.

There has been some more recent experimental work on the hydrodynamic behaviour of plant material involving charcoal (e.g. Vaughan & Nichols 1995). However, the experimental procedures used for quantifying the rates and processes of deposition of charcoal can be applied to most other categories of macroscopic plant material. This is because, in most cases, the same principles of starting with a buoyant substance which becomes waterlogged through time apply. Differences will arise in the rates at which waterlogging occurs, the size ranges used, and the length of time an experiment is run, for different materials. There may be differences between the settling behaviour of 'fresh' plant material which contains moisture and fragments which have been allowed to dry out, although experiments to investigate this have yet to be carried out.

Settling tanks

Some of the earliest experiments on the behaviour of charcoal in water were simple settling experiments (Cope 1985). These demonstrated for charcoal the same inverse relationship between size of particle and rate of settling which has also been found in pumice fragments (Whitham 1986). Large particles have a smaller surface area in proportion to their volume and longer pathways through the pores for water to reach internal parts of the buoyant object. The main drawback of these experiments is that a static water body is a poor simulation of natural conditions as in almost all circumstances there is likely to be wind creating waves across the surface or currents agitating the water and buoyant clasts. Subsequent experimental work on settling rates has therefore been carried out in agitated (wave) tanks.

Wave tank experiments

Apparatus

To simulate natural conditions, settling experiments may be carried out in a tank where a wave paddle agitates the water (Fig. 36.1). The apparatus used by Vaughan & Nichols (1995) consisted of a glass tank, 120 cm long, 40 cm wide and 50 cm deep. Smaller tanks (60 cm by 30 cm by 30 cm) have also been successfully used. In each case the water depth is two-thirds to three-quarters that of the tank depth. A paddle attached to a small electric motor is used to generate waves continuously in the tank. A variable motor speed allows for adjustment to the period of the waves generated so that the desired degree of agitation is maintained. If wave generation is slow the advantages over a simple settling tank are limited, and at rapid paddle movement there is a danger of water being forced over the edges of the tank. Once appropriate conditions have been established they are maintained for suites of experimental runs. The conditions of agitation are thus constant allowing comparison of settling rates.

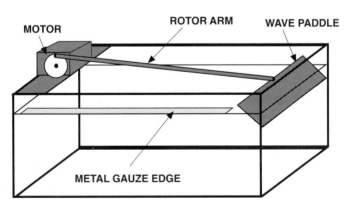

Fig. 36.1. An agitated wave tank for experiments on the settling rates of buoyant plant material. A galvanized metal gauze strip along one side helps to break up the waves and agitate the water surface.

The function of the agitation is to repeatedly submerge charcoal fragments floating on the surface such that their surfaces are continuously wetted. It has been found to be necessary to place some form of baffle, for example, a strip of metal gauze, around the edges of the tank at water level to disrupt the water surface. This prevents the formation of stationary standing waves on the water surface. Once fragments are waterlogged to the extent of achieving neutral buoyancy, they remain in suspension in the tank, circulating in the water body before further waterlogging increases the density to above that of water. Fragments which reach the bottom may saltate initially but eventually remain in contact with the base of the tank, moving back and forth with the water.

Sampling

To determine the rate at which material is becoming waterlogged, some means of sampling the floating or deposited material at time intervals through the period of agitation is required. Vaughan & Nichols (1995) used a small sieve to remove the floating material from a fixed surface area of the water: this provided a measure of the amount of material that was still floating after each time interval. The proportion in suspension was determined by siphoning off a fixed volume of water containing suspended fragments from the centre of the tank and using this as a guide to the total volume of material in suspension. The proportion which was on the base of the tank could then be calculated. The mass extracted through the sampling process at each stage was subtracted from the mass remaining in the tank for the purposes of later sampling events.

A disadvantage of using a sieve to sample the surface of the water is that it is difficult to ensure that the sample is representative of the whole surface area, as material tends to cluster in areas on the water surface. A more satisfactory method is to use some form of suction pump to remove only the settled charcoal from the base of the tank. A simple fish tank pump has been found to be effective for this purpose and a flexible hose is used to 'hoover' the settled charcoal from the floor of the tank.

The charcoal removed after set time intervals is dried for a fixed period at a standard temperature to ensure that all the material is desiccated to the same degree. The samples removed at each stage are weighed and compared to the initial mass of charcoal introduced into the tank to provide a measure of the rate at which the material is becoming waterlogged.

Results

The results of a series of experiments relating to the controls on the deposition of charcoal are presented in Vaughan & Nichols (1995). The rate at which charred material settled in agitated tanks was found to be dependent on the size of particle, temperature at which the charcoal was formed, the salinity of the water in the tank, and the nature of a substrate placed at the base of the tank (sand or clay) (Vaughan & Nichols 1995).

Flume tank experiments

A flume tank is an artificial water channel in which the processes of water flow and sediment transport can be observed and quantified. They may vary in size from small, paddle-driven elliptical channels a

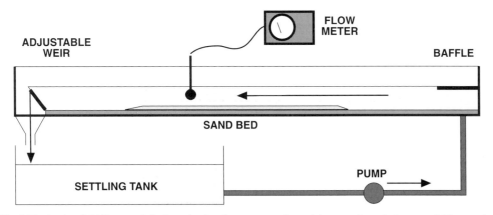

Fig. 36.2. An Armfield flume tank for investigating the processes of entraining waterlogged plant material in a sandy substrate.

few centimetres wide and deep and a few tens of centimetres long, to artificial channels metres wide and tens of metres in length. The most widely used laboratory flume tank is the Armfield Flume (Armfield Engineering) which is 30 cm wide, 50 cm deep and normally 10 m long (Fig. 36.2). Flow in the flume is maintained by a pump which recirculates water via settling tanks. The velocity of the flow can be varied by adjusting a valve on the pump and controlling the level of a weir at the upstream end of the flume (which also adjusts the level of the water). Current velocities up to a metre per second can be achieved, allowing experiments to range over the whole stability field for bedforms in sand (Harms *et al.* 1975). Current velocity is determined by a small impeller immersed in the tank and attached to a current meter, individually calibrated to provide values for flow velocities. Small impellers do not interfere with the flow and can be positioned close to the sediment–water interface.

Experiments in a large recirculating flume tank involving buoyant plant material are not practical because anything floating will become trapped in the settling tanks and would not be returned to the flume. Additionally, any material which is recirculated will pass through the pump and is likely to be broken up in the process. However, it is possible to carry out experiments on the behaviour of waterlogged material under different flow and substrate conditions. Waterlogging of material for experiments in flume tanks is carried out in a wave tank for set periods of time to achieve uniform water saturation (see above).

Experimental procedure

It takes time for an equilibrium to be achieved between the flow velocity and bedforms in a sandy substrate on the base of the tank. In the case of ripple fields formed in fine to medium sand at velocities of between 0.2 and 0.6 m s^{-1} an equilibrium is normally achieved after 10–20 min. The introduction of plant material therefore has to be delayed until stable conditions in the tank are reached. Waterlogged plant material is close to neutral buoyancy and if it is added from above at the upstream end of the flume tank much of the material is swept to the far end of the tank in temporary suspension. If the interaction between the plant material and the bedforms in the sandy substrate are to be considered, the material has to be introduced at the sediment–water interface at the upstream end of the flume. This can be achieved by burying the plant material in the sand at the upstream end of the flume and then releasing it by stirring up the sand once the flow and bedforms are in equilibrium (Fig 36.3). The released plant material then moves along the flume as bedload.

To obtain reproducible and comparable results for different flow conditions and different types of plant material a set of standard procedures has to be adopted. Stirring of the sand to release the buried material into the flow is carried out over a fixed time period (e.g. 60 s) and it is ensured that all the material is released. Flow in the tank is then maintained for a fixed time, typically four or five minutes, and then the pump rate is reduced. Care must be taken not to shut off the flow instantly as

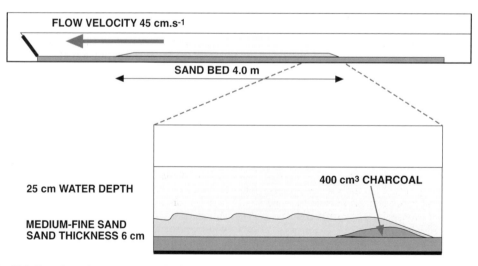

Fig. 36.3. Experimental arrangement used to introduce relatively buoyant material to the flow in a flume tank.

Fig. 36.4. Charcoal in the trough of a ripple formed in a bed of sand in a flume tank. Experiments have shown that there is an optimum velocity for the entrainment of low density particles in rippled sand.

this can cause a backwash. Similarly, when the water is drained out of the tank this must be allowed to occur slowly so that the substrate is not disturbed. To establish the amount of the introduced plant material which has been entrained in the sandy substrate, the top of the sand bed is removed and sieved to separate the plant debris which is then dried and weighed in the same manner as for the settling experiments. It should be noted that separation by sieving may not be possible if the plant material is in the same size range as the sand, and other techniques of separation must be employed (for example, by relying on the greater buoyancy of the plant material and washing it out of the collected sand).

Results

Unpublished results from experiments on the behaviour of charcoal in flume tanks supervised by the author indicate that there are optimum flow conditions for entraining material close to neutral buoyancy in flow over a sandy substrate. At low flow velocities, (<0.2 m s^{-1}) there is little or no movement of fine to medium sand; the charcoal moves along the bed surface by rolling and saltating and is not entrained within the sand bed. At higher flow velocities (>0.6 m s^{-1}) there is a flat sand bed of rolling and saltating grains: much of the charcoal is in temporary suspension at these velocities and has little residence time on the bed surface. Once again, very little of the charcoal is entrained. The greatest amounts of charcoal within the sand substrate have been found under conditions of active current ripple migration between 0.4 and 0.55 m s^{-1}. Observations indicate that this is because any plant material which accumulates in the troughs of the ripples is engulfed by avalanching sand as the ripple crest migrates downstream (Fig 36.4).

Conclusions

Experiments carried out on the rates of settling of charred plant material have shown that factors such as the size of particles, temperature at which charring occurred, the salinity of the water and the nature of the substrate are all important. Further work on the settling behaviour of the tissues of different plants or different parts of the same plant will hopefully provide more constraints. Flume tank experiments have shown that there is an optimum range of current velocities for the entrainment of clasts of low density, such as plant debris, in fields of rippled sand. Laboratory work of this type has shown that understanding of the hydro-dynamic behaviour of plant debris may be critical to the interpretation of assemblages of plant fossils in sediments.

37. Palynofacies analysis

DAVID J. BATTEN

The technique of palynofacies analysis is widely used today as an important aid for the determination of environments of deposition and the identification of source rocks for petroleum. During the present decade, its potential in sequence stratigraphic studies has also been investigated. The number of articles that focus on aspects of palynofacies analysis and related topics has increased exponentially since the beginning of the 1980s, as indicated by the extensive lists of references in the recent contributions of Traverse (1994), Tyson (1995) and Batten (1996a, b).

Palynofacies analysis requires that all types of acid (hydrochloric acid (HCl) and hydrofluoric acid (HF)) resistant organic matter (OM; Table 37.1) recovered from rock or sediment samples by palynological extraction methods are examined. It does not encompass the full range of sedimentary organic matter (SOM) such as solvent-extractable biomolecules, nor is it synonymous with the determination of the facies distribution of selected palynomorphs (e.g. dinoflagellate cysts and/or miospores (small spores and pollen grains)) without regard to the associated OM, which is usually more abundant. Critical to all palynofacies studies is the need for consistency of approach to sample-processing (Batten & Morrison 1983) and data-handling. It also helps to use a straightforward terminology that organic geochemists, coal petrographers and others who analyse SOM by different methods can understand and with which they can readily compare their observations and interpretations.

An appreciation of the enormous number of variables that affect the production and preservation of SOM is essential if data are not to be over-interpreted (Batten 1996a). Only a tiny proportion of the OM that is potentially available for deposition in sediments will become entombed. Even after deposition, preservation is by no means guaranteed; microbial and diagenetic processes can degrade and ultimately destroy all kinds of OM.

Classification and documentation of palynological matter (PM)

The various classifications of PM (Batten 1996a: POM has been used for particulate organic matter;

Table 37.1) have been the subject of much discussion, but consensus has been difficult to achieve. Typically they comprise broad groupings of palynomorphs and structured organic matter (STOM). Depending on the age of the material being examined and the environments of deposition represented, the palynomorphs will include at least some of the following: acritarchs, chitinozoans, chlorococcalean algae, dinoflagellate cysts, foraminiferal linings, fungal sclerotia, spores and other reproductive parts, land-plant spores and pollen grains, prasinophyte algae, scolecodonts, zygnematalean and other green algae, and a miscellaneous category. STOM may be subdivided into phytoclasts and zooclasts. Phytoclasts include wood, bark and cork, charcoal and other black particles, cuticles and non-cuticular tissues, fungal hyphae, and various types of tubes, filaments and hairs. Their composition again varies according to age. Among the zooclasts are graptolite siculae and arthropod cuticles. Unstructured (structureless) organic matter (USTOM) is often abundant in palynological preparations. The main component is usually amorphous organic matter (AOM). This may be determined to have a terrestrial (AOMT) and/or aquatic (AOMA) derivation. Other unstructured substances include gelified matter, resin and amber, and solid bitumen.

Size, shape and structural characteristics have commonly been used (e.g. by Whitaker *et al.* 1992) to subdivide components of the ubiquitous black and brown particles (STOM) in palynological preparations, particularly to enhance interpretations of depositional conditions in which fine-grained

Table 37.1. *Explanation of acronyms*

OM:	organic matter
AOM:	amorphous OM
AOMA:	AOM of aquatic derivation
AOMT:	AOM of terrestrial derivation
HI:	hydrogen index
PM:	palynological OM
POM:	particulate OM
SOM:	sedimentary OM
STOM:	structured OM
TOC:	total organic carbon
USTOM:	unstructured (structureless) OM

BATTEN, D. J. 1999. Palynofacies analysis. *In*: JONES, T. P. & ROWE, N. P. (eds) *Fossil Plants and Spores: modern techniques*. Geological Society, London, 194–198.

marine sediments accumulated. The preservation state of palynomorphs, cuticles and other particulate matter is also usually recorded. Thermal maturation indications reflected by palynomorph colours are noted when changes towards darker shades and increasing opacity are recognizable through thick piles of sediment and/or successions representing stratigraphic units of differing ages and geological histories. This is essential when the determination of source potential for hydrocarbons is a goal. The documentation of AOM is of particular significance both in this respect and because it is the most important organic component of the majority of petroleum source rocks.

General principles and approach to analysis

The numerous variables that affect the preservation of PM in, and its subsequent recovery from, sediments and sedimentary rocks must always be taken into account in order to reduce the temptation to read too much into palynofacies data. It has long been known that there is a strong relationship between lithology and the occurrence and relative abundance of palynomorphs and associated PM (Batten 1973). For example, some of the most diverse and well-preserved miospore assemblages occur in medium and brownish grey siltstones and silty mudstones whereas green and reddened argillaceous deposits are commonly barren. Grey mudstones and shales are more likely than sandstones to yield not only larger numbers of palynomorphs but also a greater proportion of these microfossils in the PM recovered. On the other hand, abundances and proportions may vary widely according to only slight differences in lithology and stratigraphic level, and relationships may be blurred by reworking.

Palynofacies data should, therefore, be linked as far as possible to good lithological logs of surface exposures, borehole cores and suites of other types of subsurface samples. The colour, grain-size, type of bedding, sedimentary and biogenic structures, faunal and macrofloral content, and other features of the deposits from which PM is to be extracted should be carefully documented. Cuttings samples are the least satisfactory in these respects because they comprise only small fragments of rock, and commonly a mixture of lithologies.

For all studies, large numbers of samples are also necessary if particular kinds of palynofacies are to be recognized and their palaeoenvironmental implications interpreted. Depending upon the thickness and lithological composition of the succession to be investigated, sampling horizons should normally be

closely spaced in parts if not throughout. This is because there may be significant differences between the organic composition of beds and even laminae, and the degree of variation in palynofacies characters must be ascertained before conclusions are drawn. Although repeated associations may be encountered in studies involving many samples, it should not be expected that closely comparable or identical lithologies are necessarily characterized by a particular type of palynofacies. This has been demonstrated (e.g. by Gastaldo *et al.* 1996) in palynofacies studies of modern sediments and their depositional environments.

Laboratory processing should be as routine as possible. For most samples this means beginning with a known weight or volume and digesting the inorganic matrix using only HCl and HF prior to mounting some of the PM recovered on a microscope slide for examination in transmitted light. A slide of unsieved, unoxidised PM is essential for palynofacies and related thermal maturation studies. Further treatment, which may include filtering, sieving, oxidation (usually necessary if reasonable assemblages of palynomorphs are to be extracted from coals and oil shales) and ultrasonic vibration of the residue (see Chapters 4–6), must be carefully monitored.

Data accumulation

Much palynofacies work is necessarily semi-quantitative. It may consist of visual estimations of the relative abundances of organic components recorded on a scale of three (e.g. P/present, C/common, A/Abundant) or more points, or of particle counts that, where possible, are expressed in percentages. Absolute abundance trends have seldom been documented in pre-Quaternary palynology, but when determined and combined with total organic carbon (TOC) values they have been shown to be useful (Tyson 1989). Quantification of palynofacies data by image analysis has also been attempted (e.g. Lorente 1990), and continues to be developed. Automated measurements of particle area may be analysed numerically and used, for example, as a basis for graphical representations of changes through a section.

A review of the literature has revealed that authors have commonly concentrated on particular characters of palynofacies while making only limited use of, or even neglecting entirely, some components. Although this is understandable, the degree of bias can be overdone to the extent that some potentially important information is omitted from consideration. A reasonable balance needs to be struck between the degree of subdivision of components of palynological preparations and the likelihood that useful conclusions can be drawn from the data accumulated. The typical biases are either towards phytoclasts, with minimal subdivision of the palynomorphs (e.g. very few or no taxa being identified), or towards palynomorphs, occurrences of genera and species being documented in detail whereas only the broadest groupings of the associated PM are noted. Precisely what to record from a series of palynological preparations will depend on the morphological range of the PM within a succession, basin or region. Categories that are appropriate for monotonous marine formations in which facies changes are subtle may be of little value for interpreting a basin-margin section in which sedimentological characters vary widely and partly reflect periodic freshwater influence on the environment of deposition. To a lesser extent the state of the taxonomy of the palynomorphs in a particular succession or region, i.e. whether or not most specimens can be identified reasonably easily, may also influence the decision on what to record.

It is good practice to document as part of the general palynofacies log not only the relative abundances of the major palynomorph groups but also certain taxa, such as *Pediastrum* and *Scenedesmus*, that are known to have palaeoenvironmental significance, and then to include these in separate counts of all types of palynomorphs. The latter provide a record of diversity (i.e. the number of taxa present in each sample) and, among other things (see below), also a basis for dominance plots in which the numbers of specimens of one, two or more of the most abundant species are divided by the total number of specimens counted in samples and expressed as percentages (cf. Goodman 1979).

Data handling

Quantitative data can be evaluated both by eye and numerically to assess the influence of lithological variation and stratigraphic level on palynofacies, and to determine relationships between palynomorph taxa, phytoclasts and other components of PM. Some practitioners identify types of palynofacies only after their datasets have been subjected to cluster analysis and/or other numerical techniques. Although the recognition of groupings and the categorization of some of the more nondescript palynofacies is usually aided by such procedures it is, however, preferable that most palynofacies-types are identifiable without recourse to them (Batten 1973, 1996a; Kovach & Batten 1994). The more subtle the differences in composition, the more likely it is that they are an artefact of the method of laboratory processing or data recording.

Sedimentary successions may be subdivided into zones not only by the traditional biostratigraphic method of using first and last appearances and relative abundances of palynomorph taxa but also on the basis of a variety of other quantitative and qualitative data such as ratios between selected taxa, recurrent associations, and relative abundances of different types of phytoclasts and AOM. These may have only limited value on their own but, when combined, can be used to establish trends in palynofacies characters within a stratigraphic context. Occurrences of palynomorphs can often be related to different palynofacies and hence to palaeoenvironments (Hughes & Moody-Stuart 1967; Batten 1973). Recurrent associations are commonly independent of stratigraphic level, but some may occur in the same order up-section. Zonations that combine palynofacies characteristics with occurrences of palynomorphs are likely to be erected more often in the future than hitherto as the demand for high resolution biostratigraphic and palaeoenvironmental data increases (cf. Batten 1992). Although they cannot generally be expected to have more than local application, undoubtedly parts of some will also have chronostratigraphic value. Events indicated may be tectonic and/or climatic and, in the marine realm, regional or global changes in relative sea-level. The determination of facies controls on palynomorph occurrences may be enhanced by comparing the palynology of a series of (relatively) neighbouring sections. These are more likely to yield similar palynofacies than distant locations which may also present correlation difficulties. As a result, local trends and laterally comparable associations may be recognized.

Applications

Palynofacies analysis as an aid to the interpretation of environments of deposition and the identification of source rocks for petroleum has recently been considered in detail by Tyson (1995) and Batten (1996a, b). Emphasis is placed here mainly on its significance and potential in biostratigraphic and sequence stratigraphic studies. Aspects of both, but especially the latter, have been increasingly investigated during the past few years (e.g. Oboh-Ikuenobe 1996; Schiøler et al. 1997).

When the time represented by a succession is too short for evolutionary differences to be recognizable in palynomorph assemblages, it may still be possible to erect a zonation using palynofacies characters that can be consistently recognized on a local scale. As indicated above, these may reflect not only changes in conditions of deposition but also in climate and ecology. With the oil industry currently placing considerable emphasis on improving the recovery of hydrocarbons from producing oil fields, there is a need for biostratigraphy to be applied on a very fine scale to both determine reservoir architecture and provide answers to problems associated with petroleum production and reservoir development. In such circumstances, palynological effort must rely largely on quantitative and semi-quantitative analyses of data and, hence, on palynofacies from which local changes in depositional conditions may be inferred. For the most reliable results, such studies should be based on conventional core samples. Unfortunately, for wells drilled in connection with petroleum exploration and production, only cuttings samples, and perhaps a few sidewall cores, are usually available for analysis. The stratigraphic uncertainties pertaining to these inevitably reduce the quality of the interpretations that are possible.

In subsurface studies, a sequence stratigraphic framework can be based simply on the recognition of electric log patterns for well sections that are correlatable over an entire basin. However, without biostratigraphic control the identification of sequence boundaries must inevitably be, at least partly, tentative. Hence, the integration of biostratigraphy, seismic stratigraphy, palynofacies and geophysical log correlations has become increasingly necessary in sequence stratigraphic studies. In marine successions of Late Triassic and younger ages, biostratigraphic precision is commonly provided by occurrences of dinoflagellate cysts that can be calibrated with standard ammonite, planktonic foraminiferal and nannofossil zones. Other palynomorphs must be used for older successions.

The sequence stratigraphic distribution of PM depends on both sediment supply and the degree of oxygenation of the environment, which must in turn be linked to climate and sea-level (Tyson 1996). Rapid deposition of clastic material may increase the chances of preservation of PM in oxic conditions, whereas in anoxic environments this serves mainly to dilute it. The relative importance of the presence or absence of oxygen increases as the rate of sediment accumulation falls, and tends to be greatest in transgressive to early 'highstand systems tracts' (Tyson 1996; for sequence stratigraphic terminology, see Hesselbo & Parkinson 1996, and numerous other recent publications). Productivity in shelf environments, where many successions of organic-rich sediments that have subsequently become petroleum source rocks were deposited, is also a significant factor.

It is logical that, in addition to palynomorph occurrences and zonations, there should also be relationships between palynofacies characters and sequence stratigraphic units. The environmental variables that have controlled the deposition of freshwater and terrestrially derived PM in marine deposits are particularly important in this respect.

Miospore assemblages, often in association with abundant STOM, may be diverse if sediment accumulation was not far from the source vegetation. Palynofacies of near-shore brackish-marine and inner neritic successions may contain valuable indicators of the composition of hinterland vegetation, suggesting habitats ranging from montane to lowland swamp. Such distributions are seldom manifested at sites further offshore where palynomorph assemblages can be impoverished, both numerically and taxonomically, but relative abundances of various types of phytoclasts have been used successfully to interpret more open marine depositional environments (see Batten 1996a and references therein). Concentrations of a particular taxon in unexpected places may reflect winnowing from a relatively high energy, near-shore environment and/or dispersal by currents. Anomalous abundances of this sort have been recorded most often for bisaccate pollen.

The relationship between PM of marine origin and sequence stratigraphy is more subtle because of oxidation–reduction (redox) variations not only at the sediment–water interface but also in the water column above. Changes in relative abundances and taxonomic diversity of both miospores and phytoplankton may be used to determine proximity to sediment source and hence aid recognition of relative sea-level changes within a sedimentary sequence. Dinoflagellate cysts are mainly associated with, and usually most diverse in, shallow shelf deposits. Low relative abundances may be associated with either basinal or marginal marine settings, although large numbers of just a few species may also indicate near-shore, low-salinity conditions. An increase in diversity of cysts in a sedimentary succession may, therefore, correlate with periods of relative sea-level rise when terrestrial influence on the depositional environment and, hence, the input of miospores, cuticles and wood fragments, was in decline. Problems can, however, arise in sections comprising marginal marine deposits that were swept periodically towards the centre of a basin. Submarine fan accumulations typically yield palynofacies complexes that are difficult to interpret.

The occurrence of individual species or species-groups of dinoflagellate cysts may enable the recognition of unconformities and maximum flooding surfaces in proximal settings, as Powell et al. (1996) have noted in British Palaeogene deposits. They found, for example, that some cysts suggest marginal marine, inner neritic settings (most *Areoligera* complexes of Gv-cysts, often in association with relatively coarse-grained deposits), whereas others imply open marine neritic water masses (e.g. *Spiniferites* complex of Gs-cysts) or restricted to open marine neritic conditions (e.g. *Operculodinium* complex of Gn-cysts; for definition of cyst-types, see Evitt 1985).

Restricted marine palynofacies usually differ from those of open marine conditions in being dominated by AOMA. The associated dinoflagellate cyst assemblages may also be distinct, as demonstrated by Marshall & Batten (1988) and Courtinat (1993) for Cenomanian/Turonian (Cretaceous) boundary beds in northern Germany and the Western Interior of the USA, respectively. These compositional differences reflect varying levels of oxygenation and productivity, and perhaps also climatic and other environmental changes.

A number of non-dinoflagellate aquatic palynomorphs are also useful environmental indicators. For example, acanthomorph acritarchs are usually most abundant in sediments that accumulated in relatively near-shore marine to brackish environments. Prasinophyte algae, commonly together with leiospheres (some of which may have prasinophyte affinities), are also typically found in deposits that reflect these conditions. Most associations of low diversity dinoflagellate cyst assemblages with such taxa as *Chomotriletes*, *Lecaniella*, *Paralecaniella* and various chlorococcalean algae (e.g. *Botryococcus*, *Pediastrum* and *Scenedesmus*), suggest stressed environments of below 'normal marine' salinity. Remains of the inner organic walls of (benthonic) foraminifera may be numerous in restricted brackish-marine accumulations. They are also known to be common in sediments deposited beneath areas of oceanic upwelling (Powell *et al.* 1990).

From the standpoint of petroleum potential, an especially important area of study concerns the occurrence and composition of source rocks. Many papers have been written on this topic but only a few discuss their palynological content in any detail. These include several on the Kimmeridge Clay Formation of the British area. The combined use of palynofacies data and HI (hydrogen index) vs TOC plots has suggested a promising means of assessing the relative roles of dilution, preservation and productivity through the cyclic sequences, caused by relative sea-level changes and Milankovitch climatic controls that have been recognized in the palynofacies (Tyson 1996). Waterhouse (1995) attempted to characterize and interpret lithological and organic particle cyclicity in the Kimmeridge Clay in terms of possible orbitally-forced climatic changes. According to Tyson (1996), the best development of the source rocks in the succession onshore is clearly associated with maximum flooding surface intervals.

To conclude, palynofacies analysis of a sedimentary succession requires the accumulation of a wide variety of palynological data combined with information derived from as many other geological disciplines as possible. Such an integrated approach undoubtedly enhances detailed biostratigraphic, sequence stratigraphic, palaeoenvironmental and petroleum source potential studies.

38. Particle orientation and palaeoenvironments

RICHARD M. BATEMAN

Virtually all plant fossils reach their final resting place via a taphonomic cycle that involves at least one hydraulic medium (e.g. Gastaldo 1988; Spicer 1989*b*; Bateman 1991, fig. 2.4; Behrensmeyer *et al.* 1992).

If we first consider a uniformitarian cycle, organs are shed from an individual terrestrial plant either as part of its annual phase of abscission or upon its death (necrology). Unless the plant is fully aquatic, the plant organs first pass through air, though they are rarely preserved in purely aeolian environments; most plant parts subsequently pass through an aqueous transport medium or, less frequently, through ice. During this crucial sequence of transport → deposition → burial, the plant parts are subject to several modifying processes, including fire, herbivory, microbial decay and autolysis. Notable physical modifications are mechanical abrasion/disarticulation, which reduce the size and quality of the resulting fossils, and sorting, which separates cohorts of plant fragments according to a combination of size, density and shape. At some point, a cohort of plant fossils leaves the transport system and enters its final resting place within the enclosing sediment. The hydraulic conditions prevailing at the time and place of burial are reflected in the enclosing sediments, captured in contrasting sedimentary structures, particle size distributions and particle orientations (e.g. Briggs 1977; Bateman 1990; Farrington & Bateman 1992).

More catastrophic events also initiate taphonomic cycles. Examples include major floods, hurricanes, volcanic eruptions and glaciations, where the primary hydraulic media are liquid water, air, mass flows and frozen water respectively (e.g. Bateman & Scott 1990; Bateman 1991).

This chapter uses a few case studies to discuss the analysis and interpretation of macroscopic aggregate particle orientations, commonly termed fabric analysis and more commonly practised in mainstream sedimentology. Although potentially highly informative about conditions of deposition and often (by inference) of growth, this technique remains seriously under-used in palaeobotany.

Data acquisition

Field-based orientation studies rely on the scrutiny of statistically significant populations of macroscopic particles from a single depositional unit. Most focus on inorganic particles, but organic particles such as plant parts are equally informative about the hydraulic conditions of deposition. Each particle can be reduced to three arithmetic dimensions: a long axis (*a*) defining the maximum possible dimension of the particle, an intermediate axis (*b*) defining the longest possible dimension perpendicular to the *a* axis, and a shorter axis (*c*) as a fixed perpendicular to both *a* and *b*. A thorough study records all three dimensions of each analysed particle, though strictly this is unnecessary provided that each particle exceeds pre-selected axial ratio thresholds. Here, an *a* axis exceeding 20 mm and an *a/b* ratio exceeding 2.0 are recommended, defining a size and shape that are readily orientated relative to prevailing hydraulic flows of moderate strength. However, an *a* axis exceeding 10 mm and *a/b* ratio exceeding 1.5 are, in theory, within the tolerance of the method.

The primary objective is to record the orientation of the long (*a*) axis relative to present-day magnetic north and, where possible, to the present-day gravitational vertical – values termed orientation and dip respectively (in strict structural geology parlance, the latter measure is plunge, as it represents an axis rather than a plane). They are generally recorded using a compass clinometer; less sophisticated, compact clinometers are more effective in confined spaces. In most circumstances data are gathered at the outcrop. In poorly consolidated sediment, recording both orientation and dip requires gradual excavation of the bed, typically using a trowel or chisel to cut into a vertical exposure. Each particle should be exposed sufficiently to identify the three axes; ideally, an elongate object such as a knitting needle is inserted into the exposure parallel to the long axis of the particle, acting as a physical rest for the compass clinometer and thus increasing the accuracy of the orientation and dip measurements. Where the beds have been tilted or distorted by subsequent tectonic activity, the orientation and dip of the bedding planes should also be determined and used to adjust the recorded values for individual particles to their original syn-depositional orientations and dips – no easy task in tectonically complex terrains (Bateman & Scott 1990).

Many palaeobotanical assemblages lie flat on the originally horizontal or near-horizontal bedding plane, especially where large particles such as logs

Bateman, R. M. 1999. Particle orientation and palaeoenvironments.
In: Jones, T. P. & Rowe, N. P. (eds) *Fossil Plants and Spores: modern techniques*.
Geological Society, London, 199–205.

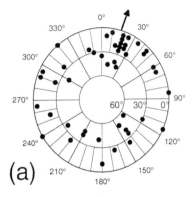

(a)

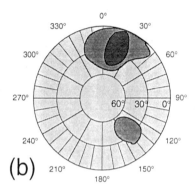

(b)

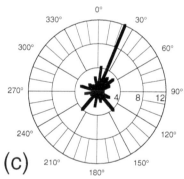

(c)

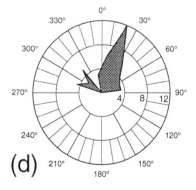

(d)

are exposed on recently revealed bedding planes (e.g. Wnuk & Pfefferkorn 1987). The resulting dip values approach horizontality (0°); dips are then of little value and best abandoned, thereby simplifying data acquisition and analysis to orientation data only. Also, identifying the precise orientation of the long axis can be challenging if the plant fragment is an awkward shape. Curved axes can be aligned by extrapolating a tangent from the mid-point, though such axes are best omitted from the study if the curvature is severe. Branched fragments can be scored, provided that one axis is distinctly more voluminous than the others; otherwise, they too are best omitted.

Obviously, the *in situ* particle excavation method cannot be applied to strongly consolidated sediments. Analyses of such deposits are rare, and largely restricted to measurements of orientation on fortuitously exposed surfaces. However, Bateman & Scott (1990; see also Bateman 1991) developed an effective (if labour-intensive) method for obtaining both orientation and approximate dip values from strongly petrified horizons in the Dinantian strata of Oxroad Bay, SE Scotland. The orientation and dip of the entire horizon was recorded in the field before the horizon was sledge-hammered into blocks of manageable size, to be reassembled into the original bed in the laboratory. A rock-saw made multiple parallel cuts through each block at *c.* 15 mm intervals, vertical to the bedding planes and perpendicular to the presumed dominant long-axis orientation of the enclosed particles (as perceived from their intersections with the fractured surfaces of the blocks). Plant (and other) fragments could then be traced between successive cut surfaces of the now loaf-like block, and the orientation of the stems, branches and petioles relative to magnetic north was thereby determined.

Data presentation

Statistically acceptable measured populations require samples of *n* = 50–100 particles (Briggs

---

Fig. 38.1. Contrasting modes of presentation of a single set of clast fabric data. Orientations and dips presented as a polar scattergram with (**a**) precise coordinates and (**b**) following contouring. Arrow on (a) is the resultant vector (see text). Orientations are then summarized as 15° azimuthal categories and dips reduced to directionality only, and (**c**) depicted as unconnected frequency bars. Dips are then ignored and orientations of diametrically opposing categories merged to yield (**d**) a 180° summary of connected frequency bars. For dip-free representations of other fabrics see Figs 38.2 and 38.4. (Single original dataset from Farrington & Bateman 1992, fig. 2b.)

1977), though strong preferred orientations can generally be detected in samples of as few as 15 individuals (Bateman 1991). A typical field record sheet consists of five columns: axis *a*, axis *b*, axis *c* (all in mm), orientation and dip (both in degrees).

The data can be presented in several ways. The most informative is a polar scattergram (Fig. 38.1a) or stereographic projection, which presents the orientation and dip of each particle as an intersection with a hypothetical hemispherical surface; individual points can then be replaced by density contouring if desired (Fig. 38.1b). Such presentations are now possible in some of the more sophisticated general computer graphics packages (e.g. with appreciable modification of default settings scattergrams can be produced via the *plot chart: special 2: polar* nested menus of *Deltagraph Professional*) or specialized geostructural packages such as *Stereo*.

Where the magnitude of the dip is deemed unimportant the data can be simplified into orientation categories (typically 10, 15 or 20° azimuthal classes) to yield a rose diagram, which can be presented as unconnected azimuthal bars (Fig. 38.1c), connected azimuthal bars (Fig. 38.1d), or azimuthal wedges (Fig. 38.4, inset). Where not only the magnitude but also the direction of dip is unavailable or judged irrelevant, data are either presented as a full rose of two reflected halves, thus duplicating the data (Fig. 38.2) or, more simply, representing the data only in the necessary half of the rose (generally the northern semicircle).

Data analysis

Many authors are satisfied to proceed directly from rose diagrams to hydraulic interpretations, but assessment of the statistical properties of the population is highly desirable. The mean dip is easily calculated as the average of the measurements taken, preferably supported by a sample standard deviation value. However, determining the preferred orientation and its statistical significance requires mathematical treatment.

Rather than simply focusing on the modal azimuth (i.e. the orientation class containing most values), a mean azimuth can be calculated using a series of geometric transformations. Even more rigorous is the vector analysis procedure that was well summarized by Till (1974) and Briggs (1977: 159–165). This yields a resultant vector (ø in degrees) that indicates the preferred particle orientation and a vector magnitude (*L* in percent) that summarizes dispersion about the resultant vector by predicting the range of orientations necessary to accommodate 68% of the observations (i.e. it is analogous to the sample standard deviation in linear statistics). Large vector magnitudes signify strong preferred orientations.

A photo-enlargeable form designed to aid calculation of these values is presented as Fig. 38.3. The number of records in each 10° azimuthal class is recorded in the **f** and **f'** columns. Their combined number **f** + **f'** is then multiplied by fixed values for both cosine and sine, and each of the three columns

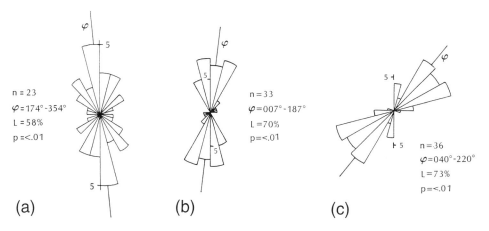

(a)   (b)   (c)

n = 23
φ = 174°-354°
L = 58%
p = <.01

n = 33
φ = 007°-187°
L = 70%
p = <.01

n = 36
φ = 040°-220°
L = 73%
p = <.01

Fig. 38.2. Dip-free, wedge-style representations of fabrics from three successive petrifaction-bearing horizons in Lower Carboniferous volcanigenic strata at Oxroad Bay, SE Scotland, showing the sample size (*n*), bi-directional resultant vector (ø), vector magnitude (*L*) and statistical significance according to the Rayleigh test (*p*). Note the upward increase in vector magnitude indicating increased hydraulic flow, and the switch in preferred orientation from S–N to SW–NE between fabrics (**b**) and (**c**). (Modified after Bateman & Scott 1990, figs 11, 14, 15; Bateman 1991, fig. 2.8.)

Ref. No.		Locality						
Recorder			Grid ref.				Altitude (m)	
Date		No. clasts		Geological age				
Deposit type								

Azimuth Θ (000–179°)	f	Azimuth Θ (180–359°)	f'	f + f'	2Θ	N–S component Cosine values		E–W component Sine values
000–009		180–189			000	x1.0000		x0.0000
010–019		190–199			020	x0.9397		x0.3420
020–029		200–209			040	x0.7660		x0.6428
030–039		210–219			060	x0.5000		x0.8660
040–049		220–229			080	x0.1736		x0.9848
050–059		230–239			100	– x0.1736		x0.9848
060–069		240–249			120	– x0.5000		x0.8660
070–079		250–259			140	– x0.7660		x0.6428
080–089		260–269			160	– x0.9397		x0.3420
090–099		270–279			180	– x1.0000		x0.0000
100–109		280–289			200	– x0.9397		– x0.3420
110–119		290–299			220	– x0.7660		– x0.6428
120–129		300–309			240	– x0.5000		– x0.8660
130–139		310–319			260	– x0.1736		– x0.9848
140–149		320–329			280	x0.1736		– x0.9848
150–159		330–339			300	x0.5000		– x0.8660
160–169		340–349			320	x0.7660		– x0.6428
170–179		350–359			340	x0.9397		– x0.3420
Totals				n =		ΣnCos2Θ =		ΣnSin2Θ =

Tan2Θ = ΣnSin2Θ/ΣnCos2Θ =

2Θ (°) =   Θ = 2Θ/2 =

Resultant Vector (φ) =

If Cos = + and Sin = +, φ = 000°+Θ
If Cos = – and Sin = +, φ = 090°–Θ
If Cos = – and Sin = –, φ = 090°+Θ
If Cos = + and Sin = –, φ = 180°–Θ

Vector Strength $(R) = \sqrt{(\Sigma n Sin2\Theta)^2 + (\Sigma n Cos2\Theta)^2}$ =

Vector Magnitude (L%) = 100(R/n) =

Mean dip (d°) =

Dip sample standard deviation (σ⁻¹) =

Fig. 38.3. Photo-enlargeable sheet facilitating vector analysis of fabric data in 10° categories. For further information see text, plus Briggs (1977). (Modified after unpublished sheet devised by the Geomorphology Laboratory, Department of Geography, Birkbeck College, University of London.)

is summated to give n, $\Sigma n\cos2\theta$ and $\Sigma n\sin2\theta$ respectively. These values are then used to calculate $\tan2\theta$, which is readily transformed into the resultant vector, taking into account the positive or negative nature of the values obtained for the summated cosines and sines (Fig. 38.4, inset). Similarly, vector strength is readily obtained from the cosine and sine columns, and can be converted into vector magnitude by taking sample size into account. Admittedly, these calculations are onerous when conducted by hand calculator, and programming is preferable. For example, Bateman & Scott (1990) and Farrington & Bateman (1992) reported results of analyses programmed in *Genstat* (Payne *et al.* 1993) by J. H. Rayner (pers. comm. 1985). The author has not yet tested more recent commercial software explicitly designed for this purpose, such as *Geoorient* and *Stereo*.

Preferred tests against randomness for orientation data are the Poisson and Rayleigh tests. The Poisson test focuses on the number of observations in the modal class relative to its breadth in degrees and the total number of observations in the population. The results are easily tabulated (e.g. Briggs 1977: 164). For example, a sample of 50 clasts divided into 20° azimuthal classes (a frequently used sampling strategy) requires a modal class of at least seven clasts to exceed the 95% confidence level and thus to have a statistically significant preferred orientation. The Rayleigh test graphically relates the total number of observations to the vector magnitude, allowing statistical significance to be read off the graph at a range of probabilities. For example, the aforementioned sample of 50 clasts requires a vector magnitude of 24.4% to reach the 95% confidence level.

Interpretation of fabrics

The interpretation and range of application of orientation data are best elucidated by brief consideration of a few case studies (cf. Bateman 1991).

The first example, admittedly of tangential relevance to palaeobotany but nicely approximating the lower boundary of statistical significance, was previewed by Farrington & Bateman (1992). Figure 38.1a shows a fabric with a modest mean dip of 22°, a resultant vector of 018° and a low vector magnitude of 30% that barely exceeds the 24.4% necessary to qualify as non-random under the Rayleigh test at $p<0.05$ for 50 clasts. This arrangement of lithic and wood fragments reflects the deliberate anthropogenic destruction of the Roman town of Colchester during the Boudiccan rebellion of AD 61. The weak preferred orientation is typical of materials laid down without directional hydraulic flow. The slight concentration of clasts

orientated a little east of north could reflect either gravity sorting on a slightly inclined surface, when clasts typically dip downslope rather than indicating the direction of principal stress under hydraulic flow. Alternatively, the weak fabric may indicate imbrication of clasts following directional stresses imposed by humans (e.g. pushing over a poorly consolidated wall).

Figure 38.2 shows an upward sequence of three fabrics (a–c) that were obtained from samples of calcareously petrified Dinantian plant stems and petioles from Oxroad Bay, SE Scotland (Bateman & Scott 1990; Bateman 1991); samples are therefore small ($n = 23$–36) and dips near-horizontal. All three resultant vectors are highly significant ($p<0.01$), revealing similar preferred orientations approximating S–N in fabrics 1 and 2 (separated by *c.* 22 m thickness of volcanigenic sediment) but a significant 33° switch to a SW–NE orientation in fabric 3 (located only 0.3 m above fabric 2, and having developed in the same transient eutrophic lake).

The strength of these orientations appears to contradict the temporary shallow lacustrine environments inferred for these deposits from a wide range of evidence, suggesting that the plant macrofossils entered the small lakes during periods of increased input from feeder streams (see also the marginal lacustrine fabrics obtained from mixed plant and bone assemblages of Permian age by Sander 1987). Moreover, increases in vector magnitude between each influx suggest overall increases in strength of flow that in the lowest horizon was insufficient to align the larger plant fragments. The rapid directional switch from fabric 2 to fabric 3 implies varying input from contrasting streams, and suggests that the data cannot be interpreted as directly indicating regional flow patterns. Note, however, that the absence of meaningful dips creates a bi-directional resultant vector and renders equally probable two opposing flow directions (e.g. N→S and S→N for fabrics 1 and 2). Moreover, bi-directional fabrics with low dips can also develop perpendicular to the primary flow direction, as traction loads.

Figure 38.4 shows much larger-scale orientations of adpressed rhizomorphic lycopsid trees and medullosan pteridosperm shrubs from Upper Carboniferous shales at Lopez, NE Pennsylvania (Wnuk & Pfefferkorn 1987). As in the previous example, dips are negligible, but in this case unidirectionality is conferred by the presence of rootstocks at the proximal ends of the trunks. Although samples are again small ($n = 16$ and 19 for trees and shrubs respectively) and no test statistics were applied, the data suggest a strong westward preferred orientation for the lycopsids and a random orientation for the pteridosperms.

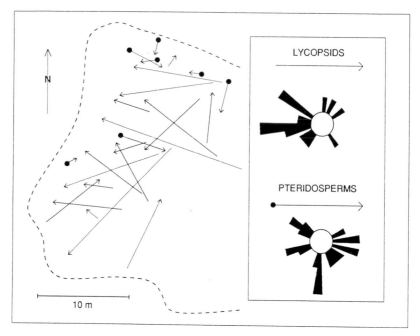

Fig. 38.4. Orientations of adpressed arboreous lycopsid and medullosan pteridosperm trunks recorded on an extensively exposed bedding plane of Upper Carboniferous strata near Lopez, Pennsylvania. Only the larger pteridosperm stems are shown to avoid confusion; a greater number contributed to the rose diagram. (Modified after Wnuk & Pfefferkorn 1987, fig. 3; Bateman 1991, fig. 2.15.)

Supported by other evidence, these fabrics were interpreted by the authors as indicating that the lycopsids were felled post-mortem and *en masse* by high velocity winds, crushing the shorter (and thus less wind-vulnerable) pteridosperms as they fell. Such an interpretation is supported by subsequent studies of modern analogues (e.g. Gastaldo 1990).

Far more extensive hurricane-felled forest have been documented in the Pleistocene of SW England (Allen 1992). However, studies of tree orientations following the catastrophic 1981 eruption of Mount St Helens in Washington State sound a cautionary note, revealing as expected a broad pattern of radiation outward from the vent but also exhibiting significant topographic modifications of trunk orientation by local channelling of pyroclastic flows through sinuous valleys and around ridges (Lipman & Mullineaux 1983).

These three examples serve to illustrate the wide range of palaeobotanical settings that are amenable to particle orientation studies and the promise that this cheap and relatively straightforward technique offers palaeoenvironmental interpretations. However, they also emphasize the paucity of such data currently available in palaeobotany, in sad contrast to the widespread use of these techniques in sedimentology (e.g. Briggs 1977; Leeder 1982)

and Quaternary studies (e.g. Lowe & Walker 1984; Gale & Hoare 1991).

No palaeobotanical examples were available to illustrate the value of obtaining large numbers of fabrics from different locations on a single landscape, especially for identifying contrasting depositional regimes (e.g. Rose 1974) or locating the likely source of deposited materials (e.g. Jupp *et al.* 1987). Similarly, direct observation of the behaviour of organic particles in modern environments (cf. Spicer 1981, 1989*b*) could allow the effective use in palaeobotany of eigenvector techniques of fabric interpretation, which have been successfully used to place inorganic data from 'unknown' past glacial regimes in a framework of known modern analogues (Dowdeswell & Sharp 1986).

Summary

As defined here, fabric analysis entails the determination from large sedimentary clast populations of two angles defined by the long axes of elongate clasts. Orientation is ubiquitously recorded and determined relative to present magnetic north, whereas dip is optional and determined relative to the dominant bedding plane. Mean dips are readily calculated for each clast population, but more complex mathematical transformations are needed to convert orientation measurements into a resultant vector (and the associated measure of dispersion, vector magnitude) that indicates preferred orientation and is subject to Poisson and Rayleigh tests against randomness.

Although data are traditionally obtained from large (>20 mm) abiotic clasts, transported fossil plant fragments are equally suitable for study.

Adpressions are recorded by exposing bedding planes (or individual clasts in poorly consolidated sediments), and petrifactions in well consolidated sediments by reconstructing fossiliferous beds in the laboratory and then repeatedly cutting blocks to trace the fossils. Singly, fabrics reflect the hydraulic conditions prevailing in the depositional environment immediately prior to burial; in aggregate, they can indicate the direction of the source community relative to the depositional sink.

39. Coal ball sampling and quantification

TOM L. PHILLIPS & WILLIAM A. DIMICHELE

Calcareous coal ball concretions from Upper Carboniferous and Permian coal deposits are the most abundant sources of anatomically preserved vascular plants in the fossil record. Coal balls provide the most direct evidence of the original swamp communities and of the botanical composition of the coal bed. Thus, their sampling and quantitative analysis are of interest to both palaeobiologists and coal geologists. Techniques employed in coal ball sampling and quantification, and in the manipulation of numerical data on taxonomic and organ abundances, depend on the opportunity to secure either random field collections or *in situ* specimens sampled directly from the coal bed as zoned vertical profiles, lateral traverses, or quadrats. Field observations, photographic records and detailed descriptions of coal ball distributions within a coal bed and their relationship to coal bed characteristics aid in palaeoecological and petrological interpretations, and contribute to studies of coal ball origins.

Field sampling

Coal balls occur in layers, which we refer to as zones, within coal beds (Fig. 39.1). Such layers may be discrete and easily separated, or grade to massive and irregular aggregates, making them difficult to delineate in the field. Coal ball zones may be determined by distinct layering and physical continuity, recurrent shapes and sizes, separation by mineral-rich bands or layers of fusain (mineral charcoal), or by restriction to distinct coal benches created by vertical changes in coal lithotype composition. Although we will focus on the collection of orientated profile samples, coal balls often are collected as 'random' samples. Random samples may be gathered from spoils where no reference to their position in the parent seam is possible, or they may be created analytically from oriented profiles. In the field we mark and identify coal ball zones with different colours of spray paint. Each zone is also numbered in sequence from the bottom up. As coal balls are removed, the tops are sprayed with the colour assigned to the zone recording original orientation within the coal bed.

Minimum sample sizes for later quantitative analysis were established by Phillips *et al.* (1977,

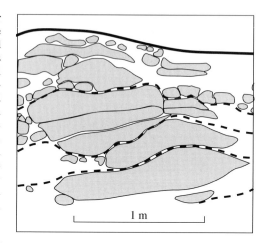

Fig. 39.1. Profile Vertical Section 4 from the Sahara Coal Company Mine No. 6, Williamson County, Illinois. Herrin coal, Carbondale Formation, Middle Pennsylvanian. Coal balls are shaded. Dotted lines are mineral partings in the coal bed. Solid line is a mixed pyrite–mineral band. Note variation in coal ball size and shape. See Phillips & DiMichele (1981).

appendix 2) for Westphalian coals. Based on a metre-wide sampling face, they determined that 10 to 15 coal balls of moderate size (hand samples to larger) generally represented a minimum area of $1500 \, \text{cm}^2$, based on a middle peel from each processed coal ball (see below). This was the minimum sample size at which quantitative composition stabilized statistically when compared with larger and smaller samples. These sample sizes are advisory only. Sampling must be adjusted to compensate for mode of preservation, degree of decay, and local variation in swamp vegetation (see Willard & Phillips 1993).

Quantification of botanical composition

Maximum surface area of permineralized peat is exposed when coal balls are cut into slices about 2.5 cm thick, at right angles to the top and bottom surfaces (Fig. 39.2). Cellulose acetate peels are prepared from each cut surface (Chapter 13). For most coal balls, only one peel from the centre cut

PHILLIPS, T. L. & DIMICHELE, W. A. 1999. Coal ball sampling and quantification. *In*: JONES, T. P. & ROWE, N. P. (eds) *Fossil Plants and Spores: modern techniques.* Geological Society, London, 206–209.

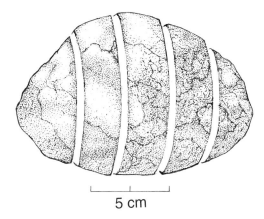

Fig. 39.2. Extracted coal ball cut cross-wise into approximately equally thick slices.

surface is analysed further; for exceptionally large coal balls, more than one peel may be examined.

In the technique developed by Phillips *et al.* (1977), the representative peel is attached to a clear cellulose acetate overlay ruled in cm^2 (Fig. 39.3). Each cm^2 is numbered. The coal ball peel with grid overlay is examined under a microscope, and for each cm^2 the following information is recorded: (1)

a choice from among the following categories: taxonomic affinity of plant remains, or unknown, or invertebrate, or mud, or calcite; (2) organ type; (3) fusinized or pyritic preservation; (4) male or female status of reproductive organs. Individual organs also are noted by outlining and counted individually. Pryor (1988) contrasted the Phillips *et al.* method with variants using either a mm^2 grid overlay, or random mm^2 method. The three approaches produce somewhat different results and their use depends on the questions of interest and constraints of time and resources. Pryor estimated the mm^2 method to be more efficient when sampling large areas of coal ball surface or when fossil peats are composed of many small plants. The random mm^2 method permits a wider array of statistical tests than frequency (total grid count) methods of any type, but does not permit quantitative study of data useful in the study of peat/coal fabric and composition, such as layering or the actual size and number of plant constituents. All methods estimate biomass through the assumption that two-dimensional area scales proportionally to volumetric measurements.

Compositional data are recorded for each coal ball on a paper copy of the numbered grid sheet on which the outline of the coal ball peel has been drawn (Fig. 39.4). Taxa, organs and preservational states are coded. Each cm^2 of peel surface is given

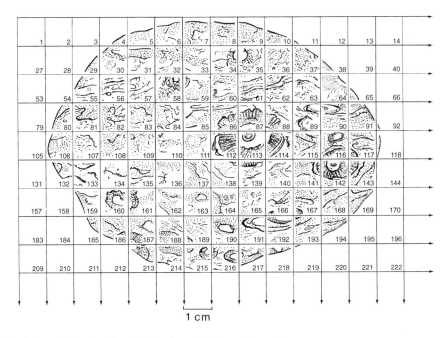

Fig. 39.3. Schematic drawing of coal ball peel overlain by counting grid.

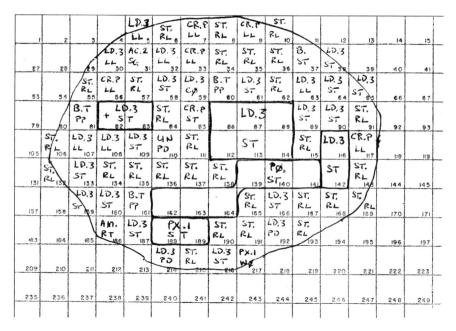

Fig. 39.4. Grid sheet of peel shown in Fig. 39.3, annotated with codes indicating taxa, organs and preservation states. In the present example the following codes are used for taxa: AC.2 = *Achlamydocarpon varius*; AM. = *Amyelon* sp.; B. = *Botryopteris* sp.; B.T = *Botryopteris tridentata*; CR.P = *Cordaites principalis*; LD.3 = *Diaphorodendron vasculare*; PO. = *Chaloneria* sp.; PX.1 = *Pennsylvanioxylon birame*; ST. = *Stigmaria* sp., UN = Taxonomically unidentifiable plant material. The following codes are used for organs: CO = parenchyma; LL = leaf lamina; PD = periderm; RL = rootlet; RT = root; SG = sporangium; ST = stem; WO = wood. The following code is used for preservation state: + = fusinized preservation. (Complete code library is available from Tom L. Phillips on request.)

a primary taxonomic or 'other' notation. If appropriate, the organ type, microsporangia/megasporangia, and special preservational states are added. To facilitate recording of data, a 'library' of taxonomic abbreviations was developed by Phillips *et al.* (1977). Each form or organ genus found in coal balls is given a one or two letter designation ending in a period; species are given a number or letter following the period (e.g. LP.1 = *Lepidophloios hallii*; A.I = *Anachoropteris involuta*). Organs are denoted by standard designations for stems, roots, leaves, seeds, etc. It is desirable to record plant identifications at the level of organ taxa because of the changes in the concepts of 'whole plants' that come with increasing research.

Analysis of quantitative data

Data are recorded from individual coal balls, whether part of a random sample or zones of a profile. For profiles, compositional data can be compiled zone by zone, or zone abundances can be averaged to create an 'after the fact' random

sample. Phillips & DiMichele (1981), Raymond (1988), and Pryor (1988) present data suggesting that random samples can accurately reflect the average botanical composition of part of a coal bed, if something is known of the original distribution of the samples (e.g. did they occur only in the top half of the coal bed), and if the random sample is sufficiently large. For example, in the Herrin Coal of Illinois, a random sample of 50 coals balls was collected between two profiles consisting of 460 coal balls; quantitative taxonomic composition of the random sample (Raymond 1988) was within 2% of that determined from the profiles (Phillips & DiMichele 1981).

Each cm^2 data record is entered into an electronic database for computer analysis. Data can be tabulated in any number of ways. We prefer first to examine whole-peat composition on a zone by zone basis, examining the relative abundances of major plant groups and unidentified tissues. In these analyses each major group can be broken down further into stem, leaf, reproductive organ and root biomass. Such data provide the most direct insights into the botanical composition of the coal bed. The most complete summary of the botanical composition of Carboniferous coals can be found in Phillips *et al.* (1985).

Further refinement of the raw data are needed for ecological analyses. First, all unidentified tissues and root biomass are removed from further calculations. Roots are eliminated because they may have penetrated from later vegetational stands, with the exception of roots from the root mantle of the tree fern *Psaronius*, 50% of which we arbitrarily treat as aerial. Thus, for community ecological analyses, particularly of profiles, non-root material is normalized to 100% identified. Hence, the aerial biomass of each zone is treated as the litter from one plant community, time averaged over a relatively brief period (tens of years). For random samples the time averaging would be considerably greater (hundreds to thousands of years). From the aerial biomass, 'whole plant' species are assembled to the most refined level possible. For many taxa, such as the lycopsid trees, marratialean tree ferns, small ferns, and small pteridosperms, the large literature on coal ball plant taxonomy and morphology permits whole plants to be assembled (expertise required). For medullosan pteridosperms and calamites it generally is not possible to assign individual plant fragments to a whole-plant species. In such cases all biomass is assigned at the genus level; estimates of biodiversity are made from the maximum number of specifically distinct organs, such as reproductive organs or leaves.

Further ecological studies of whole-plant species data use standard exploratory ecological techniques, such as dominance–diversity analysis, multivariate ordination, and an array of bivariate statistical techniques to delineate recurrent assemblages within coal seams. Other data, such as charcoal abundances, coal petrography, distributions of mineral bands, or ground cover abundances, can be superimposed on the basic vegetational patterns to assist in interpretation. Application of these techniques and approaches can

be found in Phillips & DiMichele (1981), Raymond & Phillips (1983), DiMichele & Phillips (1988), Feng (1989), DiMichele *et al.*(1991) and Pryor (1996). Phillips *et al.* (1977), Phillips & DiMichele (1981), and DiMichele & Phillips (1988) examined patterns of vegetational change within profiles and found no evidence of directional succession during peat accumulation. However, Raymond (1988) made use of the patterns of root penetration to reconstruct temporal succession, and Pryor (1996) examined and documented temporal successional patterns using a variety of sampling and statistical approaches.

How well do coal balls represent the original vegetation?

Despite the abundance of coal balls in coals of the Carboniferous and Permian, it is important to emphasize that coal balls are not encountered in most coals or in most mines. Thus, coal ball sampling and quantification provide the most direct evidence of mire vegetation and can serve as a reference base for more widely applied palynological and petrological studies. Comparative studies of coal balls with polished blocks of coal ('coal anatomy') from the same mine (Winston 1988), of coal ball palynology and coal palynology in the same mine (Mahaffy 1985), and of coal balls and palynology of coal from the same mine (Willard & Phillips 1993), along with other more broadly based studies of petrography and palynology, corroborate the validity and representative composition of coal ball analyses. Thus, the high resolution of coal ball data can be combined with broader studies of palynology and petrography to develop a comprehensive understanding of coal genesis and coal-swamp community structure and dynamics (Phillips & Peppers 1984; Phillips *et al.* 1985; Eble & Grady 1993; Willard *et al.* 1995).

We thank Mary Parrish, Department of Paleobiology, NMNH for her creation of the figures.

40. Taphonomy: field techniques in modern environments

DAVID K. FERGUSON, CHRISTA-CHARLOTTE HOFMANN & THOMAS DENK

Although one must be wary of interpreting fossil assemblages solely in terms of present day processes, without the actualistic principle as a guideline palaeobotanical interpretations would quickly relapse into the realms of fantasy (Ferguson *et al.* 1996). Therefore taphonomic fieldwork in modern environments remains essential in order to gain some insight into the processes governing the formation of fossil plant assemblages (Spicer 1981, 1989*b*; Ferguson 1985, 1995; Greenwood 1991).

Plant communities growing close to places of continuous or periodical sedimentation (e.g. along rivers, lakes) are the main sources of fossil plant assemblages (oryctocoenoses), because most plant parts are deposited at or close to their position of growth (Wolfenbarger 1946; Ferguson 1985). These communities do not reflect the entire ancient vegetation. In areas with a high humidity throughout the year, riparian elements extend deep into the arboreal vegetation. In this instance the assemblages, although they are derived from the river banks and lake margins, give a better impression of the zonal vegetation. Most depositional areas are located in lowlands, where it is possible to find species requiring good drainage growing close to elements of poorly drained soils. As observation proves, many so-called 'hinterland' taxa such as pine, beech, oak and laurel are found growing on hammocks or levées surrounded by typical wetland communities.

Modern analogues for late Cenozoic taxa are concentrated in southern China, and Japan. Unfortunately, due to human activities in the Chinese lowland, the original vegetation has largely vanished. Relict genera are restricted to montane areas, i.e. erosional rather than depositional environments, and as such are not directly comparable to the situation encountered in the past. In contrast, comparable lowland plant communities and sedimentary environments are still to be found in south-eastern North America and the south-eastern Black Sea coast (Myers & Ewel 1992; Davis 1971). Therefore for taphonomic purposes, these areas are more suitable for field observations. Before this fieldwork can be undertaken, a detailed understanding of the flora and vegetation is required.

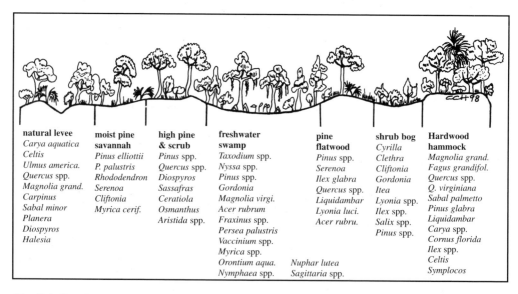

natural levee	moist pine	high pine	freshwater	pine	shrub bog	Hardwood
Carya aquatica	savannah	& scrub	swamp	flatwood	*Cyrilla*	hammock
Celtis	*Pinus elliottii*	*Pinus* spp.	*Taxodium* spp.	*Pinus* spp.	*Clethra*	*Magnolia grand.*
Ulmus america.	*P. palustris*	*Quercus* spp.	*Nyssa* spp.	*Serenoa*	*Cliftonia*	*Fagus grandifol.*
Quercus spp.	*Rhododendron*	*Diospyros*	*Pinus* spp.	*Ilex glabra*	*Gordonia*	*Quercus* spp.
Magnolia grand.	*Serenoa*	*Sassafras*	*Gordonia*	*Quercus* spp.	*Itea*	*Q. virginiana*
Carpinus	*Cliftonia*	*Ceratiola*	*Magnolia virgi.*	*Liquidambar*	*Lyonia* spp.	*Sabal palmetto*
Sabal minor	*Myrica cerif.*	*Osmanthus*	*Acer rubrum*	*Lyonia luci.*	*Ilex* spp.	*Pinus glabra*
Planera		*Aristida* spp.	*Fraxinus* spp.	*Acer rubru.*	*Salix* spp.	*Liquidambar*
Diospyros			*Persea palustris*		*Pinus* spp.	*Carya* spp.
Halesia			*Vaccinium* spp.			*Cornus florida*
			Myrica spp.			*Ilex* spp.
			Orontium aqua.	*Nuphar lutea*		*Celtis*
			Nymphaea spp.	*Sagittaria* spp.		*Symplocos*

Fig. 40.1. Co-existence of hydric, mesic and xeric plant communities in southeastern North America.

FERGUSON, D. K., HOFMANN, C-C. & DENK, T. 1999. Taphonomy: field techniques in modern environments. *In*: JONES, T. P. & ROWE, N. P. (eds) *Fossil Plants and Spores: modern techniques*. Geological Society, London, 210–213.

Southeastern United States, sedimentary environments and vegetation units

Taphonomically interesting sedimentary environments are situated along rivers flowing into the Gulf of Mexico (e.g. Mississippi, Mobile, Appalachicola). These areas are characterized by high sedimentation rates, local peat accumulation, and (if not already destroyed) various plant communities, of which approximately 20% of the woody genera are known to have existed during the Tertiary.

The vegetation cover of the lowlands is characterized by a heterogeneous patchwork of xeric, mesic and hydric plant communities (Fig. 40.1), which is mainly controlled by edaphic factors, such as small-scale relief, soil development, drainage and hydroperiod (the role of fire also requires to be investigated). From the taphonomic point of view, the close proximity of hydric ('azonal') and mesic or xeric ('zonal hinterland flora') plant communities combining arctotertiary with humid warm-temperate elements eliminates the need for large-scale reconstruction of Tertiary depositional sites, where a hinterland with mountain chains would have to be included to achieve the complete source area for the fossil plant assemblages.

Euxino-Hyrcanian relict area

The southeastern and eastern Black Sea coast yields the most important western Eurasian relict forests. The area is characterized by high precipitation throughout the year and January temperatures above freezing point. In lowland stands different plant communities occur in close proximity forming small-scale, mosaic-like patterns. A co-occurrence of temperate, submediterranean, mediterranean and relict taxa can be observed. Under humid, warm temperate conditions, a mixed assemblage does not necessarily imply the presence of different vertical vegetation belts.

Observations and field methods

What follows are some inexpensive techniques for investigating processes leading to thanato- and taphocoenoses. So far only a few of them have been carried out in the southeastern United States and the Euxino-Hyrcanian area. The first step involves inspecting the geomorphological situation including the drainage pattern, gradient and edaphic conditions, such as soils. In a fluvial environment knowledge of the drainage pattern is essential to understand the extent to which the dispersed plant material is liable to be allochthonous.

Special attention should be devoted to the woody plants, as these represent the most important elements of the vegetation from a palaeobotanical view point. The differentiation of the vegetation cover into different storeys should be documented, as this probably plays an important role in the composition of the sedimentary plant parts. A good method is to prepare different transects through the vegetation, indicating which of the species are evergreen and which deciduous (Fig. 40.2).

Litter sampling on the forest floor

Sampling plant litter can be used to assess how well the potential fossils correspond to the relative frequencies of the different species in the standing vegetation (Burnham et al. 1992). This enables us to evaluate the extent of 'over-representation' (e.g. lianas, deciduous leaves) and 'under-representation' (evergreen leaves) involved. A number of samples should be taken, as the composition of the litter varies considerably from place to place. Because both sun and shade leaves are represented, the litter gives an accurate picture of leaf variation in each of the species. This has important implications for the taxonomy of fossil leaves and their palaeoclimatic interpretation. Since leaf size can be used as an indicator of atmospheric humidity, it is important that the mean and standard deviation are established. If the leaf litter is badly damaged, the original area can be recreated by photocopying the leaves, cutting out the shapes and measuring these. Herbs and ferns do not normally abscise their leaves, so these are under-represented in leaf litter. However, this can be compensated for by parallel sampling for pollen/spores and/or diaspores (fruits and seeds). As small diaspores tend to be washed out of the litter by rain/melting snow, the underlying soil should be sieved for seeds.

Surface sampling for pollen

Sticky glass slides can be employed to determine the relationship between the pollen rain and the source vegetation. These slides are mounted horizontally. Glycerine should preferably be used as the adhesive substance, since this can be removed by ethanol if scanning electron microscopy (SEM) studies are required. When the slides are placed at regular intervals away from a source, the dispersal potential of the microspores can be demonstrated. While sticky slides represent a spot check of the pollen rain at a particular moment in time, moss cushions will enable the pollen rain accumulated over a few years to be established. The latter represents the best means of comparing fossil and recent pollen assemblages.

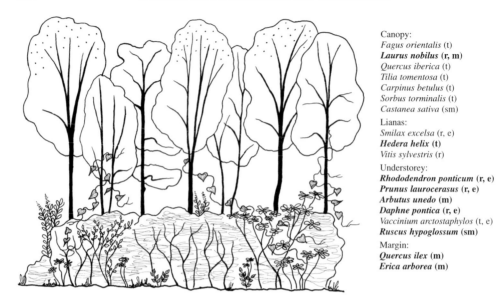

Canopy:
Fagus orientalis (t)
Laurus nobilus (r, m)
Quercus iberica (t)
Tilia tomentosa (t)
Carpinus betulus (t)
Sorbus torminalis (t)
Castanea sativa (sm)

Lianas:
Smilax excelsa (r, e)
Hedera helix (t)
Vitis sylvestris (r)

Understorey:
Rhododendron ponticum (r, e)
Prunus laurocerasus (r, e)
Arbutus unedo (m)
Daphne pontica (r, e)
Vaccinium arctostaphylos (t, e)
Ruscus hypoglossum (sm)

Margin:
Quercus ilex (m)
Erica arborea (m)

Fig. 40.2. Relict forests in western Eurasia – northern Turkey, close to the sea shore. (e) endemic, (m) mediterranean, (r) relict, (sm) submediterranean and (t) temperate species; evergreen species in bold letters.

Aerial dispersal of plant parts

As the fossilization potential depends to some extent on the distance over which plant parts are dispersed, it is important to determine the dispersal potential within a given plant community. A few isolated individuals of species with characteristic leaves and/or diaspores should be chosen. See how far the last leaf/diaspore is from the trunk and/or edge of the canopy. These observations ought to be repeated in a number of directions in order to ascertain the mean value (Ferguson 1985, fig. 9). Should a quantitative relationship be desired, a specific amount of litter (e.g. 0.25 m² × depth of litter layer) ought to be collected in polythene bags at various distances from the bole. As a negative exponential relationship is involved, most of the samples require to be taken close to the trunk. As the height of the plant is an important factor controlling the dispersal potential (Ferguson 1985, 1993), this should be recorded. Count the leaves/diaspores before they start fermenting and adhering to one another, as this makes the counting process less arduous. If this is impracticable, preserve them in a freezer.

Wind can cause the uppermost leaves in the litter to be blown further from their source. A rough guide to the amount of redistribution of leaves on the forest floor can be gained by monitoring the speed at which the bare soil, left after the litter was removed, is covered again. For a more quantitative estimation, a parallel set of samples can be taken

after a certain amount of time has elapsed. The amount of deviation from a negative exponential pattern (leptokurtic distribution) is a measure of the amount of redistribution.

How plant parts enter the aquatic milieu

Plant parts reach a water body by a variety of means. A great portion of the litter that is deposited in an adjacent river/lake originates from the emergent trees, the canopy layers and the forest margin because of the higher wind speeds encountered there, the size of the crowns and therefore the larger number of plant parts (leaves, pollen, fruits and seeds) available for dispersal.

Aerial influx into lakes and large rivers

Small, stable rafts can be used to trap the aerial influx (Spicer 1981; Middleton 1995). Styrofoam acts as a suitable float and the rafts are held in position by nylon ropes attached to a post. The rope should be long enough to allow for changes in the water level. Simple traps such as those used on land, i.e. adhesive slides for pollen, laundry baskets for leaves (Ferguson 1985), can be mounted on these rafts. As the distance from the source increases, the number of plant parts and the size of the leaves is expected to decline (Spicer 1981).

Netting litter in streams

It is important to investigate the specific composition and amount of detritus being transported downstream. Repeated sweeps made with a butterfly net are the simplest means of sampling leaves in the aquatic environment. In the temperate zone, at least 200 leaves must be collected in order to be representative (Kickinger 1997). As the mesh of such nets is too coarse for most diaspores, aquatic seed traps require another design (see Middleton 1995). However, there is a danger with such traps that once they are half full, resistance to flow will force the water with its detrital load to circumvent the inlet.

Investigating the pollen load

Commercially available water samplers (see Appendix) can be used to establish the qualitative and quantitative composition of the pollen load passing downstream. In this way it is possible to take samples at various depths. Surficial water can be collected in a bucket. The water should be evaporated to a sludge (Traverse 1990, 1992) or filtered through a 10 µm nylon mesh and the pollen prepared using current palynological techniques.

Establishing the distance over which plant parts are transported by water

By introducing exotic or labelled litter into a stream, it is, in principle, possible to investigate the actual distances over which wood, leaves and diaspores are transported in a river (Spicer & Greer 1986). These can be made more visible by spraying with fluorescent paint (Scheihing & Pfefferkorn 1984). Unfortunately, this soon wears off or gets coated by fine particulate matter. Because of this and the logistic limits to the amount of material which it is possible to employ, it is often impossible to keep track of the plant parts. Moreover, as the plant parts become water-logged and sink through the water column, they are lost to view. The distance covered as bedload remains an unknown quantity. By investigating the distance from the site of deposition to the nearest possible source of the organic matter (OM) upstream, it is possible to verify the minimum distance travelled.

Destruction of detritus at the sediment–water interface

Under aerobic conditions the plant parts undergo selective destruction by a variety of detritovores. The palatable detritus becomes selectively removed by microbes and invertebrate browsers. Other suitable OM for case-building is shredded by trichopteran larvae. Processes of destruction can be followed by putting litter into nylon mesh bags. Different mesh apertures make it possible to identify the group of organisms responsible for the damage. Care must be taken to ensure that the bags do not sink into the bottom sediments, as this can terminate biodegradation if the mud is anoxic. A marker buoy and the use of nylon cord facilitates the retrieval of samples.

Grab sampling of channel/lake deposits

To investigate the nature and amount of OM becoming embedded in the bottom sediments, these sediments should be sampled from a boat or platform. A number of types of grab samplers are commercially available (see Appendix). It is important that the jaws close with sufficient force to penetrate the bottom sediments. As these are unconsolidated, they can be washed through a set of sieves to extract the OM. The OM can be processed for palynofacies and pollen analysis.

Excavating and coring

To check which material finally gets embedded in the sediment, samples can either be extracted by coring (ideal for unconsolidated or relatively consolidated sediments) or excavation in the case of consolidated sediments. Coring is a helpful technique for analysing any changes in the amount, composition and the preservational state of OM with depth (Gastaldo & Huc 1992). Coring devices come in all sizes from small manually operated gouges to large drilling rigs mounted on trucks. While a small diameter (c. 3 cm) suffices for pollen analysis, cores for larger plant parts require a diameter of >10 cm. With such large diameters, it often proves difficult to retain the sediments intact, especially if these are still unconsolidated. By comparison, in areas which are not water-logged, it is comparatively easy to take short cores by driving rigid plastic tubes into the sediments or digging a trench. To establish whether the litter has any preferred orientation, a large area of bedding plane should be exposed. These data can be used to indicate the direction and intensity of any water currents (Boyd 1991), or degree of allochthony (Gastaldo et al. 1989).

Part of the research for this chapter was undertaken during the tenure of Austrian Science Foundation (FWF) grant no. P11412-Bio. We should like to thank Dr Carole T. Gee for suggesting a number of improvements to the manuscript.

41. Palaeosols

GREGORY J. RETALLACK

Concepts and importance

A palaeosol is a fossil soil: part of a landscape of the past altered in place by its environment, then fossilized by burial or other changes. Palaeosols are common in nonmarine sedimentary rocks, and include coal seams, underclays, cornstones, ganisters, laterites and bauxites (Retallack 1997). Unlike other fossils, a palaeosol cannot be transported and remain a palaeosol. Erosion and deposition reduce soils and palaeosols to sediments. Thus many palaeosols preserve fossil stumps, leaf litter, pollen, snails and bones in the place where they lived. Such palaeosol assemblages are preferred as evidence for ancient communities compared with fossils transported by rivers, lakes and estuaries (Pickford 1986, 1995; Dimichele & Phillips 1988; Eble & Grady 1990). For example, at the middle Miocene locality of Fort Ternan, Kenya (Figs. 41.1, 41.2), assemblages of fossil bones, snails, pollen and grasses from Chogo and Onuria palaeosols represent distinct communities of a grassland–woodland mosaic (Retallack 1991a). These palaeosols and their fossils represent times of only thousands of years and localities of only metres, compared with 'communities' abstracted from the fossil record of geological formations that can stretch for kilometers and millions of years. Palaeosols thus serve to anchor palaeoecological reconstructions, like the community they once supported.

Palaeosols were not only homes but preservational environments for fossils. Palaeosols at Fort Ternan are exceptional for their wide range of fossils: grasses (Dugas & Retallack 1993), dicot fruits and seeds (Retallack 1992a), pollen and spores (Bonnefile 1994), snails (Pickford 1995), bones and teeth (Retallack 1991a). Even here there are preservational biases related to Eh and pH that limit interpretation (Retallack 1998), such as the relatively poor preservation of leaves and pollen.

Finally, different kinds of palaeosols reflect different kinds of ancient vegetation (Retallack 1997), such as the red, clayey, blocky-structured soils of forests (Lwanda of Fig. 41.1) versus thin, brown, granular-structured soils of grasslands (Chogo and Onuria of Fig. 41.1). Palaeosols themselves may not reveal whether the trees were eucalypts, oaks or acacias, or the species of grasses.

Palaeosols are trace fossils of ecosystems, rather than of species or individuals.

Plant fossils in palaeosols

Plant fossils in palaeosols show a wide range of preservational styles, ranging from leaves freshly deposited on the ground, to leaves skeletonized in leaf litter and permineralized with the palaeosol (Retallack 1997). Fossil logs, leaves, fructifications, pollen and spores are preserved best in carbonaceous palaeosols, and not at all in organic-poor red, hematite-rich palaeosols. Charcoal persists in red palaeosols, but is not so common in them as in drab, organic palaeosols formed under chemically reducing (low Eh) conditions. Calcareous phytoliths such as pits of hackberries (*Celtis*), like snails and bones, are best preserved in calcareous palaeosols formed under alkaline (high pH) conditions (Retallack 1998). Silica phytoliths are preserved in a variety of palaeosols (Retallack 1991a, 1992a).

A field proxy for original Eh of palaeosols that can be used to assess their potential fossil record is Munsell hue (gray for reducing, red for oxidizing). A field proxy for former pH is reaction with dilute (10% of stock solution) hydrochloric acid (HCl) applied to the rock from an eyedropper bottle (reactive is calcareous and alkaline). Standard colour charts are produced by the Munsell Color Co., Baltimore, Maryland; available from many forestry supply stores. Colour and reaction can be quantified in the field (Buntley & Westin 1985; Retallack 1988).

At Fort Ternan (Figs. 41.1, 41.2), all of the palaeosols are red or brown: too oxidized for the high quality preservation of organic matter found in coal measures. Chogo and Onuria palaeosols were least oxidized (lowest ratio FeO/Fe_2O_3 in Fig. 41.2). Chogo palaeosols yielded pollen, wood, stoned-fruits and seeds. The Onuria palaeosol was buried along with a crop of its fossil grasses, and Dhero palaeosols with small tree trunks, by carbonatite-nepheline tuffs (Retallack *et al.* 1990; Retallack 1992a; Dugas & Retallack 1993). Chogo palaeosols are calcareous and highly alkaline and have yielded some 12 000 bones and teeth of antelope and other animals, mostly disarticulated,

RETALLACK, G. 1999. Palaeosols. *In*: JONES, T. P. & ROWE, N. P. (eds) *Fossil Plants and Spores: modern techniques*. Geological Society, London, 214–219.

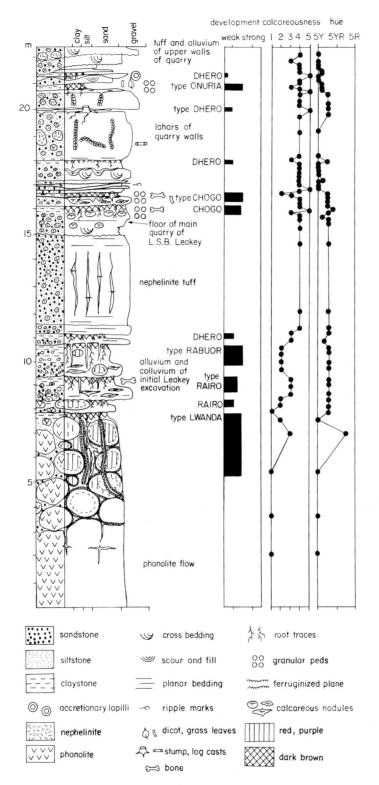

Fig. 41.1. A geological section of middle Miocene palaeosols at Fort Ternan National Monument, Kenya. Development and calcareousness of palaeosols from a scale of Retallack (1988) and hues from a Munsell Color Chart. Chogo, Rabuor, etc. are pedotypes or field-based kinds of palaeosols (from Retallack 1991a, with permission from Oxford University Press).

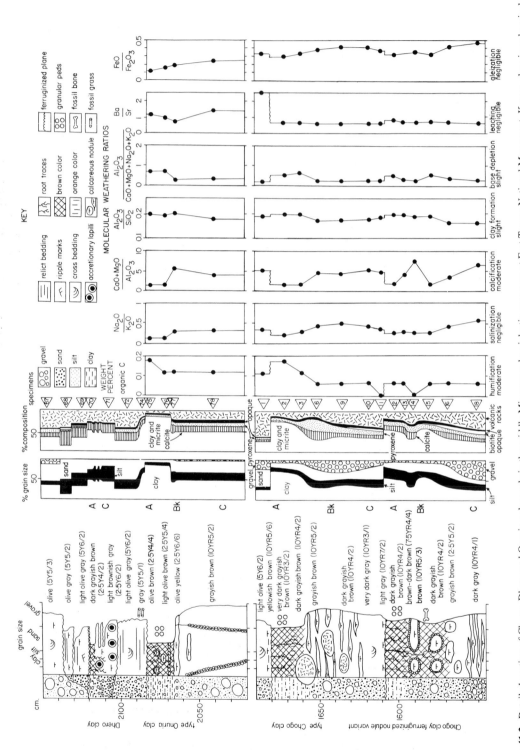

Fig. 41.2. Detailed section of Chogo, Dhero and Onuria palaeosols in the middle Miocene volcaniclastic sequence at Fort Ternan National Monument, Kenya, showing chemical and petrographic data useful for their interpretation (reprinted from Retallack *et al.* 1990, *Science*, **243**, 1325–1328, with permission of the American Association for the Advancement of Science).

with the exception of several juvenile mongoose skeletons found in a likely den (Retallack 1991a). Also common in Chogo palaeosols are calcareous shells of land snails (Pickford 1995) and endocarps of hackberry (*Celtis*; Retallack 1992a). These reflect long-term accumulation of hard parts in a soil of high pH and Eh, in contrast to exceptional catastrophic preservation of fossil grasses and mongoose skeletons.

Palaeosols also are indicators of the temporal completeness of stratigraphic sections and of time-averaging of fossil assemblages because they represent a discrete time for formation (Retallack 1998). The temporal gap in sedimentation indicated by a palaeosol can be estimated from the degree of expression of soil features such as peds and clay skins and the extent to which they obscure original features of the parent material such as sedimentary bedding, schistosity and crystalline structure. Such order of magnitude scales of soil development are widely recognized by soil scientists (Birkeland 1984) and can also be applied to palaeosols in the field. For example, at Fort Ternan the degree of development (Fig 41.1) represents a field estimate of time-averaging for each palaeosol (Retallack 1998).

Permineralization is a form of exceptional fossilization found in palaeosols. Permineralized peats of Histosols have been attributed to the chemically unusual waters of volcanic hot springs (Rice *et al.* 1995), of hypersaline lagoons (Knoll 1985) and of fen and carr (alkaline wetland) vegetation (Retallack 1986). Partial permineralization or nodular preservation of the sort called authigenic cementation by Schopf (1975), and made famous by such fossil localities as Mazon Creek, Illinois (Woodland & Stenstrom 1979), and Santana, Brazil (Maisey 1991), is largely a phenomenon of marine sea-floor diagenesis, to judge from the dominance of fish and other marine fossils. However the common Holocene dolomite-siderite nodules with fossil yabbies (*Thalassina anomala*) found in northern Australia demonstrate that fossiliferous nodules also can form in mangrove soils (Etheridge & McCulloch 1916).

Trace fossils in palaeosols

Palaeosols contain a great variety of trace fossils (Hasiotis & Bown 1992). Much can be learned about vegetation of the past from the external morphology and pattern of fossil root traces (Pfefferkorn & Fuchs 1991; Bockelie 1994). At Fort Ternan for example (Figs 41.1, 41.2), root traces are preserved as clayey streaks or tubes filled with sparry calcite. Chogo and Onuria palaeosols have abundant fine (less than 2 mm diameter) root

traces that terminate near a single level within the soil, as in sod grasslands. Other palaeosols at Fort Ternan have stout woody root traces like those of woodland trees. Palaeosols at Fort Ternan include parallel-sided burrows unlike root traces, as well as denlike burrows, insect cocoons, hymenopteran larval cells and a variety of coprolites (Retallack 1991a). These indicate the evolution of animal behaviours, as well as local conditions. For example, no aquatic fossils have been found at Fort Ternan (Retallack 1991a), all the trace fossils also are of air-breathing creatures, and the root traces penetrate deeply, so are evidence against water-logged or marshy conditions.

Palaeosols as trace fossils

Soil is an integral part of modern ecosystems, and when buried, palaeosols remain as trace fossils of ecosystems. It is a different kind of trace than a track or trail, but its texture, mineral content, bulk chemical and isotopic composition can reveal much about life of the past, even when fossils and trace fossils are not preserved (Retallack 1998). Recognizably different kinds of palaeosols or pedotypes (Retallack 1994a), represent former mosaics of vegetation in a palaeoecological approach similar to that of landscape ecology (Forman & Godron 1986).

At Fort Ternan, for example, the six different pedotypes recognized in the field (Fig. 41.1) are thought to represent as many ecosystem types, including grassy woodlands (Lwanda, Rabuor), woody vegetation early in ecological succession after disturbance (Rairo, Dhero) and wooded grassland (Chogo, Onuria). These interpretations are based on two quite separate lines of inference analogous to functional morphology and taxonomic uniformitarianism of palaeontology. The functional morphological approach selects particular features of the palaeosols, such as morphology of root traces (Retallack 1992a) or depth of calcareous nodules within the profile (Retallack 1994b), and makes inferences from what is known of such features in soils today. Using taxonomic uniformitarianism in contrast, the whole palaeosol is identified within a classification of modern soils, among which the US soil taxonomy (Soil Survey Staff 1997) and the UNESCO World Map of Soils (FAO 1974) are most useful. Paleoenvironments are then inferred to be similar to those of comparable soils today.

Petrography and geochemistry of palaeosols

Palaeosols are best studied by the time-honored combination of petrography and geochemistry.

Thin sections are especially useful for microscopic details of palaeosols, including diagnostic soil microfabrics (Brewer 1976), as well as for quantifying mineral and chemical composition (Fig. 41.2). Sampling of a palaeosol for micromorphological study should include at least two sampling levels in each recognizably different horizon. Orientation is needed for preparing petrographic thin sections vertical to bedding, and is best marked with a circle drawn with a felt pen on the upper side of a specimen in such a way that it defines a plane parallel to regional bedding. The technique of making thin sections is well known, but modifications of solvents and binders are needed for clayey and crumbling palaeosols (Tate & Retallack 1995). Point counting of thin sections can be used to quantify grain size, mineral composition or abundance of particular pedogenic structures (Eswaran 1968). About 6000 points are needed for statistically precise work (Murphy 1983), but 500 counts gives acceptable accuracy (±2%) for common components (Galehouse 1971). Size categories of sand, silt and clay can be estimated from the long-axis measurement of grains using a calibrated scale in the eyepiece of the microscope. Conversion nomograms are available for comparison with sieve analysis (Friedman & Johnson 1996). Scanning electron microscopes (SEM) provide sharp three-dimensional images of crystal forms (Smart & Tovey 1981; Sudo *et al.* 1981), and also can provide chemical analyses from energy dispersive spectrometry of X-rays, and from back-scattered electrons (Retallack & Krinsley 1993).

Soils are often studied by analysing for 'free elements'. For example, 'free iron' is the iron extractable by sodium dithionite, and does not include iron within unweathered grains. 'Free elements' of soils are most likely to be diagenetically removed or recombined burial of a soil (Retallack 1991*b*), so whole-rock chemical analyses are best for palaeosols. Although there are many local variations, average terrestrial weathering results in accumulation of SiO_2, Fe_2O_3 and Al_2O_3 and loss of CaO, MgO, Na_2O and K_2O (Chesworth 1992). These changes, and particularly the gradational variation in chemical composition with depth in soils, can be used to recognize and evaluate palaeosols (Retallack 1991a; Maynard 1992).

A variety of methods of chemical analysis are in common use (Page 1982): atomic absorption spectrometry (AA or AAS); inductively coupled plasma emission spectrometry (ICP); X-ray fluorescence spectrometry (XRF); and instrumental neutron activation analysis (INAA). Detection limits for most elements are comparable for AA and XRF (Retallack 1997). ICP is especially useful for palaeosols because a variety of elements are analysed simultaneously and samples are run in quick succession, with little opportunity for machine drift. INAA is best for accurate analysis of trace elements, particularly rare earth elements (REE). With INAA it is possible to avoid contamination from grinding, sieving and acid digestion of powders needed for other methods. Estimates of error come from counting statistics of INAA and ICP, or from the standard deviation of 10 or more analyses of the same sample, or from multiple analyses of rocks routinely analysed as standards for AA and XRF. Another indication of the quality of analyses is the weight percent total, which should be close (within 2.5%) to 100%. For many clayey and calcareous palaeosols, acceptable totals will only be achieved by including a measured loss-on-ignition (LOI) at about 1000 °C for 2–3 h. This treatment drives off carbonate, organic matter and other volatile components not reflected in major element oxides.

Other chemical methods useful for the study of palaeosols include analysis of organic carbon, nitrogen, and ferrous versus ferric iron. Organic carbon is best determined by the Walkley-Black titration (Page 1982). Total nitrogen can be analysed by Kjeldahl titration (J. B. Jones 1991). Total iron, usually in the ferric state as Fe_2O_3, is given by AA, XRF, ICP and INAA analyses, but it is important to know the proportion of iron oxidized to the ferric state versus that in the ferrous state (FeO). The amount of ferrous iron can be analysed by Pratt titration (Potts 1987), with ferric iron gained by molar difference from total iron.

Stable isotopes of oxygen and carbon also can be revealing, and are determined by mass spectrometry of gases derived from organic matter or carbonate of palaeosols (Cerling *et al.* 1989). The oxygen isotopic composition of soil carbonate can provide indications of palaeotemperature (Hays & Grossman 1991; Mack *et al.* 1991). This includes temperatures of deep burial and metamorphism, which may reset the oxygen isotopic composition of palaeosol carbonate (Mora *et al.* 1991). The carbon isotopic composition of carbonate can be used to recognize palaeosols, which are isotopically light (more negative $\delta^{13}C$ of standard notation) compared with marine carbonate and carbonate cements formed during deep burial (Driese *et al.* 1992). The carbon isotopic composition of palaeosols has also been shown to reflect ancient levels of atmospheric carbon dioxide, degrees of soil aeration and the relative proportions of woody plants (using Calvin–Benson cycle or C_3 photosynthesis) versus tropical grasses (using Hatch–Slack or C_4 photosynthesis: Cerling *et al.* 1989; Cerling 1991, 1992a; Driese *et al.* 1992). Care must be taken in sampling particular phases of carbonate, because calcite cement formed during shallow burial has been found to be misleadingly light (Wright & Vanstone 1991; Cerling 1992*b*; Retallack 1992*b*; Driese & Foreman 1992). An additional bias is the preferential preservation of woody rather than herbaceous organic matter in palaeosols (Esterle *et al.* 1989; Cohen *et al.* 1990).

A common display of geochemical data on palaeosols is a depth function, with the depth of the sample from the surface on a negative *y* axis and values of weight percent, or other manipulations of these data, on the *x* axis. Several computer software packages (QuattroPro© and SigmaPlot©) allow plotting of such data. One use of chemical data is to assess gains and losses of materials during soil formation, usually by assuming that one constituent has been unaffected and that its enrichment or depletion is due to changes in other constituents during soil formation or diagenesis (Brimhall *et al.* 1991). Such an approach assumes a parent material of uniform original chemical composition and requires analysis of unweathered parent material. Widely used stable constituents include Al_2O_3 and Zr, although each can be problematic under particular circumstances (Retallack 1997). These calculations are best converted to weight per unit volume and for this the bulk density of each sample must be known. The clod method is most appropriate for determining the bulk density of pre-Quaternary palaeosols (Klute 1986). Detailed analyses of losses and gains of constituents are impractical for cases where unweathered parent material is not known or where parent materials are suspected to have been non-uniform. In such cases, a simple index of weathering is provided by molecular weathering ratios, calculated by dividing the weight percent of an oxide by its molecular weight, and then adding and dividing as specified by the particular ratio (e.g. Fig. 41.2). Relative changes in molecular weathering ratios from horizon to horizon are important, but so are absolute values of the ratios. For example, the ratio of alumina/bases ($Al_2O_3/CaO + MgO + Na_2O + K_2O$) reaches near 100 in deeply weathered soils such as Oxisols and Ultisols, but in most other soils is less than 2. This value is a useful (but not infallible) guide for distinguishing Alfisols from Ultisols (Retallack 1997). The ratio of ferrous to ferric iron (FeO/Fe_2O_3) is an indicator of the degree of chemical reduction due to waterlogging (gleization). The ratio is close to zero in oxidized soils or palaeosols, but can be in the hundreds for unweathered mafic igneous rocks. This ratio is commonly an indicator for degree of waterlogging, but for some Precambrian soils it may also reveal

the amounts of oxygen in the atmosphere (Holland 1984).

Laboratory data can constrain considerably palaeoecological and other interpretations of palaeosols, as illustrated again by the example of Fort Ternan (Fig. 41.2). In both Chogo and Onuria palaeosols there is clear evidence of clay formation by hydrolysis of pyroxene and volcanic rock fragments from the parent material. Both palaeosols also show higher organic carbon contents than their parent material, though its markedly lesser abundance than in soils may be due to decompositon during early burial (Retallack 1991*b*). Surface clay production was not especially profound (modest values of alumina/bases and barium/strontium) and was accompanied by subsurface accumulation of carbonate nodules (subsurface peaks in alkaline earths/alumina). Weathering was not inhibited by waterlogging and the soils were moderately well drained (very low ferrous/ferric iron ratio). These indications of the soil-forming processes of humification, hydrolysis and calcification, together with dark colour and granular soil structure, allow identification of these palaeosols with grassland soils or Mollisols (Soil Survey Staff 1997). Both pedotypes are only moderately developed, neither so deeply weathered and thick as Oxisols and Ultisols, nor so little weathered as Inceptisols and Entisols. Soils with comparable nodular horizons form on comparable parent materials of the Serengeti Plains of Tanzania on surfaces some 200–9000 years old (Retallack 1991*a*). Carbon isotopic study of these palaeosols and of antelope teeth from them has shown that this was an entirely C_3 ecosystem (Cerling *et al.* 1997), and so is best compared with high elevation grassland–woodland mosaics of the Isuria–Mara area of Kenya, as also indicated by the site's fossil snails (Pickford 1995) and pollen (Bonnefille 1994). Chemical and petrographic study of palaeosols not only quantifies soil-forming processes and products of palaeosols, but can lead us to analogous modern soilscapes.

Field observations and fossil collecting remain central to any study of palaeosols. Petrography and geochemistry also are emerging as essential for the characterization of palaeosols. However, palaeosols can be viewed in many ways: as palaeoprecipitation gauges, as barometers of ancient atmospheric composition, as trace fossils of former ecosystems, as partial ancient landscapes and as indicators of timescales intermediate between ecological and geological time. Methods for their study will continue to be as varied as these different approaches.

42. Plant macrofossil biostratigraphy

CHRISTOPHER J. CLEAL

In the early days of stratigraphical science, it was common for time periods and even rock units to be defined by the presence of particular species of fossil. Today, however, a tripartite stratigraphical classification is used, with sequences being divided up separately by time (chronostratigraphy), rock- and facies-type (lithostratigraphy) and fossil content (biostratigraphy).

Although a number of abiotic alternatives have been developed (Dunay & Hailwood 1995) biostratigraphy remains the most reliable and widely used means of correlating sedimentary rock sequences. Most sedimentary rocks are marine deposits in which animal fossils are most often used as biostratigraphical indices (ammonites, trilobites, graptolites, corals, etc.). In rocks of non-marine origin, however, plant macrofossils have played a major stratigraphical role, especially in the Upper Palaeozoic, from where most of the cases quoted below originate. There is no reason why the same principles could not equally be applied in the Mesozoic, or Tertiary, but to date there have been few attempts to apply rigorous biostratigraphical methodologies to the plant fossil record of these eras. The literature still regularly contains statements such as, '... the Bathonian flora of area X is typified by the following species and thus correlates with the floras in area Y'. Such an approach is wide open to circular arguments and false correlations, and has little value for stratigraphical or floristic work.

Meyen (1987) and Cleal (1991) have discussed plant macrofossil biostratigraphy, but mainly the principles rather than the practicalities. The following will look at these practicalities in more detail: how rock sequences are classified biostratigraphically, how the divisions are named, what sort of plant fossils produce the most reliable results, and what are the controls and limitations of biostratigraphy. Further details of currently used biostratigraphical schemes can be found in Dilcher & Taylor (1980), Meyen (1987), Cleal (1991) and Vakhrameev (1991).

Biozones

In biostratigraphy, a sequence of rocks is divided into a succession of units, defined exclusively on their fossil content. The standard unit is the biozone. For many years they were just called zones but, with the introduction of chronozones in chronostratigraphy, the prefix bio- may be added if there is any potential for confusion. Biozones can be divided into subbiozones; they can also be clustered in to superbiozones but, to the best of my knowledge, this has never been done in plant macrofossil biostratigraphy.

Various types of biozone are currently recognized (Bassett 1990; Doyle *et al.* 1994; Salvador 1994). The simplest are range zones, which are defined by the fossils found within a particular body of strata. They can be taxon range zones, assemblage range zones or concurrent range zones, depending on the criteria used in their definition. Examples are given by Read & Mamay (1964) for the Carboniferous and Ash (1980) for the Upper Triassic of North America. Banks (1980) referred to the biozones in his biostratigraphy for the Silurian and Devonian as assemblages zones, but they are in fact mostly interval zones as currently interpreted (see below).

Range zones are especially useful in areas where the stratigraphical sequence is poorly understood, as they can be identified by the presence of the index taxon or taxa in isolated assemblages. Where the full succession of strata in an area is better documented, however, greater biostratigraphical precision is normally possible using a fundamentally different type of biozone: the interval zone. These are defined purely by their upper and lower boundaries, which are placed in the stratigraphical sequence at defined levels called biohorizons, where there is a significant change in the fossil record, such as the lowest or highest occurrence of a taxon or taxa, or by a marked change in abundance. For example, the base of the upper Westphalian D *L. vestita* Biozone is defined at a biohorizon where a series of species have their lowest occurrences (Fig. 42.1). Because it is based on a change in the fossil record through the rock sequence, an interval zone can only be reliably identified in a continuous stratigraphical succession. The taxa whose ranges define the boundaries of an interval zone may not be restricted to that biozone, and so their presence in an individual assemblage cannot be taken as evidence that the assemblage belongs to that biozone. Such interval zones have proved especially useful in the

CLEAL, C. J. 1999. Plant macrofossil biostratigraphy. *In*: JONES, T. P. & ROWE, N. P. (eds) *Fossil Plants and Spores: modern techniques.* Geological Society, London, 220–224.

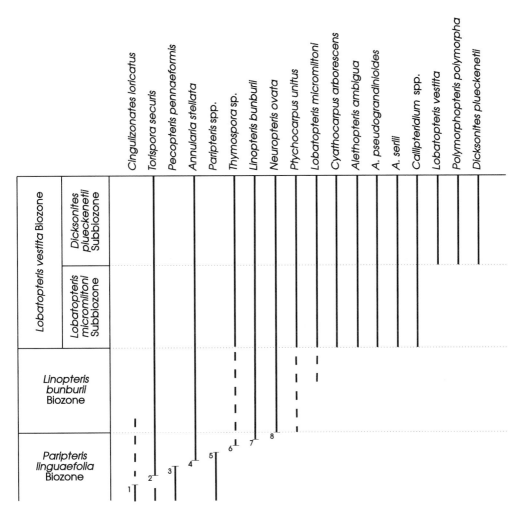

Fig. 42.1. Interval zones used to classify upper Westphalian strata in Europe and eastern North America. The base of the *L. bunburii* Biozone is defined using sequential biohorizons that are numbered on the chart 1–8. The bases of the *L. vestita* Biozone and *D. plueckenetii* Subbiozone are defined by multitaxon biohorizons. Based on data from Laveine (1977), Cleal (1978, 1984) and Zodrow & Cleal (1985).

Carboniferous of the palaeoequatorial belt (e.g. Wagner 1984; Josten & Laveine 1984; Cleal 1984; Cleal & Thomas 1994) and the results contrast with the rather coarser definition produced using assemblage range zones (e.g. Read & Mamay 1964).

Biohorizons can be based on a single taxon. More useful, however, is a multitaxon biohorizon, where several taxa appear and/or disappear at a particular level, such as that used to define the base of the *L. micromiltoni* Subzone (Fig. 42.1). Then, if one taxon appears late or disappears early, the other taxa should still be capable of indicating the

biohorizon. Another approach is to use sequential biohorizons (Laveine 1977; Cleal 1978, 1984; Zodrow & Cleal 1985). By looking at the fossil record near the interval zone boundary, it should be possible to recognize a succession of biohorizons reflecting the broad pattern of vegetational changes occurring at the time. One of these biohorizons is then chosen as the index for the interval zone boundary. For example, eight biohorizons have been recognized near the base of the *Linopteris bunburii* Biozone, with the eighth (the lowest occurrence of *Neuropteris ovata*) being taken as the index to the zonal boundary (Fig. 42.1). By examining its position in the context of the other biohorizons, it should be possible to recognize if the index biohorizon in a particular sequence is occurring unusually high (or possibly low) due to abnormal environmental conditions. This was well demonstrated by Zodrow & Cleal (1985), who were able to identify the base of the *L. bunburii* Biozone in the Sydney Coalfield (Cape Breton Island, Canada) despite the unusually high position of the index biohorizon. It is possible that all the biohorizons could be similarly diachronous, but it is far more likely that different taxa will respond differently to environmental change and thus cause the biohorizon succession to get out of order.

Biozonal nomenclature

As with botanical taxonomic nomenclature, there is a central organization responsible for standardizing stratigraphical nomenclatural practice: the International Stratigraphy Commission of the International Union of Geological Sciences. The organization presides over a codified set of rules covering nomenclature, the most recent edition being Salvador (1994). Although this code is not as prescriptive as the biological nomenclature codes (its rules are more akin to Recommendations in the biological codes), it has become a widely accepted guide in the field and the editorial policy of many journals is that they will only accept papers if the recommendations are adhered to.

The naming of biozones has caused some misunderstanding. In principle, biozones can be given any sort of designation provided it is unambiguous. Especially in the early development of a biostratigraphy, a sequential lettering or numbering system can be used (e.g. Dix 1934). In more mature systems, however, biozones are normally named after a particular taxon and it is here that confusion can arise. A taxon range zone is obviously named after the taxon whose range is used in the definition. In biozones defined on the ranges of two taxa (e.g. concurrent range zones) both names can be used. However, the stratigraphical code recommends that no more than two taxa should be used to name (rather than define) a biozone and, ideally, just one should be used. This need not be one of the taxa used to define the body or boundaries of the biozone, and certainly need not be restricted to the biozone (although it would obviously be unwise to name a biozone after a taxon which never occurs in it!). The taxon is merely a name-giver, providing a convenient label to assign to the interval. Except in total range zones, therefore, there should be no expectation that the nominal taxon is either restricted to or ranges throughout the biozone.

Data used

The ideal group of fossils for biostratigraphy should be abundant, occur widely and across as many facies as possible, and represent organs that exhibit consistent behaviour over a wide range of biostratinomic processes. Most fossil plant remains are fragments of the whole organism and so the best candidates (1) were abundantly produced, (2) were open to the natural forces (e.g. wind) that would detach them from the plant, (3) had sufficient taxonomically useful characters to allow easy identification, and (4) were dorsiventral so that they tend to be preserved showing as many as possible of these taxonomic characters.

Leaves are the obvious candidates here and it is no coincidence that virtually all plant macrofossil biostratigraphies (at least from the Carboniferous upwards) have been based on foliage adpressions. Tree and shrub foliage is the best; compared with herbs and ground-cover plants, they produce relatively more leaves that are more exposed to wind. However, their potential biostratigraphical value depends on there being enough useable morphological characters to enable a robust taxonomy to be developed. Because of the problems of leaf shape variation, plants that have relatively small, entire leaves are often poor biostratigraphical tools. For instance, glossopterid foliage is extremely abundant and diverse in the Permian Gondwanan floras (e.g. Chandra & Surange 1979) and should have considerable potential for biostratigraphy. However, the apparent morphological plasticity of the leaves and their relatively simple venation has meant that there is little consensus as to their taxonomy and so their biostratigraphical potential has never been properly developed. Angiosperm leaves can also show similar morphological plasticity but there is increasing evidence that their more complex venation patterns combined with leaf margin characters might hold out hope for improving their taxonomy (Hickey & Wolfe 1975) and thereby their biostratigraphical potential. In larger, compound leaves, such as ferns and pteridosperms, the morphology of the segments (pinnae, pinnules, etc.) tends to be less variable than that of the whole leaf and can be the basis of a useful taxonomy. These have the added advantage that, provided there is sufficient understanding of the variation of the segments within the leaves, the segments can be identified from relatively small fragments, making them especially useful when working with borehole cores.

Twigs and small branches of such large plants are also exposed to the elements, but lack the range of taxonomically useful characters when preserved as adpressions. Seeds are in most cases only produced periodically and rarely show large numbers of taxonomically useful characters except in the rare circumstances that they are anatomically preserved. Pollen- and spore-producing organs have more taxonomically useful characters, but are normally delicate structures with a low fossilization potential; even where they are preserved as adpressions, the effects of compression usually make them difficult to identify. Cones and strobili can often be fairly robust structures and have many taxonomically useful characters, but compression again can make their identification difficult.

Geologically orientated palaeobotanists have consequently tended to take a much greater interest in the taxonomy of leaves. Unfortunately, it is only given a superficial treatment in most standard palaeobotanical textbooks and details of the systematics and identification of fossil foliage has to be obtained from the primary literature. The taxonomy of some foliage fossils of the Upper Palaeozoic has become highly refined, incorporating both morphological and anatomical features (e.g. Kerp & Haubold 1988; Cleal & Shute 1995). Mesozoic gymnosperm taxonomy also relies heavily on foliar features (e.g. Harris 1964, 1969); even with their living relatives, the infrequency with which some of the plants produce reproductive structures has meant that foliage has played an important taxonomic role (e.g. cycads, Lamb 1923). Until recently, botanists have regarded angiosperm leaves as having little taxonomic significance and it has only been through the efforts of palaeobotanists such as Hickey & Wolfe (1975) that their importance has been realized, opening up their potential for biostratigraphical studies in the upper Mesozoic and Tertiary.

This traditional taxonomic approach to plant macrofossil biostratigraphy has found only limited use in the Silurian and Devonian. Although land plants were undergoing rapid evolution at that time, their fossilized remains tend to be rare and fragmentary. The morphological simplicity of the plants also means that the fragmentary fossils rarely have enough characters for identification; in most Silurian–Devonian fossil floras, identifiable remains are the exception, most fossils being little more than 'indeterminable plant debris'. To help overcome this limitation, Banks (1980) added simple morphological criteria to the more traditional taxonomic definitions to his biozones; for instance, the appearance of true seeds was used to help define the base of the *Rhacophyton* Biozone, as well as the appearance of *Rhacophyton*. Gerrienne & Streel (1994) took this further, by only using the presence or absence of morphological and anatomical characters ('biocharacters'), irrespective of whether the fossils can be identified. At a particular locality, a score is given for each

biocharacter found, depending on whether the biocharacter is primitive or derived, and these scores are then used to calculate a coefficient that reflects the relative evolutionary development of the assemblage. By comparing it against coefficients obtained from well documented and dated localities, it is possible to get some idea as to the relative stratigraphical position of the new locality. It remains to be seen how widely applicable and accurate this method proves, although an attempt has also been made to use it in palaeophytogeography (Raymond 1987).

What controls biozones

Plant biozones and biohorizons reflect the underlying changes in fossil assemblages which, in turn, mirror a complex interaction of evolution and environmental change in the original vegetation. In some cases, we are probably directly seeing evolutionary change. One of the best documented examples of this is the progressive change from *Neuropteris* to *Reticulopteris* in the Westphalian of northern Europe (Josten 1962), which seems to be a true evolutionary change rather than a reversible, phenotypic response (Zodrow & Cleal 1993; Cleal & Shute 1995).

Many biohorizons appear, however, to be merely reflecting environmental changes, that caused species to decline or become locally extinct, and other species to replace them in the habitats sampled by the fossil record. There is the risk that this sort of change does not occur synchronously in different geographical areas, and is thus of limited value for correlation. The main way of controlling this is to look at the positions of the principal biohorizons in the context of the overall changes in the plant fossil record, such as by using the sequential biohorizon model mentioned above.

There are no hard and fast rules for making a biostratigraphically robust set of biohorizons. The effects of environmental change can never be avoided, even when an event or trend in the fossil record is suspected of reflecting an evolutionary change. All that one can hope for is an internally consistent set of changes in the record that can be identified over as wide an area as possible.

Limitations

Even the best biostratigraphical schemes are limited in their application. The most obvious restriction is geographical. Most plant macrofossil species are restricted to the higher ranked *phytochoria* (palaeokingdoms), and are therefore all but useless for correlation between such phytochoria. Apparent similarities in form-genera between palaeokingdoms are normally superficial (e.g. Meyen 1969) and should not be used as a basis for correlation. This is not just a problem of plant macrofossils, as even planktonic and nektonic marine animal fossils tend to be at least partially constrained within faunal provinces. At times of high biotic provincialism, such as the Permian, global stratigraphical correlations can only normally be achieved through abiotic methods.

Even within palaeokingdoms, biostratigraphical correlations using plant macrofossils can have a geographical limitation. Vegetational changes do not occur synchronously over wide areas, even when viewed on a geological timescale. Evidence for potonieacean pteridosperm trees (Laveine *et al.* 1993) suggests that species migrated at about 0.9 m per year, as they extended their range from China to central North America during the Carboniferous. While such a rate is unlikely to have a major influence on the positions of biohorizons between areas separated by hundreds of kilometres, when the separation is nearer thousands of kilometres the effect will be more marked (Laveine *et al.* 1989). This has been well documented by Fissunenko & Laveine (1984), who showed numerous discrepancies in the relative positions of biohorizons between western Europe (principally northern France) and the Ukraine.

Another major constraint is the facies in which the plant macrofossils occur. The fossil record usually only preserves remains of lowland vegetation. Occasionally, however, so-called 'upland' or extra-basinal vegetation is preserved, and this can show apparent discrepancies in the time of appearance and disappearance of species (e.g. Mamay & Mapes 1992). Even within the lowland vegetation, there can be significant differences in the composition of the vegetation, depending on variations in the physical environment, such as edaphic conditions. Which of the lowland vegetation-types is being represented by the fossil record is often constrained by the aero- and hydrodynamics of the depositional system that generated the sedimentary succession, and this in turn is reflected by the facies of the strata produced. Hence, a major change in facies often produces a major change in the plant fossil record, but which

may be strongly diachronous. A well documented example of this is the diachronous appearance of conifer remains in the Upper Palaeozoic, which is mainly controlled by Variscan tectonic uplift draining the tropical wetlands (Lyons & Darrah 1989). Similarly, the appearance of the 'typically' Lower Carboniferous *Sphenopteridium* and *Archaeocalamites* in Lower Permian red-beds of North America (Mamay & Bateman 1991; Mamay 1992) is because those red-beds were probably sampling habitats with similar edaphic conditions to those represented by the Lower Carboniferous parallic deposits. It is not the plants that have changed significantly, but the sedimentary processes that generated the strata and their plant macrofossil content.

Relationship between biostratigraphy and chronostratigraphy

Similarity in the arrangement of biozones between different areas is referred to as homotaxy. Where homotaxy occurs, the biozones can obviously be correlated and lines drawn between the sections at the biozonal boundaries. It is important to remember, however, that these are not timelines, and it underscores the fundamental difference between biostratigraphy and chronostratigraphy. Chronostratigraphical units (systems, series, stages, etc.) are bounded by time-planes and the only place where a boundary can be unequivocally identified is in its boundary stratotype section. Everywhere else, the positions of chronostratigraphical boundaries can only be estimated. The most useful biohorizons can approximate to time-planes, at least on the scale of geological time and over a relatively restricted geographical area. But it is only an approximation and any claim that a chronostratigraphical boundary can be identified in a sequence (other than its stratotype) by the presence of a biohorizon has to be rejected. Nevertheless, provided these limitations are borne in mind, homotaxy remains the best means of making this estimation and of constructing near-chronostratigraphical correlations between sequences.

43. Spore and pollen biostratigraphy

GEOFFREY CLAYTON & PETER COXON

Fossil spores and pollen occur in vast numbers in many sediments and sedimentary rocks ranging in age from Ordovician to Quaternary. Their abundance and small size enables samples of limited volume to be used effectively; an advantage soon recognized in attempts to establish the age of rocks penetrated during oil exploration where only small fragments ('cuttings') of the rocks drilled are normally available. An additional advantage of spores and pollen in biostratigraphy is that their dispersal and subsequent transport often result in their presence in sediments representing a wide range of terrestrial and marine depositional environments, thereby enabling correlation of marine and non-marine sections. Problems associated with reworking may occur but reworked specimens can generally be recognized from their different state of preservation or organic maturation level. Their entire stratigraphic range may also be older than the age of the assemblage as indicated by the other (indigenous) taxa present. In this chapter, the term 'spore' is used in a restricted sense covering the reproductive cells of bryophytes and free-sporing pteridophytic vascular plants.

N. Green is credited with observing the first pollen grains under a primitive lens system in 1640 (Bradbury 1967). By the middle of the nineteenth century several workers including Witham and Hooker had described *in situ* spores in thin sections of Carboniferous coals and in 1881 Reinsch made the first successful attempt to extract spores from coals using a mixture of nitric acid and potassium chlorate. Pollen analysis and Quaternary palynological research dates from von Post's pioneering publication in 1917. The origins of pre-Quaternary stratigraphic palynology are less clear. These can be traced back to Bennie & Kidston's (1886) description of differences in spore content between certain Scottish Carboniferous coals, but modern biostratigraphic work essentially dates from Potonié's publications in 1932 and 1934 and papers by Raistrick & Simpson (1933) and Raistrick (1934). A comprehensive account of the history of palaeopalynology has recently been given by Jansonius & McGregor (1996) to which reference should be made for all the works cited in this paragraph.

A fundamental difference in methodology exists between Quaternary biostratigraphic studies and investigations of older sections. In the former, identification and quantification of pollen and spores of extant plant taxa are generally used to establish patterns of climate change that can then be correlated with independently dated sections. The Quaternary is characterized by high magnitude variability in climate which is principally controlled by orbital forcing (i.e. the astronomical relationship of the Earth and the Sun). The consequent environmental change exerts considerable pressure on the global biota with marked alteration in the ranges of taxa due to rapid transformation of environments. Astronomical forcing produces 'metronomic' variability in climate but the magnitude and frequency of the climatic changes are far from uniform (see Lowe & Walker 1997). The product of such change varies spatially but globally a sequence of complex cold and warm stages of different lengths and intensities (some of which include glacial episodes) can be identified (see Fig. 43.1). The impact of Quaternary environmental change on the flora has been the subject of detailed investigation in Europe since the early 1900s (West 1981). The warm stages are well represented in the terrestrial sedimentary record although successive phases of erosional cold climate processes (glacial and periglacial) have removed much evidence. Our knowledge of the cold stage floras of mid-latitudes is far more fragmentary but the palaeobotanical records from some sites in lower latitudes can be remarkably complete (see Lowe & Walker 1997; MacDonald 1996). In pre-Quaternary investigations, first appearances and extinctions of extant spore and pollen taxa are established and these form the basis for correlation. These events are often assumed to represent evolutionary changes in floras though, in fact, many first appearances and disappearances may record local climatic changes. Current knowledge of the natural affinities of fossil pollen and spores gradually decreases back through time to the Devonian where the parent plants of less than 5% of 'species' are known. The extinct spore and pollen taxa erected from pre-Quaternary sections are based entirely on morphological characters such as shape and size. In some cases they may approximate to natural species but in others they are purely arbitrary.

CLAYTON, G. & COXON, P. 1999. Spore and pollen biostratigraphy. *In*: JONES, T. P. & ROWE, N. P. (eds) *Fossil Plants and Spores: modern techniques*. Geological Society, London, 225–229.

Ribains (MIS 5e, 122-132ka)

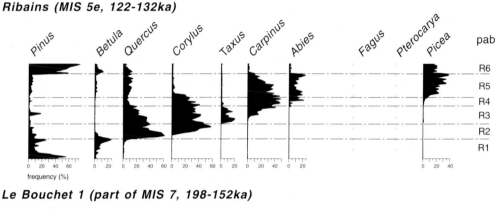

Le Bouchet 1 (part of MIS 7, 198-152ka)

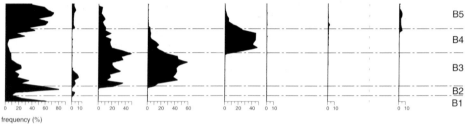

Landos (MIS 9, 302-338ka)

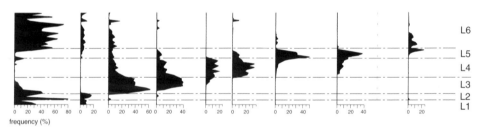

Praclaux (MIS 11, 352-428ka)

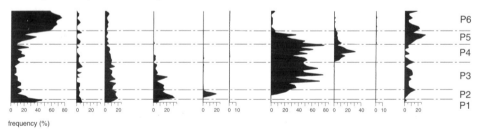

Fig. 43.1. Relative percentage pollen diagrams (selected taxa) of four successive Middle and Late Pleistocene temperate stages (interglacials) in the Velay region of France. The correlation to marine isotope stages (MIS) and tentative ages of the deposits are shown. The behaviour of the individual taxa (e.g. *Carpinus*) during each temperate stage and the unique succession of pollen assemblages that are apparent throughout each stage are clearly shown. Possible local pollen assemblage biozones are marked and these could be subdivided where necessary to produce more detailed descriptions of assemblages. The regional disappearance of taxa, e.g. *Pterocarya* after the Middle Pleistocene (MIS 11) and *Fagus* by the last interglacial (MIS 5e), is also apparent. After Reille & De Beaulieu (1995).

Biostratigraphic practice

Pre-Tertiary spore and pollen assemblages may be quite diverse, sometimes comprising more than 100 taxa. Rarely, stratigraphic ranges of spores and pollen are very short; *Radiizonates aligerens* (Knox) Staplin & Jansonius, for example, is restricted to the upper part of the Langsettian Stage within the Silesian (Upper Carboniferous) of Europe. Occasionally, taxa have both restricted stratigraphic ranges and widespread geographical distributions enabling them to be used effectively in intercontinental biostratigraphic correlation. One of the best known examples of this type is *Retispora lepidophyta* (Kedo) Playford which first appears in the upper Famennian Stage of the Upper Devonian and disappears at the Devonian/Carboniferous boundary, probably in response to some global climate change. However, stratigraphic ranges of individual taxa are normally relatively long, often extending through several stages (see Fig. 43.2).

Many different codes and guides to stratigraphic classification have been published; some accepted locally or nationally, others intended to be internationally applicable. Several of these are discussed in detail by Christopher & Goodman (1996) in the context of palynology and biostratigraphy. Definitions of different types of biozones and the nomenclature applied to them vary somewhat from scheme to scheme but there is general agreement on some of the more important types of biozone used in spore and pollen-based biostratigraphy.

Pre-Quaternary

Since most pre-Quaternary spore and pollen taxa have relatively long stratigraphic ranges, most of the zones erected are concurrent range biozones and partial range biozones (*sensu* Holland *et al.* 1978), based on the overlapping ranges of several taxa. In the Devonian / Carboniferous example shown in Fig. 43.2, the LN Biozone is a concurrent range biozone. The base of the biozone is defined by the first appearance of *Verrucosisporites nitidus* and its top is defined by the base of the succeeding *Vallatisporites verrucosus–Retusotriletes incohatus* (VI) Biozone and by the last occurrence of *Retispora lepidophyta*. The VI Biozone is a partial range biozone with its top defined by the base of the succeeding HD Biozone at the level of the first appearance of *Kraeuselisporites hibernicus* and *Umbonatisporites distinctus*. In this case, the VI Biozone index species, *Vallatisporites verrucosus* and *Retusotriletes incohatus* both have ranges that extend well above and below the boundaries of the VI Biozone. Other types of biozone have been established but are relatively rare. The *Radiizonates aligerens* Biozone in the Langsettian Stage of the Silesian is a total range biozone (*sensu* Holland *et al.* 1978), its base and top being defined by the first and last appearances of the taxon respectively. Quantitatively defined biozones based on relative proportions of taxa have been established but are always subject to the suspicion that these proportions reflect parameters other than evolutionary changes. Relevant factors include palaeoecology, sediment transport history and diagenetic environment.

Quaternary

The principal unit of Pleistocene pollen biostratigraphy is the pollen assemblage biozone (pab). Such zones are defined locally (local pabs) and correlated to regional pabs and to type localities, chronozones and stages. Some workers generate the pab's using numerical analyses (Birks 1986). Although extinctions are not particularly useful in Pleistocene biostratigraphy regional disappearances can be as the ranges of certain taxa retract and expand with environmental change. Regional disappearance is progressive throughout the Pleistocene because taxa are unable to recolonize from distant refugia and, as such, disappearance can be used biostratigraphically (Coxon & Waldren 1997) with caution (see Fig. 43.1). The climatically driven nature of the record has produced recognizable cyclicity in pollen assemblages as glacial, cold, cool and warm conditions alternate (e.g. Reille & De Beaulieu 1995). This has led to a number of schemes of describing the cyclic temperate stages and their pabs (e.g. Turner & West 1968). Shorter records of cold, cool or warm phases which do not describe a complete cycle are simply described in terms of pollen assemblages. The Holocene (10 ka to present) falls within the range of radiocarbon dating and, as such, the time transgressive nature of the biostratigraphic boundaries are well documented and can be placed within a detailed chronological framework. Analyses of the spatial and temporal changes in pabs have allowed appraisals of global palaeoenvironments to be made and such research is at the forefront of Quaternary palynology (e.g. MacDonald 1996).

Applications of particular spore and pollen groups

The more important spore and pollen groups are briefly discussed below in order of the first appearance in the fossil record.

Cryptospores

'Cryptospores are spores without trilete or monolete tetrad marks, and with or without contact

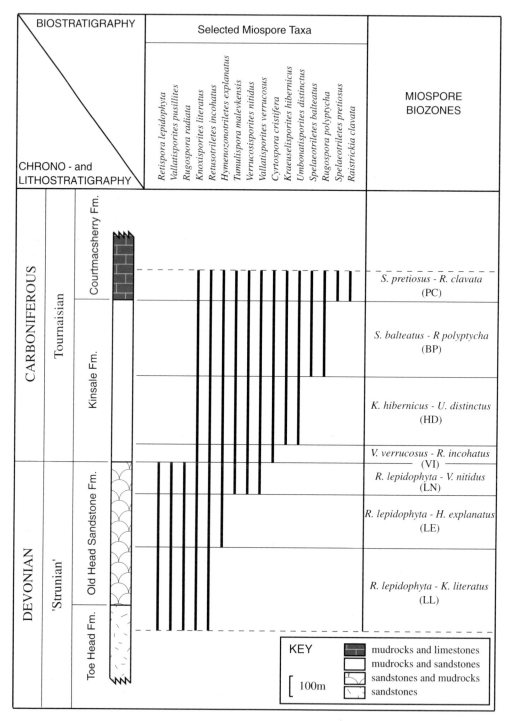

Fig. 43.2. Miospore zonation of late Devonian–early Carboniferous rocks in the Old Head of Kinsale–Seven Heads area of south County Cork, Ireland (data from Higgs *et al.* 1988).

features; they include "permanent" tetrads, dyads and alete monads.' Richardson (1996, p. 555). These simple spores which were probably produced by bryophytes are proving useful in dating and correlating rocks from the late Ordovician to the early Devonian; see, for example, Williams *et al.* (1996).

Miospores

Trilete spores first appear within the Llandovery Series of the Silurian System and dominate Devonian and Carboniferous spore/pollen assemblages in terms of both numbers of individuals and species. Monolete spores first appear in the Devonian but are rare below the upper Dinantian. The differences between isospores, microspores, small megaspores, prepollen and pollen are functional rather than morphological. This difficulty in identification led to the introduction of the term 'miospore' by Guennel (1952) to cover all these groups in dispersed assemblages.

Megaspores

Dispersed fossil megaspores are typically defined as being larger than 200 µm in diameter. They first appear in Devonian rocks where many taxa span this arbitrary size boundary separating megaspores from miospores. Some of these small megaspore taxa such as *Ancyrospora* Richardson, have been used successfully for biostratigraphic purposes (e.g. Higgs & Scott 1982). However, the large size of most megaspores results in their palaeoecological and palaeogeographical distribution being more limited than miospores of the same age.

Gymnosperm pollen

The earliest fossil seeds occur in rocks of latest Devonian age, proving the existence of gymnospermous plants by this time. However, the first undisputed pollen grains do not appear until high in the Dinantian (Lower Carboniferous). Clearly, some early pollen grains exist that cannot be distinguished morphologically from microspores or isospores. This also applies to many non-saccate taxa in the Upper Palaeozoic and Mesozoic and lends support to the use of the term 'miospore' discussed earlier.

Monosaccate pollen grains such as *Potonieisporites* Bharadwaj first appear in the mid-Carboniferous and become gradually more abundant through the Silesian Subsystem (Upper Carboniferous). They are of limited stratigraphic value in this interval. Bisaccate pollen first appear in the Silesian but are initially rare, becoming much more abundant in the Lower Permian. In terms of biostratigraphy, saccate pollen are most important in the Permo-Triassic where they tend to numerically dominate assemblages. One group, the striate/taeniate bisaccates, characterized by parallel strap-like thickenings on the surface of the body, becomes especially diverse in the Permian and lower Triassic where it constitutes the basis for several palynological zonal schemes (see for example Hart 1970). Saccate pollen have remained abundant from the Triassic through to the present day and in Tertiary/Quaternary assemblages they are common in high latitude and montane assemblages. Quaternary saccate pollen is predominantly derived from the Pinaceae and (to a lesser extent) Podocarpaceae families. Identification within those families is often possible to genus, and occasionally to species (e.g. Hansen & Cushing 1973). Other gymnosperm pollen found throughout the Tertiary and Quaternary includes numerous inaperturate types referable to the Taxodiaceae, Cupressaceae and Taxaceae families. Again, within these families some genera (and even species) can be distinguished.

Angiosperm pollen

Angiosperm pollen, with its distinctive wall structure, is believed to have appeared in Early Cretaceous time (e.g. see Jarzen & Nichols 1996) with *Clavatipollenites hughesii* which has a columellate, tectate exine. Triaperturate angiosperm pollen appears during the mid-Cretaceous with tricolpate, tricolporate and triporate forms appearing successively (Lidgard & Crane 1990; Jarzen & Nichols 1996). A distinct provincial pattern appeared by the Late Cretaceous with triaperturate pollen remaining the most common type up to the present day. By the mid-Tertiary most assemblages contain morphotypes characteristic of modern pollen assemblages although the Poaceae and Asteraceae expanded dramatically in the Late Tertiary. Some morphologies peaked in the Cretaceous and subsequently declined. The development of distinctive angiosperm pollen morphologies is reviewed by Jarzen & Nichols (1996); the Cretaceous pollen succession is discussed by Batten (1996c).

Part Eight   Palaeoclimatology

44. Fossil leaf character states: multivariate analyses

JACK A. WOLFE & ROBERT A. SPICER

We base this methodology on the assumption that there has been prime selection for those features of leaves that confer the maximum functional advantage under a variety of environmental conditions. These features centre on maximizing photosynthetic capacity (for example by maximizing leaf surface area and stomatal size/numbers) while minimizing water loss (for example by developing coverings largely impervious to water, reducing stomatal size/numbers, minimizing leaf surface area), and concurrently minimizing the energy invested in photosynthetic and structural components. Only a limited number of engineering solutions can approximately satisfy these conflicting constraints under a given set of environmental conditions; not surprisingly, land plants growing under similar environmental conditions but geographically widely separated tend to develop similar morphologies despite marked floristic differences. Moreover, these morphologies (physiognomic traits) are constrained by the laws of physics, which should have remained fixed since the advent of land plants, and we thus assume that palaeoenvironmental interpretations can be made using morphologies that have been calibrated with extant land plants growing under known climatic parameters.

These constraints affect all land plants, but some plant groups appear to have evolved more sensitive physiognomic responses to climate than have other groups. Long-lived woody angiosperms, for example, have higher levels of foliar diversity and phenotypic plasticity in leaf morphology than do gymnosperms (e.g. cycads and conifers) or ferns (Spicer 1989a). This gives woody angiosperms (especially the subgroup of the dicotyledons) a wide array of morphologies that possibly can be calibrated with environmental factors.

Existing vegetation has been described and mapped without reliance on taxonomic similarities or differences, i.e. on the physical structure (including leaf structure) of the plants. The resulting patterns of plant distributions have clear correlations to climate, and indeed before meteorological stations became common, vegetation often served as a proxy for inferring climatic patterns. These important observations imply that the physiognomy of individual organs, whole plants, and vegetational units up to the scale of global

biomes is strongly influenced by (and thus indicative of) climate. In turn, such relations imply that physiognomic character states are controlled directly by environment, although the experimental basis for this concept has only been demonstrated in some cases (Givnish & Vermeij 1976; Givnish 1979, 1986; Parkhurst & Loucks 1972).

Physiognomic adaptations to environment should be robust in an evolutionary context, and we should be able, within certain limits, to quantify these relations to infer pre-Quaternary climates. The method that has been in use longest is that of leaf margin analysis. The seminal work of Bailey & Sinnott (1915, 1916) demonstrated a marked correlation between some physical character states of dicotyledon leaves (especially those of woody plants) and general warmth of climate. Using regional floras of hundreds to thousands of species, Bailey & Sinnott concluded that generally the higher the proportion of species that had untoothed (entire) margins, the warmer the climate. At the same time, these authors noted some exceptions, e.g. the tendency for very cold and/or dry (but not necessarily warm) climates to have moderately high proportions of untoothed species; but these authors suggested that, despite such exceptions, the kind of leaf margin could provide a botanical index of climates for the Late Cretaceous and Tertiary, independent of inferred phylogenetic relationships of fossils to extant plants. Wolfe (1979) expanded that methodology and from floristic lists of vegetation growing in drought-free environments in southeastern and eastern Asia plotted the percentage of entire margined (untoothed) leaf species against mean annual temperature (T). This relation degrades when water is limiting to growth or the growing season is short and/or cool and so can only be applied to palaeobotanical data when the original vegetation grew in drought-free regimes and the growing season was comparatively long (>4.3 months) and/or warm (mean of warmest month >15°C).

Development of CLAMP

Although the approximate relation between woody dicotyledon leaf margins and at least one climatic factor – temperature – has been demonstrated, other leaf character states could correlate with other

WOLFE, J. A. & SPICER, R. A. 1999. Fossil leaf character states: multivariate analyses.
In: JONES, T. P. & ROWE, N. P. (eds) *Fossil Plants and Spores: modern techniques.*
Geological Society, London, 233–239.

climatic variables. Leaf size is likely to be related to precipitation or water availability, as experimentally demonstrated (Parkhurst & Loucks 1972). Consider also the contrast between desert and rain forest vegetation. In deserts leaf size is small; large trees with large leaf loads are absent, and some plants have dispensed with leaves altogether and photosynthesize using their stems which are also adapted for water storage, and woody plants are widely spaced. In rain forests leaf size ranges to the very large (some more than 1 m^2), large trees with large leaf loads are common, and the plants form a complex structure made up of several shrub and tree layers with many lianas. Note, however, that although leaf sizes can be large in temperate rain forests, the largest leaves occur in tropical rain forests.

If dryness has a secondary influence on the leaf margin and temperature on leaf size, then to consider change in any single leaf character state to have a one-to-one relation to change in a given environmental factor would seem unlikely to produce the most accurate calibration for any given environmental factor. Leaf morphology represents a compromise solution to conflicting constraints; for example, size is a function of the need to intercept as much light as possible while minimizing water loss and structural cost. From this, we suggest that the most accurate calibration of leaf physiognomy to environment would be produced in a multivariate context. Further, the original leaf-margin analysis by Bailey & Sinnott (1915, 1916) and as later explored by Wolfe (1979) was based largely on regional floras comprising hundreds or even thousands of species, and a given large sample could include different climates (i.e. calibration is very approximate). If calibration of leaf physiognomy to environment is the desired product, then the basis for the calibration should be modern samples that are comparable in size and in restriction to a local environment, and in turn to fossil samples.

The database for the calibration of leaf physiognomy to environment is being developed by collection of modern samples in a small area (typically only a few hectares) that is close to a site where meteorological data have been recorded. Each sample comprises a minimum of 20 (the mean is now c. 30) species of woody dicotyledons, and each species was collected so that the voucher contains the full physiognomic range displayed by that species in the sampled area; for example, both sun leaves and shade leaves for a species are collected. Exotic species are not collected for analysis. At the present time, the database includes about 170 samples; the original database included about 100 samples (Wolfe 1993). Now included are samples from tropical rain forest (e.g. Fiji, Puerto Rico), Sonoran desert, dry tropical forest (e.g. southern Sonora), mesothermal chaparral (e.g. California) and closed-canopy analogues (e.g. southeastern USA), and various microthermal vegetational types, ranging from wet, closed-canopy forests (Japan) to dry, open-canopy woodlands (e.g. Utah) and to boreal forest.

In the laboratory, each sample is scored for 31 character states. These are 7 categories for margin, 9 for size, 4 for the apex, 3 for the base, 5 for length to width ratio, and 3 for general shape. As shown in Fig. 44.1, the full range of physiognomic variation for each species is scored, the sums for a given character state for the sample are summed, and these sums are then converted to percentages. These comprise the database for CLAMP (climate–leaf analysis multivariate program).

As discussed by ter Braak & Prentice (1988), multivariate analyses of organisms and their environments can first be categorized by whether

Chuzenji-ko, Honshu	Form	Teeth--------------------------------------					Size---							
Uemura Oct. 20, 1991	Lobe	None	Regular	Close	Rnd	Acute	Cmpd	Nano	Lep 1	Lep 2	Mi 1	Mi 2	Mi 3	Me 1	Me 2	Me 3
Pterocarya rhoifolia			1	1		1	0.5					0.5	0.5			
Betula maximowicziana			1	1		1	1							0.33	0.33	0.33
Betula schmidtii			1	1		1	1					1				
Acer distylum			1	0.5	1		0.5						0.33	0.33	0.33	
Acer japonicum	1		1	1		1	1					0.5	0.5			
Pterostyrax hispida			0.5			1	0.5						0.25	0.25	0.25	0.25
Fraxinus sp.			1	0.5		1	0.5				0.5	0.5				
Viburnum wrightii			1	1		1	0.5						0.5	0.5		
Total 43 species	7.5	6	36	28.5	9.5	27.5	23	0	0	0.66	3.4	12.7	13.6	7.3	2.24	2.91
Percentage	17	14	84	66	22	64	54	0	0	2	8	30	32	17	5	7

Fig. 44.1. Part of a score sheet for a CLAMP database sample. In a sampled area, each species is collected so the voucher has the full range of observed physiognomic variation. The range for each species is scored: for example, under Cmpd (i.e. teeth compound), a 0.5 indicates that some of the teeth are compound and some are simple, and under Size, a score of 1 is portioned equally among the size categories displayed by the leaves of that species. The sums in the penultimate line are converted to percentages, which are the data entered into the species data file to be run in the CANOCO software program. See Fig. 44.5 for the full names of the size categories.

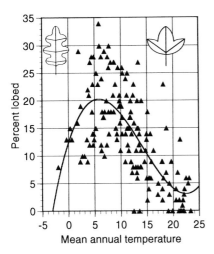

Fig. 44.2. Plot of percent lobed species versus mean annual temperature (*T*). Lobing is generally absent or infrequent in megathermal (*T* >20°C) vegetation, increases in mesothermal (*T* 13–20°C) vegetation, and reaches a maximum between 4 to 12°C in warm microthermal (*T* <13°C) vegetation. The decrease in lobing in cool microthermal vegetation is very valid; diversity in lobed genera such as *Quercus* (oaks) and *Acer* (maples) decreases markedly at low values of *T*. The relation between temperature and lobing is decidedly non-linear.

the organism/environment relations are linear or non-linear. As emphasized by Wolfe (1995), the relations between physiognomic character states and climatic parameters are typically non-linear (Fig. 44.2), and these non-linear relations exclude the use of methods such as principal components analysis or multiple regression analysis, which assume linear relations. Wolfe (1990, 1993) initially used correspondence analysis, which, although assuming a Gaussian distribution of an organism along an environmental gradient, is capable of validly portraying a relation that might be linear. A second categorization of multivariate methods is direct or indirect. In correspondence analysis, the environmental gradient is not directly (objectively) related to the biological distributions included in samples, whereas in canonical correspondence analysis (CCA) the analysis directly relates supplied environmental data to the samples and their constituents (ter Braak 1986). As previously discussed (Wolfe 1995), CCA is the preferred technique of analysing physiognomic data and relating them to climatic parameters. We have used the CANOCO software developed by ter Braak (1987–1992), which has several multivariate programs but was especially developed to run CCA on a species (physiognomic character states in the

present context) database derived from sampled sites and on an environmental (climatic parameters in the present context) database for the sampled sites.

CCA also has desirable aspects that are absent in methods that assume linearity. The CLAMP database comprises sets of closed categories, whose values, comprising percentages, are related. For example, if the percentage obovate shape increases, the combined percentage of elliptic shape and ovate shape must decrease, i.e. the categories covary. Similarly, some meteorological parameters must also covary to different degrees; the mean of the warmest month will generally be higher in areas of high mean annual temperature, and thus these parameters have some degree of colinearity. Some character states also tend to covary with other character states; for example, samples with the largest percentage of compound teeth also tend to have the largest percentage of lobing. Multiple regression analysis and principal components analysis are highly sensitive to, and thus their results influenced by, colinearity; if colinear factors are eliminated, information can be lost. In the previous example, if either lobing or compound teeth were eliminated because both character states indicate microthermal climates, we would lose the discriminatory fact that lobing tends to occur in both wet and dry microthermal climates whereas compound teeth are more common in wet than in dry microthermal climates. Covariance and/or colinearity are inevitable in climatic data, in particular that relating to foliar physiognomy, and in physiognomic data.

Figure 44.3 shows the ordination of 141 of the 170 samples on the first two axes. The remaining sites are from high altitudes or latitudes and comprise a well defined subalpine nest. These samples consistently plot together because the leaf morphology is uniquely adapted to freeze-induced drought, snow cover, short seasons, but no significant day-length effect. Because of the very small leaf size many taxa have lost marginal teeth that would otherwise indicate cool conditions and as a consequence this subalpine nest consistently suggests warmer conditions than are observed. Further, each sample typically contains some evergreen species that survive the frigid winters by overwintering beneath the snow cover. Most fossil floras are preserved in lowland settings, and it is legitimate to exclude subalpine vegetation from the reference set; however, for studies of Tertiary elevation change (e.g. Povey *et al.* 1994; Wolfe *et al.* 1998) or high latitude Neogene floras (Wolfe 1994*b*) the inclusion of the subalpine sites is necessary.

The spatial relations of the climatic parameters and of some physiognomic character states on axes

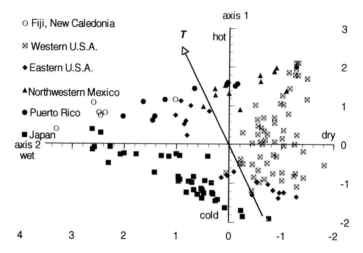

Fig. 44.3. Canonical correspondence analysis plot of 141 leaf samples of modern vegetation. Axis 1 (shown here as vertical) has an eigenvalue of 0.147 and accounts for 48.2% of the physiognomic variance, and axis 2 (horizontal) has an eigenvalue of 0.042 and accounts for 13.6% of the variance. If each sample is projected orthogonally to the mean annual temperature (T) vector, the samples are approximately ranked according to their T values. Megathermal desert samples plot in the upper right quadrant and megathermal rain forest samples plot to the far left. Mesothermal samples plot on axis 1 between megathermal and microthermal samples. Despite marked floristic differences, a sample from the western (dry) side of New Caledonia plots close to samples from Florida and Puerto Rico. Similarly, a sample from coastal Washington plots very close to three samples from Maryland (the samples grouped between –0.6 and –0.8 on axis 1) have no species and only three genera in common.

1 and 2 are shown in Figs 44.4–6. All could, of course, be plotted on the same graph but are here separated for clarity. Note that leaf sizes can be subparallel to water-stress factors (the largest leaf sizes) or to temperature factors (the smallest sizes).

When the sample plots are orthogonally projected to a vector such as mean annual temperature (Fig. 44.7), the samples are approximately ranked for that meteorological parameter. The T vector undoubtedly represents a compromise positioning, and we might expect that the physiognomic compromises evidenced in dry vegetation might be somewhat different from those apparent in wet vegetation. That this is so is indicated by the regressions obtained from separating into cohorts the samples that plot to the left of the T vector from the samples that plot to the right; the standard error of either cohort is less than that obtained from regressing all 141 samples.

Although regressions of most meteorological parameters are most accurate by projecting sample plots on axes 1 and 2, in the instance of warm-month mean temperature (WM) the projection from plots on axes 1 and 3 provides the most accurate estimate (Fig. 44.8). On axis 3, T, which typically has a marked colinearity with WM, receives a negative score whereas WM receives a moderately high score, i.e. the relation between T and WM is separated on axis 3. With valid estimates of both T

and WM, estimates of the cold-month mean temperature (and hence mean annual range of temperature) can thus be obtained; T is the approximate mean of cold-month and warm-month mean temperatures, and mean annual range is the difference between cold-month and warm-month mean temperatures.

Applications

CLAMP was developed primarily to produce repeatable and valid estimates of standard meteorological parameters of temperature and precipitation for fossil leaf assemblages. Application of CLAMP to a variety of Tertiary floras in western North America has produced results that are internally consistent, i.e. the estimates of T in a given time interval decrease in a northerly direction (Wolfe 1994a). Similarly, estimates of mean annual range of temperature in a given time interval increase from the coastal region into the interior. The CLAMP estimates of sea-level climatic changes during the Tertiary in western North America are consistent with changes inferred from the marine record, and the CLAMP estimates add the significant dimensions of seasonality of temperature and of precipitation, as well as estimates of significant changes in precipitation. Estimates of T derived

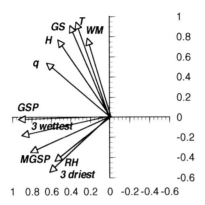

Fig. 44.4. Correspondence analysis plot of environmental parameters used in CLAMP. The relative lengths of the vectors indicate the relative significance of the different parameters. From top centre in a counterclockwise direction, the parameters are warm month mean temperature (*WM*); mean annual temperature (*T*); growing season (*GS*), which includes all weeks during which mean temperature is >10°C; mean annual moist enthalpy (*H*); mean annual specific humidity (*q*); mean growing season precipitation (*GSP*); mean total precipitation of the three consecutive wettest months during the growing season (*3 wettest*); mean monthly precipitation during the growing season (*MGSP*); mean annual relative humidity (*RH*); and mean total precipitation of the three consecutive driest months during the growing season (*3 driest*). The arrow tips are at the scores for each factor and can be viewed as vectors that can be extended indefinitely (as shown in Fig. 44.3), including in the direction opposite the arrow for any given factor. Any sample point (Fig. 44.3) can thus be orthogonally projected to any given vector for the ranking of the sample with respect to all other samples relative to the given factor.

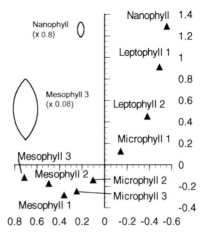

Fig. 44.5. Scores on axes 1 and 2 for leaf sizes. The sizes plot from the smallest (nanophyll) in the upper right in a clockwise direction to the largest (mesophyll 3). When viewed in multidimensional space, the curve represents an approximate spiral. Note that these scores do not represent loadings but plot with the samples that have the highest percentage of the particular size. Thus, the smallest size plots with Sonoran Desert scrub and the larger leaf sizes (mesophyll 1 through 3) plot with rain forest samples. Samples of intermediate water stress and the intermediate leaf sizes plot near the intersection of the two axes.

from CLAMP for near-polar Late Cretaceous floras (Herman & Spicer 1996), moreover, are consistent with other proxy data and also add estimates for the additional climatic parameters.

CLAMP can, of course, be applied to geological problems that relate to altitudinal changes, because *T* generally decreases from sea-level to higher elevations. The rate of that decrease, however, can vary greatly, even within the same geographic region (Meyer 1992). If, for example, a coastal sea-level fossil flora had a *T* of 20°C and an interior, isochronous flora had a *T* of 10°C, this could imply an elevational difference of perhaps as little as 1 to 2 km or as much as 5 km (cf. Wolfe 1994*a*). Fortunately, moist enthalpy (*H*), which is a concept based on conservation of energy and hence should be applicable to the past, provides a more accurate measure of palaeoelevations (Forest *et al.* 1995). Determinations of *H* in modern environments

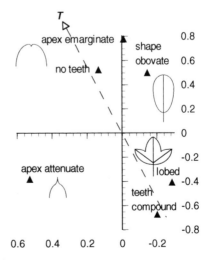

Fig. 44.6. Scores on axes 1 and 2 for some other leaf character states. Note that, although the score for no teeth is close to the *T* vector, the score does not fall on that vector; the score for teeth compound is just as proximal to the *T* vector.

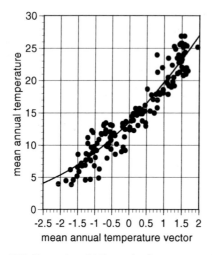

Fig. 44.7. Regression of 141 samples for mean annual temperature (T). The r^2 is 0.90 and the standard error is 1.85°C. The standard error can be decreased by separation of the samples into wet and dry cohorts (cf. Wolfe 1993).

depend on knowing T, specific humidity (q), and relative humidity (RH). All these meteorological parameters are to some extent reflected in leaf physiognomy (Fig. 44.4); H, however, can be estimated from leaf physiognomy with a standard error that produces an altitudinal estimate of <1 km (Wolfe *et al.* 1997, 1998).

To simplify the obtaining of climatic estimates from CLAMP, we have developed, with the help of A. B. Herman, a spreadsheet. After a CANOCO run, the scores for samples are copied from the CANOCO solution file and placed in the spreadsheet; previous geometrical projections of samples onto each of the 10 meteorological vectors were regressed against the actual values for each parameter, and the resulting formula incorporated into the spreadsheet. On placing the axis scores for a new sample (e.g. a fossil sample) into the spreadsheet, predictions (estimates) for each of the 10 parameters are automatically calculated. A copy of this spreadsheet and copies of the CLAMP databases (both physiognomic and meteorological) can be obtained by sending a formatted floppy disk to either author (PC format to Wolfe and Macintosh format to Spicer).

Future work

Our experience with CLAMP suggests that the ordination methods might be improved by allowing samples to be projected to a vector that lies in a space formed by at least three axes. Indeed, the nearest neighbour method used by Stranks & England (1997) to relate leaf physiognomy of New Zealand and Australian samples to Northern Hemisphere samples essentially positions samples in physiognomic space. The samples of the subalpine nest might be similarly treated, inasmuch as these, although plotting proximal to warm and

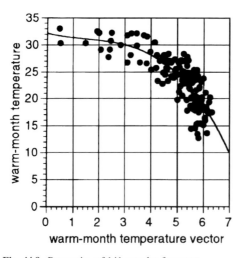

Fig. 44.8. Regression of 141 samples for mean temperature of the warmest month. The regression is on the warm-month vector in a plot on axis 1 and axis 3, which yields a significantly longer vector than a plot of the vector on axis 1 and axis 2. The r^2 is 0.69 and the standard error is 2.3°C.

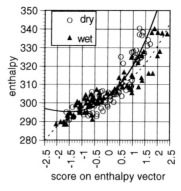

Fig. 44.9. Regression of samples ($n = 69$) that plot to right (dry side) of specific humidity (q) vector compared to regression of those ($n = 72$) that plot to left (wet side) of the vector for mean moist enthalpy. Regression of the dry samples (solid curve) produces an r^2 of 0.83 and a standard error (s) of 5.3 kJ kg^{-1}, in contrast to regression of the wet samples, which produces an r^2 of 0.86 and a standard error of 4.3 kJ kg^{-1}. If all 141 samples are regressed together, r^2 is 0.80 and s is 5.4 kJ kg^{-1}.

dry samples in two dimensions (axes 1 and 2), typically become far removed from these warm samples on minor axes.

The CLAMP database is strongly orientated toward Northern Hemisphere vegetation, although samples from Fiji and New Caledonia are included. Based on herbarium material (this could be highly biased especially relative to leaf sizes), Jacobs & Deino (1996) were able successfully to analyse some African fossil leaf assemblages, which suggests that CLAMP may be applicable to African vegetation. However, both modern leaf samples from New Zealand and Australia appear somewhat anomalous relative to Northern Hemisphere

samples, which is the primary reason for the employment of the nearest neighbours method by Stranks & England (1997). Clearly an enlarged database incorporating samples from South America and from Africa, as well as from as yet unsampled regions, will resolve these problems.

Also emphasized is that taphonomic distortions might alter the physiognomic signals. Certainly taphonomy does influence the floristic composition of fossil assemblages (Spicer 1989b), but the influence on leaf physiognomy and especially on CLAMP estimates is poorly known. The possible effects have been only cursorily investigated and with few samples (Wolfe 1993).

45. Palaeobotanical databases and palaeoclimate signals

PETER McA REES & ALFRED M. ZIEGLER

Environment, climate and geography

This chapter assesses how palaeobotanical data can be compiled and analysed to reconstruct palaeo-climates, ranging from local to global scales. A number of factors influence the distribution of plants, including environment, climate and geography (Fig. 45.1), and the relative contribution of each may be unravelled using different sampling strategies. Our interest is primarily in the climate signal and its role in biogeography, as well as the potential for elucidating 'global change' and its influence on evolution. We believe that the effect of climate on fossil plant distributions has often been underestimated by previous workers. Our multi-variate statistical approach to data analysis and climate interpretation may be used at various scales, provided the sampling strategy is appropriate.

At the local environment or ecological scale (Fig. 45.1A), sampling must be done on a bed-by-bed basis in order to reconstruct each of the communities that may be preserved in a single geological formation. The transportation and tapho-nomic history of the deposit must be well understood. Variations between plant assemblages may represent elevational changes, riparian effects, or communities in various successional states. The depositional settings and plant communities may be determined from the sedimentology and the preserved plant remains (e.g. Bateman 1991 and references therein).

For climate scale studies (Fig. 45.1B), detailed sampling is usually impractical, so a different approach is used whereby the data are compiled in the form of 'whole flora' lists from the strati-graphical and palaeobotanical literature. Lists from individual formations may be merged, both temporally and spatially (c. 100 km), to minimize community or Milankovitch variations (Ziegler et al. 1994, 1996). The precipitation balance may be determined from broad patterns in the ratio of coals to evaporites (Lottes & Ziegler 1994), while some concept of relative temperature may be gained from general palaeolatitudinal relationships. The fossil plants themselves provide information on relative precipitation and temperature from their leaf physiognomic adaptations, and on seasonality from wood growth ring studies (e.g. Francis 1986; Wolfe 1993; Spicer et al. 1994; Ziegler et al. 1996; Rees et al. in press).

The geographical scale (Fig. 45.1C) may be similar to the climate scale, so what we mean by geography is the effect of geographical barriers on plant distributions, especially oceanic barriers. Deserts may provide similar barriers, but we classify deserts as climatic effects. Geographical barriers are the main cause of disjunct plant distributions while climate and ecology are typified by gradual transitions across the Earth's surface. At the geographical scale, a widely distributed genus or family can be selected and examined for disjunct species distributions indicating endemism. To eliminate environmental or climatic effects, only species from equivalent communities and climate zones should be used in this analysis. Species

	CONTROL	SCALE	UNIT
A	Environment (e.g. elevation)	Local (c. 10 km)	Community
B	Climate (e.g. temperature, precipitation)	Zonal (c. 1000 km)	Biome
C	Geography (e.g. ocean barrier)	Continental (scale variable)	Realm

Fig. 45.1. Spatial controls on plant distributions at different scales.

REES, P. McA & ZIEGLER, A. M. 1999. Palaeobotanical databases and palaeoclimate signals. *In*: JONES, T. P. & ROWE, N. P. (eds) *Fossil Plants and Spores: modern techniques.* Geological Society, London, 240–244.

distributions should be plotted on palaeogeographic maps to determine the nature of the geographical barriers. Finally, this type of analysis should be performed on as many taxa as possible to establish the reality and temporal evolution of the geographical barrier of interest.

Using the palaeobotanical record – why and how

We can determine climates (Fig. 45.1B) for intervals in the geological past by studying the morphology and distributional patterns of fossil leaves. These provide a 'palaeoclimate spectrum' between end-member lithological indicators of climate such as coals and evaporites, which provide information about the precipitation/evaporation ratio. There are three main reasons for believing this palaeobotanical approach to be valid: (1) global distributional patterns of modern vegetation show a strong relationship with climate, especially temperature and precipitation, and the way these parameters are distributed through the annual cycle (e.g. Walter 1985; Prentice et al. 1992; Neilson 1995); (2) leaves are a plant's means of interacting directly with the atmosphere, and their morphology is often adapted to and reflects prevailing environmental conditions; and (3) these relationships appear to have remained fairly constant since terrestrial vascular plants became established (e.g. Meyen 1973). Fossil leaf genera and species are typically delimited taxonomically on the basis of relatively coarse characters such as size and shape; they do not necessarily define natural taxa. Although such uncertainties may hinder evolutionary studies, these coarse subdivisions can be useful for palaeoclimatic studies if one accepts that leaf morphologies represent environmental adaptations.

The foliar physiognomy/climate relationship is best understood for angiosperms, from which quantitative climate estimates have been derived (e.g. Bailey & Sinnott 1915; Wolfe 1993). However, non-angiosperms also exhibit a distributional pattern linked most strongly to (1) the evaporation/precipitation ratio or (2) temperature and growing season length, relationships often reflected in their foliar physiognomy. Two different quantitative foliar physiognomic approaches, one for angiosperms the other for non-angiosperms, have been developed to determine palaeoclimates. These include detailed analyses of selected sites using CLAMP (Climate Leaf Analysis Multivariate Program – see Wolfe (1993) for methodology) on Cretaceous angiosperm leaves (e.g. Herman & Spicer 1996; Spicer et al. 1996), and correspondence analysis of non-angiosperm leaves and floral localities combined with lithological data (Ziegler

et al. 1994, 1996; Rees et al. in press). Both approaches have their limitations, the first because quantitative climate estimates using angiosperm leaves are limited to the last c. 120 million years (the time when angiosperms became significant components of vegetation). There are also uncertainties regarding the climate tolerances of non-angiosperm fossil taxa, given that today most are either extinct or have 'relictual' distributions. Nevertheless, there is a wealth of potential climatic data for pre-angiosperm times that has previously been limited to the demarcation of floristic provinces and climate zones based upon the distributions of only a few non-angiosperm plant genera or orders (e.g. Vakhrameev et al. 1978; Krassilov 1981; Dobruskina 1982; Vakhrameev 1991).

Statistical approach

One means of compensating for uncertainties inherent in the non-angiosperm climate signal is to use a global 'whole-flora' approach to the collection of fossil data. Although imperfect, owing to factors which include taphonomic, taxonomic and collection bias, it provides our best proxy for original vegetation and therefore climate regimes in the geological past. We have conducted multivariate statistical analyses of non-angiosperm leaf genera to explore the foliar physiognomy/climate relationship and to identify phytogeographic patterns and climate zones in a more rigorous and repeatable manner.

Before illustrating our approach with some results from Lower Jurassic analyses, it is worth outlining the general statistical method. We chose correspondence analysis (CA), which is used commonly in studies of modern ecology and vegetational succession. The method can be used at the local (environment) through to global (climate) scale. The version used is one of the programs in the Canonical Community Ordination (CANOCO) package compiled by Ter Braak (1987–1992). Figure 45.2 is designed to illustrate the fact that an initial data matrix (Fig. 45.2A) may appear to have no structure, but by rearranging the vertical, locality axis (Fig. 45.2B) and then the horizontal, genus axis (Fig. 45.2C), a pattern emerges. The palaeobotanist may be faced with a data array like Fig. 45.2A (or 45.2B if, for example, the palaeo-latitude is known for each locality), and the computer effectively rearranges the matrix to produce the 45.2C plot. This could be done by hand, but with data matrices containing hundreds of columns and rows, this becomes impractical.

Figure 45.2C shows a very simple matrix, reflecting perhaps latitude, whereas in reality of course there may be more than one source of variance in the data. The CA can ordinate the

(A)

GENUS

	A	B	C	D	E	F
1		X	X	X		X
2	X	X			X	X
3	X	X	X			X
4			X	X		X
5	X	X			X	

LOCALITY

(B)

GENUS

	A	B	C	D	E	F
5	X	X			X	
2	X	X			X	X
3	X	X	X			X
1		X	X	X		X
4			X	X		X

LOCALITY

(C)

GENUS

	D	C	F	B	A	E
5				X	X	X
2			X	X	X	X
3		X	X	X	X	
1	X	X	X	X		
4	X	X	X			

LOCALITY

Fig. 45.2. Idealized data matrices for 6 genera from 5 localities, showing how an apparently random array of data (**A**) actually contains increasingly obvious patterns when ordered first by localities (**B**) and then localities plus genera (**C**).

various influences on the data array, such as temperature, precipitation, geography and succession. Two-dimensional plots are produced showing variance within datasets on two axes. We use CA as a means of arranging all of the elements relative to axes in multidimensional space according to their similarity to each other. Most of the variation occurs on the first axis, with other axes accounting for progressively less. The output

consists of two plots – one for localities and the other for genera. So, localities which share many floral elements plot closest together on axis 1, whilst those with little in common plot furthest apart. The same applies to the generic plot – genera which frequently co-occur plot together and vice versa. The advantages of CA are that it provides the same scaling of sample (locality) and character (taxa) plots, enabling direct comparison, and can accommodate 'incomplete' data matrices where some information is missing (Hill 1979; Gauch 1982).

A Lower Jurassic example

For the Jurassic, we assembled a database of some 8000 leaf genus occurrences from 950 plant localities worldwide and, using CA, arranged these according to their relative similarity to each other (Rees *et al.* in press). This represents an attempt to quantify gradations between floral provinces that have already been described and interpreted qualitatively (e.g. Vakhrameev *et al.* 1978; Krassilov 1981; Dobruskina 1982; Vakhrameev 1991). Due to limitations in stratigraphical correlation and dating, our analyses were carried out on data summed over relatively long time intervals (i.e. Early, Middle and Late Jurassic).

Ordination results for Lower Jurassic genera from Northern Hemisphere localities are shown in Fig. 45.3a. Microphyllous cycadophytes and microphyllous conifers plot to the left of axis 1, with macrophyllous conifers and ginkgophytes towards the right. These plants define opposite ends of a spectrum, which makes sense if we consider their leaf morphologies in terms of climate: small leaves with thick cuticles adapted to hot dry environments, large and presumably deciduous leaves adapted to seasonally cool and/or dark conditions. Other plant groups such as macrophyllous cycadophytes, ferns and sphenophytes occupy the central and right portions of axis 1, presumably since few of these were tolerant of water stress. It should be emphasized that the symbols on the generic plot indicate only the centroids of the various floral elements and individual taxa may have wide ranges (Ziegler *et al.* 1996).

The corresponding locality plot (Fig. 45.3b) shows a broad correlation between axis 1 score and palaeolatitude. However other factors, such as longitudinal east vs. west, continental interior vs. maritime, and even topographic variations are important – just as in the modern world. The effects of these can be seen when the localities are plotted on palaeogeographic maps (Rees *et al.* in press). The correspondence analysis simply provides an objective assessment of the variance in the original data matrix. Both generic and locality plots show

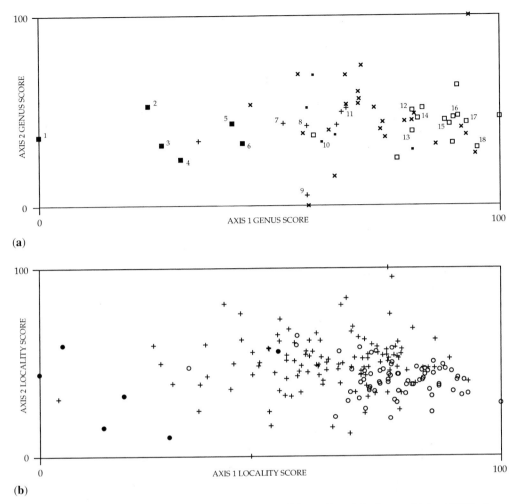

Fig. 45.3. Correspondence analysis (CA) axis 1/axis 2 plots for 57 Lower Jurassic leaf genera (**a**) from 195 Northern Hemisphere localities (**b**). In (a), the genera have been assigned to broad morphological categories: microphyllous cycadophytes, microphyllous conifers and *Pachypteris* (large solid squares); macrophyllous cycadophytes (vertical crosses); ferns, sphenophytes and lycophytes (diagonal crosses); 'unassigned' conifers (small solid squares); macrophyllous conifers and ginkgophytes (open squares). Numbers refer to the following leaf genera: 1 *Zamites*, 2 *Otozamites*, 3 *Brachyphyllum*, 4 *Pachypteris*, 5 *Ptilophyllum*, 6 *Pagiophyllum*, 7 *Pterophyllum*, 8 *Taeniopteris*, 9 *Nilssonia*, 10 *Elatocladus*, 11 *Ctenis*, 12 *Podozamites*, 13 *Baiera*, 14 *Ginkgo*, 15 *Pityophyllum*, 16 *Sphenobaiera*, 17 *Czekanowskia*, 18 *Desmiophyllum*. For the corresponding locality plot (b), symbols represent palaeolatitude: 0° to 40°N (solid circles), 40° to 60°N (vertical crosses), 60° to 90°N (open circles).

that the data arrays are gradational rather than disjunct, indicating that climate influenced the patterns and not significant geographical barriers. This poses a problem in classification because there are no natural breaks in the distributions, but this is often true of the Recent as well.

From leaf genera to biomes and climates

An individual leaf genus is defined by morphological characters that can be interpreted in terms of prevailing environmental conditions. The relative position of each genus on the generic ordination plot is defined by its degree of association with other leaf genera. The relative position of each floral locality on the corresponding locality ordination plot is defined by its constituent leaf genera.

There are two extremes in our Jurassic example: localities comprising wholly microphyllous forms (of conifers and cycadophytes) and localities comprising wholly macrophyllous conifers and ginkgophytes. Based on leaf morphologies, these plants can be interpreted as being adapted to hot dry and seasonally cool and/or dark conditions respectively. These plant types do occasionally co-occur but it is relatively easy to define end-member biomes based on the locality scores defined by these leaf genera. The microphyllous plant localities occur at low palaeolatitudes and can be assigned to a seasonally dry biome, this being consistent with evaporite distributions. The macrophyllous conifer/ginkgophyte localities occur at high palaeolatitudes and can be assigned to a cool temperate biome, based upon the deciduous nature of the foliage. It is harder to define the latitudinal boundaries of these and the intermediate warm temperate biome, but the presence of macrophyllous cycadophytes and ferns, and changes in their relative abundance with respect to microphyllous and macrophyllous/ginkgophyte forms, together with coal distributions, enables subdivisions of the floral and climate spectrum (Rees *et al.* in press).

Multivariate analysis serves to identify the degree of variance in the data but cannot, of course, specify the sources of the variance. It is the physiognomy implicit in the names of individual fossil leaf genera that ultimately enables the determination of global palaeoclimates. Ordinations of fossil leaf genera and localities, combined with lithological data, enable climate zones (biomes) to be drawn on palaeogeographic maps. We use Walter's (1985) biome scheme, in which the 'macroclimate' of the present-day land surface is reduced to nine major biomes. The scheme was developed using data from some 8000 meteorological ground stations worldwide and was combined with details of corresponding vegetation. In effect, the choices of climatic boundary con-

ditions were influenced by natural transitions in the vegetation. One attractive aspect of Walter's scheme is that it is simple and therefore applicable in the geological past (Ziegler 1990; Rees *et al.* in press).

The statistical whole-flora approach enables palaeobotanical evidence of past climates to be interpreted in a more rigorous and repeatable manner, and also provides 'non-specialist' geologists and palaeoclimate modellers with a means of utilizing directly and easily the detailed work of the palaeobotanical community. Since the climate models are global, the proxy climate data should be analysed at the same scale. One advantage of this approach is that it highlights key areas requiring detailed studies, particularly where global data and climate model results differ. Comparison and reconciliation of these results provides a more certain means of understanding past climates, as well as vegetation responses and feedbacks.

Our technique analyses palaeobotanical data using statistical methods. However, this is augmented by a range of other geological evidence and also requires an understanding of the strengths and limitations inherent in the fossil plant record. Our methods are sometimes at odds with traditional fossil 'bin' taxonomy, since we explore the nature of what is, in reality, a near-continuous spectrum. The fact that meaningful patterns do emerge indicates both the quality of the fossil plant record and the robust relationship between plants and their environments through time.

We thank D. B. Rowley, M. L. Hulver, R. A. Spicer, M. C. Boulter and two anonymous reviewers for their contributions.

46. Fossil tree-ring analysis: palaeodendrology

GEOFFREY T. CREBER & JANE E. FRANCIS

Tree rings are an important source of information about past climates and fossil environments. Unlike tree-ring analysis of 'modern' wood, probably thousands of years old or less, fossil tree rings cannot be used for dating, (some cross-dating was found by Ammons *et al.* (1987) and Jefferson (1982) but these are rare examples). Fossil tree rings are, however, a unique source of detailed information about seasonality, annual growing conditions, water availability, limiting temperatures and forest productivity in the geological past. The main methods of analysis are outlined below.

Ring production

Within the bark of a tree there is a cylindrical layer of actively dividing cells termed the vascular cambium. As the cells produced internally by this layer expand, they force the cambium to move outwards and increase its circumference. Thus, with production of this additional wood required to support the growing tree, the girth of the tree enlarges. In many tree species, especially those from temperate latitudes, but also some in equatorial regions, cambial activity is not constant throughout the year. The cessation of cell division during the unfavourable part of the growing season leads to the formation of growth rings in cross-sections of the trunk, branches and larger roots of a tree (Fig. 46.1A). The ring boundaries (Fig. 46.1B) are emphasized by larger cells produced at the beginning of the growing season (the earlywood, Fig. 46.1B) followed by smaller cells formed as the season closes (the latewood, Fig. 46.1B).

As the production of a ring can take several months, the environmental influences upon the tree during this period are recorded in the wood. In other words the wood becomes a form of 'data store' of external factors influencing the tree during the growing season (Creber 1977). For example, a late frost may cause actual physical damage or at least a temporary cessation of cell division which produces a feature that is termed a 'frost ring'. A 'false ring' (Fig. 46.1C) may be caused by a severe drought in the growing season resulting in the production of a few very small cells which mimic an end-of-season boundary within the growth ring. Other data that may be recovered include: ring widths, year-to-year variations in ring width, the

radial diameters of cells throughout one ring, the relative proportions of earlywood and latewood. The annual forest productivity, as mass of timber per unit area of forest floor (kg ha^{-1} a^{-1}), may be calculated from ring-widths and the spacing of the trees.

Mean and annual sensitivities

One tree ring frequently differs in width from the ring before and the one after. Indeed, a noticeable pattern of a few rings that differ very markedly from one another is known to dendrochronologists as a 'signature' which is often discernible in ring sequences within neighbouring trees. The variation in width between one ring and its neighbour can be statistically represented by a term called the 'annual sensitivity' (AS) (Douglass 1928) and calculated from the formula:

$$\text{Annual sensitivity} = \left| \frac{2(x_{t+1} - x_t)}{x_{t+1} + x_t} \right|$$

where x is the ring width and t is the year number of the ring.

The 'mean sensitivity' (MS) (Douglass 1928) is the mean variability in ring width over a series of rings and is calculated from the formula:

$$\text{Mean sensitivity} = \frac{1}{n-1} \sum_{t=1}^{t=n-1} \left| \frac{2(x_{t+1} - x_t)}{x_{t+1} + x_t} \right|$$

in addition to x and t as above, n is the number of rings in the sequence.

Most MS fall between the figures of 0 to 0.6; conventionally those below 0.3 are termed 'complacent' while those above are 'sensitive'. A value of 0.6 would result from growth under a restricted and intermittent water supply whereas values of 0.3 or less indicate that trees had an adequate annual water supply and produced rings of approximately constant width.

The frequency of AS values can provide an indication of growth patterns when plotted as histograms. Figure 46.2 was constructed from data from two wood specimens. One was an extant larch (*Larix decidua* Mill.) grown in Argyll, Scotland, and the other was *Metacedroxylon scoticum* Holden, a Late Jurassic conifer from Helmsdale,

CREBER, G. T. & FRANCIS, J. E. 1999. Fossil tree-ring analysis: palaeodendrology.
In: JONES, T. P. & ROWE, N. P. (eds) *Fossil Plants and Spores: modern techniques.*
Geological Society, London, 245–250.

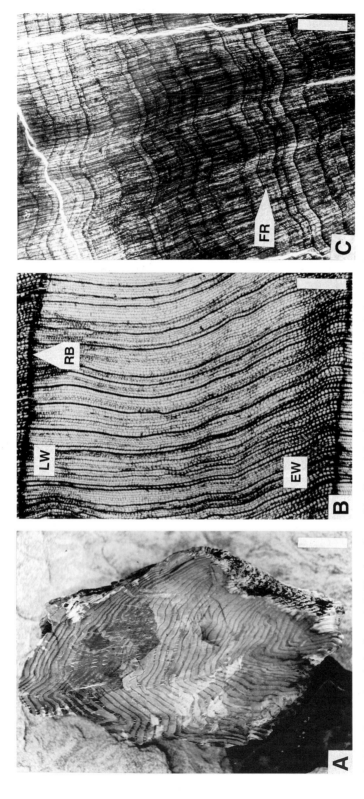

Fig. 46.1. Growth rings in fossil wood. (**A**) Hand specimen of fossil wood showing prominent wide growth rings. Permian age, Allan Hills, Antarctica. Scale bar = 6 cm. (**B**) Thin section of fossil wood illustrating the large number of cells per ring and the abrupt ring boundaries (RB). EW = early wood, LW = latewood. Permian wood from Allan Hills, Antarctica. Scale bar = 0.7 mm. (**C**) Thin section of Jurassic fossil wood showing very irregular growth rings, reflecting intermittent supply of water in a semi-arid environment. FR = false ring caused by drought during the growing season. Late Jurassic/Early Cretaceous wood, southern England. Scale bar = 6 mm. (Francis 1984).

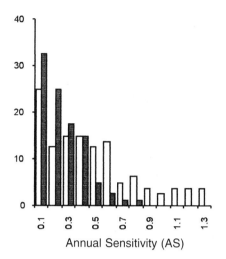

Fig. 46.2. A histogram of annual sensitivity distribution in a Jurassic conifer (unshaded columns), compared to that in a Recent larch (shaded columns).

East Sutherland, Scotland. The histogram of the modern tree shows all the AS grouped at the lower end of the scale, and its low MS of 0.207 indicates that it grew under very equable conditions with a constant supply of all of the necessary requirements for growth. The pattern of the fossil tree presents a considerable contrast. AS of up to 1.3 occur, producing a MS of 0.393. This wood is from a tree that probably grew under conditions that varied widely from year to year, particularly in respect of water supply.

Intra-ring cell analysis

The radial diameters of the cells across an individual ring can provide information about environmental conditions within one growing season. The mean radial cell diameter is calculated and the cumulative sum of the deviations from the mean is obtained. When plotted, a curve is produced allowing interpretation of events during that growing season. The graph in Fig. 46.3A is a plot derived from a wide (12.8 mm) ring at the base of the trunk of a pine (*Pinus sylvestris* L) grown near Bracknell in southeast England. It would appear that growth proceeded steadily in the early part of the season until it was checked, probably by shortage of water, then later relieved by further supplies. In the last part of the season, increasing numbers of latewood cells were formed, which is reflected in a steady downward trend in the curve towards zero.

Figure 46.3B illustrates cell size data from a trunk of fossil wood (Glossopterid type) of late

Early Permian age from Allan Hills, Antarctica (Francis *et al.* 1994). Since this site was at about 80°S at the time, the annual daylight regime would have consisted of a period of 180 days in which 60 were of continuous daylight. This type of growing season is strongly reflected in the shape of the curve which is completely symmetrical about the middle of the growth ring. This suggests that growth commenced at the onset of daylight in September. Cells mainly larger than the mean were

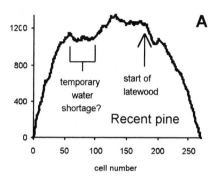

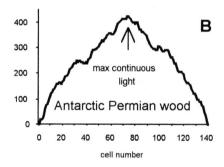

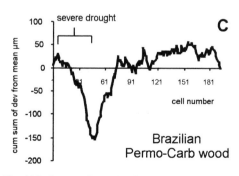

Fig. 46.3. Pattern of annual cell development in (**A**), a Recent pine (**B**), Antarctic Permian wood and (**C**) Brazilian Permo-Carboniferous wood (see text for explanations).

produced until December. Smaller ones followed until late March. The curve suggests that the rate of wood growth of this tree, with a constant water supply, was dominantly controlled by the input of solar energy, the latter being vital for photosynthesis and the production of a favourable ambient temperature. It is interesting to note that in both hand specimen and thin section the ring boundary is quite abrupt, a feature often cited as characteristic of high latitude woods due to the supposedly abrupt onset of low light levels. However, careful measurement of cells as illustrated above indicates that this sharp boundary is an illusion.

In contrast, the graph in Fig. 46.3C was derived from data obtained from a tree that grew at about 550 S in the Rio Grande do Sul, southern Brazil, during the Permo-Carboniferous. This tree appears to have suffered a very severe drought not long after the beginning of the growing season. It recovered towards the middle of the season but a further period of drought followed, with only a final burst of growth at the end of the season.

Earlywood–latewood ratio

This is the ratio between the width of that part of the ring which is formed early in the growing season and the remainder formed at the end. Earlywood cells tend to be thinner-walled and larger in diameter, whereas latewood cells are smaller and thick-walled. In general a longer, more favourable growing season will lead to the production of a higher percentage of latewood in a growth ring (Creber 1977).

Forest productivity

Using the techniques employed in present day forestry (Assmann 1970; Hamilton & Christie 1971) it is possible to use growth-ring measurements to assess the productivity of fossil forests. Some examples are discussed below.

Tertiary fossil forest, Arctic Canada

Francis (1988) described a 50-million-year-old fossil forest from Strathcona Fiord, Ellesmere Island, Arctic Canada. At the time of growth the locality was at about 78°N. Most of the stumps were of the order of 0.5 m in diameter. Using this measurement and the formula of Niklas (1994) it is possible to obtain an estimate of the height of the trees. The critical height of a tree is found from the following:

$$H_{crit} = C \left(\frac{E}{\rho}\right)^{1/3} D^{2/3}$$

where C is a constant, 0.792; E is Young's modulus, $(10^6$ kg m$^{-2})$; ρ is the wood density (kg m^{-3}) ; D is the diameter (m). Niklas cites a specimen of extant *Pinus banksiana* Lamb. for which E was 868×10^6 kg m^{-2}, ρ was 461 kg m^{-3} and D was 0.631 m . If the equation is solved for this tree H_{crit} is found to be 59.0 m. This is the height at which the trunk will fail mechanically leading to its collapse. In practice trees develop safety factors of up to 4 or more and in the *Pinus* example the actual height of the specimen of *P. banksiana* was 27.7 m, with a safety factor of 2.1. Since the wood data of *P. banksiana* are typical of many conifers, it is reasonable to use them to calculate H_{crit} for an Arctic Tertiary tree of diameter 0.5 m at Strathcona Fiord which is found to be 58.7 m. Applying the safety factor of 2.1 a height of 28.0 m is obtained.

One method of estimating modern tree volumes is to use a polynomial taper equation to model the shapes of trees (Goulding & Murray 1976; Demaerschalk & Kozak 1977). However, such equations need to be validated against a large number of trunks. Goulding & Murray used 1200 and Demaerschalk & Kozak used over 32 000 in a British Columbian forestry database. Clearly, these numbers are not available in palaeobotany and so we have used a very reliable rotation paraboloid formula (Gray 1956).

Gray's formula for calculating the parabolic volume of a tree trunk is:

$$v = \frac{\pi r^2 h}{2}$$

where r is the basal radius and h is the height. Using the figures for the Tertiary Strathcona tree given above, the existing trunk wood would have a volume of 2.75 m^3. If the tree puts on a growth ring of 2.5 mm, the new radius will be 0.2525 m and the new volume will be 2.8 m^3. Subtracting the two volumes reveals an annual increase in tree volume of 0.05 m^3. The distribution of the stumps at Strathcona Fiord was one per 27 m^2 so that the annual forest productivity was 18.5 m^3 ha^{-1} a^{-1}.

Lower Cretaceous fossil forest, Antarctica

Jefferson (1982) described a fossil forest in the Lower Cretaceous of Alexander Island, Antarctica (palaeolatitude 70°S). In one continuous exposure there were 31 conifer stumps in an area of 550 m^{-2}, a density of one per 17 m^{-2}. The largest stumps were 0.22 m in diameter. Using the same critical height formula as above it is found that H_{crit} is 34.3 m. Applying the same safety factor the height of one of these trees can be estimated as about 17 m. Some of Jefferson's trees had ring widths of 5 mm. Jefferson stated that the average ring width was 2.5 mm. The volume of wood added by each tree per year would have been 0.03 m³. At a distribution of one tree per 17 m⁻², this gives a forest productivity of 17.65 m³ ha⁻¹ a⁻¹.

Such a productivity and also that of the Strathcona trees above can be seen in comparison with some forest productivities at the present day. Ovington (1961) calculated a productivity of 12.6 m³ ha⁻¹ a⁻¹ in a forest at Thetford, Norfolk UK, of *Pinus sylvestris* L. Hamilton & Christie (1971) give the following examples of temperate forest productivities: *Picea sitchensis* (Bong.) Carr (Sitka spruce) 14 m³ ha⁻¹ a⁻¹, *Pinus contorta* Dougl. (Lodgepole pine) 10 m³ ha⁻¹ a⁻¹, *Pseudotsuga menziesii* (Mirb.) Franco (Douglas-fir) 16 m³ ha⁻¹ a⁻¹. The higher productivities of the polar trees can be attributed to their being able to benefit from receiving the full 4380 hours of solar input in their growing season. This is the quantity of solar input received in a given year at any point on the planet. However, in the temperate zones a distinct quantity of solar radiation falls outside the growing season and cannot be used for wood production. Furthermore an additional benefit accrued to the polar trees in past geological time through the continuous maintenance of translocation of photosynthate from the foliage to various sinks during the 24-hour periods of daylight in the middle of their growing season. In the temperate trees' growing season, translocation would be considerably curtailed during the summer nights owing to lack of sucrose consequent on the cessation of photosynthesis on the onset of darkness (Canny 1984).

Isolated fossil wood specimens

In cases where there are no fossilized stumps *in situ*, data from isolated specimens of fossil wood may be used. The method is that of Assmann (1970) who has used it on extant trees. He calculated the additional area increment added by each successive growth ring to the pre-existing cross-sectional area of the trunk. This additional area is directly proportional to the amount of wood produced by the entire trunk during the year. The advantage of this method is that the area increments do not depend upon the ring widths alone but are influenced by the diameters of the cross-sections of the trunks on which they accrue. The larger the initial trunk, the larger will be the area increment for a given ring width. The area increment added by a ring of width *x* mm to the existing trunk cross-section can be found by using the following formula:

$$\text{area increment} = \pi(r + x)^2 - \pi r^2$$

where *r* is the radius of the trunk before the new ring is added. If it is supposed that a tree has a

sequence of 1 mm ring widths, it is possible to calculate the area increments by the addition of 1 mm annually to the existing radius. A graph of these increments is a curve of a certain slope. The process may be repeated with ring widths of 1, 3 and 5 mm to produce curves of increasing slopes. By reference to Hamilton & Christie (1971), these curves can be seen to represent tree growth of high (5 mm), medium (3 mm) and low (1 mm) annual productivity. Fossil ring-width series can be plotted on the same graph as the sequences for 1-, 3- and 5 mm ring widths and an assessment can then be made of the productivity represented by the fossil series (Creber & Francis 1987).

The formation of growth rings in tropical regions

The formation of secondary wood without rings is generally related to a uniform, seasonless climate. Thus, for example, most fossil wood from the Carboniferous does not have rings, which may have been related to its growth in the vast area of lowland swamps that extended from present-day Kansas to the east coast of the USA and from Western Europe to the Donetz Basin in Ukraine. However, in wood specimens drawn from the entire Carboniferous period some growth rings have been recorded and their significance has yet to be determined.

Studies on modern tropical forests have revealed that a number of tree species may form rings, particularly those growing on coarse, well drained soils which may lead to edaphic drought and dormancy. Seasonal flowering, fruiting, flushing and leaf-fall may result in identifiable changes in the radial growth. It was shown by Ash & Creber (1992) that there were interruptions in the growth of the wood of the Upper Triassic trees, now preserved on the desert surface in the Petrified Forest National Park, Arizona. However, these interruptions are quite irregular in occurrence and many do not make a complete circuit of the trunk. This situation was seen as being quite compatible with the trees having grown at a palaeolatitude of 18°N, the calculated Upper Triassic palaeolatitude for that site.

The analysis of growth rings (or their absence) in fossil wood is a valuable tool for determining past environments and climates, especially where fossil trees are the only preserved remains of terrestrial vegetation. No other source of palaeoclimatic data can be resolved so readily on an annual, or even intra-annual, time scale. Further studies on fossil forests and other wood collections are required to build up a database of tree-ring information over a wide geographical and stratigraphical spread, which in association with other geological data, can provide information about global climate change. We have yet to understand fully the complex influences on tree growth in the past, particularly in the unique palaeoenvironments that have no living counterparts such as forests growing in the polar regions, but the records are there in the tree rings, waiting to be read.

We gratefully acknowledge valuable assistance with the calculations from Dr John Whiteman and help from two referees and the editors.

growth can be controlled indirectly by careful selection of the study site, using information from pollen and plant macrofossils and isotopic records from ocean and terrestrial sediments. Controlling for environmental effects can be achieved, in part, by calculating stomatal index from measurements of stomatal and epidermal cell densities on fossil cuticles.

Temperature

Experimental evidence for the effects of temperature on stomatal density and index is rather limited (see data reviewed by Beerling & Woodward 1996). Growth of seven populations of the dwarf shrub *Vaccinium myrtillus* at two temperature regimes (15/5°C day/night temperature and 22/12°C) led to only one population showing a significant increase in stomatal density at the higher temperatures (Beerling & Woodward 1996) and none for stomatal index. Data for puma rye grass (*Secale cereale*) indicate that lower temperatures during leaf growth resulted in the development of leaves with a higher stomatal density (Huner *et al.* 1981). Clearly, further experimental work in this area is required since, on geological timescales, CO_2 and climate are likely to have covaried through the 'greenhouse effect'. Therefore, the influence of both on stomatal development needs to be determined, and quantified separately, if a more secure CO_2 signal is to be obtained from the fossils. Moreover, such experiments will need to distinguish between the effects of atmospheric leaf-to-air vapour pressure deficit (VPD) and temperature which are strongly correlated (Jones 1992). Bakker (1991) reported that some species of agricultural plants grown at high VPD's developed leaves with a lower stomatal density. Other species may be less sensitive. Observations for the dwarf shrub *Salix herbacea* grown across a 5–25°C temperature range and a corresponding VPD gradient of 0.5–2.0 kPa resulted in no significant effects on the stomatal density or index of mature fully expanded leaves (D. J. Beerling, unpublished). Theoretically, temperature may affect stomatal density through its influence on leaf expansion, although calculation of stomatal index would remove this effect, as would measurements made on mature fully expanded leaves.

Water supply

Plant water availability influences stomatal density directly through its effects on leaf expansion via changes in epidermal cell size. The data from the experiments of Clifford *et al.* (1995) on the semi-arid species *Arachis hypogaea* L. grown at ambient and elevated CO_2 concentrations clearly illustrate the differential effects of drought on leaf stomatal density and stomatal index. Growth of plants at either CO_2 concentration under droughted conditions, led to an expected increase in stomatal density, relative to plants in irrigated plots, whereas stomatal index, which allows for increases in epidermal cell size, remained constant (Fig. 47.2). In this case, only well-irrigated plants showed a significant reduction in stomatal index with CO_2 enrichment.

Irradiance

The light environment during leaf development and expansion (Schoch *et al.* 1980) can affect leaf stomatal density and index, as shown by classical studies on sun/shade morphology and physiology (Boardman 1977), and this has led to concern regarding its potential influence on CO_2 reconstructions (Poole *et al.* 1996). Detailed studies of modern and fossil oak leaves (Kürschner 1996) have shown that distinct sun–shade morphotypes are recognizable in the fossil record for that species. However, the degree to which this feature of leaf anatomy can be used to distinguish between sun and shade leaves remains uncertain since CO_2 enrichment has been shown to increase leaf thickness, at least for the herbaceous species *Rumex obtusifolius* (Pearson *et al.* 1995). It is possible to help minimize the effects of irradiance in stomatal studies on materials from herbaria by sampling only leaves attached to flowering shoots and collected from isolated trees (Woodward 1987). This approach assumes, not unreasonably, that the majority of flowering shoots occurred on the outside of the tree crown. With respect to studies of fossil leaves, it might be that the transport processes responsible for sorting leaf material prior to fossilization offer a greater abundance of sun morphotypes, and obtaining details of the depositional environment of the sites from which the leaf fossils were collected aids an assessment of this possibility (see Poole & Kürschner (Chapter 48) for further details).

Biological effects

Interspecific variation.

Salisbury (1927) demonstrated large inherent differences in stomatal characters of different species. As a consequence, studies aiming to detect a change in atmospheric CO_2 concentration based on interpreting changes in stomatal density and index should attempt, where possible, to study leaves of a single identifiable species through the time period of interest (e.g. Van der Burgh *et al.* 1993; Beerling *et al.* 1995; Wagner *et al.* 1996).

Studies on leaf fossils reaching back beyond the late Cretaceous inevitably deal with extinct species, and therefore raise the question as to whether a CO_2 signal can be read from this material. McElwain &

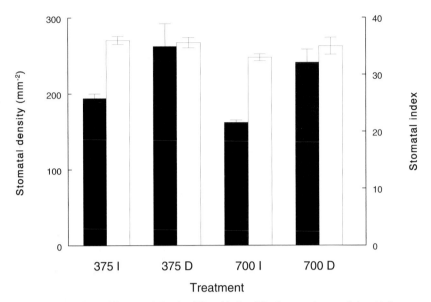

Fig. 47.2. The response of adaxial stomatal density (■) and index (□) of mature leaves of *Arachis hypogaea* grown under droughted (D) and irrigated (I) conditions at ambient (375 ppmv) and elevated (700 ppmv) CO_2 concentrations for 114 days after sowing (redrawn from Clifford *et al.* 1995).

Chaloner (1995, 1996) proposed that this aim could be achieved by comparing data from fossil plants with those data collected from the nearest living equivalent (NLE) to the fossil, that is species with close ecological and/or structural similarity to their Palaeozoic counterparts. Whilst the stomatal characters of plants vary between species, comparative analyses have shown that taxa from similar habitats tend to have similar stomatal densities (Peat & Fitter 1994; Kelly & Beerling 1995). Therefore, the approach has some merit in attempting to interpret past changes in CO_2 from valuable Palaeozoic plant fossils and has been developed further more recently (McElwain in press). Beerling & Woodward (1997) took an alternative approach and surveyed stomatal density/index measurements made on fossil leaves from plants dating across the entire Phanerozoic. These authors found that the absolute values were sufficient to make some inferences about the growth CO_2 environment. Although both studies showed changes in the stomatal density of fossils consistent with a CO_2 influence there is a need to acknowledge the difficulties in attributing the observed changes solely to the effects of CO_2, particularly for Devonian–Carboniferous plant fossils (Edwards *et al.* 1998). Throughout the Devonian, terrestrial vegetation was subject to rapid evolutionary development in response to changing conditions of water stress, nutrient availability and light intensity. Therefore other features of the environment may

have driven adjustments in the stomatal characters of the early land plants, especially given the continuous nature of the linkage between root system development, water conducting tissues, leaf transpiration rates and stomatal function. Studies on single taxa with a similar growth form through the entire Devonian would be helpful for disentangling CO_2 effects from other environmental factors.

An emerging method for detecting the influence of past changes in atmospheric CO_2 on the stomatal characters of terrestrial plant leaves comes from the application of the evolutionary comparative methods (ECMs) to stomatal data obtained from a wide range of species (Peat & Fitter 1994; Kelly & Beerling 1995; Beerling & Kelly 1997). ECMs control for taxonomic relatedness by removing the effect of phylogeny, i.e. the possibility that a target response (in this case the response of stomatal density to changes in the concentration of atmospheric CO_2) may persist because of the evolutionary lineage of the species rather than being a response driven solely by the environmental stimulus. Technical details and specific worked examples of the approach can be found in Harvey & Pagel (1991) and Beerling & Kelly (1997). In one application, a variety of ECMs were used to analyse stomatal density changes of a wide range of woodland plant species collected in 1927 and 1996. Ice core studies and direct measurements indicate that this sampling interval spans a 50 ppmv increase in atmospheric CO_2. The results indicated a significant reduction in stomatal density had occurred in these plants, after removing the effects of taxonomy, consistent with the effects of an increase in atmospheric CO_2 concentration over this time. Used in this way, ECMs offer the potential to detect fluctuations in atmospheric CO_2 by comparing the stomatal density and index of a wide range of taxa from different fossil floras dating across the time interval of interest. Analysis of the stomatal characters of fossil floras in this way assumes that species have the inherent capacity to adjust their stomatal index to the new CO_2 concentration given sufficient time of exposure.

Intraspecific variation

Besides species-specific stomatal densities there is also inherent spatial heterogeneity in stomatal density across the surface of a leaf (Salisbury 1927; Poole *et al.* 1996; Weyers & Lawson 1997). Therefore to minimize spatial heterogeneity effects, stomatal characters should be measured from a standardized position on the leaf surface to reduce unnecessary noise (Beerling & Chaloner 1992). With studies on historical collections of leaves and fossils it is more difficult to correct for possible ontogenetic effects (Tichá 1982) (see Poole & Kürschner (Chapter 48) for details of developing and optimizing sampling and counting strategies).

Stomatal based palaeo-CO_2 studies and the geological record

Pliocene studies

The work of Van der Burgh *et al.* (1993) and Kürschner *et al.* (1996) illustrates a single-species stomatal study reconstructing past CO_2 variations and a comparison of the results with independent palynological evidence. These authors measured the stomatal index of fossil oak (*Quercus petraea*) from leaves of late Miocene, Pliocene and early Pleistocene age from the Lower Rhine Embayment and calibrated the changes by constructing a 'training set' from modern samples regressing stomatal index from herbarium leaves of the same species collected between 1873 and 1991 against the corresponding CO_2 concentration. Reconstructed changes in CO_2 show strong covariance with an independent climate curve inferred from the late Miocene–Pliocene pollen record in the Lower Rhine Embayment. In this comparison, warm climatic episodes, characterzied by mixed evergreen–deciduous forests, corresponded with high CO_2 concentrations inferred from the calibrated stomatal index of fossil oak leaves. Furthermore, independent CO_2 estimates derived from isotopic analyses of marine organic carbon (Freeman & Hayes 1992; Raymo *et al.* 1996) and palaeosols (Cerling 1992c) show similar values, within the errors of each method, to those of Kürschner *et al.* (1996).

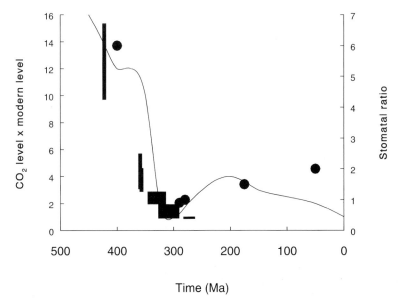

Fig. 47.3. Comparison of Berner's (1994) CO_2 curve through the Phanerozoic with palaeosol estimates of Palaeozoic CO_2 concentration (filled boxes) and the ratio of stomatal index of nearest living equivalent and its Palaeozoic counterpart (●) (from Beerling 1997 and references therein).

Palaeozoic studies

A second example illustrating comparison of stomatal-based CO_2 inferences with independent geological data reaches back into the Palaeozoic. For this interval, Berner's (1994) model of the long-term carbon cycle suggests large CO_2 excursions in the Upper Palaeozoic, with a Siluro-Devonian peak succeeded by a Carbo-Permian low. Working on the hypothesis that such large changes in CO_2 influenced the stomatal characters of vegetation, McElwain & Chaloner (1995, 1996) and Beerling & Woodward (1997) both investigated trends from fossil leaves across this time interval. The results of these studies show changes in the ratio of the stomatal index of the fossil to the NLE (see above) consistent with the predictions of Berner's (1994) model and with CO_2 reconstructions based on isotopic analysis of Palaeozoic soil carbonates and organic matter (Fig. 47.3). Further morphological studies on a wider range of taxa of Palaeozoic plant fossils are required. Nevertheless, the results from different approaches to interpreting the fossil record for evidence of past CO_2 changes for this interval appear to be converging to provide similar overall long-term trends.

Conclusions

This chapter has sought to emphasize the importance of controlling for environmental effects on the stomatal characteristics of fossil leaves in an effort to read a stronger signal of past CO_2 change. Where the quality of cuticular preservation is suitable, this control can be achieved by calculating stomatal index, rather than density. Indeed, from this review of the limited available evidence, it appears that stomatal index has the fortuitous property of being relatively insensitive to changes in temperature and water availability (Fig. 47.2) but sensitive to the concentration of atmospheric CO_2 at the time of leaf growth (Fig. 47.1). Because considerable variation in stomatal characters exists between species, quantitative measurements of changes in the stomatal index of single-species probably offer the most powerful approach for reconstructing past changes in atmospheric CO_2 concentrations. The non-linear nature of the response of stomatal index and density to CO_2 concentrations may reduce the sensitivity of the approach, although studies on fossil leaves from Palaeozoic, Mesozoic and Cenozoic settings all appear to indicate stomatal changes consistent with CO_2 shifts inferred from independent geological data. This suggests that mechanistic information is urgently required on how plants adapt their stomatal characters to CO_2 concentrations above ambient, the length of time required for this response, as well as its implications for the ecophysiology of the plants themselves.

I gratefully acknowledge funding by the Royal Society.

48. Stomatal density and index: the practice

IMOGEN POOLE & WOLFRAM M. KÜRSCHNER

The use of stomatal characters for assessing historical past climates and palaeoatmospheric carbon dioxide (palaeo-CO_2) levels is a new technique in palaeobotany. At present it is still at a relatively preliminary stage but has the potential to become a very valuable, independent tool in trying to determine CO_2 levels. The main problem when using this approach is to overcome the intrinsic variation in stomatal distribution across the leaf surface. This variability is well known from research of leaf structure or physiology (e.g. Salisbury 1927; Tichá 1982; Weyers & Meidner 1990; Willmer & Fricker 1996; Kürschner et al. 1997; Weyers & Lawson 1997 and references cited therein). Species, site and aspect of the plant, coupled with environmental factors (such as light intensity, water availability, carbon dioxide concentration), are enough to affect the distribution of stomata across a leaf surface. The palaeobotanist is, therefore, immediately at a disadvantage because the environment in which the parent plant grew is unknown, as is the location of that leaf within that plant. Despite these variations there is still potential to obtain valuable data. A discussion of the intrinsic and extrinsic factors affecting stomatal characters is given by Beerling (Chapter 47). Such heterogeneity within and between leaves impacts on the experimental procedure and subsequent data analysis. This chapter will be concerned with the experimental protocol and ways of overcoming some of the inherent problems when dealing with fossil material. Details and references concerning the preparation of fossil cuticle material is presented by Kerp & Krings (Chapter 11) and Dilcher (1974).

An idealized approach

The main approach to using stomata as a palaeo-CO_2 indicator has been via stomatal density (sometimes referred to as stomatal frequency) and index (e.g. Woodward 1987; Beerling & Chaloner 1994; McElwain & Chaloner 1995), although no detailed methodology has been published. Stomatal density is expressed as the number of stomatal apertures per unit area of leaf. Stomatal index is the number of stomata calculated as a percentage of the total epidermal cells (other than guard cells) per unit area (Salisbury 1927). In order to compensate for the effects of leaf expansion, which is one source of variation, the use of stomatal index is preferred over stomatal density (Fig. 48.1). However, when studying fossils it might not always be possible to obtain epidermal cell counts due to poor preservation and therefore only stomatal density values can be obtained. If this is the case then stomatal variability and its causes need to be considered when interpreting the data.

Stomatal density (SD) is the total number of stomata per unit area:

$$SD = \frac{\text{total number of stomata}}{\text{area}}$$

Stomatal index (SI) is the number of stomata expressed as a percentage of the total number of cells per unit area:

$$SI = \frac{\text{total number of stomata}}{\text{(total number of stomata + total number of epidermal cells)}} \times 100$$

Stomatal density and index may appear to be simple measurements of the aerial density of stomata and epidermal cells over the leaf surface, but there are a number of problems associated with obtaining relevant data from the leaf surface.

First, after careful consideration of which surface to examine (as leaves are usually hypostomatous but can be hyperstomatous or amphistomatous) an unbiased decision needs to be made concerning the inclusion of stomata and epidermal cells on the edge of a field of view (Kubínová 1994). The usual approach is to use a rectangular field of view and to include all those stomata or epidermal cells overlapping two predefined sides and the corner between them, but to exclude those overlapping the two remaining sides and the three remaining corners (Fig. 48.1). Counts should be made using the same field area because the calculated density per mm^2 and index can vary with magnification (Fig. 48.1) because the stomata are not necessarily evenly distributed and there are the associated problems with multiplying up small differences. Furthermore, in order to compare counts made in different laboratories it is necessary to use similar magnifications. The appropriate magnification for stomatal counts should first be determined in a pilot study (cf. Swan & Sandilands 1995) which has to consider the distribution pattern of the stomata (i.e.

POOLE, I. & KÜRSCHNER, W. M. 1999. Stomatal density and index: the practice.   257
In: JONES, T. P. & ROWE, N. P. (eds) *Fossil Plants and Spores: modern techniques.*
Geological Society, London, 257–260.

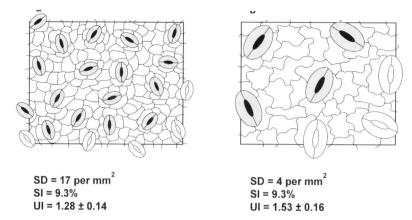

SD = 17 per mm^2
SI = 9.3%
UI = 1.28 ± 0.14

SD = 4 per mm^2
SI = 9.3%
UI = 1.53 ± 0.16

Fig. 48.1. Two different stomatal distributions of, for example, (**a**) a sun and (**b**) a shade leaf each within an area of 1 mm^2. Both diagrams illustrate the sampling protocol whereby only those stomata touching or straddling the top and left-hand side including one corner are counted (shaded). Those touching the bottom, right-hand side and other three corners are ignored (white). The same procedure applies to the epidermal cells. This illustrates the increased reliability from using stomatal index as opposed to stomatal density which does not take into account leaf expansion. Whereas there is a four-fold difference between stomatal densities, the stomatal indices remain the same. Changing the area of the field of view radically changes the SI values. For example, using 0.25 mm^2 (a quarter of the shown area) would result in a change in SI values, for the leaf shown in (a) SI = c. 7.8% and for the leaf shown in (b) SI = c. 8.3% (exact values will vary depending upon location of field of view). The undulation index (UI) was measured with an image analyser QWin 1 (Leica Cambridge UK), the values are means ± standard deviation ($n = 30$ in each case). From the UI values, the leaf in (b) is more likely to have grown in the shade (UI is higher) than leaf (a).

regular, uniform, random, clustered or anisotropic etc.) within the interveinal leaf area. The size of the area should be chosen in such a way that a representative field of the interveinal area is visible. Experience shows that the field areas should be as large as possible and certainly greater than 0.03 mm^2.

The use of an image analyser system is recommended to undertake the stomatal and epidermal cell counts, as large datasets and precise densitometrical and geometrical measurements are needed for analysis. Fortunately, there are good PC-based systems and software available. Alternatively, a microscope linked to a television monitor via a video camera can be used. To ensure that the counts are as accurate as possible, the cells can be marked off on an acetate sheet covering the monitor screen. A more simplistic approach would be to use a camera lucida attachment to a microscope although care must be taken when calculating the area of the field of view.

Second, a decision needs to be made concerning whether or not samples from veinal areas (i.e. those areas which include a vein) should be included, as the epidermis in these regions generally has no stomata (Weyers & Lawson 1997). It might be advisable not to include such areas because of the possible variation that they may cause. Even so, inclusion or not, should be stated.

Third, there appears to be a major problem concerning the number of stomata and epidermal cells that should be counted. A typical medium-sized leaf with an area of 5000 mm^2 will have in the region of 500 000 stomata and sampling just 1% of the stomata would involve 5000 counts (Weyers & Lawson 1997). Therefore, it is unrealistic to count the whole population and due regard must be given to the sampling strategy. The number of readings (i.e. the number of fields of view) required per site to show any intrinsic variation can be estimated by undertaking a pilot study and using objective statistical criteria (for example following the method given by Sokal & Rohlf (1995) in Box 9.13 pp. 255–257). Alternatively, plots of cumulative mean versus sample number can be used whereby the sample size is increased until the fluctuation of the mean is within acceptable limits (A. Jones *et al.* 1996), this is easily programmed into standard spreadsheet software. Although the precise number of readings per site need not be stated, this protocol is considered to be a fundamental prerequisite to any stomatal density or index investigation. A stratified sampling procedure (A. Jones *et al.* 1996) can then be used to determine the centre of each site across the leaf surface. It is recommended that at least one such sampling site should come from each 100 mm^2 of leaf surface where possible (Fig. 48.2). If only part of the leaf or cuticle has been preserved

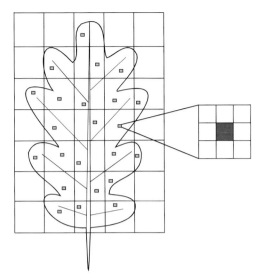

Fig. 48.2. Sampling protocol for an entire specimen. A grid composed of 100 mm² squares has been superimposed upon the specimen. One sample site (filled box) has been selected from each square using a stratified sampling strategy. Within each site nine fields of view (number determined from using statistical criteria) have to be considered. The central field of view, and hence the centre of that site, has been shaded.

then the relative area studied and the total number of sites sampled should still be stated so that the real significance of the data can be assessed (see below). For each site a mean stomatal density and index can be calculated. Once the data have been collected the methods of statistical analysis must be in accordance with the distribution pattern (i.e. normal or otherwise) of the data.

The modified approach

Modifications to the above approach, based on careful decisions, have to be made when dealing with fossil material. It is recommended that only leaf remains with at least 50% visible leaf area are used in order to ensure that they can be consistently studied from one specific leaf region. The best area to use is the mid-lamina region because in this region stomatal density and stomatal index are more consistent (e.g. Salisbury 1927; Poole *et al.* 1996). In addition, smaller leaf fragments of taxa with relatively little intrinsic variation may also be used if the variability has been assessed in more complete specimens, or if marginal pieces, usually the apical or basal leaf region with extremely high or low stomatal densities, are excluded from the sample set.

Detailed morphological and anatomical studies can enable the recognition of distinctive leaf morphotypes in modern and fossil leaf material (Kürschner 1997). Besides intrinsic variation, the variation between different leaf morphotypes of an individual taxon has to be studied carefully. Leaf morphotypes encountered in the fossil record are mainly sun and shade leaves, in addition to spring and *lammas* leaves. However, photomorphogenesis of plants in general, and particularly the development of leaves, greatly depend on the amount of incident light available during growth (Lichtenthaler 1985). Therefore, the resulting leaf anatomical differences found between the sun and shade morphotypes are, by far, the most profound and involve significant changes in stomatal density (for further discussion see Poole *et al.* 1996; Kürschner 1997). Gross features such as leaf area, degree of lobing, venation density as well as cuticular properties such as **trichome** frequency, surface texture, epidermal cell density, epidermal cell area and the degree of undulation of the epidermal anticlinal cell walls are very useful characters for distinguishing sun and shade morphotypes. Besides describing the degree of undulation qualitatively (Fig. 48.1), this important feature can be quantified by using the 'undulation index' (Kürschner 1997) as the undulation pattern is frequently more pronounced in shade than in sun leaves:

$$UI = \frac{C_e}{C_o} = \frac{C_e}{2 \times \pi \times \sqrt{\dfrac{A_e}{\pi}}}$$

where *UI* represents the undulation index, C_e (µm) the circumference of the cell, C_0 (µm) the circumference of the circle with the same area as the cell, and A_e (µm²) the area of the cell. If the preservation of fossil material permits, for example in the case of mummified or permineralized leaves, the mesophyll anatomy can reveal convincing evidence for a sun or shade morphotype. Generally, the mesophyll tissue of extant sun leaves, and in particular the palisade parenchyma, tends to be thicker due to additional cell layers. This has also shown to be valid in some fossil angiosperm leaves, for example Miocene *Quercus pseudocastanea* (Kürschner 1997). Only after this careful groundwork has been undertaken can the stomatal density and index of fossil leaves be interpreted in terms of palaeo-CO_2 levels.

In contrast to studies on modern leaf material, palaeo-CO_2 reconstructions by means of stomatal analyses of fossil leaves must also take into account the taphonomic processes (Kürschner 1997). Most depositional systems are selective and tend to bias the composition of the leaf assemblages (e.g. Roth & Dilcher 1978; Ferguson 1985; Spicer 1989*a*).

Therefore, although an increased population yields a more reliable dataset, it is unnecessary to study hundreds of leaves from one particular horizon because of the potentially wide variation of leaf morphotypes preserved. However, selective transport in fluvial and lacustrine environments favour the preservation of sun morphotypes. Consequently, this process filters out much of the natural variability observed in field studies on modern material (Kürschner 1977). The predominance of (allochthonous) sun leaves in the taphocoenosis can evoke a highly confident reproducibility of both stomatal index and stomatal density values per stratigraphic unit (Kürschner 1997). However, because of the high variability of density values, they should be used only in large datasets or from one particular leaf morphotype, preferably from sun leaves. Fossil sun leves were exposed to a CO_2 palaeoenvironment which corresponds to the bulk palaeoatmospheric CO_2 level. Since the sun leaves photosynthesized under non-limiting light conditions their adaptation to the prevailing atmospheric CO_2 was not restricted by light supply. Mires, on the other hand, can yield autochthonous leaf assemblages composed of both sun and shade morphotypes that have experienced only limited lateral wind transport. The relative abundance of sun and shade leaves in peat deposits is dependent upon the successional status of the adjacent vegetation. In this case shifts in stomatal density alone cannot unambiguously be considered to reflect a carbon dioxide response as it may be the result of a changing vegetation (Wagner, pers. comm.). In this situation the stomatal index remains the only indisputable parameter pertinent to CO_2 concentrations of the ambient atmosphere.

Using the data obtained

Stomatal data are highly suitable for plotting as contour maps using geographical mapping programs (cf. Poole et al. 1996). These programs require x and y spatial coordinates indicating the central position of the sample on the leaf surface and a z coordinate which is the measured variable (Poole et al. 1996; Weyers & Lawson 1997). Care must be taken in choosing the algorithm used for data 'smoothing' as this may take either a 'too literal' or 'too liberal' account of individual data points giving rise to artificial patterning (Weyers & Lawson 1997). However, this technique provides a useful visual representation of values and variation.

The fossil record of plants is by nature only fragmentary, and information concerning the micro habitat (light, humidity, etc.) of leaves and the growth position in the tree crown is lost or can be considered only indirectly. However, over the past decades palaeobotanists have established methods based upon foliar architecture and cuticular anatomy in order to assess the wide morphological and anatomical variability of fossil angiosperm leaves and their significance for taxonomic research (e.g. Ferguson 1971; Dilcher 1974; Kvacek & Walther 1978), in addition to palaeo-ecological and palaeoclimatological interpretation (e.g. Roth & Dilcher 1978; Wolfe 1993). Even so, stomatal density and index analyses of angiosperm leaves can be used in two ways for palaeo-CO_2 reconstructions.

In the first approach, extant taxa can provide quantitative information through comparisons of the fossil data with standardized calibration curves which describe the stomatal density adaptation of the modern plant or recent equivalent to a series of known atmospheric carbon dioxide concentrations. These standard curves can be obtained from historical herbarium leaf collections, growth experiments (Van der Burgh et al. 1993; Kürschner et al. 1996) or natural archives of annual leaf shedding recovered from peat deposits (Wagner et al. 1996). This method allows the study of the continuous adaptation of stomatal characters of living trees or populations under known growth conditions. It may be possible to calibrate extinct taxa with their nearest living relative although no conclusive data have yet been published due to the inherent discrepancies when comparing different taxa.

The second approach is concerned with the relative changes in the palaeo-CO_2 concentration, over a geological time interval, which may be revealed from a sequence of a specific fossil taxon over this period. However, to date no detailed case study for this has been published.

We would like to gratefully acknowledge many collaborators who have discussed ideas regarding the use of stomatal characters. These include T. Lawson, J. D. B. Weyers (University of Dundee, UK), F. Wagner, H. Visscher, J. van der Burgh (Utrecht University, The Netherlands) and D. L. Dilcher (University of Florida, Gainesville, USA). WMK acknowledges the financial support of the Netherlands Geoscience Foundation (GOA) and The Netherlands Organization of Scientific Research (NWO). This is Netherlands Research School of Sedimentary Geology (NSG) publication no. 970144.

49. The nearest living relative method

VOLKER MOSBRUGGER

A basic task of palaeoclimatology is the reconstruction of palaeoclimatic parameters such as: MAT = mean annual temperature; CMMT = cold month mean temperature; WMMT = warm month mean temperature; MAP = mean annual precipitation. Quantitative palaeoclimate data are preferred over qualitative data, and should provide high climatic resolution and have high statistical significance as well as small error bars. All palaeoclimate reconstructions have to rely on climate proxies; organisms, land plants in particular, are among the most useful for this task. This chapter focuses on one of the oldest techniques used in the reconstruction of palaeoclimates, the nearest living relative (NLR) method.

The underlying premise of the NLR method is straightforward. If a fossil organism or an assemblage of fossil organisms, have a close living relative, then we might assume that the climatic requirements of the fossil organism or of the fossil assemblage were close to those of its nearest living relative. Thus, morphological or systematic similarity is assumed to reflect similarity in climatic tolerance. As early as the nineteenth century, Heer (1855–1859) systematically used the NLR technique for Tertiary palaeoclimate reconstructions.

Today, the NLR technique still provides one of the best methods for palaeoclimate reconstructions in the Cenozoic, and numerous variations of this approach are in use. For the purpose of this overview, we will describe four types of NLR technique: those that are based on taxa versus those that are based on syntaxa (i.e. ecologically defined groups of organisms); those that aim at qualitative versus those that aim at quantitative palaeoclimate reconstructions.

Qualitative taxa-based approaches

Concept and applications

In the most basic version of the NLR method, a fossil taxon or several fossil taxa are used to infer palaeoclimates qualitatively (e.g. warm, cool, warming trend, cooling trend). Therefore fossil organisms are interpreted as indicators of specific climates, based on the climatic requirements of their NLRs. For instance, generally speaking, for Cenozoic vegetation, Lauraceae, palms, Zingi-

beraceae, etc. are considered to be indicators of warm-tropical to subtropical climates; deciduous trees such as Fagaceae, Ulmaceae and Betulaceae are assumed to reflect temperate climates; conifers are considered to be typical of boreal or dry; and *Ephedra* of semi-arid climates. Based on the relative abundance of the various climate indicators, it is possible to provide qualitative assessments of palaeoclimates and palaeoclimate change (cf. Mai 1995).

This qualitative indicator species (or indicator taxa) approach (Birks & Birks 1980) has a long tradition, and is still the most widely used for the Tertiary (e.g. Suc 1984; White *et al.* 1997) and Quaternary (cf. examples cited in Birks & Birks 1980; Moore *et al.* 1991; Lang 1994). Specific mention should be made of the 'Central European Model' for the Tertiary (Boulter 1984), where qualitative climate changes are derived from variations in the relative abundance of arctotertiary and palaeotropic elements (e.g. Zagwijn & Hager 1987; Mai 1991). Palaeotropic elements are those plants that are evergreen and prefer tropical to subtropical climates (based on NLR); arctotertiary elements encompass deciduous plants characteristic of temperate climates. Although for some plants it may be disputed whether they belong to the palaeotropic or arctotertiary group (cf. Zagwijn & Hager 1987; Mai 1995), this approach has proved to be very popular in Europe (see Mai 1991, 1995 for an overview). In Quaternary palaeoclimatology, the construction and climatic interpretation of pollen diagrams also belongs to this category of the NLR method (for details see, for instance, Birks & Birks 1980; Birks 1981).

In a very generalized way, the qualitative indicator taxa approach is also used for the Permo-Carboniferous and Mesozoic (e.g. Vakhrameev *et al.* 1978; Behrensmeyer *et al.* 1992b for overviews). For instance, ferns are generally considered to represent more humid climates, whereas seed-plants are assumed to be more common in drier habitats. Hence, the spore : pollen ratio is a common palaeoclimate indicator, particularly for the Mesozoic. However, because most Palaeozoic and Mesozoic plants are so distantly related to modern plants, the application of NLR methods for pre-Cenozoic times is limited.

MOSBRUGGER, V. 1999. The nearest living relative method. *In*: JONES, T. P. & ROWE, N. P. (eds) *Fossil Plants and Spores: modern techniques*. Geological Society, London, 261–265.

Problems and limitations

The advantages of qualitative taxa-based variations of the NLR method are that they provide rapid results, and are easy to apply to many kinds of fossil floras (leaves, fruits/seeds, pollen/spores, wood). On the other hand, they also have a number of shortcomings. First, the basic assumption of the NLR method, that morphological or systematic similarity between Recent and fossil taxa reflects similarity in the climatic requirements, limits its applicability. Obviously, there are many reasons why this basic assumption may be wrong, and the potential for errors almost certainly augments with increasing age. For instance, there is no conclusive reason why the Schizaeaceae of the Permo-Carboniferous should have the same climatic requirements as the modern representatives of this family. Hence, all palaeoclimate reconstructions based on the NLR method are most reliable in the Cenozoic.

There are, however, other problems and limitations. The methods described so far yield only qualitative palaeoclimate data and hence are hardly sufficient to serve as a basis for palaeoclimate modelling. Moreover, they do not have the status of an objective standardized methodology. Hence, for the same fossil flora somewhat different palaeoclimate results may be obtained, depending on the taxa considered and on the interpretations of the scientist (see, for instance, table 1 in Mosbrugger & Schilling 1992). An even more serious problem is that the presence, absence or relative abundance of those taxa that are used for climatic interpretations are influenced by the sedimentary environment and taphonomy. For instance, it is a well known problem that evergreen (and thus palaeotropic) elements are consistently more abundant in peat than in clastic environments because leaf persistence also represents an adaptation to nutrient-poor (oligotrophic) soils (Monk 1966; van der Burgh 1973). The influence of taphonomy and sedimentary environment on palaeoclimate reconstructions with the 'Central European Model' is discussed by Boulter (1984).

Overall the qualitative taxa-based approaches of the NLR method have several advantages and have proven successful for a wide stratigraphic range and floral types. On the other hand, they suffer from a number of shortcomings (qualitative data, no objective and standardized methodology, taphonomic influence) that severely limit their applicability as well as the climatic resolution and reliability of their results.

Quantitative taxa-based approaches

Concepts and applications

Quantitative taxa-based approaches of the NLR method, which use fossils and their NLRs for deriving quantitative estimates of palaeoclimate parameters, overcome some of the problems

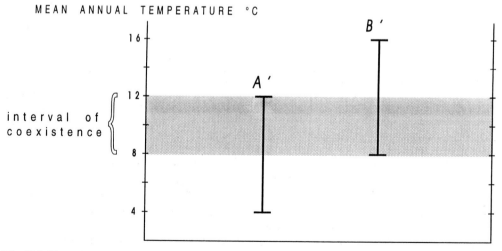

Fig. 49.1. Illustration of the basic principle of the CA. A′ and B′ are the nearest living relatives of fossil taxa A and B, respectively. The bars indicate the mean annual temperature range tolerated by A′ and B′. There is a mean annual temperature interval between 8 and 12°C, in which A′ and B′ can (or could) co-exist. This interval of co-existence is considered to be the best estimate for the mean annual temperature of a fossil flora with fossil taxa A and B (from Mosbrugger & Utescher 1997).

described above. The basic assumption of quantitative taxa-based approaches of the NLR method is similar, but more rigorous than that of the qualitative approaches. Fossil taxa are not only considered to be characteristic of the same type of climate as their NLRs, but also to have the same quantitative climatic requirements. For instance, if today Mastixiaceae tolerate a MAT between 15 and 28°C, then we may assume that for a fossil flora containing Mastixiaceae the MAT was between 15 and 28°C.

Since its first use by Heer (1855–1859) the quantitative indicator taxa approach has found numerous applications in the Cenozoic (cf. Mai 1995) and even in the Mesozoic (e.g. Horell 1991). However, in most studies, only one or a few taxa of a fossil flora have been used to derive quantitative estimates of palaeoclimate parameters, and this may cause a number of problems. Most taxa have relatively wide climatic tolerances and hence, do not provide a high climatic resolution. Moreover, taphonomy and sedimentary environments may again influence the presence and absence of a specific taxon. Mosbrugger & Utescher (1997) recently stated that the effect of these shortcomings can be reduced by using all the taxa of a fossil assemblage. They introduced the co-existence approach (CA) as a new version of a quantitative taxa-based NLR method.

The underlying idea of the CA is simple (Fig. 49.1). Consider a fossil flora with two taxa A and B with their corresponding NLRs A′ and B′. If A′ requires a MAT between 4 and 12°C, and B′ between 8 and 16°C, then there is an interval between 8 and 12°C, where both NLRs can (or could) co-exist. This co-existence interval is then used as the best estimator for the MAT under which the fossil taxa A and B lived. The aim of the CA is to find for a given fossil flora and a given climate parameter the climatic interval in which all nearest living relatives of the fossil flora can co-exist. To allow for a rapid application of the CA, a database CLIMBOT has been developed containing over 800 Tertiary plant taxa, their NLRs, and the climatic requirements of the NLRs with respect to 10 different climate parameters (MAT, CMMT, WMMT, MAP, maximum monthly precipitation, minimum monthly precipitation, precipitation of the warmest month, relative humidity, potential evaporation, aridity index). Moreover, we have devised a computer algorithm CLIMST, which, based on the taxon list for a given flora, extracts the information from the database and determines the co-existence intervals for the various climate parameters as well as some descriptive statistics (see Mosbrugger & Utescher 1997 for details).

The CA has a number of advantages which are mostly related to the fact that all taxa of a fossil

flora (at least those with well-defined NLRs) are used.

1. The climatic resolution is potentially increased, because the co-existence intervals for the climatic parameters are narrower than the climatic ranges tolerated by a single taxon. Usually, the co-existence intervals will become narrower the greater the diversity of the flora. In general, if more than 10 taxa are considered, reliability and resolution of the climatic data obtained with the CA are reasonably good (mostly between 1 and 4°C) for the temperature-related parameters.
2. The CA is able to reconstruct past climates that are different from today because different plants define the co-existence intervals of the various climate parameters.
3. The CA yields co-existence intervals which can be interpreted as confidence intervals.
4. The CA produces results that are statistically highly significant, as was demonstrated by Monte Carlo simulations (see Mosbrugger & Utescher 1997 for details).
5. Errors and inconsistencies that may occur in the application of the CA can generally be detected.
6. The CA is a relatively robust technique that is not sensitive to minor errors.
7. Taphonomic, sedimentological and ecological factors may influence the presence/absence of taxa and thus the width of the co-existence interval, but they will not affect the applicability and the correctness of the CA as long as the fossil flora is derived from a single ecosystem.

The CA has been applied to numerous Tertiary (Oligocene to Pliocene) floras from Europe (cf. Mosbrugger 1995; Mosbrugger & Utescher 1997; Köhler in press; Pross et al. in press). The results are largely consistent with other palaeoclimatic data (e.g. derived from terrestrial carbon isotopes, marine oxygen isotopes), and indicate that the CA represents a reasonable, robust and most widely applicable technique for the Tertiary. (Software and database are available from the author on request.)

Problems and limitations

The CA as the most advanced quantitative taxa-based NLR method is based on only a few assumptions and requirements (cf. Mosbrugger & Utescher 1997).

1. The fossil taxa are correctly identified.
2. For fossil taxa systematically closely related, nearest living relatives exist and they are correctly identified.
3. The climatic requirements of a fossil taxon are similar/identical to those of its NLR.

4. The climatic requirements or tolerances of a NLR (and hence of a fossil taxon) can be derived from its area of distribution. It is assumed that a modern plant lives at least somewhere within its distribution area close to its minimum and maximum tolerances with respect to the various climate parameters.

5. The meteorological stations provide adequate and reliable data to describe the climatic tolerances of modern taxa.

Of course, some or all of these requirements or assumptions may be wrong. Some taxa of a fossil flora or the NLR of a fossil plant may be mis-identified The climatic requirements of a fossil plant may be different from those of its NLR. For some modern plants, in particular those occupying a relictual area, their distribution area may not cover their climatic tolerances. The meteorological stations may not provide the required type and quality of data to describe the climatic requirements of plants. Fortunately, all these errors can be detected if they lead to climatic outliers and inconsistencies. In ideal situations (i.e. no errors) the CA will result in co-existence intervals in which 100% of the NLRs of a flora can co-exist. If, however, one or several of those errors occur, then the CA will lead to co-existence intervals containing less than 100% of the taxa. Thus, the co-existence value, that is the percentage of taxa that can co-exist within a co-existence interval, provides information about the reliability of the co-existence interval and about the frequency of errors.

Our analyses of fossil floras with the CA show that all these errors, although present to a certain extent, do not seriously affect the CA in applications to Oligocene, Miocene and Pliocene floras; here the CA generally provides good results with co-existence values between 88 and 100%. As yet we have not applied CA to pre-Oligocene flora assemblages. Theoretically, with the increasing age of the flora, the reliability and the climatic resolution of the CA decreases. Moreover, the climatic resolution of the CA is generally better for leaf and fruit/seed floras than for wood or pollen/spore floras.

Qualitative and quantitative syntaxa-based approaches

Concepts and applications

Vegetation units or syntaxa can be used for qualitative and quantitative palaeoclimate reconstructions using the NLR method in the same way as for plant taxa. For qualitative reconstructions, the basic assumption is that if a modern vegetation unit is indicative of a certain climate, then it is reasonable to assume that a very similar fossil vegetation unit is restricted to a similar climate. Such qualitative syntaxa-based NLR approaches are widely used in Tertiary and Quaternary palaeoclimatology. For a description of classic vegetation types that can be used for qualitative palaeoclimatic interpretations see Frenzel (1968), Wolfe (1985), Webb (1987), Lang (1994) and Mai (1995).

There also exist various quantitative syntaxa-based approaches. For the Tertiary of the Northern Hemisphere, the modern vegetation units of North America and in particular of China generally serve as a reference base (cf. the series Ecosystems of the World, e.g. Goodall 1986; see Wang 1961 for vegetation types of China). First, for a given Tertiary vegetation its NLR vegetation type is determined from the literature (e.g. from Wang 1961). Based on recent climate data (the atlas of Walter & Lieth 1967 is most commonly used) the tolerances of several climate parameters are determined for this NLR, and therefore the Tertiary vegetation´s climatic conditions are determined. Numerous quantitative palaeoclimate reconstructions for the European Tertiary are based on this approach (e.g. Gregor 1989; Mai 1995); however, its climatic resolution is usually not very high because the various vegetation units have a wide climatic tolerance. Moreover, this technique is not able to reconstruct past climate conditions which do not exist today.

In Quaternary palaeoclimatology similar quantitative techniques are applied (cf. Birks & Birks 1980; Frenzel et al. 1992). In addition, so-called transfer function techniques are increasingly used. Numerous variations of these transfer functions exist (cf. Webb & Bryson 1972; Huntley & Prentice 1988; Guiot et al. 1992), but they all are based on the same theoretical concept, which is only briefly described here (cf. Guiot 1994). Theoretically, it should be possible to describe vegetation dynamics by the response function

$$R: X = R\ (C, D),$$

with X = state of the vegetation, C = climatic factors, D = non-climatic factors. This equation states in general terms that the vegetation X is a function of (or depends on) climatic factors C and non-climatic factors D. Provided that the non-climatic factors D are constant or largely irrelevant for the observed vegetation response, a simplified response function can be defined

$$R_c : X = R_c(C),$$

it describes the state of vegetation X as a mathematical function of the change of climatic factors C. The inverse of response function R_c is the transfer function

$$T: C = T(X)$$

which links the vegetation state X to climatic parameters C. The transfer function can be determined or calibrated by correlating modern vegetation states X with the corresponding modern climate parameters C. Based on this transfer function, fossil vegetation data X' can then be used to determine the palaeoclimatic parameters C'.

For the Quaternary, these transfer functions provide the most detailed palaeoclimate reconstructions with the best climatic resolution and reliability as compared with other methods. The climate-dependent biological response most commonly considered in transfer functions is the vegetation structure as reflected by the relative abundance of pollen and spores. Obviously, calibrating such a transfer function is a difficult and time-consuming task.

Problems and limitations

The syntaxa-based NLR-methods demand more rigorous assumptions than taxa-based methods. They require that not only the fossil taxa, but also the fossil syntaxa have NLRs, and that both fossil taxa and syntaxa have the same or similar climatic requirements as their NLRs. In addition, in the case of transfer functions it is assumed that the same transfer function T is valid for the Recent and the fossil vegetation, implying for instance that the non-climatic factors D, including taphonomy, do not effect the transfer function (for a more detailed discussion see Birks 1981; Guiot 1994). Because of these assumptions, it is expected that in the pre-Quaternary syntaxa-based NLR methods are less reliable than taxa-based. In particular, it is obvious that transfer functions as they are used in the Quaternary cannot work in the pre-Quaternary. Already by the Tertiary, vegetation units were quite different from those today. Many of the taxa (e.g. *Sequoia, Taxodium, Glyptostrobus*) that lived together in the Tertiary have NLRs that no longer co-exist (today *Sequoia* is restricted to western North America, *Taxodium* to eastern North America and Mexico and *Glyptostrobus* to China). Even within the Quaternary, the reliability of transfer functions will rapidly decrease with stratigraphic age. Another weakness of transfer functions is that reasonably reliable results are only obtained within the climatic range that has been used for calibration.

Part Nine   Palaeoecology

50. Palynology/ecology interfaces

ALFRED TRAVERSE

Ecology is the study of the environment and its impact on, and feedback relationship with, particular items (normally organisms) that are, of course, also parts of the environment. Palynology was originally the study of pollen and spores of all sorts, but especially those of terrestrial green plants. The subject is now much bigger, including microscopic resistant-walled remains of protists, animals and fungi. Therefore, the relationships between palynology and ecology are also very diverse, including, for example, study of airborne pollen and spores in relation to human allergy, and investigations of insect pollen-foraging. This chapter concentrates on some of the ecological aspects of palaeopalynology.

Palaeopalynology

Because the exterior walls of most pollen and spores consist of a very tough organic compound, sporopollenin, and the walls of many fungal spores are made of another resistant compound, chitin, the outer walls of spores and pollen tend to resist decay before and after being incorporated in sediment: peat, sand, silt, clay, as well as in lime and other precipitates. The usually somewhat flattened spore-wall 'shells' can be extracted from such sediments, and rocks derived from them, by various techniques (see Traverse 1988) and identified microscopically. Such study is called palaeopalynology, a sub-discipline of palynology. People who do such studies have discovered that various other microscopic bodies composed of sporopollenin or chitin occur in the same rocks as the spores/pollen and can be harvested from the rocks by the same techniques. Among such items are dinoflagellate cysts, and acritarchs (algal bodies of uncertain relationship). These may have sporopolleninous walls, and are prevailingly found in marine sedimentary rocks, as is also true of some protist and animal palynomorphs consisting of chitin.

Palaeopalynologists use the term palynomorph to lump spores and pollen with the non-spore items just mentioned, making up the subject matter of palaeopalynology. Dinoflagellate cysts and acritarchs are the most important of the non-spore palynomorphs. It is the ecological study of all palynomorphs obtained from sediments and rocks that comprises the basic subject matter treated here.

The general layout of the concepts employed is presented in Fig. 50.1.

Physical palynological ecology

Geological environments

Ecology includes physical and chemical reactions between the whole environment, and particular, usually biological, items of it. Palynomorphs of all sorts are participants in such reactions, and the study of them can be quite revealing. It has been shown by various palynologists, for example, that closely associated different sorts of sedimentary rocks, such as coal, siltstone and sandstone, often contain characteristic assortments of palynomorphs (Farley 1990). Indeed, Chaloner (1968) has even shown that palynofloras (assemblages of palynomorphs) of rocks of different ages but of similar lithology (rock type) may have uncanny resemblances to each other in such matters as percentage of pollen with attached sacs. Similarly, because palynomorphs are silt-size particles, siltstone tends to have more palynomorphs per gram than does sandstone, because all silt-size particles, whether mineral grains (clasts) or spores, are subject to the same sorting processes in water. Sporopollenin has a specific gravity of about 1.4, whereas mineral matter is about 2.5 on average; therefore, palynomorphs sort with silt-size mineral clasts somewhat smaller than they are. Various studies have shown that dinoflagellate cysts with spines and other elongated processes are more likely to be found in sediments deposited in high-energy (more turbulent) water than in quiet, sometimes brackish water, where relatively smooth forms predominate (see, for example, Traverse 1978). It has also been discovered, for example in Great Bahama Bank by Traverse & Ginsburg (1966), that palynomorphs sediment out of quiet water more rapidly than they do out of active (high-energy) water, and for low-density pollen such as saccate conifer grains, the difference is dramatic. Sediments deposited close to shore tend to contain more palynomorphs per gram than those deposited far from land, and there is a regular drop-off between the two (Traverse 1988; Caratini 1994).

Once deposited, conditions in the substrate sediment begin to affect the palynomorphs.

TRAVERSE, A. 1999. Palynology/ecology interfaces. *In*: JONES, T. P. & ROWE, N. P. (eds) *Fossil Plants and Spores: modern techniques*. Geological Society, London, 269–273.

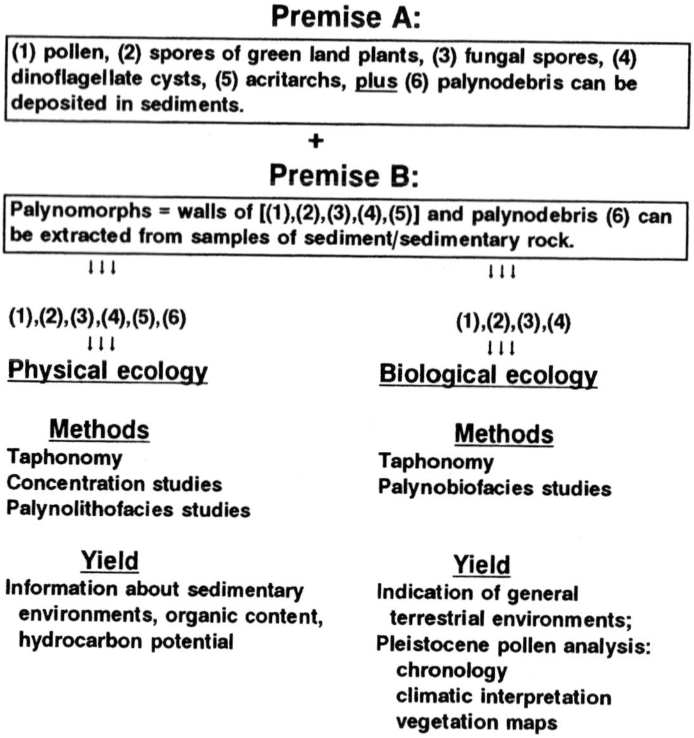

Premise A:

(1) pollen, (2) spores of green land plants, (3) fungal spores, (4) dinoflagellate cysts, (5) acritarchs, plus (6) palynodebris can be deposited in sediments.

+

Premise B:

Palynomorphs = walls of [(1),(2),(3),(4),(5)] and palynodebris (6) can be extracted from samples of sediment/sedimentary rock.

↓↓↓   ↓↓↓

(1),(2),(3),(4),(5),(6)   (1),(2),(3),(4)
↓↓↓   ↓↓↓
Physical ecology   **Biological ecology**

Methods   **Methods**
Taphonomy   Taphonomy
Concentration studies   Palynobiofacies studies
Palynolithofacies studies

Yield   **Yield**
Information about sedimentary   Indication of general
  environments, organic content,   terrestrial environments;
  hydrocarbon potential   Pleistocene pollen analysis:
                                                            chronology
                                                            climatic interpretation
                                                            vegetation maps

Fig. 50.1. Flow chart showing basic aspects of the relationships between palaeopalynology and ecology. Assume (**Premise A**) that palynomorphs (items 1–5) and palynodebris (item 6) can be deposited in sediments as clastic particles along with mineral clasts. Also assume (**Premise B**) that all items (1–6) can be extracted from sediments and sedimentary rocks by palynological maceration. Then, ecological methods aimed primarily at the physical environment, or primarily at the biological environment, yield information either about the source rocks, including, for example, hydrocarbon potential, or about the biological environment, chiefly with regard to palaeoclimates and their derivatives.

Oxidizing conditions, and to a lesser extent alkalinity, erode and ultimately destroy spore walls. Sometimes such processes are selective and result in concentration of certain kinds of palynomorphs with relatively thick or resistant walls. Such concentration can be related to the sorts of plants producing the spores or pollen, thus being partly biological in its significance. High temperatures, whether from depth of burial (geothermal gradient) or from volcanic flows or intrusions, can cook palynomorphs from their original pale yellow colour to opaque (black), not permitting microscopy by transmitted light. Thus, the condition of the walls of sporomorphs is a valuable indicator of the physical environment and chemical conditions to which they have been subjected. The colour or reflectivity of spore walls has been quantified as a measure of maturity of the organic matter in rocks for evaluation of hydrocarbon potential; see discussion in Marshall & Yule (Chapter 31) and

Traverse (1988). Such matters, dealing with the natural history of fossils after the death of the original living organic material, are features of the taphonomy of fossil palynomorphs. Taphonomy is an important aspect of palaeoecology, to which palynology has made unique contributions.

Palynolithofacies and palynodebris

The palynomorph composition of the palynoflora of a layer of rock tends to be characteristic of that stratum and is sometimes called its palynofacies (see Batten, Chapter 4). However, there are really two ways of looking at the palynofacies of a rock entity: The first approach is to look at the palynoflora-facies in relation to the sedimentary circumstances that yielded the rock, for example, the concentration of sporomorphs per gram of rock. I call facies of this sort palynolithofacies, emphasizing the palynomorph/rock relationship, and it is clearly palaeoecological. In recent years there has been a surge of interest in palynofacies, and the concept has been extended to include not only sporomorphs and other palynomorphs, but also plant tissue fragments (both relatively unchanged and charcoalified), amorphous organic matter, and other organic 'microjunk,' sometimes collectively referred to as palynodebris. (For a thorough description of the constituents of palynofacies, see also Batten 1996a.) When palynomorphs and palynodebris are considered as sedimentary particles *per se* they are obviously part of what constitutes palynolithofacies (Traverse 1994). Study of this sort of palynofacies can reveal much about the organic fraction of rocks and has been shown to be useful in evaluating sedimentary rock basins for hydrocarbon potential (cf. Hart 1994; Batten 1996b). This is an example of applied palynological palaeoecology. (For detailed information about the sedimentation of all sorts of organic material, see Traverse 1994 and Tyson 1995.)

Biological palynological ecology

The second way of looking at palynofacies is to consider the total complex of palynomorphs characteristic of a sediment or sedimentary rock from a biological point of view. I have suggested calling such complexes palynobiofacies. Sometimes the emphasis is on death assemblages: forms found together as fossils, whether or not they were associated when alive. This is thus an aspect of taphonomy, which, as we have seen, may also have palynolithofacies significance. In palaeopalynology a taphonomically influenced assemblage may result from the greater durability of some forms and their concentration following the destruction of palynomorphs with lower preservation potential. In my experience, pollen of Chenopodiaceae/ Amaranthaceae and spores of many ferns are examples of forms that are often so concentrated. Thin-walled pollen such as that of grasses are often preferentially destroyed, by hydrolysis and by fungi and bacteria. Such taphonomically influenced assemblages, of course, do not accurately reflect the source vegetation.

Of much greater importance, however, is the fortunate fact that the spore/pollen floras of a sediment or sedimentary rock typically do reflect, to some degree, the vegetation from which they were derived. Inasmuch as vegetation is in turn an accurate indicator of climate and other environmental factors on land adjacent to the basin of deposition, palynofloras can be used to interpret environmental trends on the land masses from which they were derived.

When long records are available from cores, terrestrial long-term moisture and temperature trends can be demonstrated, as Fowell *et al.* (1992) have shown for a record of hundreds of thousands of years in the Triassic–Jurassic of the Newark Basin in New Jersey, USA. Sporomorphs in pre-Cenozoic deposits can sometimes be interpreted climatologically despite the lack of close links with living plants, because certain groups of morphologically similar sporomorphs have been shown to be climatic indicators. For example, van der Eem (1983), working in the Triassic, has shown that dominance of saccate pollen indicates relatively dry conditions, whereas abundant lycopod spores such as *Aratrisporites* indicate wet environments; various other morphological groups have other ecological significances.

In the Cenozoic, direct comparisons with related living forms can often be made. Palmae in Eocene deposits surely mean warm climate, just as they do today, and, from at least late Oligocene time, plant associations are essentially modern in generic composition and climatological implications.

Marine pollen records from sediments deposited far from continents must be interpreted with caution, but in some cases, such as Neogene sediments of offshore northwest Africa and southwest Europe, the marine pollen/spore records reflect accurately the vegetation patterns of the continent (Hooghiemstra *et al.* 1992)

Relatively nearshore marine deposits, such as those of the continental shelves, and non-marine sediments, such as lagoonal, fluvial, lacustrine and swamp deposits, contain palynofloras representing almost entirely the regional or even the local vegetation. Long cores of such deposits yield amazingly detailed records of climatic oscillations, with evidence for the profound effect these have on flora and fauna and on such geological matters as oxidation/weathering rates.

It should be noted here that dinoflagellate cysts can be used for ecological interpretations of marine sediments. Some species indicate nearshore and others far offshore conditions. Some dinoflagellate taxa indicate certain biogeographic zones, and analysis of changes in dinoflagellate composition at different levels in cores has shown a relationship to palaeoclimatic change (Lentin & Williams 1980; Habib, *et al.* 1994).

The special case of pollen analysis

In Scandinavia about a century ago, Lagerheim and von Post (Traverse 1988, p. 12 ff.) observed that pollen and spores in peat from bogs produced since the retreat of Pleistocene ice reflect very accurately the climatic trends at the place of deposition. Indeed, we know now that such pollen comes primarily from plants that grew near the site where the peat occurs. Von Post, Erdtman, Iversen, Faegri, Firbas and others in northern Europe decades ago put pollen statistics (= pollen analysis) on a sound basis, enabling its extension over much of the Northern Hemisphere. Even before radiocarbon dating they developed a chronological scheme with subdivisions based on the pollen complexes and adjusted for latitudinal differences, for the last 10 000 years. With some refinements, and with the addition of absolute years from radiocarbon measurements, the schemes are still in widespread use, though each is limited geographically in its applicability to a specific region where there is floral continuity, for example, England, central Europe, the Appalachians (USA), Kyushu (Japan).

The pollen statistics methods employed by the pioneers depended mostly on percentage calculations, and it was recognized fairly early that it didn't necessarily follow that a pollen sample with 50% pine pollen came from a forest consisting of 50% *Pinus* trees. Some taxa, usually wind-pollinated, produce prodigious amounts of pollen, and some abundant insect-pollinated plants produce relatively little. Some sorts of pollen have very resistant sporopollenin walls, others have relatively thin walls that are easily destroyed. Some types of pollen are more buoyant in air than others and are therefore more widely distributed by winds. In addition, the sedimentation rate of the sand, silt and clay which incorporate the pollen and spores may be quite uneven, so that the total concentration of palynomorphs is abnormally low when the sedimentation rate is high. Various palynologists have suggested sophisticated mathematical techniques to compensate for all of these barriers to reconstructing the source vegetation accurately from the pollen and spore record (Traverse 1988, p. 386 ff.). In fact, even without these corrections, percentage-based pollen analyses can usually be interpreted accurately enough for practical purposes. For example, Hase & Iwauchi (1985) established six stratigraphic zones for late Cenozoic sediments in Kyushu, based on percentages of pollen, mostly of trees and shrubs. The *Picea* zone is defined by very high percentages of spruce pollen, and the zone is easy to recognize on this basis, even though, without mathematical interpretation, there is no certainty that 50% *Picea* pollen in the sediment means 50% spruce trees in the source forests. Palynological studies of cored sediment of the Present Interglacial (= Post-glacial = Holocene) is ecologically very significant to us, as this is the time period of modern civilizations and their immediate precursors. The pollen record was the first clear indication of a post-glacial climatic optimum in Europe (Boreal, Atlantic, and Subboreal pollen stages = Firbas zones V–VIII) and North America beginning about 9000 and ending about

2500 years ago. Correlations with the high points in Mediterranean civilizations are obvious. The Little Ice Age during much of the last thousand years shows clearly in pollen analyses. One of the many results of this cold period was the failure of the Norse settlement of the Western Hemisphere. While other sorts of study now are more quantitative, for example, oxygen isotopic studies, no method more directly measures what was going on with the vegetation on which humans and other animals depend. For example, pollen analysis of beach deposits in Oslo Fjord, Norway, has made it possible to assign the deposits now found at various altitudes to specific substages of the standard post-glacial (= present interglacial) diagram, thus proving the gradual and very considerable rising of the land by isostatic rebound since the melting of the glacial burden. Such changes of relative sea-level have had profound effect on humans and other forms of life. The dating of sea-level by palynological analysis of beach deposits provides very useful information for understanding the history of the concerned area (Traverse 1988, pp. 373–374).

In both eastern North America (Delcourt & Delcourt 1981; Delcourt 1987) and northwest Europe (Huntley & Birks 1983) palynological analyses of peat and other sediments from many cores has permitted preparation of both vegetation maps, and maps of the distribution of key taxa, for various intervals during the whole of the present interglacial (about 10 000 years). These maps have many uses, among which is the reconstruction of probable land use in the past by humans at different levels of civilization. Such studies also provide a valuable check on the probable effects on vegetation of future climatic alteration.

Extension of the Pleistocene pollen analytical method

Although pollen statistics was originally aimed at the Present Interglacial, the method has been applied to much longer time periods. The famous Grande Pile core in France (Woillard 1978) enables the tracing of the waxing and waning of forest types for hundreds of thousands of years. The past few million years have witnessed very large migrations of forests and other vegetation types, but the taxa of plants, at least at the generic level that pollen analysis can detect, have not changed much. Therefore, the method proved useful with cores from the Black Sea spanning the time period from present to late Miocene (about 7 Ma). Studies in the Black Sea (Traverse 1982) showed that alternation of forest dominance, indicating warm-moist conditions, and steppe dominance, indicating cold-dry climate, could be estimated for the enormously large drainage basin by calculation of ratios between characteristic forest species pollen (oak, pine, elm, beech, etc.) and steppe species pollen (grasses, chenopods/amaranths, *Artemisia*).

In fact, there are few problems involving the study of the interaction of vegetation with other organisms and with various ecological processes, to which palynology cannot potentially make a contribution. If it is important to know whether an area in Illinois was tundra or prairie at a certain time in the last 10 000 years, for example, one of many deposits of sediment representing the time in question (the age usually measurable by radiocarbon studies of wood fragments) in Illinois can be analysed palynologically. In fact, the data are already available in the literature. The floral constituents are very different for these two contrasting environments. Pollen analysis has been used on Neanderthal grave sites to reveal that this human species probably used floral tributes as part of its burial practices (Leroi-Gourhan 1975). If it needs to be known whether the Mayan Indians in Honduras were cultivating maize at a certain time, study of sediments from nearby lakes may solve the problem. It can be necessary, for legal reasons, to know what sorts of plants honey bees were visiting during a critical period. Did the application of insecticides to certain crops cause mortality in a nearby apiary? Pollen from the raw honey may help to answer the question. If there is no pollen from the suspect crop, the bees probably weren't visiting it. These last two examples are from the author's unpublished consulting work. It is clear that an astonishing wealth of ecological information is available to us because of the fortuitous circumstance that sporopollenin and chitin protect the identity of incomprehensibly abundant reproductive bodies of plants and fungi: pollen and spores.

51. Techniques for analysing unconsolidated lake sediments

STEPHEN T. JACKSON

Quaternary palaeoecologists have long utilized unconsolidated sediments of small to moderate-sized lakes (10^{-1}–10^2 ha) as a source of information about past vegetation and environment. Lakes provide continuous sedimentary records, with temporal resolution ranging from 10^0–10^2 years. Radiocarbon dating of organic materials can provide age models for sediments spanning the past 40 000–50 000 years.

Tephrochronology provides another dating tool when volcanic ashes of known age are present in sediments; this technique can provide chronologies for sediments beyond the range of radiocarbon dating. High-resolution dating of sediments spanning the past two centuries can be accomplished using the ^{210}Pb method, and by correlation of pollen stratigraphy with known historical events (e.g. *Ambrosia* rise, *Castanea* decline in eastern North America). Lake sediments provide an excellent preservational environment for pollen, spores, plant macrofossils, charcoal and other materials. Interpretation is facilitated by extensive networks of modern pollen assemblages, allowing formal numerical searches for the best modern analogues of fossil assemblages (Overpeck *et al.* 1985), and by theoretical and empirical studies of pollen–vegetation relationships (Bradshaw & Webb 1985; Prentice 1985, 1988; Jackson 1994; Sugita 1994). The latter have led to formal approaches to pollen–vegetation calibrations (Prentice & Webb 1986; Jackson *et al.* 1995). Recent theoretical and empirical studies have established firm foundations for inferences from plant macrofossil assemblages (Birks 1973; Dunwiddie 1987; Jackson 1989; Jackson *et al* . 1997) and charcoal data (Patterson *et al.* 1987; Clark 1988*a*; Clark & Royall 1995; Whitlock & Millspaugh 1996). Palaeoecological techniques for analysing lake sediments are diverse; in this chapter the most generally useful techniques are described and an incomplete guide to the literature is provided. Some of the specific techniques reflect the author's own preferences; these preferences are explained and alternatives identified.

Sediment coring

Cores of lake sediments can be obtained using a variety of devices. Uncompacted sediments in the upper portions (50–200 cm) of lake sediments can be obtained using gravity (Hongve) corers, freeze-corers, or Plexiglass piston-corers. Compacted sediments are best obtained using piston corers (core diameter 2–10 cm), which can usually be hand-operated from simple floating platforms or ice. Mineral-rich and deep organic sediments may require chain-hoists or machine-powered devices for driving and extraction, with accompanying needs for additional buoyancy, reaction force, etc. Large-diameter cores (7.5–10 cm) provide more material for macrofossil and radiocarbon analysis and better stratigraphic detail, but are more difficult to obtain. Specific guidelines for design, construction and use of coring devices are available from several sources (Wright 1980, 1991; Wright *et al.* 1984; Neale & Walker 1996). Sediment-coring devices can be custom-made in a well-equipped machine shop. Piston corers, rods and other devices are also available for purchase (see Appendix).

Sediment cores can be obtained anywhere in a lake, but continuity and temporal resolution are best where sediments are thickest (usually the deepest part of the basin). Macrofossils are usually scarce in sediments more than *c.* 100 m from shore (S. T. Jackson, unpublished data). Macrofossil studies are best done using cores obtained nearshore or from small lakes ($\leq$2 ha).

Pollen extraction

From the viewpoint of a palynologist, lake sediment consists of pollen, spores and charcoal embedded in a matrix of organic and mineral material. The organic materials, which include the pollen and charcoal, are diverse, but for our purposes can be classed into three general groups: alkali-soluble, cellulose and refractory. Alkali-soluble compounds primarily consist of humic and other organic acids. Cellulose, a long-chain glucose polymer, is a primary constituent of cell walls of green algae and plants, and is typically a major constituent of the organic fraction of sediments. The refractory material includes stable organic molecules that are resistant to all except strong oxidizing reactions. These latter include sporopollenin (i.e. pollen and spores), elemental carbon (i.e. charcoal), lignins and chitin. The mineral constituent of typical lake sediments includes

JACKSON, S. T. 1999. Techniques for analysing unconsolidated lake sediments. *In*: JONES, T. P. & ROWE, N. P. (eds) *Fossil Plants and Spores: modern techniques.* Geological Society, London, 274–278.

silicates (diatoms, chrysophyte cysts, sponge spicules, clastic particles) and carbonates ($CaCO_3$, $CaMg(CO_3)_2$). Lake sediments also contain other minerals (e.g. pyrites, magnetites, sulphates) and organic compounds (e.g. lipids, carotenoids), but these are usually of little consequence to pollen-sample preparation. Both the organic and mineral constituents of lake sediments occur in a wide range of size fractions.

Extraction of pollen, spores and microscopic charcoal from lake sediments consists of a series of sievings, dispersions and chemical digestions aimed at eliminating as much extraneous material as possible without losing or damaging pollen grains. Because pollen, spores and charcoal are among the refractory organic constituents, strong reactions can be used to digest other materials. Pollen counting is still done 'manually' at the microscope, so efficiency and accuracy of analyses are increased by minimizing the junk-to-pollen ratio in residues. Techniques of pollen-sample preparation have been standardized for decades, and have been applied successfully throughout the world. For typical organic-rich lake sediments, the standard recipe includes the following steps:

(1) disaggregation;
(2) alkali-soluble digestion;
(3) sieving;
(4) carbonate digestion;
(5) silicate digestion;
(6) cellulose removal (acetolysis);
(7) residue suspension.

These steps and solutions to specific problems are described more fully in standard references (Gray 1965; Berglund & Ralska-Jasiewiczowa 1986; Traverse 1988; Fægri & Iversen 1989; Moore *et al.* 1991). Detailed protocols can be obtained from the author or from other active Quaternary palaeoecology labs.

Sediment samples of *c.* 1 cm^3 are usually sufficient for pollen analysis of organic-rich lake sediments. Reactions are best carried out in teflon or polypropylene centrifuge tubes (15–50 ml) and beakers. Initial mixing of samples and reagents can be done, with care, using a vortex mixer. During treatments, samples should be agitated regularly using stainless-steel spatulas, teflon rods, or disposable wooden applicators. Each sample treatment is followed by centrifugation (3–5 min at 3000 rpm is usually sufficient; longer centrifugation times may be required for denser reagents such as hydrofluoric acid (HF)) and careful decanting. All steps involving strong reagents or solvents should be carried out in a fume hood, and eye protection and acid-resistant aprons and gloves should be worn. Disposal of waste chemicals (storage, dilution or neutralization) should be done in accordance with institutional and governmental guidelines.

(1) The sediment sample should be first disaggregated and dispersed to maximize reactive surface area. For clay-rich sediments, this first step consists of a 10 min treatment with 5% $Na_2P_2O_7$ (sodium pyrophosphate) in a hot-water bath. For organic-rich sediments (e.g. algal gyttja, peat), this step can be omitted. Disaggregation of such sediments can be combined with the second step, alkali-soluble digestion, which consists of a 10 min treatment with 10% potassium hydroxide (KOH) (some use 10% sodium hydroxide (NaOH)) in a hot-water bath.

(2) The sieving step removes large clasts and organic debris, which ensures that reactants in subsequent treatments are used more effectively in digesting extraneous materials. Sediment samples are suspended in distilled water, and washed through 180 µm mesh stainless-steel wire-cloth into a beaker. Material retained in the screen can be discarded after thorough washing, or can be retained for macrofossil analysis and/or radiocarbon dating. Beaker contents are returned to centrifuge tubes for concentration and further treatment.

(3) Carbonate digestion consists of a 10 min room-temperature treatment with 10% hydrochloric acid (HCl). If high carbonate concentration is suspected (indicated by marl flecks, presence of molluscs or ostracods), the acid should be added very slowly and monitored for effervescence to prevent sample loss. This step should be carried out even if sediments have little or no carbonate. $CaCO_3$ reacts with HF in the next step to form CaF_2 (an insoluble precipitate). Any and all carbonates should be removed before HF treatment.

(4) Silicates are digested by concentrated HF. The length and nature of the treatment varies depending on the nature of the sediments. For peat, algal gyttja, and other organic-rich sediment, a 10 min treatment in a hot-water bath is usually sufficient to digest biogenic silicates (diatoms, spicules, chrysophyte cysts, etc.) as well as the few clastic particles. Samples with substantial clay, silt or fine sand will require additional and often repeated treatment. Samples can be left in HF at room temperature for 12–24 h or more, although settling will inhibit reactant circulation. Periodic stirring of samples, or automated agitation (e.g. shaker table), will greatly increase the effectiveness of digestion. Digestion can be monitored by rubbing some of the residue against the centrifuge-tube wall

with a spatula or rod; if silts and/or sands are still present, a distinct gritty texture can be felt. HF treatment should be continued or repeated until silts and sands are completely digested. HF treatment should be followed by a distilled-water rinse. Some authorities (e.g. Fægri & Iversen 1989; Moore et al. 1991) recommend that a treatment with 10% HCl follow HF treatment to remove colloidal silicates and silicofluorides. We omit this step in this laboratory, with satisfactory results.

(5) Cellulose removal is the most complex step. The primary reactant, acetic anhydride [$(CH_3CO)_2O$], reacts violently with water, so samples must be dehydrated before treatment. This is accomplished by treatment with glacial acetic acid, which should always precede cellulose digestion. After glacial acetic acid treatment and centrifugation/decantation, the sample is treated with a 9:1 (approximate) mixture of acetic anhydride and concentrated sulphuric acid (H_2SO_4). The H_2SO_4 acts as a catalyst for an acetylation reaction, in which the cellulose is esterified to form cellulose triacetate, which is soluble in acetic acid (the other reaction product). This acetylation is usually referred to as acetolysis, and the acetic anhydride–sulphuric acid mixture as acetolysis mixture.

The acetolysis mixture should be prepared during or immediately before the acetolysis process. In some laboratories, a batch of acetolysis mixture is prepared and added to the individual samples. In this laboratory, the mixture is prepared in the individual sample tubes (e.g. 5 ml acetic anhydride are added to each tube, followed by 0.5 ml H_2SO_4, followed by mixing). This can be done quickly using Nalgene fixed-volume dispensers or pipette-flasks. In either case, the H_2SO_4 should be added slowly and carefully; it will generate heat as it mixes with the acetic anhydride. Once the acetolysis mixture has been mixed with samples, the samples are heated in a boiling-water bath for 1–5 min (a 2 min treatment is a safe standard for most lake sediments). Glacial acetic acid should be added to each sample tube after removal from the water bath to cool the sample and slow the reaction. Following centrifugation and decantation, samples should be treated again with glacial acetic acid to remove remaining cellulose triacetate and acetic anhydride.

(6) If samples are clay-rich, an additional treatment with warm 5% sodium pyrophosphate followed by 2–3 water rinses will be useful at this point to help disaggregate residues before suspension. Water-mount slides of the residues should

be scanned to determine whether clay removal and dispersion has been effective. If pollen concentrations are low relative to clay, the sample can be dispersed again in sodium pyrophosphate and sieved using 7 or 8 μm mesh nylon screen (Cwynar et al. 1979).

The sample is dehydrated after all acids, bases and detergents have been rinsed from it. Dehydration consists of an initial treatment with 70% ethanol, followed by two treatments with tertiary-butanol [$(CH_3)_3COH$] (aka 2-methyl-2-propanol). Following the second tertiary-butanol treatment, the sample is transferred to a 1-dram vial. We use small amounts of butanol to wash the sample from the centrifuge tube into the vial. In some instances, the volume of butanol required to wash the sample completely from the centrifuge tube exceeds that of the vial. In such cases, the vial can be centrifuged and decanted or pipetted to make more room. Once the entire sample has been transferred to the vial, silicone oil (dimethylpolysiloxane) is added to the vial. The silicone oil should be approximately twice the volume of the uncompacted sample residue. The sample is stirred or vortexed to completely dissolve the silicone oil in the tertiary-butanol. The vial is then left uncapped in a warm environment (preferably a fume hood) to evaporate the butanol. Samples can be stored indefinitely in silicone oil, which also serves as the mounting medium for slide preparation.

Staining is largely a matter of preference. Acetolysis usually darkens the grains somewhat, but many workers prefer to heighten the contrast between pollen and other materials by staining with basic fuchsin (1% in 95% ethanol) or safranin O (1% aqueous solution). The staining step can be undertaken immediately before dehydration. One or two drops of stain added to each sample suspended in distilled water is usually sufficient. Overstaining, which often occurs in samples where pollen concentrations are high relative to lignins and undigested cellulose, obscures exine structure and can make identification difficult. Wet-mount monitor slides should be examined for selected samples before moving on to dehydration. Samples can be de-stained by treatment with acidified ethanol (1:19 concentrated HCl: 95% ethanol).

Estimation of pollen concentrations

If estimation of pollen concentrations in sediments is required (e.g. for pollen accumulation-rate estimation), sediment samples should be measured volumetrically before dispersion and pollen extraction. We use a spatula to pack sediment into a porcelain weighing spoon of predetermined volume. With due care to prevent air pockets, this technique works well for compressed, plastic sediments (gyttjas, clays, silts). Alternative techniques are discussed by Maher (1981), Fægri & Iversen (1989), and Moore *et al.* (1991). The samples are 'spiked' with a known quantity of marker particles (plastic microspheres, exotic pollen grains or spores), which are added to the centrifuge tube along with the sample before initial dispersion. *Lycopodium* tablets of known concentration (see Appendix) are convenient and widely used. The grains are acetolysed before tablet preparation, so they can usually be differentiated from *Lycopodium* spores in sediments (the two acetolysis treatments render the 'spiked' spores darker and more degraded in appearance). Pollen concentrations in sediments can be calculated from the ratio of sediment-grains to marker-grains (Berglund & Ralska-Jasiewiczowa 1986). Routine spiking of samples with marker-grains is useful to determine whether absence of pollen grains in slides results from loss during sample preparation (no markers, no pollen) or absence of pollen in sediments (markers but no pollen). Sample contamination by domestic pollen can be monitored by periodically inserting 'blank' samples (i.e. marker grains only) into batches of sediment samples during preparation.

Pollen identification and counting

Pollen residue can be mounted on microscope slides in the silicone-oil suspension, which has excellent optical properties and does not appear to alter the size or morphology of pollen grains. Silicone oil comes in a wide variety of viscosities. We use 12 500 cs silicone oil. The high viscosity permits semi-permanent slides to be prepared without a sealant, which allows the cover-slip to be agitated or moved so that grains can be reorientated for examination. Many labs use silicone oil of lower viscosity (1000–2000 cs), but this usually requires that cover-slips be sealed (e.g. with nail varnish), making reorientation difficult.

Pollen identification and counting can be done on any transmitted light microscope that has magnification of *c.* 400 × and 1000 × and is capable of Koehler illumination. Of course, better optics (especially high numerical apertures on objectives and condensers) yield better resolution. Phase-contrast and interference microscopy are rarely used in routine work. Pollen counts are done while scanning evenly spaced transects of the slide-mount. Pre-printed tally sheets or mechanical tally-counters aid tabulation of grains and other particles. We enter pollen data directly into a tabulation program (available from the author) on notebook computers at the microscope. Guides and keys are available to assist in pollen identification for many parts of the world, but a vouchered modern reference collection is indispensible.

Extraction and analysis of plant macrofossils

Extraction of plant macrofossils from lake sediments is simple, consisting of dispersion of a known volume of sediment (typically 50–500 cm^3) followed by sieving. Dispersion can usually be done with water; clay-rich samples may be dispersed using 5% sodium pyrophosphate and strong agitation. A nest of sieves is recommended to differentiate the macrofossils into two or more size fractions to facilitate scanning and identification. Mesh sizes of 710 and 350 μm have worked well for a variety of lake and wetland sediments studied in this laboratory during the past decade. We also retain a 180 μm sieve fraction, although identifiable macrofossils are rare. Sieving is best accomplished in a sink; a gentle jet of water from a rubber hose attached to the tap is useful for dispersing clods of sediment and for concentrating residues in one portion of the sieve before removal. All particles in the sieve should be washed gently using the hose to detach and disperse matrix. Sieve residues can be removed mechanically using a spatula, or by tilting the sieve over a small pan and back-washing the screen with a hose or squirt-bottle. Sieve fractions are stored separately in vials or jars. Storage media vary widely among investigators. We use distilled water in a refrigerator or cold room for short-term storage (6–24 months), and 70% ethanol for long-term storage or archiving. Samples stored in ethanol must be sealed tightly to prevent evaporative dilution. In humid regions with high spore counts, chemical preservatives may be necessary even for short-term storage. Weak solutions (*c.* 1–5%) of either formalin or phenol, in either glycerol or water, have been used as preservatives.

Macrofossil samples are scanned under 5–20 × magnification using a stereo-microscope. A boom-stand permits the sieve residues to be spread out in a shallow pan, which can be slid under the microscope for scanning. We use pans with painted 1 cm wide lanes, and slide the pan lane-by-lane along transects within the field of view, picking and/or tallying macrofossils as they pass by. Other workers place sieve residues on one side of a pan, move small portions of the residue into the field of view for picking and tallying, and push scanned residue into the opposite side of the pan. Manipulation of residues and removal of macrofossils can be done using a camels-hair brush with most of the bristles removed, or with very fine forceps.

Some readily identifiable macrofossil morpho-types often occur in large quantities (e.g. Charophyte oospores, *Picea* sterigmata), and hence may be tallied during scanning and left with bulk residues. Macrofossils that require more detailed examination or archiving, or that can be used in other studies (dating, stable-isotope, molecular), are removed and stored in vials. Reliable macro-fossil identification is best accomplished using a vouchered modern-reference collection. Regional floras, systematic monographs and seed atlases are helpful in identification, but there is no substitute for direct examination of comparative material.

Charcoal analysis

Charcoal occurs in a wide range of size fractions, each of which provide information about fires at different spatial scales (Clark 1988a; Clark & Royall 1995). The size fractions are extracted and analysed in different ways. Microscopic charcoal (particle size of <60 μm) is retained in pollen residues and can be analysed during pollen counts. Macroscopic charcoal (>60 μm) can be obtained by sieving, similar to macrofossil analysis. Large charcoal particles can be separated during macro-fossil scans. Small subsamples (1–10 cm^3) of sedi-ment can be fine screened (e.g. 50, 150, 250 μm mesh) and scanned to estimate macroscopic charcoal (e.g. Whitlock & Millspaugh 1996).

Charcoal fragments must be distinguished from other particles, particularly lignified debris, incom-pletely combusted material, pyrite microspheres, and industrial ash. Microscopic charcoal can be quantified in a variety of ways, including tallying of fragments in various size-classes, measurement of one or two longest dimensions, and area estimation using a grid reticule or video-based image-analysis software (Tolonen 1986; Patterson *et al.* 1987). Sieved charcoal can be tallied in size-classes (Millspaugh & Whitlock 1995) or dried and weighed (Kearsley & Jackson 1997). Clark (1988b) has developed a petrographic thin-section tech-nique for macroscopic-charcoal analysis of lamin-ated and other lake sediments.

Data presentation, display and archiving

Stratigraphic diagrams of pollen, macrofossil and charcoal abundances are the standard method for primary display of data from single sites, and conventions are well established (Berglund & Ralska-Jasiewiczowa 1986; Fægri & Iversen 1989). E.C. Grimm has developed DOS-based programs, TILIA and TILIAGRAPH, that are specifically designed for management, manipulation and diagramatic presentation of pollen and other stratigraphic data from lake and other sediments. These programs have a number of options that allow plotting of many kinds of data from different contexts. Data stored in TILIA format can be transferred directly to international databases for Quaternary paleoclimate data (e.g. European Pollen Database (EPD), North American Pollen Database (NAPD), North American Plant Macrofossil Database (NAPMD), Latin American Pollen Database (LAPD), etc.).

52. Collection and analysis techniques for palaeoecological studies in coastal-deltaic settings

ROBERT A. GASTALDO

Many assumptions have been applied to the interpretation of Phanerophytic plant communities with relatively little actuopalaeontological data and data analysis to support or refute them. Plant histology has not changed fundamentally since terrestrialization, and the decay or preservation of plant tissues has always been dependent upon the geochemical conditions prevailing in the sedimentary regime at the time of burial. For at least a century and a half it had been assumed by many workers that all plants, regardless of their bauplan or histological composition, had an essentially equal chance of becoming part of the plant-fossil record if conditions suitable for preservation were present. We now realize, based upon empirical data collected in modern depositional systems, that this is not true (e.g. Gastaldo 1988, 1992; Spicer 1989*b*). It is becoming clear that not every plant-

life form in each vegetational tier of a habitat has the same probability of preservation (Burnham 1994), and that the taphonomic filters operating on those plant parts that are transferred from the biosphere to the lithosphere are facies-dependent (see Gastaldo 1989). Hence, it is becoming increasingly important to develop a contextual framework in Holocene depositional regimes that can be used for paleoecological purposes.

Transitional settings of the coastal-deltaic regime are most commonly encountered in the stratigraphic record of the Phanerozoic. This is because they are geographically marginal marine and not only form during the culminations of highstand (maximum flooding and progradation of the coastline seaward) and lowstand systems tracts (maximum sea-level fall with shoreline pushed onto the shelf), but also during transgression when

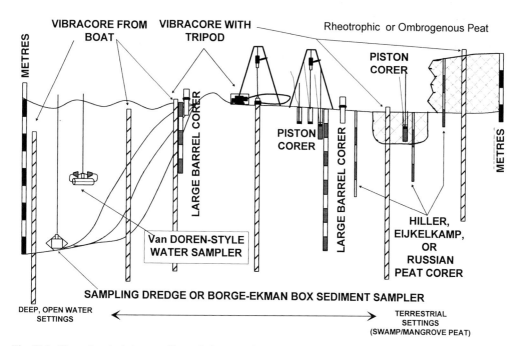

Fig. 52.1. Illustration depicting sampling techniques used to obtain actuopalaeontological data in modern coastal-deltaic regimes.

GASTALDO, R. A. 1999. Collection and analysis techniques for palaeoecological studies in coastal-deltaic settings. *In*: JONES, T. P. & ROWE, N. P. (eds) *Fossil Plants and Spores: modern techniques*. Geological Society, London, 279–284.

deposition occurs within incised valleys (formed within shelf or continental deposits during low-stand). Collection of macrobotanical and micro-botanical samples in Holocene coastal-deltaic regimes involves sediment recovery in both aqueous and terrestrial sites utilizing a variety of sampling devices. There are both advantages and disadvantages to each method outlined in this chapter.

Rivers, bayous, bays and marginal marine settings

Techniques for sample collection in shallow water differ from those in deeper water (Fig. 52.1) and are dependent upon the hydrodynamics (river flow velocities and tidal regime) of the sampling site. Water-column samples for palynofacies (see Batten, Chapter 4) and palynological (see Traverse, Chapter 50) analyses are easily retrieved using a Van Dorn-style water sampler. This device is composed of a one-litre transparent acrylic cylinder with rubber end plugs that are held within the cylinder by rubber tubing. Metal braided wires on the exterior of each end plug are attached to a trigger mechanism on top of the cylinder. When the cylinder is lowered to the desired sampling depth using a calibrated line, a brass weight (traveller or messenger) is sent to the release mechanism. The braided wires are disengaged, the rubber end plugs are released, and the cylinder is sealed. After recovery, the water sample can be removed through an outlet mounted on the side. Recovery of macro-botanical specimens in open water is more difficult because of specimen dilution within the water column. Although seining has been attempted (e.g. Scheihing & Pfefferkorn 1984; personal observ-ation), the results are unproductive, and in shallow water may reflect what has been re-entrained from the sediment–water interface. Inasmuch as plant part preservation is dependent upon the water chemistry, chemical characterization of the water column (and sediments) should include pH, Eh, dissolved O_2, CO_2 alkalinity, sulphide, nitrates, salinity and iron. Although sediment traps anchored at different depths have been useful for the collection of pollen, the dilution of macrobotanical remains within the water column generally precludes this approach.

Sample recovery from the sediment–water interface can be accomplished by one of several commercially available, bottom-sampling devices. Sampling dredges are designed for use on soft sediments (sand or silt) and are composed of two open boxes hinged at the centre. The device is lowered to the sediment–water interface while a simple trigger holds the sampler open. A scissor design closes the sampler, obtaining a sample that is then raised to the surface. With no spring-lever cocking mechanism to malfunction, the Birge-Ekman-style box sampler overcomes some of the problems encountered with simple sampling dredges in river systems. This device is designed with two spring-loaded jaws that are held open during descent by braided wires attached to a triggering device (similar to the Van Dorn-style sampler). Once the sampler is resting on the sediment–water interface, a messenger is dropped down the line to strike a release bar that causes the external coil spring to snap shut, trapping the sediment within. Overlapping cover plates loosely hinged at the top of the device permit overflow of water during descent and close on the ascent to prevent wash-out of sediment samples.

In shallow waters (<1.5 m), sediment–water interface samples can be recovered using a box-corer, whereas shallow subsurface samples can be recovered using a large-diameter (6″ – 15.5 cm) coring device (Burnham 1988). This device allows for a single sample to be taken rather than suc-cessive samples from within a small area. The advantage over narrow diameter PVC pipe corers (Scheihing & Pfefferkorn 1984) is that the large barrel diameter reduces sediment compression and distortion, but only allows for recovery to a depth of up to 0.45 m. Deeper subsurface samples must be recovered either using one of the various hand-coring devices (see below), a piston corer or a vibracorer.

Piston corers have been used primarily in lakes (Spicer 1981), although their use may be applicable in quiet-water bays and swamps (Cohen & Spackman 1980). A continuous, relatively undis-turbed section of core can be recovered using this device. Limitations of this device, and modifi-cations thereof, include a 5 cm core diameter and individual core segments of about 1 m (e.g. Moore *et al.* 1991). A new core barrel must be used for each subsequent segment, and it must be re-inserted into the same hole (a difficult task when covered in water, although made easier with the use of plastic casing; see Wright 1980, 1991; Wright *et al.* 1984). Jackson (pers. comm. 1998) adheres to a strict rule of extruding core segments in the field between successive drives in order to assess what has been recovered and what to expect in the next drive. Although it has been estimated that piston cores can recover samples to depths of as much as 50 m, realistic recovery depths are limited to approxi-mately >10 m in subaerial peat and subjacent incipient soils. Longer, individual core segments can be recovered using the compressed air sampler modification of the Livingston sampler (Mackereth 1958), but this apparatus was made obsolete with the development of the vibracorer.

Vibratory coring devices were originally designed for use on the Inner Continental Shelf and were used for decades from research vessels before these designs were modified to make them more portable for sediment recovery within barrier islands (Hoyt & Demarest 1981) and other coastal settings (e.g. Thompson *et al.* 1991). A 2- or 4-cycle, 4–5 horsepower, air-cooled, gasoline engine that is designed for use as a concrete vibrator is used as the power source for the coring system.

This engine may be either a portable (enclosed within a steel frame for transport) or backpack model, and can be obtained from a number of manufacturers (see Appendix). The portable engine vibrator unit weighs 110 lb (50 kg) and is mounted on a swivel base; the backpack unit weighs approximately 30 lb (15 kg). A vibrator head with a flexible shaft (additional extension shafts are available) is attached to the engine, and the vibrator head is secured within a clamp (Fig. 52.2) that is

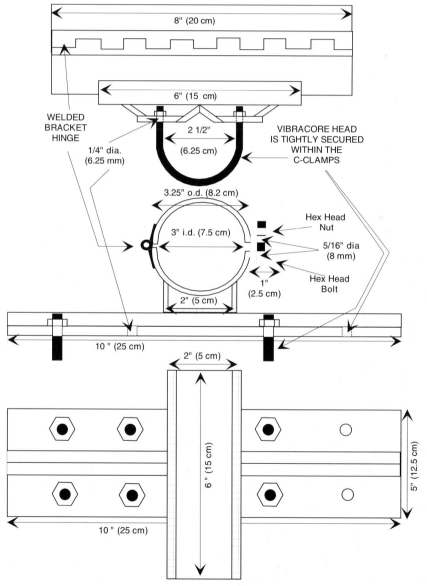

Fig. 52.2. Diagram for construction of clamping device used to secure the concrete-vibrator head to the aluminium coring tube used in vibracoring.

placed around a desired length of thin-walled
(0.05″ – 1.25 mm), 3″ (7.5 cm) diameter alumin-
ium-irrigation pipe. The coring procedure is easily
accomplished by two individuals, whereas the
length of the vibracore is limited only by the length
of aluminium irrigation pipe and the composition of
subsurface sediment.

Once the vibrator head is secured around the
aluminium pipe near the top (it is recommended
that the vibrator head be attached as high as
possible), the pipe is raised to an erect position, the
engine started, and the throttle increased to where
the engine is supplying approximately 10 000
vibrations per minute. The vibrations are passed
along to the pipe. A standing wave is established
allowing the pipe to slide into the ground because
the sediment adjacent to the wall of the pipe
becomes thixotropic. The pore water within the
sediment acts as a lubricant, allowing the core to
penetrate. Eventually, enough friction develops (or
more cohesive clay-bearing sediment is encountered) that stops further penetration. Normal
penetration is 5 to 8 m, although cores exceeding
11 m have been recovered. Once the coring is
completed, the clamp is moved to the sediment
interface, the excess pipe is cut free, and orientation
to north is marked on the side of the core barrel
(allowing for ease in determining the split
orientation when evaluating plant part deposition
relative to water flow direction). A metre-stick is
lowered into the core barrel to determine the
difference between ground level and the core top,
providing some estimate of compaction (usually
less than 0.5 m in 10 m depending upon sediment
composition). The core barrel is filled with water
and capped with an expandable plug (available
from any plumbing supply store), preventing the
loss of sediment during extraction. A 10–13 ft
(3–4 m) aluminium tripod is placed over the core
barrel, and a pulley device (1.5 or 2 ton capacity
come-along or winch) is attached around the core
barrel; the pipe is manually extracted. When fully
extracted, the core is laid down and the bottom
capped with a plastic end cap. North orientation is
marked along the entire length of the core barrel. It
is then cut into 1 m length sections using a hack-
saw, capped and transported to a processing area.
Here, the aluminium pipe is cut on opposite sides
using a carbide-tipped, hand-held circular saw
modified with a cutting guide (the depth of which
allows the blade to penetrate 2 mm below the pipe
wall). The core is split with monofilament line (a
sharp knife may be used to cut matted rhizomes and
saturated wood) and opened along the cut. One side
of the core is photographed (Fig. 52.3) and
archived, while the other side is described and
sampled. On-site Eh and pH measurements can be
taken using meter probes inserted into the split core

sediments (Gastaldo & Huc 1992), and additional
pore-water chemistry, as well as total organic
carbon (TOC), Rock Eval, and sediment analyses,
can be performed in the laboratory. Disadvantages
to this technique may include 'rodding' (occurs
when a compacted clay plug gets stuck in the core
barrel, preventing complete recovery at depth),
compaction (dependent upon the physical nature of
the cored sediments), and core loss upon extraction
(when sandy sediments are oversaturated; e.g.
quick sand).

The portable system has been used for sampling
in deep water from boats or barges as well as
terrestrial settings (Gastaldo & Huc 1992); the
backpack system has been equally successful
(Gastaldo et al. 1996) in all these settings. The
advantages of size, weight and transport (particu-

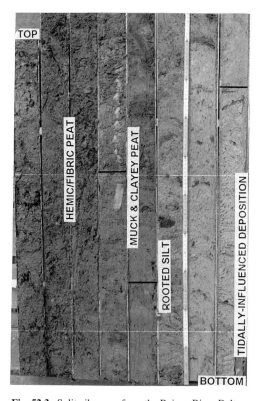

Fig. 52.3. Split vibracore from the Rajang River Delta,
Sarawak, East Malaysia, which has been recovered in an
ombrogenous peat swamp. Cores are cut to 1 m lengths;
core barrel is 7.5 cm in diameter (3″). Top of core is to
the upper left; bottom of core is to bottom right.
Approximately 3.5 m of undisturbed hemic/fibric peat,
>2 m of undisturbed inceptisol, and >2.5 m of sediments
deposited under tidal influence can be seen. A woody
root penetrates from the base of the well-developed peat
into the muck and peaty clay soil. See Gastaldo & Staub
(1999) for details.

larly over rough terrain) make the backpack system preferable. Hoyt & Demarest (1981) note several advantages of the vibracore system over most other coring systems used in similar settings (including terrestrial clastic and peat; see below and Fig. 52.3). Equipment cost is affordable (approximately $1500.00) and the relatively simple operation uses all hand-operated equipment that is easily transported. Cores can be taken virtually anywhere on land and in moderately deep waters (using modified boats or pontoon craft), and sediment cores are virtually undisturbed except for a 1–2 mm zone adjacent to the core pipe. The coring device has been used successfully in fine to moderately coarse sediments (including pebble conglomerates, personal observation). It must be noted that the system is not perfect. Core sites are limited to where access to water-saturated sediment is available, although vibracores have been extracted from floodplains in Coeud Alene, Idaho, by saturating the ground above the water table prior to coring. The depth of penetration is limited by subsurface sediment composition (plastic clays, consolidated sediments, and medium-to-coarse, well-sorted sands are very difficult to impossible to penetrate). Additionally, vibracores can get a compact plug (sediment, wood, or root) stuck in the end virtually at any depth, which prohibits collection of sediment when the coring tube is introduced through the sediment.

Terrestrial environments

Sampling protocols for collection of ecological data in various ecosystems are well established (e.g. Kent & Coker 1992) and have been used in actuopalaeontological investigations that address litter production, accumulation, and representation (e.g. Burnham 1994). These techniques include: sampling quadrats, and the concepts of minimal area, species-area curves, and vegetation pattern within quadrats; species abundance as measured either through subjective (estimate using a Domin or Braun-Blanquet scale) or objective (presence/absence, density counts, frequency and biomass) methods; and line-intercept, transect, gridded, or plotless sampling methods; leaf and pollen traps (see Moore et al. 1991).

Subsurface sampling has generally been restricted to what has been recoverable using hand-coring devices of limited capacity (although vibracores overcome this problem, providing a higher fidelity subsurface record). These samplers are the modified Hiller (Thomas 1964), Eijkelkamp and Russian peat (Jowsey 1966) samplers, costing the same or more than a vibracore (see Appendix). With the use of extension rods, these devices can provide subsurface samples to depths >10 m.

The Hiller sampler, and modifications thereof, is a chamber sampler fitted with an auger, requiring it to be twisted clockwise as it penetrates the sediment. By changing the motion to a counter-clockwise direction once the depth of sampling is reached, the inner rotating flanged chamber opens and scores a sample from the adjacent sediment. The disadvantages of this apparatus are noted by Moore et al. (1991) to include: contamination due to entrapment of roots and other subsurface plant detritus during descent; not only is the sample disturbed by the auger head, but material beneath the sample to a depth of 10–20 cm is disrupted; and the intact core cannot be removed in its entirety from the sampling chamber.

The Russian peat corer does not have an auger head to disturb the sediment during emplacement and, hence, must be pushed vertically into peat or saturated, soft sediment substrates. The sampler consists of a half-circular tube with a centrally hinged main blade. Upon emplacement, the handle is turned 180° cutting out a half-cylinder of adjacent sediment. The blade remains stationary during sampling and is the only part that is in contact with the sediment to be sampled during descent. Moore et al. (1991) note that the advantages of this device include: a simple design strategy that limits contamination during emplacement; minimal sediment disturbance; and the ability to view and collect a full core exposure. Peats can also be sampled by excavation and the removal of monoliths, which is especially useful in tundra and alpine settings (Jackson, pers. comm. 1998), using a 10 cm piston corer with serrations on the core barrel (see Wright et al. 1984).

Data retrieval

Holocene macrobotanical remains collected either at the soil–air or sediment–water interface, or from the subsurface should be stored in ethanol or a 1:1:1 mixture of glycol, ethanol and water to prevent degradation, and preferably refrigerated. A dispersant is usually needed to disaggregate the organic remains from the siliciclastic matrix, and the residuum can be gently wet-sieved using a 250 μm (2 Φ) screen to recover fruits and seeds. Clastics can be removed from fruits and seeds using a 30% hydrofluoric acid (HF) bath for 24 h, followed by 30 minutes in 30% hydrochloric acid (HCl).

Data analysis

Plant litter recovered from marginal marine, coastal plain, and deltaic settings can be analysed using established ecological procedures with the caveat that the investigator recognize whether or not the accumulation is autochthonous, parautochthonous, or allochthonous. There are limitations in translating many of these procedures to fossil assemblages because of limited outcrop exposures, sample size, preservational quality and the lack of a sedimentologic and taphonomic framework.

In autochthonous assemblages where plants are preserved erect (*in situ*), as forest-floor litters or peat (lignite/coal), it may be possible to determine the plant-life form, although presently accepted life-form categories (Du Rietz or Raunkiaer) may not be applicable because of the characteristics upon which some are based. Additionally, it may be possible to: ascertain physiognomy; calculate density, spacing pattern (e.g. DiMichele & Demaris 1987), and frequency in standing assemblages (Mosbrugger *et al.* 1994); determine basal area, girth and diameter in standing assemblages (e.g. Mosbrugger *et al.* 1994); estimate cover and biomass production; and map vegetation (application of Burnham (1994) to forest-floor litters). If exposure is extensive, gradient analysis (a variety of methods to simply represent a continuum), ordination (such as correspondence analysis or reciprocal averaging (these techniques can also be applied to parautochthonous assemblages), Spicer & Hill 1979), detrended correspondence analysis (DiMichele *et al.* 1991), and non-metric multidimensional scaling (MDS) can be applied (Phillips & DiMichele 1988).

In all assemblage types it is possible to determine diversity indices, although Kent & Coker (1992) note that confusion exists over the meaning of the term, the methods for measuring and assessing diversity, and interpretations of different diversity levels. Two types of species diversity are recognized generally along a gradient – α diversity is the number of species within a collection, whereas β diversity is the difference in species diversity between collections (and sometimes termed habitat diversity). The most commonly employed diversity indices that are based on both species richness and equitability (evenness of species abundance) are the Shannon–Wiener (e.g. DiMichele *et al.* 1991), McIntosh's, and Simpson Indices, whereas dominance-diversity curves are based upon the plot of the log-transformation of proportional species abundance in a sample against their rank from most to least abundant. The form of this line is then used to describe the evenness of species distribution and relative species dominance in the assemblage. In compression assemblages it has been common to either (1) count hundreds of leaves per site, each identified to species, with relative abundance calculated on the proportion of specimens per taxon, or (2) treat each block of rock as a separate quadrat and score any taxon as present in that quadrat (Pfefferkorn *et al.* 1975; Wing & DiMichele 1995). Comparisons of these two methods of estimating species abundance have shown that both methods estimate similar species richness and rank-order abundance (e.g. DiMichele *et al.* 1991). Not only should extreme care be taken when comparing data from autochthonous/parautochthonous assemblages with allochthonous assemblages due to the inherent bias towards sampling of riparian elements in these latter accumulations, but it has been demonstrated that forest-floor litters from forests inhabiting different climate zones should be treated with a climatic filter when estimating plant diversity in the past (Burnham 1993).

The application of parametric statistical analyses to these data require that there is an underlying assumption that the data are normal in distribution. Quite often, particularly in fossil assemblages, there is no way to test for normality. Hence, the application of non-parametric statistical tests (those that make no such assumptions about the distribution of the background population or sample) provide a suitable alternative (see Shi 1993 for a review).

When contemporaneous or coeval modern or fossil assemblages are being compared, many different measures exist to assess sample similarity (the degree to which species composition of samples matches is alike) or dissimilarity (the degree to which two samples differ). Some techniques are qualitative (e.g. presence/absence), while others are quantitative (e.g. abundance data). The Jaccard and Sorenson (Burnham 1993) coefficients are generally applied to presence/absence data (but see Archer & Maples 1987), whereas the Czekanowski coefficient (Pryor 1996) and coefficient of squared Euclidean distance may be applied to either type of data. There are many other coefficients that have been used (see Prentice 1980 for review). The resultant matrix of similarity or dissimilarity coefficients may be further analysed by cluster analysis (Kovach 1989) to determine underlying patterns within the data (Gastaldo *et al.* 1996).

53. Calcareous algae: analytical techniques

BEN J. WILLIAMSON, TIM P. JONES & KELLY A BÉRUBÉ

This chapter describes some of the commonly used techniques for the analysis of fossil calcareous algae in soft sediments (see Van den Hoek *et al.* (1995) and Riding (1991)). The techniques described will be illustrated using representatives of the *Halimedaceae* and *Characeae*, as these are the algae with which we are most familiar. However, these methods can also be applied to a wide range of biomineralizing organisms and in a variety of fields such as palaeobotany, phycology, taphonomy and carbonate biogeochemistry.

The analysis of calcareous algae provides palaeoenvironmental information not usually found in fossil plants. Fossil plant fragments made up of organic carbon are invariably altered, or lost, during diagenesis, and the chemical composition of the remains will therefore reflect the burial conditions rather than the environment in which the organism lived. The original calcium carbonate of calcareous algae, aragonite (for example, *Halimedaceae*) or calcite (for example, *Characeae*), may be preserved in sediments unaffected by diagenesis. Geochemical and isotopic studies therefore enable us to unlock the environmental information stored in unaltered biogenic carbonates, particularly relating to palaeotemperatures and water chemistry. *Coccolithophoridae*, for example, have been used in palaeoenvironmental studies of the deep ocean (Anderson & Steinmetz 1981), *Halimedaceae* have been used for shallow shelf marine settings (Aharon 1991), and *Characeae* in freshwater environments (T. P. Jones *et al.* 1996). Because the measurement of stable carbon and oxygen isotopes is of prime interest, this chapter provides a review of commonly used isotopic techniques. It also aims to illustrate the types of rigorous mineralogical and geochemical studies that must be carried out prior to isotopic analysis to ensure that the samples have not been affected by diagenetic alteration.

Sample collection

Soft sediment can be collected as either core or bulk (grab) samples; core samples should be carefully wrapped in plastic film (e.g. clingfilm) and kept in cold storage (see Jackson, Chapter 51). Bulk field sampling of soft sediment should be carried out using a bricklayer's trowel (or similar) with the sediment sealed in strong plastic or cloth bags. The term 'soft sediment' can be misleading, so when visiting new locations always take appropriate equipment; strong knives, garden spades and forks. A minimum of around 10 kg should be collected from each horizon of interest (see Hooker *et al.* 1995); a sensible rule of thumb is to collect too much rather than too little. Due attention should be paid during sampling not to unnecessarily damage the site and therefore degrade its future scientific value.

Soft sediment maceration

Maceration is the process of breaking down sedimentary rocks, and cleaning and separating out the material of interest. Wet sediment samples should be air-dried or dried in a low temperature warming cabinet (<50°C) or microwave oven. The use of a microwave oven is an efficient way of rapidly processing large numbers of samples. Samples are placed in a shallow microwave dish, covered with clingfilm (perforated with small holes), and microwaved for several minutes. The time required varies between types of sediment and microwave oven, but is easily found by experimentation. The dried sample can then be 'crumbled' or broken down by hand into small pieces and placed in boiling distilled water that can be agitated, stirred or sonicated. The material can then be processed through a series of sieves. If cleaning in boiling water is inadequate, then more vigorous chemical maceration, such as in hydrogen peroxide, should be undertaken. For some Recent calcareous algae, such as the *Halimedaceae*, the plates may be held together by organic matter which, if removed by oxidation, will result in sample disintegration. For calcareous fossils, not even dilute acids should be used. Once removed from the sediment, the sieved fraction should be washed carefully with distilled water and then dried. The residue can be viewed under a binocular dissecting microscope and algal remains picked out either with tweezers or a paint brush, depending on particle size and fragility.

Removal of organics and contaminants

Recent or sub-fossil algal material commonly contains organic matter that can be removed by immersing samples in 5% sodium hypochlorite for

WILLIAMSON, B. J., JONES, T. P. & BÉRUBÉ, K. A. 1999. Calcareous algae: analytical techniques. *In*: JONES, T. P. & ROWE, N. P. (eds) *Fossil Plants and Spores: modern techniques*. Geological Society, London, 285–289.

24 h. This treatment was found not to affect the stable isotope composition of oosporangia from Recent *Characeae*, compared with material cleaned using manual techniques (T. P. Jones *et al.* 1996). An alternative method used on cyanobacterial carbonates is low temperature (<80°C) oxygen plasma ashing of the material for 3 h in a Bio-Rad PT 7300 plasma barrel etcher (Andrews *et al.* 1993).

The preparation of Recent and sub-fossil *Halimedaceae* for scanning electron microscopy (SEM) often requires the removal of organic material so that the fine internal carbonate structure can be seen clearly. This may, however, result in the disintegration of more fragile specimens. To overcome this, the material should be mounted in cold-setting epoxy resin on an SEM stub prior to removing the organics. When set, the algal plate can then be broken open to reveal the interior. The entire stub is then immersed in 5% sodium hypochlorite for 24 h, gently rinsed in distilled water, air-dried and then carbon- or gold-coated for SEM study. The SEM images in Fig. 53.1a and 53.1b show how well the structural integrity of plates can be preserved using this technique.

Gyrogonites (fossil oosporangia from the *Characeae*) collected from soft sediments commonly have interiors filled with sediment (Hooker *et al.* 1995), which has to be removed prior to geochemical analysis. Although this can be achieved by careful multiple washings in hot distilled water combined with sonication, the effectiveness of the procedure can only be verified if the gyrogonite is broken open. This is achieved by gently applying pressure with the point of a needle. If the exposed core is not completely clean, the fragments must be further sonicated and rinsed in distilled water.

Resin embedding

Techniques such as cathodoluminescence and X-ray element mapping (see below) usually require the preparation of calcareous algae as polished resin blocks (see Jones, Chapter 16). A common problem is that many calcareous algal fossils have hollow cores causing incomplete embedding. This may be overcome by vacuum or pressure embedding, which are commonly used to impregnate porous plant fragments. If these methods are not available, an alternative method is to embed the specimens and then grind them down to expose the 'hollows'. Resin can then be smeared into the exposed surfaces, the excess resin ground away and the surface can be finished with a final polish. Cold-setting polyester resin is usually adequate for this preparation. Once embedded in the resin, the algae are unlikely to be plucked from the block

during grinding. The Recent and fossil *Characeae* in Fig. 53.1e and f were embedded using these techniques.

Scanning electron microscopy

A variety of mounting methods can be used for preparing calcareous algae for SEM. Large algal specimens need to be securely mounted in cold-setting epoxy resin (*c.* 8 h cure), for example, *Halimedaceae* plates as described earlier. Relatively small specimens such as Tertiary *Nitellopsis (Tectochara) latispira* sp. gyrogonites (Fig. 53.1d) can be mounted easily using 'sticky carbon tabs' although the use of epoxy resin is commonly preferred as the 'sticky carbon tabs' contain more volatiles which may contaminate the SEM column. Material made up of fine crystals (for example, *Halimedaceae*) may be difficult to observe because of 'charging' under the electron beam. This can usually be overcome by improving the conductance between the specimen and stub by double-coating the sample with carbon or gold. Excessive coating, however, may produce artefacts, such as extraneous surface textures, when viewed at high magnification.

Geochemical, isotopic and mineralogical analysis

A broad range of techniques are available for the study of biogenic carbonates; three of these are particularly suitable for the analysis of fossil algal remains as outlined below.

X-ray element mapping

X-ray element mapping is a widely available and relatively simple technique for studying the distribution of different elements in samples prepared in polished resin blocks or as polished sections. This type of analysis may be crucial for understanding complex patterns of biomineralization or when considering the suitability of material for isotopic analysis. For *Halimedaceae*, for example, sections through individual plates can be mapped for Mg. This could be used to indicate the presence of diagenetic Mg–calcite which may have replaced original biogenic aragonite (Alexandersson & Milliman 1981; Braga *et al.* 1996). Examples of X-ray element maps for fossil plants are shown in Chapter 30.

X-ray diffraction (XRD)

Arguably the most useful and widely available technique for identifying the types and proportions

Fig. 53.1. (**a**) Scanning electron micrograph (SEM) of a broken section through a Holocene *Halimedacean* plate. (**b**) High magnification field emission SEM photomicrograph of aragonite crystals in (a). (**c**) X-ray diffraction pattern for Holocene *Halimedaceae* compared with aragonite and calcite (intensity $\times 0.17$) standards. (**d**) Tertiary *Nitellopsis (Tectochara) latispira* sp. gyrogonite. (**e**) Cathodoluminescence micrograph of a Recent *Chara globularis* oosporangia. (**f**) Cathodoluminescence micrograph of a Tertiary *Grovesichara distorta* gyrogonite.

of different minerals in calcareous alga is XRD, see Chapter 30 (Kerkar 1994; Kerkar & Untawale 1995; Medakovic *et al.* 1995). An understanding of mineralogy is essential when undertaking diagenetic studies where biogenic minerals may have been replaced by those formed during diagenesis. From the XRD pattern for Holocene *Halimedaceae*

(Fig. 53.1c), it is clear that the sample is made up almost entirely of original biogenic aragonite. There is only a small peak for calcite, calculated at less than 1% of the sample (using techniques described in Chapter 30), which may be of sedimentary or diagenetic origin. The main advantage of XRD is that it requires only a small amount of powdered sample (c. 0.01 to 0.1 g) and therefore permits analysis of individual specimens such as c. 2 mm diameter gyrogonites. The powder may often also be reused for geochemical or isotopic analysis.

Cathodoluminescence (CL)

CL requires algal specimens to be prepared as polished resin blocks or polished sections (see Chapter 36). Resins can be problematic because they also show varying degrees of luminescence. This is not a problem for algae with solid carbonate walls which do not become infiltrated with the resin, such as oosporangia from Recent *Chara globularis* or the Tertiary *Grovesichara distorta* gyrogonites illustrated in Fig. 53.1e and f, respectively. The photomicrographs show original biogenic patterns which can be directly related to calcification processes of the oosporangia (Leitch 1991). These patterns occur as broken lines of brightly-luminescing calcite inside the cells of the fossil material (Fig. 53.1f), and as banding of brighter and darker luminescence inside the cells of the modern material (Fig. 53.1e). Their preservation provides compelling evidence that the fossil gyrogonite (Fig. 53.1f) has not undergone major diagenetic alteration.

Stable isotope analysis

Stable carbon and oxygen isotope analysis of carbonates using phosphoric acid digestion is a routine procedure in most isotope laboratories. The experimental methods used to obtain isotopic compositions of Recent *Chara globularis* and fossil gyrogonites are described in T. P. Jones *et al.* (1996). Details of the notation for stable carbon isotopes are given in Chapter 26. Oxygen isotopic compositions are commonly expressed as $\delta^{18}O$ values in per mil (%) notation such that:

$$\delta^{18}O\ (\%) = [[(^{18}O{:}^{16}O)_{sample} - (^{18}O{:}^{16}O)_{standard}]/(^{18}O{:}^{16}O)_{standard}] \times 10^3$$

where the usual standard material for carbonates is PDB, a late Cretaceous belemnite from the Pee Dee Formation, or SMOW (Standard Mean Ocean Water). An important application of oxygen isotopes in the study of carbonates is in calculating palaeotemperatures.

For calcite:

$$T(°C) = 16.0 - 4.14\Delta + 0.13\Delta^2$$
(Anderson & Arthur 1983),

where $\Delta = (\delta^{18}O_{calcite\ (PDB)} - \delta^{18}O_{water\ (SMOW)})$.

For aragonite:

$$T(°C) = 20.6 - 4.34\Delta \text{ (Grossman & Ku 1986)}$$

where $\Delta = (\delta^{18}O_{aragonite\ (PDB)} - \delta^{18}O_{SMOW})$.

The amount of carbonate required for analysis depends on the type of mass spectrometer used and preparation protocols. The laboratory manager should be consulted for the amount of material required. Large numbers of samples are commonly run on an automated system where powdered carbonate is loaded into metal 'buckets', which are sequentially dropped from a rotating daisywheel into phosphoric acid at 25°C. The resulting CO_2 gas is automatically processed through the mass spectrometer. Techniques exist for the accurate processing and measurement of very small carbonate samples, such as individual *Chara globularis* oosporangia, although laboratory managers should again be consulted for exact details.

Interpretation of isotopic compositions

Isotopic compositions can be interpreted both in terms of absolute values and as relative changes over a given interval. There is growing evidence that certain calcareous algae biomineralize carbonate in oxygen isotopic equilibrium with the environment in which they grow (Anderson & Arthur 1983; T. P. Jones *et al.* 1996). Whether this is also true for the carbon isotopes remains controversial. Detailed studies need to be undertaken on the carbon and oxygen isotope chemistry of living and Recent material to better understand their biomineralization. These studies will identify potential problems such as 'vital effects', i.e. biomineralization out of equilibrium with the water in which they live. The main problem with palaeotemperature calculations is that they require an estimate of the oxygen isotope composition of the water in which the algae lived. This can be estimated with more assurance for organisms which lived in the open ocean, but is problematic for algae found in lagoonal or restricted marine environments. In these settings, the oxygen isotopic composition of the water can be affected by input of ^{16}O-enriched terrestrial water or by evaporation which results in enrichment in ^{18}O (Faure 1986, Jones *et al.* 1996). Independent means of assessing palaeoseawater chemistry are therefore required. One of the most promising methods is the measurement of strontium isotope compositions, which can be compared with known open ocean Sr isotope values for the time; samples that experienced variable freshwater/seawater conditions will give different Sr isotope values (Vonhof & Wesselingh 1997).

Oxygen isotope variations within terrestrial hydrodynamic systems are extremely wide ranging, and this restricts the use of freshwater algae for

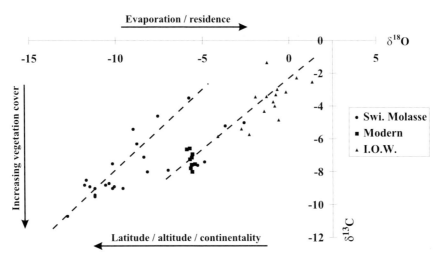

Fig. 53.2. Redrawn from T. P. Jones *et al.* (1996), original diagram based on Talbot (1990), Swiss data from Berger (1990). Modern algae from Malham Tarn (Yorkshire, UK), and fossil algae from the Isle of Wight (UK) and Switzerland. Principal environmental controls on the stable carbon and oxygen isotopic compositions of water bodies of different morphology and geographical setting. The distribution of the datasets is interpreted as representing the greater 'continentality' and increased vegetation cover of the Swiss depositional environment relative to that of the material from the Isle of Wight.

palaeoenvironmental interpretation (Stuiver 1970). Lacustrine carbonates, for example, may show strong vertical carbon isotopic stratifications (Oana & Deevey 1960). Long-term covariant trends between carbon and oxygen isotopes can be found within individual basins (Talbot 1990). Oxygen isotopes are mainly controlled by latitude, altitude, continentality and residence time, whereas carbon isotopes are mainly controlled by lake vegetation, residence time and primary production (Fig. 53.2, based on Talbot 1990). The angle of the slope of the trends relates to surface area:depth ratios of the water bodies, where a shallow slope indicates a low ratio and a steep slope a high ratio. This relationship is a function of a number of variables includ-

ing isotopic variations in the water column, the rates of isotopic exchange between the water surface and the atmosphere, and hydrodynamic inputs and outputs (Talbot 1990).

In this chapter we have described techniques to extract meaningful and diverse palaeontological information from fossil calcareous algae. It is becoming increasingly apparent that the quality of this information is dependent on the state of preservation of the material and the burial conditions to which it was subjected. The material must therefore be characterized using a variety of analytical techniques to fully understand its geological context, and only then can meaningful palaeoenvironmental interpretations be made.

54. Archaeobotany: collecting and analytical techniques for sub-fossils

ISABEL FIGUEIRAL & GEORGE WILLCOX

Archaeobotany or palaeoethnobotany are terms used to define the study of archaeological plant remains, which provide information on the relationship between human populations and plants (Van Zeist *et al.* 1991).

Such studies were carried out in the last century, but it was not until the 1960s that specialist laboratories which had acquired comparative reference collections were developed, and systematic sampling and analysis were established. The main organization for the diffusion of research in this discipline is the 'International Work Group for Palaeoethnobotany', which meets every 3 years. Each meeting has produced a publication. One of these publications *Progress in Old World Palaeoethnobotany* (Van Zeist *et al.* 1991) presents an overall view of the discipline. A specialist periodical, *Vegetation History and Archaeobotany* has also appeared.

Macrofossils which are identified include fruits and seeds (particularly cereals: glumes, rachis parts, awns, parts of testa), capsules, pods, roots, stems, stalks, rhizomes, leaves, fungi, coprolites and bryophytes among others. Macrofossils also include wood and charcoal, but these remains are usually considered separately. This is why this chapter will be divided into two distinct parts, the first under the title 'Palaeoethnobotany' and the second 'Wood remains'.

Micro-remains such as spores, pollen, diatoms and silica phytoliths may also survive in archaeological contexts. However, when micro-remains are found on aerobic sites they are considered problematic because of possible contamination by older fossil-bearing sediment brought on to the site, or through percolation from biologically active upper levels, including the surface.

Palaeoethnobotany

Preservation

Most archaeological deposits are aerobic, resulting in rapid decomposition of buried plant material. However, remains do survive as a result of mineralization (often associated with metals, calcium carbonate and salt), impressions (usually from chaff tempering in daub or pottery), desiccation (desert areas, for example, Tutankamun's tomb in Egypt, or at Nahal Hemar in Israel: see Kislev 1988), and charring (arrested combustion in hearths and other fires); the latter is the most common form of preservation. Intact or partly decomposed seeds do occasionally occur at aerobic sites. They should be regarded with extreme caution since in most cases they represent contamination. Anaerobic waterlogged deposits occur near major rivers, on the edges of lakes, peat bogs, wells and cess-pits. They have produced very extensive information about lake settlements (e.g. Jacomet *et al.* 1989), and urban sites such as London or the Viking levels at York. Bodies preserved in peat bogs have provided information on plants identified from stomach contents (Hillman 1986). Waterlogged archaeological plant remains are treated in the same way as peat or uncompacted deposits (Jacomet *et al.* 1989).

This section will focus on charred plant materials, because they occur frequently at most archaeological sites, although they do not survive well under conditions of active root growth, earthworm activity or when humidity fluctuations lead to the crystallization of common salt or gypsum, as in some arid areas. The advantage of charred remains is that they are resistant to biological decomposition and represent the remains of plants which have been collected or cultivated by humans for a range of purposes. The majority of charred seeds, fruits etc. represent food remains, but plants used for fodder, dyeing, rituals, medicines also occur. Charred remains are rare at hunter–gatherer sites, either because deposits are superficial or because compaction over long periods of time led to fragmentation. However, they are common at agricultural sites and for this reason research has concentrated on the origins, development and diffusion of domestic crop plants, crop processing techniques and agricultural adaptations in different geographical areas.

Sampling strategy

At an archaeological site, sampling of sediment can be total, random, interval or judgmental (M. K. Jones 1991). The first, presents practical problems due to the potential volume of sediment and the second and third are problematic because of the

FIGUEIRAL, I. & WILLCOX, G. 1999. Archaeobotany: collecting and analytical techniques for sub-fossils. *In*: JONES, T. P. & ROWE, N. P. (eds) *Fossil Plants and Spores: modern techniques.* Geological Society, London, 290–294.

heterogeneous nature of archaeological deposits. For this reason archaeobotanists tend to prefer sampling from sediments that are obviously rich (judgmental). This method is then best combined with some random or interval sampling as a control. The sampling unit is defined by the archaeological feature such as a pit, hearth, floor, destruction layer, or a depositional episode. Depending on the size of the structure, sampling may be partial or total. Sample size is ideally recorded in volume (litres) of sediment, although some researchers use weight instead of volume.

Sampling techniques

No system is 100% efficient, and loss and breakage occur at all stages of investigation (Pearsall 1989; Greig 1989). Flotation combined with wet-sieving has now become a standard method for recovery of charred remains. On waterlogged sites wet-sieving alone is the usual technique except in the case of some urban sites, such as London, where flotation has been used successfully (Willcox 1977). Domestic water softeners can be used, while sieving to break up heavy clay soils. Various flotation machines have been developed, the Siraf machine now being the most widely adopted (Williams 1973).

(i) Sediment is introduced into a tank of water which contains a wet sieve to recover the heavy fraction which recovers a wide range of materials – archaeological small finds, small vertebrate bones and teeth, shells and carbonized material which do not float.
(ii) Material that floats is carried over a weir into another sieve attached to the exterior to recover floating material.

The standard sieve size for flotation or wet-sieving of waterlogged sites is 300 μm. In the flotation tank an ideal mesh size is 1 mm; however, this requires a binocular microscope for sorting, and is therefore only practical with small samples. It is therefore advisable to use 2.5 mm mesh-size and to sub-sample with 1 mm as a control. The slurry which passes through the wet sieve can also be sorted as a control.

Sorting and identification

Charred remains recovered by flotation are dried slowly and then stored in rigid containers. Finds from waterlogged deposits should be stored in a liquid preserving medium, such as Topane (see Appendix).

Sorting and identification are carried out using a binocular microscope at × 10–75. Seed and fruit identification depends on a good comparative collection and the use of identification atlases (for a complete list see Nesbitt & Greig 1989). Morphological details preserved in carbonized grains and seeds are compared with the corresponding details on living plants. Changes in size, shape and proportions caused by heat must be taken into account and descriptive biometric analyses can be used as an aid to cereal and seed identifications. In many cases, particularly in the case of waterlogged sites, identifications at the species level are possible (as opposed to pollen, for example), (Fig. 54.1).

Biochemical signatures from fatty acids and DNA extracted from charred seeds have also been used (Hillman et al. 1993). This type of analysis is still in the experimental stage. Seeds and other items are stored in small plastic tubes available from medical suppliers.

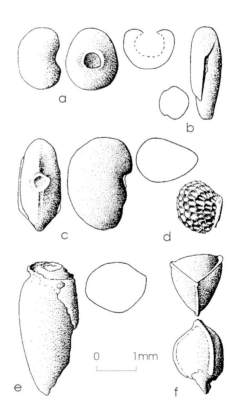

Fig. 54.1. Seeds from Djade, an early Neolithic site (9200 BP non cal.) in northern Syria. These drawings are of potential weed taxa. (**a**) (sample 37) *Galium* sp.; (**b**) (sample 69) Cruciferae, not identified; (**c**) (sample 69) small-seeded legumes, type *Astragalus*, *Trifolium*, *Melilotus* etc.; (**d**) (sample 37) *Glaucium* sp.; (**e**) (sample 69) *Centaurea* sp.; (**f**) (sample 69) *Polygonum* sp.

Quantification and numerical analysis

The first stage involves a numerical description of the material sampled which, can be carried out at various levels: region, site, period or sampling unit. Because isolated samples may not be representative of either the plant economy or the vegetation, single or solitary finds are of little value. A large number of samples is necessary to compare different units, phases, periods or sites. Presence/absence is the simplest description, which can be quantified by a percentage presence when enough units or samples are available. Abundance can also be based on absolute counts of items which can then be compared. Clearly in this case some taxa will be over-represented and others under-represented. One can also calculate the density of plant remains in the sediment by comparing the volume of flot (floating fraction of sample) to the volume of sediment. Once the material has been identified multivariate statistical analysis is frequently used (see G. Jones 1991).

Interpretation of palaeoethnobotanical data

Much interpretation depends on a knowledge of pre-industrial plant economies and their processing techniques(e.g. Jones et al. 1995) which may be supplemented by historical information from ancient texts. Practical experimentation as an interpretative tool has been used to study the effects of charring, decomposition and cultivation of primitive crops to help understand early farming. Where sites have been adequately sampled, reconstructions of gathering and agricultural activities have been described, often in surprising detail, to the point where crop processing and storage activities have been identified or seasonal activities shown to exist. Archaeobotanical research in Europe and southwest and central Asia (and to a lesser extent the Americas) has provided evidence for the adoption, diffusion, introduction and later the importation of both crops and plant materials (Zohary & Hopf 1993). Information on the evolution of 'weed floras', and the influence of agriculture on the vegetation has also come to light. These results can be seen at both a regional and a local level, the latter providing evidence for regional diversity. In other areas such as Africa and the Far East, palaeoethnobotanical data are still very scarce.

Wood remains

The preservation of wood remains at archaeological sites depends on a number of conditions: (**1**) the presence of oxygen-poor sediments (waterlogging prevents the survival of many organisms, such as

fungi, which degrade wood); (**2**) charring (charcoal is resistant to biological decomposition); (**3**) desiccation (organisms that destroy wood require the presence of moisture).

Traces of wood can also be found in more specific archaeological contexts: (**1**) in association with metal corrosion products or minerals; (**2**) as impressions in baked clay; (**3**) as stains in the soil (i.e. the wood has rotted away but a stain remains in the soil) (Shackley 1981*b*; Taylor 1981). This section will focus on waterlogged wood and charcoal, which are most frequently preserved wood remains in archaeological contexts.

Sampling methods, conservation and storage

Waterlogged wood

The techniques for excavating and recovering waterlogged wood have been recently described by the Somerset Levels Project (Coles 1975). Waterlogged wood should be excavated during the cooler hours of the day, and extracted very carefully to avoid fragmentation resulting from heating/cooling. After excavation, the wood must be kept wet and sent to specialized laboratories for conservation. Various techniques are currently in use which include: (1) freeze-drying, (2) alcohol-ether, (3) Lyofix (synthetic resin with a melanine and formaldehyde base) (see Appendix), (4) carbowax, and (5) polyester (polymerization by y-rays) (Schweingruber 1978). The best results appear to be achieved using the first three methods.

Charcoal

The recovery of charcoal fragments from archaeological sites is carried out by: (1) hand picking of larger fragments (<3 cm) directly from the sediment; (2) flotation of archaeological sediments in water; and (3) wet- and/or dry-sieving of sediment. Flotation and water-sieving methods are described above. Under field and/or laboratory conditions, wet fragments should be allowed to dry slowly (24–48 h), and away from direct light and drafts, to avoid cracking. Sampling should cover the largest area possible at each site in order to obtain a representative sample. As charcoal is inert, storing of archaeological charcoal is straight forward and material can be stored dry, in envelopes or plastic boxes.

Identification methods

Four main routine techniques are used to observe the three anatomical planes of wood and charcoal fragments.

Transmitted light microscopy
This is used for thin-sectioned charcoal embedded in paraffin (Liphshitz & Waisel 1973), resin (Couvert 1970) or a combination of resins (Longo Marziani & Iannone 1986). Light microscopy is also used to observe impressions on acetate paper (Plu 1979), and for thin-sections of wood embedded in paraffin and coloured with safranin (Schweingruber 1978). Preparation of thin-sections is a long process requiring embedding followed by sectioning with adjustments for varying materials (Schweingruber 1978).

Incident (reflected) light microscopy. (for a historical review of this method see Heinz 1990). Charcoal fragments are fractured manually and placed at the desired orientation in a shallow container of poppy seeds (*Papaver setigerum*) and observed directly, with a magnification range between $\times$ 50–800. The method is rapid and a great number of charcoal fragments can be identified in a relatively short time (see Chapter 18). Furthermore, the material is unaffected by resins, etc. and may therefore be used, subsequently, for $^{13}C:^{12}C$ analyses and ^{14}C dating purposes. Some authors consider that the image obtained with this method is sometimes blurred, which led to the use of applying ammonium chloride vapour to the specimen to enhance the contrast of the surface (Castelletti 1975).

Interference microscopy
A compound microscope is equipped with polarizing filters and a Wollaston–Nomarski prism (Thinon 1988). This method allows the study of very small fragments and fine anatomical details may be observed at magnifications higher than $1000 \times$.

Scanning electron microscopy
Critical identification criteria, such as cross-field pitting, vessel punctuation, may be verified with a scanning electron microscope (SEM). Suitable sample preparations are described by Collinson (Chapter 12) and Figueiral (Chapter 18).

Identification

The identification of genera and species is based on the descriptions in atlases of wood anatomy (for complete list see Schweingruber 1990), and/or on comparisons with thin sections from extant wood reference collections. Charcoal anatomy can also be compared with charred modern woods from reference collections. Identifications restricted to the level of family are not unusual. Computer identification programs have been developed recently, which may also help in the identification

of problematic genera and species (Espinoza de Pernia & Miller 1991). In addition to wood identification, other characteristics may be studied such as the observation of growth rings, the age of the trees, the collecting season and variations in climate and available humidity.

Analytical methods

Most waterlogged wood remains represent either construction material such as dwellings, tracks, or items of everyday life, such as agricultural or building tools, shields, sword and dagger handles, bows and basketry. These types of remains provide direct evidence of the exploitation of wood and the selection of species according to characteristics and properties. Twigs and branches may occasionally be found and represent either the vegetation growing nearby or fragments of timber transported from elsewhere.

Archaeological charcoal has been used as evidence for ancient forests and for identifying patterns of cultural development. The importance of charcoal analysis as a palaeoecological and palaeoethnological discipline has long been recognized. However, while the ethnological approach is not generally questioned, the relationship between charcoal analysis and the reconstruction of past vegetation has long been discussed (for complete references see Chabal 1997; Smart & Hoffmann 1988; Neumann 1992). The controversy about applying qualitative and quantitative approaches to interpreting charcoal data from sediments continues. Those adopting qualitative approaches believe that charcoal is not suitable for quantification, and consider that taxa frequencies should be given only as presence / absence data. This reduces biases induced by factors such as selection of species by humans, availability of species, charcoal preservation and field sampling.

Those favouring a quantitative interpretation of data attempt to eliminate at least some of the intrinsic biases by distinguishing dispersed assemblages from concentrated charcoal accumulations and by analysing large numbers of charcoal fragments from the former. According to these authors, concentrated charcoal from hearths etc. may indicate a short-term selection of preferred woods while dispersed charcoal represents a long-term sampling of the vegetation, and is therefore more likely to reflect the composition of the local vegetation. Taxonomic and relative frequency curves (Fig. 54.2) are plotted to determine the minimum number of fragments that should be identified (per archaeological layer) in order to obtain maxima for both qualitative and quantitative studies. Recent comparisons have shown that analyses based on both sample weight and number

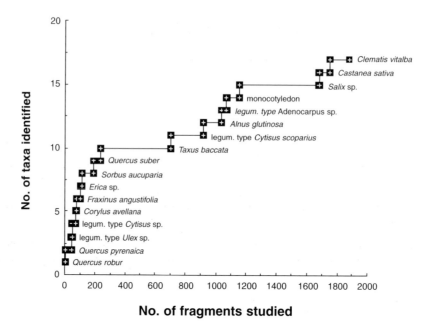

Fig. 54.2. Taxonomic curve plotted to investigate the minimum number of plant charcoal fragments that should be identified for each archaeological layer studied. In this figure (Site at Castelo de Matos, NW Portugal, Layer 03, Late Bronze age), identifications were carried out to determine the largest number of taxa possible in this Atlantic type of vegetation. A total of 17 taxa were identified after inspection of over 1800 specimens

as counted units per species produce similar results (Chabal 1997). Whenever long chronological sequences are available, diagrams can be drawn to illustrate changes in vegetation over time. Detailed comparisons with present-day ecosystems are useful when interpreting archaeological charcoal data and multivariate statistics may be applied in different samples at different levels.

55. Dendrochronology

MIKE G. L. BAILLIE

The ring patterns of ancient and modern timbers of the same species can be successfully cross-dated over quite large distances. Thus ancient, naturally-preserved, samples have played an important role in the construction of long, Holocene, tree-ring chronologies. The trees occur as stumps and trunks in a variety of depositional settings, including inland and coastal peats, lake margins and river gravels. Where numbers of such trees occur together they can be related in time, as remnants of original regenerating woodland systems. This allows the construction of long site-chronologies which in turn form the building blocks in the overall chronology-building process. Continuous year-by-year chronologies now exist for up to 9000 years. These chronologies provide information about the depositional environments from which the trees were recovered. They represent the master chronologies against which prehistoric timbers, both natural and archaeological, can be dated. They provide absolutely-dated samples for radiocarbon calibration and stable isotope research. The annual resolution ring patterns provide a parallel environmental history which both complements and refines human historical and archaeological records.

Chronology construction

Since the early twentieth century, and with increasing pace since the late 1960s, workers in various areas have been constructing 'local' tree-ring reference chronologies. 'Local' is an inexact term in dendrochronology but normally refers to some geographically restricted area within which the dendrochronologist perceives that it will be possible to cross-match the ring patterns of trees of the same species. Since cross-matching will operate over larger areas where there is a spatially coherent climate, e.g. in the semi-arid southwest of the United States, there is no fixed rule governing the area to which a 'local' chronology applies. The only ground rules for this fundamental tree-ring work are that the year-by-year chronologies must be precisely dated, and replicated to a degree which ensures that there are no missing or duplicate years in the chronology.

At a practical level, the dendrochronologist acquires large numbers of samples of the chosen species and proceeds to overlap the ring-patterns of successively older samples far back in time. Ideally the whole chronology is anchored to the present through the use of living trees. In extreme cases the total length of the available chronology coincides with the maximum age of the living specimens. The giant redwoods of California are a good example: the oldest specimens defining the chronology back to around 1200 BC (Hughes *et al.* 1996). Similar remarks could be made of the 3600 year *Fitzroya* chronology from living trees in Chile (Lara & Villalba 1993). In some areas chronologies many millennia long have been constructed using combinations of living trees and naturally preserved ancient samples, for example, the bristlecone pine chronologies of California (Ferguson 1969). In this high-altitude location, living trees yield millennia-long ring patterns while dead specimens existing in the vicinity, allow the extension of the year-by-year chronology back to beyond 6000 BC. Similarly in Tasmania, the decay-resistant huon pines found in river deposits have allowed the extension of living-tree chronologies back to around 2000 BC (Cook *et al.* 1991). The extreme ages of the individual trees characterizes all these examples.

In more temperate areas, particularly Europe, very long-lived trees do not exist and timbers must be collected in large numbers from a wide variety

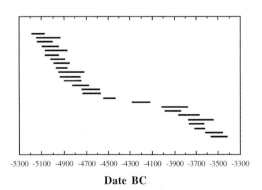

-5300 -5100 -4900 -4700 -4500 -4300 -4100 -3900 -3700 -3500 -3300

Date BC

Fig. 55.1. The time placement of 25 ancient oaks randomly sampled from the DerryMacFall fenland site, N. Ireland, showing a typical regeneration history.

BAILLIE, M. G. L. 1999. Dendrochronology. *In*: JONES, T. P. & ROWE, N. P. (eds) *Fossil Plants and Spores: modern techniques*. Geological Society, London, 295–300 of sources, some 'natural' and others anthropogenic. Typically, oak chronologies have been constructed by overlapping the ring patterns of living trees with those from buildings, from archaeological sites, and from natural sources such as bogs and river gravels (Baillie 1995). Irrespective of the timber sources involved, chronologies have normally been built within the smallest possible geographical region. This limits, as far as possible, the unknowns associated with cross-matching during the initial construction phase. Most chronologies have also been species specific. It is now known that for European oak (*Quercus robur* and *Quercus petraea*) the underlying cross-matching 'signal' can be traced over long distances for some periods. Some abrupt environmental events, for example the one following the dust-veil in AD 536, shows up widely in the Northern Hemisphere in different species (Baillie 1995).

Dendrochronology of naturally preserved timbers

Natural sources provide the ancient timbers used to construct the long chronologies. In each case, whether Tasmanian huon pine logs from river beds or German river-gravel oaks, the aim has been to acquire sufficient numbers of long-lived specimens to allow the construction of well-replicated, calendrically-precise, chronologies. Once such fundamental chronologies have been built, they are available to answer research questions. In the case of the huon pine the principal aim is direct temperature reconstruction. In the case of the 9000-year German oak chronology the initial aim was elucidation of the history of German river valley development, supplemented by the desire for precisely-dated samples for radiocarbon calibration purposes (see Chapter 56). Direct dating of prehistoric archaeological oak timbers represented an additional bonus (Becker 1993). These latter two objectives also underpinned the development of the 7000-year oak chronology in Ireland, the oaks in this case having been preserved in peat bogs (Baillie 1995). In Fennoscandia, although there is still a tree-ring gap in the first centuries BC, pines preserved in northern lakes have been exploited to provide a sensitive palaeo-temperature record comparable in length with the German and Irish oaks (Briffa 1994).

These three sources, rivers, lakes and bogs – have provided large numbers of tree trunks for dendrochronologists to study. In return, dendrochronologists can provide three broad classes of information. First, information deriving from the practicalities of the chronology construction. Second, information on historical processes within the river, lake and bog systems. Third, additional information derived from exploitation of the chronologies, such as radiocarbon calibration, environmental reconstruction and archaeological dating.

Chronology construction

Most dendrochronologists dealing with ancient timbers have been confronted with large numbers of tree trunks and stumps of unknown age. These trees come mostly with no stratigraphic information, and preservational factors such as colour or condition provide few clues to relative age. Thus sub-fossil chronology building usually relies heavily on the ability of dendrochronologists to cross-match ring patterns without prior information. Fortunately it turns out that many species exhibit sufficiently good cross-dating to allow chronology building even when using what are effectively random samples. In retrospect, groups which were 'randomly sampled' were not random in any real sense. First, in most areas, such as Europe or Tasmania (although not New Zealand), the sub-fossil trees are restricted to the Holocene. These trees were part of natural regenerating systems and most site collections of even 10 to 20 trees quickly yield overlaps between the ring patterns of some specimens, see Fig. 55.1. In fact, in Europe, it was found that site chronologies much longer than the age of any individual tree could be constructed rapidly. One classic example from the English site at Croston Moss, Lancashire, consisted of 100 oaks which gave two site chronologies spanning 3198 BC to 1682 BC and 1584 BC to 970 BC, respectively (Baillie 1995). Chronology building is therefore simplified to the construction of lengthy, robust, site chronologies and their subsequent overlapping. Particular difficulties were experienced where local depletions (for whatever reasons) left gaps. The Fennoscandian/Finnish pine gap in the first centuries BC was noted above. Similarly Becker & Schmidt (1982), working in Germany, found it impossible to find timbers whose ring patterns spanned the sixth century BC. They were forced to use Hollstein's archaeological chronology to bridge the gap (Hollstein 1980). In Ireland no sub-fossil timbers could be found to bridge the period 229 BC to 13 BC, although archaeological timbers narrowed the gap to 95–13 BC (Baillie 1995). In this case the gap was finally bridged with archaeological chronologies from English Roman sites. Clearly, using sections of chronology from different areas to bridge local gaps is a situation of last resort. Ideally, any local chronology should be constructed solely from local timbers of the same character, that is, it would be preferable to build separate chronologies for 'land grown' and for 'bog-grown' timbers, as these may retain different aspects of climate signal. In the initial, or 'pioneer', chronology-building exercises that is not always possible, and compromises have to be made. However, once the pioneer chronologies are completed, and as fresh samples are added to the archive, sub-chronologies of timbers from different origins can be constructed. Thus over time, within a local area, it is possible to envisage chronologies for bog-grown trees, for land-grown trees, those from archaeological and river gravel sites, and for lake-edge trees.

The critical factor in all chronology building is the ability to replicate the chronologies. Most site chronologies are internally replicated (primary replication). Over time, with the collection and analysis of additional timbers, both site chronologies and links between site chronologies are replicated by new chronologies (secondary replication). The ultimate check on the absolute nature of these chronologies is comparison with chronologies produced by independent workers (tertiary replication). In the case of European oak, the original German/Irish chronology reported by Pilcher *et al.* (1984) was replicated by an independent bog and river-gravel chronology produced by Leuschner & Delorme (1984) working at Göttingen. In America the bristlecone pine chronology published by Ferguson (1969) was replicated back to 3300 BC by the independent work of LaMarche & Harlan (1973).

Source information

Once a long chronology has been constructed it then becomes possible to review the exercise. Simple statistics, such as sample frequency, give an overall impression of periods of sample abundance versus periods of depletion, although this can be made complex due to sampling factors. By their nature, stumps preserved in lake margins grew when water levels were relatively low for long periods. They were preserved by the raised water levels, and their recovery was due to reduced levels in recent times. Figure 55.2 plots the frequency of Irish bog oaks through time, together with the dates of oak stumps from lakes. It is apparent that the relatively dry episodes indicated by the occurrence of the lake-edge oaks is reflected in the relative abundance of oaks growing on bog surfaces.

Trunks recovered from river gravels originally grew on mineral soils and were washed into rivers during erosion or flood events; such trees tend to be wider-ringed than the oaks which grew rooted on peat (Leuschner & Delorme 1984). Bog oak trunks grew mostly on the surfaces of raised bogs, and have survived through being blown over and buried

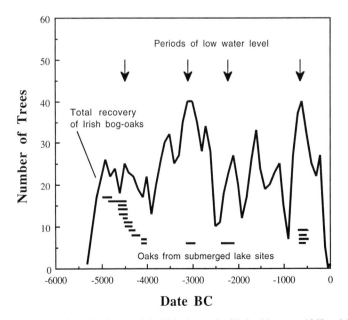

Fig. 55.2. Frequency through time of oaks sampled within the north of Ireland between 1968 and 1995, and subsequently dated. The time span of *in situ* oak stumps and oaks from submerged lake sites are also plotted to show the tendency for reduced lake levels to be coincident with increased frequency of bog oak survival.

in the peat. Stumps represent trees which died and stood until they rotted.

It is clear that a range of information can be obtained immediately from the dated trees, based upon their depositional setting and plant anatomy. Apart from identifying periods of lower lake levels and wash-out or flood events, in bog-oak frequencies we can identify periods of relatively dry bog surfaces, separated by wetter intervals. Clusters of death dates for bog trees provide some clues to storm events, when a lot of trees are blown down simultaneously. Equally, reaction wood hints at removal of competition or leaning due to storm damage. In some cases coastal tree remains give clues to the dating of isostatic and eustatic processes. All this information can be derived from dated assemblages.

Cross species deductions are possible where, for example, an abrupt growth reduction in bog pines in Ireland (Pilcher *et al.* 1995) in 2911 BC is followed by a period of enhanced growth. This coincides with the 'release' of one bog oak (a very narrow ringed tree suddenly shows a massive increase in growth just at this time), see Fig. 55.3. The release in the oak being due presumably to the removal of competing trees, possibly as the result of a storm or human activity. The date is made more interesting by the observation that it coincides with the end of a period of lake-edge building at Portalban on Lake Neuchâtel, Switzerland, which

had lasted from 2917–2912 BC (Orcel *et al.* 1992). It also appears to show up in the high altitude bristlecone pine chronology from Campito Mountain, California (LaMarche & Harlan 1973).

Applications of chronologies

The most significant outcome of long chronology construction has been the ability to calibrate the radiocarbon timescale for the last 9000 years (Pearson *et al.* 1993; Stuiver & Becker 1993). While the original calibration measurements were made on pre-existing American chronologies (Suess 1970), some long chronologies, such as those in Ireland and central Germany, were built specifically to provide precisely-dated wood samples for calibration (Becker 1993; Baillie 1995). Radiocarbon is a widely-used dating method and it is now possible to correct radiocarbon age ranges to 'real' age ranges for most of the Holocene. This calibration work continues as increasingly refined radiocarbon measurements are indicating regional variations in radiocarbon activity in same-age samples. Results such as these have important environmental implications regarding carbon sinks (McCormac *et al.* 1995).

Once regional tree-ring chronologies exist, irrespective of why they were built, they can be used to date samples from natural deposits or

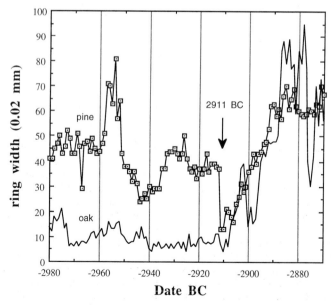

Fig. 55.3. An ancient pine chronology, based on numerous trees from Garry Bog, Co. Antrim, N. Ireland (Pilcher *et al.* 1995) showing the extreme growth reduction at 2911 BC, plotted with a single oak from Bally Murphy, Co. Down, which shows growth 'release' starting at the same time.

human constructions. Thus 'spot dates' can be assigned for any natural deposit which contains the remains of trees of the correct species. Dating archaeological remains defines precise dates within normally flexible archaeological timescales. In Europe this has led to a revolution in chronological refinement with previously enigmatic structures such as bog trackways and settlements now being among the best dated remains in the archaeological record. For example, the Sweet Track in Somerset, England, dates to 3807 BC (Hillam *et al.* 1990), and the Corlea Trackway in Longford, Ireland, dates to 148 BC (Raftery 1990). The most important archaeological applications of dendrochronology relate to the ability to compare calendar dates across large geographical distances. If all tree-ring chronologies are absolutely dated, through the application of the same standards of replication, then all dates derived from them are directly comparable worldwide.

Another important aspect of dendrochronology is the new-found potential to reconstruct at least a proxy picture of environmental change. This can be illustrated in two ways. First, in some areas such as Fennoscandia, it is possible to infer summer temperature variations at annual resolution from the pine trunks recovered from northern lakes (Briffa 1994). Such records of relative annual summer temperature are continuous over thousands of years, and the hope exists that within a few years the dating of these long prehistoric temperature-sensitive chronologies will be absolute. Second, for Irish and European oaks, extreme events have been isolated which appear from their dates to be related to similarly-aged acidic layers in the Greenland ice records (Baillie 1996). The extreme environmental conditions appear therefore to be due to major volcanic dust-veil events (Baillie & Munro 1988). Such an approach allows the specification of what can be thought of as 'marker dates', that is dates for large scale environmental downturns which may show up in widespread records (Baillie 1995). These events serve to break up prehistoric time into more manageable units, and to synchronize aspects of past environmental change directly with the records of human history. Once these dates are specified, additional information begins to broaden our understanding, giving clues to cause and effect. For example, one of the narrowest-ring events in the Irish oaks at 3195 BC takes on added significance, when it is found that two low-lying English regions provide chronologies which start at 3198 BC and 3207 BC, for Lancashire and East Anglia respectively. To this can be added the more recently observed sulphate anomaly in the thirty-second century BC, in both the GISP2 (Zielinski *et al.* 1994) and GRIP ice cores from Summit Greenland. It is concluded from this package of observations that sea-level change may well be a significant factor in the events at that time.

Overall, dendrochronology of ancient timbers is opening up a new level of understanding of past environmental change at annual resolution. Because of the absolute precision of well-replicated chronologies, evidence can be compared worldwide. It is hoped that in the not too distant future a comprehensive series of event-dates will be available, thus enabling a better understanding of the Holocene.

Practical considerations

Sampling and preparation

The fundamental building blocks within dendrochronology are the ring patterns of individual trees. An ideal tree-ring sample is a horizontal slice through the main trunk of a tree, taken at 'mean-breast height', that is about 1.5 m above the ground. Such slices, when prepared to render the growth rings clearly visible, allow individual rings to be inspected around their circumference, and the widths of all the individual growth rings to be measured. Ancient natural timbers, discarded building and archaeological timbers are sliced with power saws. As felling is not always appropriate with living trees, and slicing may not be appropriate with timbers in standing buildings, or with valuable artefacts, alternative means of extracting the ring patterns have been devised. Living trees and historic beams can be cored; hollow metal tubes with sharp or toothed rims are power-driven into the wood in a radial direction to obtain as complete a ring pattern as possible. With valuable objects X-ray techniques can be employed.

With a suitable sample obtained, the rings must be rendered visible for measurement. Much depends on the condition of the samples. The surface of dry samples can be sanded. Robust, modern or ancient timbers acquired wet can be dried or their transverse surfaces can be pared while wet. Friable samples are normally kept wet or frozen and pared in this condition. In almost all cases ring visibility is enhanced by the application of a contrasting medium such as chalk. Where felling or death dates are required, much importance attaches to the survival of the final growth ring beneath the bark. The survival of sapwood in an anthropogenically-important species such as oak, is critical for dating cultural activity (Baillie 1995).

With the rings rendered clearly visible, the width of each growth ring is measured, from as close to the centre of the tree to as close to the bark as possible, in order to maximize the useful pattern length. The resulting set of measurements, the ring pattern, represents a record of the response of the tree to its growing conditions. The measurements can be made with any suitable device from a magnifying glass with internal scale to, normally, a travelling stage with binocular microscope. Most tree-ring measuring devices comprise a moving stage linked to a computer. The sample, viewed through a binocular microscope with cross hairs, is aligned so that the vertical cross hair lies along the start of the first growth ring. The stage is moved until the hair aligns with the start of the next growth ring, and the horizontal distance moved is recorded. This is repeated for the whole pattern, with each tenth and hundredth ring being marked on the sample as a guide to later checking. The measurements, after checking, are plotted against a time axis as either raw or semi-log widths and are stored as a set of numbers, with a laboratory identifier unique to the sample. Visual and computer cross-dating is then employed to fit the ring pattern to the appropriate master chronology (Baillie 1982).

Visual and computer cross-dating

Empirical evidence from around the world demonstrates that recognizably-similar patterns of wide and narrow rings occur in trees of the same species, which grew over the same time interval in the same geographical region. Visual cross-dating of graphical representations of individual ring patterns, or master chronologies, involves pattern recognition skills on the part of the practised dendrochronologist. Computer programs aid this process by sliding numerical datasets past one another in one-year steps, calculating correlation coefficients at every relative placement of the data. High correlations occur where the data represents tree-ring series which grew simultaneously. Most correlation programs are enhanced versions of program CROS first published in 1973 (Baillie & Pilcher 1973), see, for example, Yamaguchi & Allen (1992). Computer packages such as COFECHA (Holmes 1983) allow statistical checking of large assemblages of long ring patterns by performing a correlation matrix on consecutive sub-sets, thus identifying any patterns which go out of phase with the majority.

It is widely recognized in dendrochronology that computer programs are an aid to, and a check on, the practised dendrochronologist. In itself, a high correlation does not guarantee a correct cross-match, and most dendrochronological dating involves several levels of replication in addition to simple correlation.

The research recorded here was at least partly supported by EU Grants EN5V-CT94-0500 and ENV4- CT95-0127.

56. ^{14}C dating sub-fossil plant remains

RUPERT A. HOUSLEY

The purpose of this section is to provide a guide to ^{14}C dating as used to determine the age of Holocene and Late Quaternary sub-fossil plant remains (in this context sub-fossil refers to the remains of plants that have undergone little or no chemical change subsequent to death). It is not a basic introduction to radiocarbon dating, although a brief outline is included. Readers who require more explanation of the scientific principles should consult Gillespie (1984), Mook & Waterbolk (1985), Aitken (1990) or Bowman (1990). Here, practical concerns such as extraction and selection of samples for submission to a ^{14}C laboratory are emphasized. For this reason considerable attention is given to issues such as how to decide on which samples to date; the choice of appropriate materials; the quantities typically required by the laboratories; the types of packing that can be used; and how best the samples should be kept and handled. Some explanation is given as to what the results may mean once dates have been received from the dating laboratory, in particular the question of conventions and calibration procedures.

Basic principles

The principles of radiocarbon dating can be concisely stated and readily understood, although in practice there are a number of complicating factors. Carbon-14 is one of three naturally occurring isotopes of carbon. It is the least common of the three and is unusual in being weakly radioactive, unlike its two stable sister isotopes, ^{13}C and ^{12}C. What makes it special is the fact that ^{14}C is continually being formed in the upper atmosphere. After formation, ^{14}C combines with oxygen to produce carbon dioxide which mixes throughout the atmosphere, dissolves in the oceans, and enters the biosphere via photosynthesis. Thus, theoretically, a dynamic equilibrium exists between the formation and decay of ^{14}C, with a constant concentration being maintained in all living organisms and throughout the atmosphere. Upon death, an organism stops exchanging carbon with the biosphere, ^{14}C is no longer replenished, and the level falls at a rate determined by the law of radioactive decay. Thus by determining experimentally the number of ^{14}C atoms remaining, and

the equilibrium number at the start, the time elapsed since death can be obtained.

The measurement of ^{14}C is achieved by one of two methods. Conventional, or radiometric, dating measures the decay activity of the sample; the number of electrons emitted per unit of time and weight of a sample. Accelerator mass spectrometry (AMS) directly counts a proportion of the number of ^{14}C atoms relative to ^{13}C or ^{12}C. It is a more recent technique and requires much smaller samples than radiometric counters, although the costs are often higher. The initial concentration of ^{14}C is determined by measurement of modern reference standards.

Method of reporting

Radiocarbon dates are expressed according to a set of conventions:

- ^{14}C ages are always in uncalibrated radiocarbon years BP, where 0 BP is defined as AD 1950;
- the Libby half-life of 5568 years is used, rather than the more accurate 5730 half-life;
- modern ^{14}C activity is defined in relation to a US NIST oxalic acid standard;
- a ± 1σ error term should be quoted (rounded to 10 years if > ± 50 years and to 5 years if less);
- δ^{13}C values are normalized to –25‰;
- each result has a reference number (lab identifier followed by a number).

These conventions are adhered to, in part, to prevent misunderstandings, but also to overcome certain complicating factors, some of which are outlined below.

Limitations

Limitations regarding quantity and choice of appropriate material for successful ^{14}C dating are detailed in a separate section. Otherwise, the main limitations are in relation to age limits, and the level of precision that can be achieved.

Maximum age limit

Although the maximum age limit is determined by different criteria depending on whether AMS or conventional radiometric counting is concerned, in practice the upper age limit is very similar

HOUSLEY, R. A. 1999. ^{14}C dating sub-fossil plant remains. *In*: JONES, T. P. & ROWE, N. P. (eds) *Fossil Plants and Spores: modern techniques.* Geological Society, London, 301–305.

regardless of the method used, i.e. around 40 000 years. However, there is some variation between laboratories. With radiometric counters the maximum limit is determined by the level of the background count rate; for AMS it has more to do with machine stability and modern contamination introduced by the pre-treatment of small samples. It is possible to measure greater ages, up to about 75 000 years, by means of isotopic enrichment, however this is not routinely done as it demands sample sizes an order of magnitude larger.

Some explanation is required as to the distinction between a finite age, a minimum age and an 'infinite' or 'as background' age. A **finite age** is one where the sample count-rate is more than twice the counting-error above the background level. It takes the usual form of a ^{14}C determination, i.e. is quoted as a mean $\pm 1\sigma$. A **minimum age** is one where the sample count-rate is less than twice the counting-error above background, but still positive. A result like >43 000 BP is a minimum age. Finally, if the sample count-rate is indistinguishable from background then it is termed '**infinite**' or '**as background**' and is reported as such.

Younger age limit

Radiocarbon ages on material less than about 200 calendrical years old are rarely of value for a number of reasons. This, in part, is due to the fact that atmospheric ^{14}C levels have been disturbed by human actions like the burning of fossil fuels and the testing of nuclear weapons. It is also, in part, due to the nature of the calibration curve (see below) over this time period. These factors do give rise to a form of determination where the ^{14}C activity is much higher than the modern activity defined by the international oxalic acid standard. Such measurements are normally reported as 'greater than modern' ages and are expressed as a percentage above the modern activity, e.g. 183.9 ± 0.7 (pMC $\pm 1\sigma$).

Limits of precision

Because radiocarbon dating is an experimental process, all measurements have an experimental error term ($\pm 1\sigma$), that needs estimation. In all but very old samples ^{14}C errors approximate to a Gaussian distribution, such that $\pm 1\sigma$ means there is a 68.3% chance that the true age lies within $\pm 1\sigma$ of the experimental result, a 95.4% chance that it lies within $\pm 2\sigma$, and 99.7% within $\pm 3\sigma$. Whilst more ^{14}C counts generally mean a smaller error term (achievable by longer counting time or increasing the sample size), other systematic non-Poisson factors influence the overall error and have a greater role when dealing with the age of older or high-precision ($\pm 1\sigma \leq 20$ years) samples.

It is important to distinguish precision from accuracy. The level of precision is expressed by the error term – a smaller number after the $\pm$ indicates a more precise measurement than a larger number. Precision is strongly influenced by laboratory considerations, such as the length of time the sample was in the counter or the stability of the accelerator, although the amount of carbon and its age may also be influential. However, the error term gives no indication of the accuracy of the measurement, by which is meant the proximity of the measured result to the true age. The accuracy of a measurement is influenced as much by the actions of the researcher as by the procedures of the dating laboratory – no amount of subsequent pre-treatment will compensate for poor initial selection. Of precision and accuracy probably accuracy is of more importance, in that an imprecise but accurate result is often a useful approximation to the true age, whereas an inaccurate but precise measurement is simply misleading. For this reason the 'high precision' measurements available from a small number of laboratories are only worthwhile in situations where confidence in the dating material is exceptionally good. The presence of systematic dating errors can be revealed by independent inter-laboratory tests, although such exercises are no substitute for continual self-checks. Upon inquiry, most laboratories will be able to supply details as to what procedures they have in place to monitor potential drift.

Materials suitable for ^{14}C dating

In the context of sub-fossil plant material, it is probably fair to say that almost all remains can be ^{14}C dated within the time frame explained above, provided sufficient matter is available. In all but a few cases, the remains chosen would normally be the larger macrofossils – fruits, seeds, wood, leaves, buds, scales, spines and other parts of plants (Wasylikowa 1986). Microfossils such as pollen are ^{14}C datable (Long et al. 1992; Richardson & Hall 1994), but extraction procedures are only in their infancy as there are technical ^{14}C difficulties still to be overcome (Vogel 1995). Although virtually all sub-fossil remains are theoretically datable, there are sometimes valid reasons why certain remains are probably best not chosen unless the researcher has a specific question in mind.

Problems with age at death

The use of wood, whether as charcoal or uncharred, is material which needs careful consideration. Radiocarbon dating assumes that the time of death and the cessation of exchange with the biosphere are contemporary events. For seeds and grasses with only a single season of growth this assumption is valid. However, if the radiocarbon age of the organism at death is not zero, an 'age offset' results. Samples of wood suffer from this in that trees (usually, although not invariably) add growth rings annually, and so the time of felling is not the same as when the rings grew. Once formed, the rings cease to significantly exchange with the biosphere, meaning that for a 200-year oak, the inner heartwood produces a radiocarbon date 200 years older than does the outer sapwood. This is known as the 'old wood' effect (Warner 1990, p. 160).

An allied problem that also affects wood is the 'time-width' of the sample. Suppose a radiocarbon sample consists of wood from a number of growth rings, then the measured ^{14}C activity will be an average of the relative proportions of the many annual rings (Waterbolk 1971, p. 21). However, should the sample consist of numerous discrete fragments of wood or charcoal, the overall time-width could be both very variable and incalculable thereby increasing the uncertainty of the age estimate.

Problems of reservoir effects

The remains of plants that obtain a proportion of their carbon from the marine environment need careful consideration when deciding what material to date. Carbon-14 does not mix into the oceans as quickly as in the atmosphere and the biosphere, for in the time spent mixing the ^{14}C radioactively decays. The effect is to produce an 'apparent age offset' of the oceans relative to the atmosphere and biosphere. For this reason modern ocean deep water has an apparent radiocarbon age of several millennia. Plants that take a proportion of their carbon from the marine environment exhibit a similar offset. Although there are general measurements of the 'marine reservoir effect' for broad oceanographic regions (Stuiver & Braziunas 1993), local effects like upwelling may predominate making accurate quantification difficult.

Freshwater environments do not, in general, suffer the marine reservoir effects but they do experience another effect, namely hard-water. The name comes from the presence of calcium ions produced through the dissolution of calcium carbonate of geological age, for example chalk or limestones, although the carbon can also come from non-calcium carbonate sources such as fossil soil humus. The effect is to dilute the ^{14}C concentration dissolved in the water thus making organisms which get their carbon from such environments appear older than they really are – often by several centuries. It is very clearly a problem when measuring aquatic plants in hardwater areas, however there is little evidence to suggest it affects terrestrial and emergent plants (Marčenko et al. 1989).

Problems of sedimentary depositional processes

Sedimentary processes, such as erosion and reworking of older organic sediments, can lead to the deposition of sub-fossil plant matter where different components have dissimilar ages. In such situations, the bulking of plant matter of differing age in a sample will result in a biased ^{14}C determination. Similar problems may occur with plant remains from archaeological sites where the mixing of remains is the product of human disturbance. Other relevant issues may include the delayed use of materials, the possible re-use of remains (especially timbers), and the question of residuality when considering botanical remains from archaeological contexts.

The final issue to take into account when selecting samples is the choice of ^{14}C laboratory to use. Certain laboratories only take AMS samples, others only conventional (radiometric) ones. Some specialize in a certain type of sample. Given that the process of dating may influence the choice of material, it is wise to liaise with the laboratory well in advance.

Practical considerations

Sample size

This is specific to individual dating laboratories and relevant details should be obtained directly. Examples of amounts needed are shown in Table 56.1, although it should be emphasized that requirements do change making direct consultation essential.

Storage, handling, packaging

Also laboratory specific. In general it is important not to introduce contamination when taking the sample. If the plant remains are to be collected by flotation, no chemicals containing hydrocarbons should be used, however hydrogen peroxide is permissible for breaking up clay-rich sediments. Most chemical preservatives contain carbon of a different age to that of the sample; if added they are often difficult to remove and will introduce bias. Avoid ordinary organic packaging materials (paper, cotton wool, string, cellotape and cardboard). Ensure labels are permanent and cannot get detached or erased. Glass containers are fine but suffer the risk of breakage. Plastic containers are all

Table 56.1. *Required quantities of dry plant matter for conventional (radiometric) and AMS dating for three laboratories*

	Beta Analytic		Belfast	
	recommended (g)	*minimum* (g)	*routine* (g)	*high-precision* (g)
Conventional				
charcoal (and related charred plant matter)	30	1.7	5–10	40
wood	100	7	30	160
peat	100	15	50	250

	Beta Analytic		Oxford	
	recommended (mg)	*minimum* (mg)	*recommended* (mg)	*minimum* (mg)
AMS				
charcoal (and related charred plant matter)	50	5	30	5
wood	100	10	50	20
peat	100	15	50	20

Laboratories cited are: (1) Beta Analytic Inc: 4985 S.W. 74th Court, Miami, Florida; (2) Belfast: Radiocarbon Dating Laboratory, Palaeoecology Centre, School of Geosciences, The Queen's University of Belfast; (3) Oxford: Radiocarbon Accelerator Unit, Research Laboratory for Archaeology and the History of Art, Oxford University.
This is a general guide. Always liaise directly with the laboratory.
No value judgements should be inferred from the figures quoted or from the inclusion of any given laboratory.

right but beware of contamination from plasticizers (polythene is generally better than poly vinyl chloride) however the danger is minimal unless really small-sized samples are involved. The use of clingfilm to wrap cores or monoliths is acceptable but dating samples should ideally be taken from cleaned surfaces. Aluminium foil is accepted by some laboratories for some samples; however, acid peats and organic sediments from intertidal deposits can dissolve the foil. Waterlogged sub-

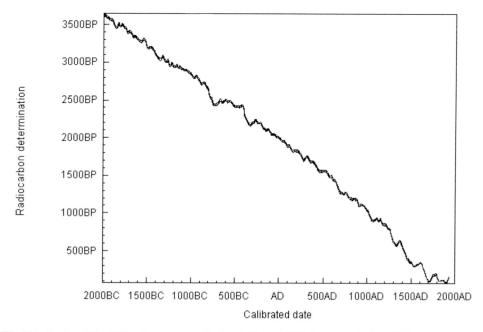

Fig. 56.1. Section of the 1986 calibration curve (Stuiver & Pearson 1986; Pearson & Stuiver 1986) showing atmospheric ^{14}C levels for the last 4000 calendar years.

fossil plant remains should be kept cool and wet; freezing will prevent infestations but ice crystal formation is destructive of structure. Charred remains can be air-dried. Bear in mind that laboratories do not respond well to samples which need laborious extraction from a mass of sediment. The main point to stress is the need for direct liaison with the laboratory.

Calibration

Why calibrate? The reason is that production of ¹⁴C has not been constant over time – hence radiocarbon years are not calendar years. Discrepancies can be corrected using a calibration curve (Fig. 56.1); the product of measuring the ¹⁴C content of tree rings whose precise calendar age is known by dendrochronology (Baillie 1995).

There are now several long chronologies that cover most of the Holocene (Stuiver & Kra 1986; Stuiver *et al.* 1993). Although the 1993 calibration curve extends back the furthest (to *c.* 11 400 years),

doubts exist as to its validity, and so the Belfast & Seattle 1986 curves (Pearson & Stuiver 1986; Stuiver & Pearson 1986; Pearson *et al.* 1986) are to be preferred*. Calibrated dates are complex mathematically by being non-Gaussian. For convenience, they are often expressed as ranges even though this is only an approximation. For example, 3150 ± 40 BP gives two ranges: 1520–1380 and 1350–1320 cal BC at the 95.4% confidence level. The term 'cal' makes clear the dates are calibrated. Computer calibration programs (e.g. van der Plicht & Mook 1989; Niklaus *et al.* 1992; Stuiver & Reimer 1993; Bronk Ramsey 1995) are now well established and have become important tools for handling suites of ¹⁴C measurements.

---

*Since this section was written a new calibration curve has been published in the December 1998 issue of *Radiocarbon* (vol. **40** (3)). This supersedes the previous 1986 and 1993 curves and allows calibration to as far back as 24 000 calendar years ago. The 1998 curve is likely to become the recognized standard and its use is recommended.

57. $^{13}C/^{12}C$ in growth rings and leaves: carbon distribution in trees

GERHARD H. SCHLESER

Carbon isotopes of tree rings are widely used to reconstruct past climates. The method is based on the assumption that weather conditions such as temperature and humidity or precipitation primarily control the ratio of the carbon isotopes within trees. Trees are, however, rather complex systems and many different effects, also including variations of soil moisture, nutrient availability, pollutants, etc. have to be considered. The causes of isotope patterns and trends in tree rings are not yet fully understood, especially with regard to the combined effects of several climatic or environmental quantities. Nonetheless, isotope data can yield valuable palaeoclimatic and/or palaeoecological information.

Definitions and biological discrimination

The carbon isotopes of tree tissues (C_t) or chemical compounds thereof, are measured as CO_2. The abundance ratio of a sample, $R_t = {}^{13}CO_2/{}^{12}CO_2$, is compared with the corresponding ratio of a reference (R_{ref}) and given in the δ notation as:

$$\delta^{13}C_t = [(R_t - R_{ref})/R_{ref}] \times 1000‰. \quad (1)$$

The reference is a fossil belemnite from the Pee Dee Formation, Upper Cretaceous, of South Carolina, USA. It is denoted as PDB, with $R_{ref} = 0.01124$ (Craig 1957). $\delta^{13}C$ values are normally multiplied by 10^3 and expressed as 'per mil' (‰). Note, that 'per mil' is not a unit: $\delta^{13}C$ values are dimensionless. $\delta^{13}C$ values of tree tissues are negative, because $^{13}C/^{12}C$ of atmospheric CO_2 is always greater than ratios of tree tissues. The discrimination Δ which expresses the isotope shift between air, R_a, and tree material, R_t, is given by Δ $= (R_a-R_t)/R_t$. In the δ-notation, in per mil, Δ results in:

$$\Delta [‰] = (\delta^{13}C_a - \delta^{13}C_t)/(1 + \delta^{13}C_t \times 10^{-3}). \quad (2a)$$

In most cases $\delta^{13}C_t \times 10^{-3} \ll 1$. Therefore, Δ is to a good approximation given by:

$$\Delta \cong (\delta^{13}C_a - \delta^{13}C_t). \quad (2b)$$

On the PDB scale atmospheric CO_2 has a value of about –8‰. It gradually decreases due to CO_2 inputs to the atmosphere from combustion of fossil fuels and land use changes (e.g. deforestation)

(Mook et al. 1983). Total wood shows values around –25‰.

Photosynthetically produced matter is associated with isotope fractionations during CO_2 fixation. The process is considered as a step-by-step fractionation, comprising diffusion, dissolution and the initial carboxylation reaction. An expression for the ratio of carbon isotopes in plants in its most elementary form (Farquhar et al. 1982) is given by:

$$\delta^{13}C_t = \delta^{13}C_a + \varepsilon_D(1 - c_i/c_a) + \varepsilon_C(c_i/c_a). \quad (3)$$

ε_D is the fractionation for diffusion (–4.4‰) while ε_c is the fractionation for carboxylation (–29‰) and c_i and c_a are the leaf-intercellular and ambient air concentrations of CO_2, respectively. From equations (2b) and (3) follows the discrimination as:

$$\Delta \cong -\varepsilon_D(1 - c_i/c_a) - \varepsilon_C (c_i/c_a). \quad (4)$$

which shows that the discrimination is not merely the sum of the individual fractionations. If c_i decreases, the fractionation for diffusion, ε_D, becomes more important and vice versa. Thus, Δ reflects the conditions under which trees incorporate their CO_2.

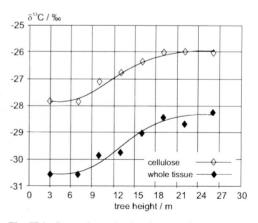

Fig. 57.1. Comparison of carbon isotopes from α-cellulose and whole tissue of leaves collected from different heights in a beech tree (Schleser, unpublished results).

SCHLESER, G. H. 1999. $^{13}C/^{12}C$ in growth rings and leaves: carbon distribution in trees. *In*: JONES, T. P. & ROWE, N. P. (eds) *Fossil Plants and Spores: modern techniques.* Geological Society, London, 306–309.

Carbon isotope pattern in trees

The basic fractionations take place at the leaf level which, in a broader sense, determines the carbon isotope level within a tree. However, metabolic processes occurring subsequent to leaves can lead to further isotope changes. Therefore, isotope values vary considerably among and within plant parts. Carbon isotope investigations in trees are generally based on cellulose, rather than on whole tissue because cellulose deposited in a particular place is practically immobile. This also holds for old or fossil wood material. Nevertheless, cellulose, precisely α-cellulose, and whole tissue broadly result in the same relative isotope changes, although they are distinctly different isotopically (Fig. 57.1). Unless otherwise stated, the following results are valid for cellulose as well as for whole tissue.

Figure 57.2 illustrates $\delta^{13}C$ variations typically encountered in trees. Leaves, especially of forest trees, are exposed to rather contrasting micro-environments. This leads to various physiological states and thus gives rise to different leaf

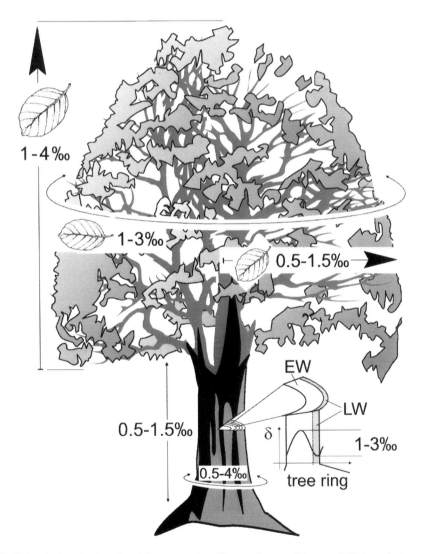

Fig. 57.2. Carbon isotope trends and variations encountered in trees. Large solid arrows indicate an isotope gradient towards more positive values. EW and LW indicate early and late wood, respectively (compilation of literature data and author's data).

developments. Therefore, leaves sampled from different positions in a tree show different $\delta^{13}C$ values. Leaves positioned close to the ground exhibit lower $\delta^{13}C$ values than those higher up in a tree. Differences of up to 4‰ have been measured. Leaves, originating from the outer region of a crown can show higher isotope values than those from the inner part of a crown, even if they originate from the same height. These different $\delta^{13}C$ values for dissimilar positions in a tree reflect either various source values (Vogel 1978; Medina & Minchin 1985) and/or different physiological conditions due to contrasting c_i/c_a ratios (eqn. 4), based on different stomatal resistivities for CO_2 (Francey et al. 1985; Schleser & Jayasekera 1985). Intercostal tissue from different places in a leaf do not show different $\delta^{13}C$ values (Schleser 1990).

Isotope trends and variations are also seen in twigs and branches (e.g. Leavitt & Long 1986). These phenomena are partly due to leaves being attached to various parts along branches where they differently fractionate the carbon isotopes (Panek & Waring 1995). [13]C trends that have been measured in lower branches of forest trees can be explained as gradients developing partly due to a mixing of carbon isotopes from different origins in a tree having different ^{13}C values (Fig. 57.3, Schleser 1992).

Tissues from single rings but different heights in a trunk do not show comparable isotope variations, if investigations are restricted to one radial direction. A vertical gradient is absent, though fluctuations of 0.5 to 1.5‰ exist (Fig. 57.2). These fluctuations almost disappear, however, along the wood fibres which do not normally follow exactly the vertical direction, mostly due to torsional effects imposed on a tree. Fibres, thus have their own individual ^{13}C signatures. The circumferential variation of $\delta^{13}C$ values from single rings can be large, i.e. 0.5 to 4‰ and these intra-ring variations are not necessarily correlated with corresponding ring width variations (Tans & Mook 1980; Leavitt & Long 1986). However, thorough examinations of consecutive years generally exhibit the same circumferential ^{13}C pattern. This similarity justifies, to a certain degree, the restriction of investigations to only one core. If possible, investigations of several cores from different directions are preferable.

Rings do not show a uniform ^{13}C content in their radial direction, but a rather clear-cut and annually recurring pattern, schematically given in Fig. 57.2 (Leavitt & Long 1982; Loader et al. 1995). Up to now there is no clear evidence to what extent this radial isotope pattern within a ring mirrors the seasonal development around the tree or points to

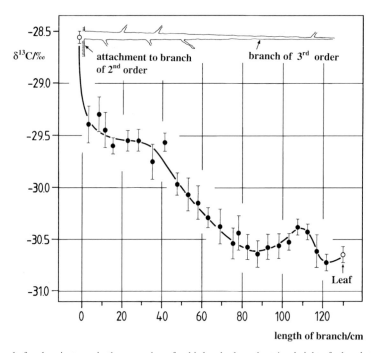

Fig. 57.3. Trend of carbon isotopes in the outer ring of a third-order branch at 4 m height of a beech tree in a forest (Schleser, unpublished results).

special weather events. Some studies have linked the seasonal $\delta^{13}C$ variation in tree rings with seasonal microclimate variation. In these studies relations were given between intra-annual trends of $\delta^{13}C$ and relative humidity and temperature, or vapour pressure deficit and temperature, or soil moisture and precipitation (Loader *et al.* 1995; Ogle & McCormac 1994; Leavitt & Long 1991). In many cases the relative trend seems to be independent of weather conditions, presumably featuring certain specific biochemical reactions in conjunction with particular isotope fractionations (Hill *et al.* 1995). The causes of this ^{13}C pattern are not yet fully understood. Deciduous trees are typically depleted by about 3‰ compared with coniferous trees from the same stand. Otherwise inter-tree variations at a site amount to roughly 2–3‰, including trees of different species.

Reconstructions of past climates can be carried out, provided atmospheric $\delta^{13}C_{CO_2}$ and pCO_2 remained constant. Since atmospheric $\delta^{13}C_{CO_2}$ and pCO_2 affect the isotope ratio of organic matter, either directly ($\delta^{13}C_a$) or indirectly (c_i/c_a), the interpretation of $\delta^{13}C$ values from fossil or sub-fossil wood material has to be viewed with some caution. For investigations covering the Holocene or parts thereof, this is of no concern, except for the last 50 years. Finally it should be noticed that the relative $\delta^{13}C$ trends in tree rings of whole tissues and cellulose from fossil woods of the Neogene are largely identical, even though the cellulose content of some woods varies by a factor of up to 6 due to degradation processes (Frielingsdorf 1992).

Techniques

Isotope analyses are normally performed on cellulose rather than on total tree material, especially with regard to climate reconstruction on the basis of tree rings. The technique of cellulose extraction is based on an acidified sodium chlorite oxidation method (Green 1963). Lately, improvements have been introduced to cope with small samples such as small shavings (Leavitt & Danzer 1993; Loader *et al.* 1997). Carbon isotopes are measured as CO_2 in a mass spectrometer. CO_2 is produced by combusting samples in an excess of oxygen at 800 to 1000°C. It is then measured in a dual inlet isotope ratio mass spectrometer (IRMS). Nowadays an elemental analyser interfaced to a dual inlet IRMS or to a continuous flow IRMS is commonly used. The precision achieved is better than ±0.1‰ which is much smaller than the isotopic inhomogeneities of many organic samples. Sample sizes down to 100 µgC can be measured routinely and with some additional efforts, samples down to 10 µgC can be analysed. The most modern generation of instruments combines the precision required for isotope analysis with the ability to handle carrier gas flows with extremely small sample sizes. These are irm-GC/MS instruments, e.g. isotope ratio monitoring GC/MS machines.

Summary

The ratio of the stable carbon isotopes ($^{13}C/^{12}C$) in trees is significantly different from the isotope ratio of atmospheric carbon dioxide from which it is derived, because of isotope fractionation during the photosynthetic uptake of CO_2. The isotope ratio fixed in the leaf photosynthates is, however, not representative for all compartments in a tree, such as e.g. leaves, branches, the trunk or even within different sections of a tree ring. First, the isotope value of atmospheric CO_2 may, in space and time, not be evenly distributed around a tree. Second, due to isotope fractionations at various biochemical branch points of the metabolism, isotopic enrichments and depletions occur. The reconstructions of environmental quantities, based on carbon isotopes in trees is largely carried out by means of trunk material.

58. Techniques in the study of plant–arthropod interactions

ANDREW C. SCOTT & FREDERICK R. TITCHENER

Palaeontologists tend to study either fossil animals or plants and evidence of their interaction and co-evolution is a rather neglected field. It is clear, however, that a consideration of their interactions may provide valuable data on the evolution of herbivory, ecosystem complexity and co-evolution (Scott *et al.* 1992; Labandeira 1998).

Evidence of plant–arthropod interactions in the fossil record comes from three major sources:

1. study of animals in terms of functional morphology (e.g. Labandeira & Beall 1990; Labandeira 1997);
2. study of plants and their morphological and anatomical modifications (e.g. Crepet *et al.* 1991);
3. study of trace fossils, both on the plants and as coprolites of animals (e.g. Scott 1992).

Interactions between plants and arthropods may be mutualistic, that is of benefit to both groups, or antagonistic, that is of detriment to one group. Such interactions include plants as food with no obvious benefit to the plant through to where the plant uses the arthropods as transporters or pollinators and to where the animals use the plants for shelter and camouflage. Clearly some of the interactions are more easily identified than others and this chapter will concentrate on the traces of animals remaining on the plants rather than on detailed morphology of insects which is more rarely encountered in the fossil record (see Labandeira 1997).

There are three basic steps involved in the study of plant–arthropod interactions: recognition of an interaction, then its characterization and interpretation. Recognition of distinct traces, such as some leaf mines and galls, may be relatively easy. However, the discrimination of physical and biological mechanisms, such as pre- and post-mortem timing for other forms of leaf damage may be problematic. In addition to this, another major problem is that damaged specimens are often not collected by researchers nor kept by museum curators. In addition, it may also be difficult to determine precisely the functional morphology of arthropods and plants and to infer correctly any corresponding adaptations. In this regard there are three approaches commonly used: (1) comparative and functional morphology; (2) comparative analogy; and (3) ichnotaxonomy. Traditionally

there has been little attempt to quantitatively analyse plant–arthropod interactions and in most cases work has concentrated on the first stratigraphic occurrences of the interaction (e.g. Scott *et al.* 1992; Stephenson & Scott 1992; Labandeira 1998). Recently attempts have been made first by modern biologists (Landsberg & Ohmart 1989) and then by palaeobiologists (Labandeira *et al.* 1995) to quantify the extent, frequency and diversity of plant–arthropod interactions in a range of ecological and geographical settings through time.

Recognition

Figure 58.1 shows the range of damage that can be caused by an arthropod on a leaf. Galls and traces of foliar feeding require little or no preparation work for their recognition and can be readily and easily studied. They may occur on the foliage of any terrestrial plant. However, recognition of the causal agent of feeding traces may be difficult as normal decay and post-mortem processes can produce traces similar to those of the original causal organism.

Thus recognition of these feeding traces, as opposed to galls, on fossils is usually but not exclusively through the presence of wound reaction tissue; this is observed as a localized thickening and browning of the trace margin, forms only on living plant material and therefore provides definitive evidence of pre-abscissional damage. A problem exists, however, that some wound tissue may be produced by fungal infection so that whilst in most cases the style and distribution of damage may confirm arthropod interaction, occasionally definitive proof may be lacking. In addition, the shape and position of the damage may be used to eliminate potential physical agents, such as wind damage (Wilson 1979) or fluvial transport (Spicer 1989*b*), which tend to be angular and/or linear. Feeding traces on leaves are best observed on impression fossils where the wound-reaction tissue may be identified by either a distinctive darker colour or indentation around the damage. The presence of wound-reaction tissue on leaf compression fossils may be more difficult to determine, especially when the leaf and surrounding matrix are of a similar colour.

Scott, A. C. & Titchener, F. R. 1999. Techniques in the study of plant–arthropod interactions. *In*: Jones, T. P. & Rowe, N. P. (eds) *Fossil Plants and Spores: modern techniques.* Geological Society, London, 310–315.

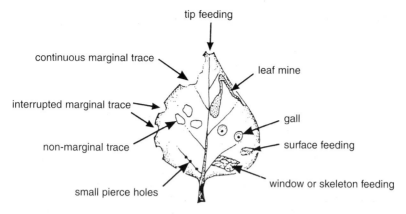

tip feeding

continuous marginal trace

leaf mine

interrupted marginal trace

gall

non-marginal trace

surface feeding

small pierce holes

window or skeleton feeding

Fig. 58.1. Some traces of plant–animal interactions on a leaf (after Scott 1992).

The most common plant–arthropod interactions observed on fossil plants are feeding traces on foliage (Fig. 58.1). Feeding traces may be grouped as marginal or non-marginal (e.g. Scott *et al.* 1992). Marginal damage may originate from a single or several bites of an arthropod resulting in the removal of a large portion of the leaf lamina. The damage may also be restricted to one part of the leaf such as on the leaf tip (Fig. 58.1, Fig. 58.2a–e). Interrupted marginal feeding is often found as regular bites along a leaf margin (Fig. 58.2a). Non-marginal damage may have a very variable form (Fig. 58.2a, b & e). For example, leaf surface feeding may result from the stripping of one cuticular layer but leaving the other layer, whereas skeletonization results from feeding and removing all the tissue between the veins. Skeletonization and surface feeding is also produced by both terrestrial and aquatic leaf decomposing organisms which may lead to an overestimation of herbivory if observation of wound-reaction tissue is not used as a criterion for identification of pre-abscissional damage. Circular feeding traces are common (Fig. 58.2a, b & e) and aspects of shape and size as well as position and density need to be included in any study. Some holes, however, may be the result of the decay of leaf mines or the abscission of galls.

Some insect (and mite) larvae feed on tissues from between the two leaf cuticles. The leaf not only acts as a food source but also as shelter from dehydration and predators. Mines can be divided by morphology into two distinct categories: blotch mines (Fig. 58.2h & d) and linear mines (Fig. 58.2g & i) (e.g. Needham *et al.* 1928; Lang *et al.* 1995). The point of origin, the size and course of the mine and associated frass (concentration of coprolites within the plant tissue) may be very specific to the causal taxon and, indeed, host specific (e.g.

Labandeira *et al.* 1994). Mines are recognized by a colour variation in the leaf in which mined areas are thinner and thus lighter. A frass trail may be seen as a darker line or series of continuous dark dots within the mine. Mines, however, are very prone to losing key morphological characters during transport, decay and burial. In particular, shallow blotch mines are especially vulnerable because the top surface of the mine is often removed and the frass detached leading to a superficial resemblance to surface feeding traces (Fig 58.2d & h).

Galls are produced as a reaction or response by a plant to insects living and growing on a plant and most commonly on leaves. As they result from a morphological modification of the plant they may be recognized on fossils. Galls may be regular in shape and host specific but are often three-dimensional in life so that they seldom maintain their original morphology, i.e. they are most frequently compressed (Fig. 58.2j). The shape, size and position of galls is important in their identification (Scott *et al.* 1994), for example, they have been identified in Carboniferous permineralized plants (Labandeira & Phillips 1996*b*) where the details of all growth has been recognized using standard acetate peel techniques.

Some abnormalities in cell growth in Carboniferous plants may have been caused by the piercing and sucking activity of some insects or other arthropods (Labandeira & Phillips 1996*a*). Likewise, abnormal growth in the cells of stems of *Rhynia* from the Lower Devonian of Rhynie, may also be suggestive of such an interaction (see Scott *et al.* 1992 for a discussion).

Boring by insects or other arthropods (e.g. mites) may take place while the plant is living but occurs more often after death of the plant. Borings can be recognized commonly by the regularity of size,

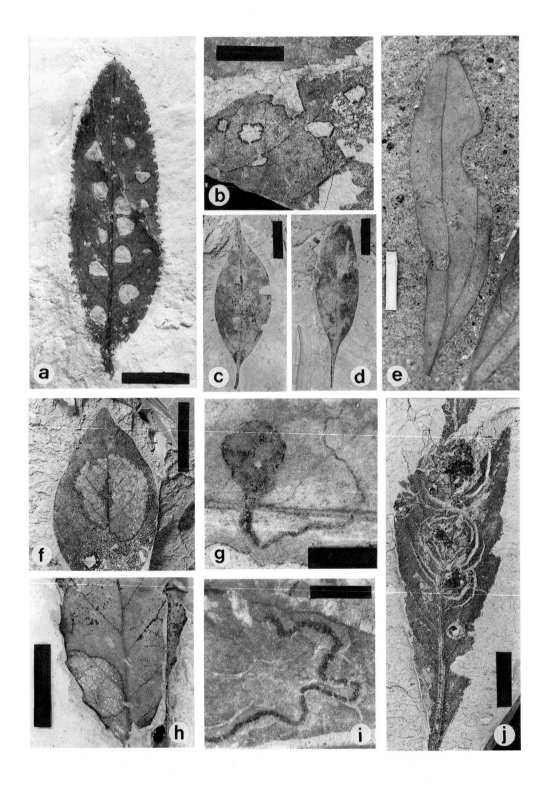

shape and position as well as the occurrence of frass (e.g. Scott 1992; Labandeira *et al.* 1997). Borings may be host specific, for example the bark borings of Scolytid beetle lavae which create elaborate chambers just below the bark surface (see Jarzembowski 1990; Scott *et al.* 1992). Other studies include those of Labandeira *et al.* (1997) who have reconstructed mite borings in Carboniferous plants using serial peels from coal balls. In addition to wood, other plant organs may show evidence of boring, such as seeds or spores (see Scott 1992 for a discussion).

Morphological adaptations of host and causal organism in conjunction with extant analogues can allow interpretation of an interaction. Arthropod mouthpart morphology can provide us with an insight into the method of feeding and also the range of potential traces created by an arthropod. The presence of functional mandibles is indicative of chewing or cutting whereas more specialized morphologies such as stylets in the Hemiptera are used for piercing plant tissues and the proboscis of adult lepidoptera which are used for sucking nectar (Labandeira 1997). Other morphological adaptations which insects may have evolved as a response to interaction with plants include the pollen collecting apparatus of Hymenoptera, blunt mandibles for kneeding wax, ovipositors for laying eggs under a leaf surface (Labandeira & Beall 1990).

Mimicry, where insects appear like plants, is a strategy frequently seen in the modern biota but its identification in the fossil record has proved problematic (Scott *et al.* 1992). The suggested similarity of cockroach wings with pteridosperm pinnules in the Carboniferous has been cited by a number of authors (e.g. Scott & Taylor 1983) but has been refuted by others (e.g. Jarzembowski 1995). Plant-arthropod interactions may not only be to the advantage of the animal but also to the plant, particularly in the case of pollination and dispersal

(Strong *et al.* 1984). Angiosperms have successfully exploited this interaction. The evolution of nectaries and other floral structures visible in fossils such as Cretaceous and Tertiary flowers invites this interpretation (Crepet *et al.* 1991). Arthropods may also be involved with seed or even spore/pollen dispersal and may have adapted interactions with features of the propagules, such as spines and hooks (e.g. Collinson 1998).

Characterization and interpretation

There are three basic approaches to the classification of plant–arthropod interactions.

1. Plant and animal comparative morphology and functional anatomy is the most commonly applied, especially with respect to Tertiary interactions (Labandeira & Beall 1990). However, this is reliant on direct analogy with extant organisms and thus is only possible when such interactions produce a number of unique morphological characteristics (such as an unusual mine type made by one insect type). Paucity of the arthropod fossil record, especially during the Palaeozoic and Mesozoic makes this problematic.

2. Analogy uses modern taxa simply as a method of describing the observed interaction, so that a fossil and its analogue may not be linked nor the causal organisms identified (Lang *et al.* 1995).

3. Ichotaxonomy may be used to classify and name traces of plant–arthropod interactions. It is important to realize that with an ichnotaxonomic classification the interaction is not linked to a causal organism but described purely as a morphological trace. For example, marginal bites from leaves have been described under the ichnotaxon *Phagophytichnus*. Such a system has not yet been widely applied (see Givulescu

---

Fig 58.2. Plant–arthropod traces on Tertiary angiosperm leaves. (**a**) Interrupted marginal and non-marginal feeding trace on an angiosperm leaf from the Clairborne Formation, Eocene, USA. Specimen PP7745, Field Museum of Natural History, Chicago. (**b**) Non-marginal traces with exceptionally distinct wound reaction tissue on an angiosperm leaf from Bechlejovice, Oligocene, Czech Republic. (**c**) Marginal feeding traces on *Diopyros brachysepala* from the Brestany Clay, Oligocene, Czech Republic. Specimen G453, National Museum, Prague. (**d**) Marginal feeding trace and blotch mine on an angiosperm leaf from the Brestany Clay, Oligocene, Czech Republic. Specimen G7615, National Museum, Prague. (**e**) Marginal and non-marginal trace on *Daphnogene bilinica* from Ipolytarnoc, Miocene, Hungary. Specimen 54.939.1, Hungarian National History Museum, Budapest. (**f**) Surface feeding trace on a member of Lauraceae, Brestany Clay, Oligocene, Czech Republic. Specimen G3921, National Museum, Prague. (**g**) Linear-blotch mine on *Heteromeles* sp. from Fingerrock Miocene of Nevada, USA. University of California Museum of Paleontology × 1.5. (**h**) Blotch mine on *Quercus urophylla* from Erdobenye, Miocene, Hungary. Specimen 54.768.1, Hungarian National History Museum, Budapest. (**i**) Sinuous-linear mine on *Arbutus* sp. from Fingerrock, Miocene of Nevada, USA. University of California Museum of Paleontology. (**j**) Compressed galls on *Quercus rhenana* from the Brestany Clay, Oligocene of the Czech Republic. Specimen G7647. National Museum, Prague. Scale bars; a, c, d, e, f, h, j = 20 mm; b, g, h = 10 mm.

1984). Both the use of analogy and ichno-taxonomy only identify a functional/causal mechanism for plant–arthropod interactions and their use in evolutionary studies is limited to gaining knowledge of the timing and diversification of interactions. These two approaches are not, however, constrained by the paucity of the fossil record nor on the reliability of taxonomic determinations.

Non-quantitative studies

The majority of plant–arthropod interaction studies have been non-quantitative, concentrating on the first occurrence either of a trace-forming mechanism (Scott *et al.* 1992) or a taxonomic specific interaction: for example, gall production in the Carboniferous (Labandeira *et al.* 1996) and spangle galls on Cretaceous oak leaves (Larew 1986) respectively.

Quantitative studies

The identification and subsequent characterization of an interaction is just one aspect of any study. It is often desirable to determine the extent and frequency in a temporal and/or environmental setting of an individual or suite of interactions. Two methods are discussed here: numerical frequency (e.g. Scott *et al.* 1994) and quantification by area coverage (e.g. Beck *et al.* 1996).

Eliminating bias: Prior to any quantitative analysis it is necessary to account for any potential bias. First, the survival potential of an individual fossil taxon may vary markedly; this applies to host, causal organism and any resultant trace. Leaves that are small, thick and coriaceous (sun leaves) and appeared high in a tree's canopy had a greater fossilization potential than large, thin, papery, shade leaves (Ferguson 1970; Greenwood 1992). The presence of an interaction or any resultant changes, either chemically or physically in a host, may affect its potential for fossilization. Plants with high secondary metabolite contents may produce leaves which decompose at a slower rate than those with lower levels of secondary metabolites (Spicer 1989b). Additionally, it cannot be assumed that a suite of interactions on a range of fossil taxa is truely respresentative of the original living biota. Fossil floras are usually over-represented by autochthonous foliage and therefore, by any traces of interactions which may be specific to these taxa. Presently there is no method for analysing these biases, so caution must be exercised and comparisons only made between data from similar taphonomic settings or identical taxa. Thus tracing a single taxon temporally or geographically in a

similar depositional environment might be one way of controlling local ecological and taphonomic variation. Collection of material must be exhaustive, as not only pristine specimens should be collected for examination and analysis. Changing attitudes in fossil collecting, whereby all material irespective of preservation is preserved, together with an increasing awareness of the importance of recognizing traces fossils of plant–arthropod interactions should help significantly expand our current database.

Numerical frequency: Such studies may be conducted using any three of the potential characterization methods discussed earlier. No preparation work is required and the methodology is based just on simple observation, thus enabling quick and quantitative results. The frequency of each interaction and its occurrence on each host taxon allows a crude measure of the importance, diversity and host range. Comparison of a number of floras or of key taxa may allow environmental, taphonomic and temporal trends to be identified.

Area coverage: Numerical frequency and diversity studies do not produce a quantitative assessment of the amount of herbivory. Thus it is often desirable, for example, to measure the area removed by feeding. Such an analysis can be undertaken by visual estimation and the use of range zones, for example, removal of a leaf by marginal feeding where less than 20% is removed, 21–40% or greater than 40%. Studies on modern vegetation using visual estimation of leaf area removed have been found to be quite reliable (Wint 1983). Exact values can be measured using image analysis techniques. Beck *et al.* (1996) have developed an additional calculated measure called the herbivory index which is

the average herbivorized area per leaf ÷ average total area per leaf × 100.

This measure is, therefore, indended to be taxon independent and allow the increasing use of plants by arthropods as a food resource to be tracked through time. Another method is to calculate the percentage of leaves damaged of a taxon or of the total leaves in a flora which provides an insight into feeding intensity and the range of leaves used as a food source.

The study of the levels of herbivory using measured values of area leaf loss or damage in both fossil (Labandeira *et al.* 1994) and even modern floras (Landsberg & Ohmart 1989) is fraught with difficulties. Many herbivores preferentially feed on young foliage, often consuming the whole leaf and hence this is not represented in the fossil record. In addition, damage created by feeding on young foliage expands as they grow thus leading to an overestimation of area removed (Landsberg & Ohmart 1989). Modern biologists can deal with this problem by monitoring area lost and damage expansion on tagged leaves over a period of time. This is clearly not viable with fossil foliage, although correction factors calculated from measurement of closely related extant plants could be used (Robertson & Duke 1987).

Wider considerations

It has long been recognized that the development of plant–arthropod interactions through time has played a significant role in the evolution, and indeed co-evolution, of each group (see Chaloner *et al.* 1991 for a discussion). This is markedly seen in the evolution of the angiosperms and insects (see Crepet *et al.* 1991), as well as on the diversification of plant and arthropod groups (and indeed extinctions) and on the evolution of new feeding strategies, in the case of arthropods, and protection strategies, in the case of plants (see Labandeira 1997, 1998; Scott *et al.* 1992 for discussion and references). Whilst it is easy to see how insect mouthparts may have evolved to cope with new food sources, it is not so easy to prove how herbivory may have acted as a selective pressure on plant evolution. It has been suggested, for example, that the production of toxins in plants as an anti-feedant strategy can be recognized even in fossils from the presence of interrupted bite marks along leaves (e.g. Fig. 58.2a, see Scott *et al.* 1992) and even the presence of a toothed margin on a leaf may act as a feeding deterrent to some animals (see Chaloner *et al.* 1991 for a fuller discussion of these issues).

59. Plants and animal diets

MARGARET E. COLLINSON

Plant contributions to animal diets can be recognized by studies of fossil plants in gut contents and coprolites, trace fossils of animal feeding on plants, and plants in food caches. Indirect lines of evidence include the overall morphology and microwear of vertebrate teeth as well as $\delta^{13}C$ data. Evidence from fossil insect mouthparts is summarized by Labandeira (1997, 1998) and discussed by Scott & Titchener (Chapter 58). If possible, all lines of evidence should be combined prior to any interpretation.

Gut contents

Palaeozoic arthropod gut contents are exclusively of pollen or spores (Labandeira 1997). Post-Palaeozoic examples (Labandeira 1998, pp. 165–166) are exclusively of pollen. Farlow (1987) discussed the few claims for plant material in dinosaur gut contents all of which are equivocal. Seeds and leaves occur in the gut contents of Eocene mammals (Figs 59.1 & 59.2) and birds from Lake Messel (Schaarschmidt, in Schaal & Ziegler 1992). These prove that *Propalaeotherium* (a relative of the early horses) (Fig. 59.1) was a browser, eating broad-leaved foliage of trees and shrubs (e.g. Lauraceae, Juglandaceae) and occasional fruit (Vitaceae), and not a grazer like modern horses.

Gut contents (Figs 59.1 & 59.2) can be studied directly by reflected light microscopy or by removing material (Fig. 59.2) for light microscopy

Fig. 59.1. *Propalaeotherium parvulum* an early horse relative with gut contents containing broad-leaved foliage. Eocene, Messel, Germany. Height at the shoulder approximately 30 cm. Illustration courtesy of J.L. Franzen. Reproduced with permission from J.L. Franzen and Natur-Museum Senckenberg. Photograph E. Pantak/U.Wegmann, Senckenberg Museum.

COLLINSON, M. E. 1999. Plants and animal diets. *In*: JONES, T. P. & ROWE, N. P. (eds) *Fossil Plants and Spores: modern techniques*. Geological Society, London, 316–319.

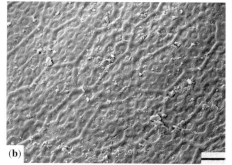

Fig. 59.2. Gut contents from a rodent *Masillamys*, shown by SEM to be fragments of seeds which occur as complete specimens in the same deposits. Eocene, Messel, Germany (Collinson 1988). (**a**) Portion of gut contents, scale bar 100 µm; (**b**) detail of seed coat surface, scale bar 10 µm.

(LM) or scanning electron microscopy (SEM) (Collinson 1988 and Chapter 12). Schaarschmidt (in Schaal & Ziegler 1992, fig. 84) used epifluorescence microscopy to study pollen and cuticles *in situ* in insect guts. Gut contents could possibly be studied *in situ* using the low vacuum (LV) SEM or environmental SEM (ESEM) with minimal risk to the specimen.

Fossilized gut contents represent the last meal(s). This may be the normal diet or an unusual food which caused the death of the animal. Furthermore, some contents could be 'accidental' intake, e.g. pollen and spores on leaves or amongst detritus. This poses a problem for distinction between herbivores and detritivors. Good evidence for ancient diet is the repeated occurrence of similar gut contents e.g. foliage in many Messel *Propalaeotherium* (Fig 59.1) (Franzen, in Schaal &

Ziegler 1992). Even then, there may be biases due to the relative resistance of plant material to conditions in the alimentary canal and subsequent decomposition. Materials such as sporopollenin, lignin and cuticles will be favoured (van Bergen *et al.* 1995), hence gut contents may not include all parts of the diet.

Coprolites

Contents of small arthropod coprolites are best studied by SEM (Chapter 12). Palaeozoic examples are known for their spore content (Edwards *et al.* 1995*b*; Labandeira 1998; Hooker & Collinson in press) but also include pollen and other taxon-diagnostic plant tissues including cuticles, trichomes, papillae and secretory cells (Labandeira 1998, p. 334). Labandeira (1998) concluded that

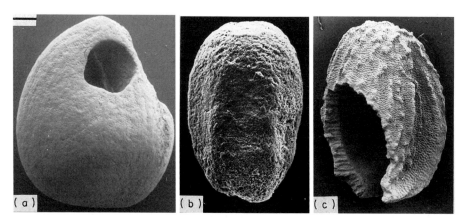

Fig. 59.3. SEM showing trace fossils and coprolite evidence of plant-feeding. (**a**) *Rutaspermum* seed with insect exit hole, Eocene, Germany; (**b**) coprolite of dry wood-feeding termite, Palaeocene , southern England; (**c**) gnaw marks on a *Stratiotes* seed indicating seed predation by a rodent, late Eocene, southern England. Scale bar on (a) measures 500 µm, on (b) 50 µm, and on (c) 650 µm. Reproduced with permission of Academic Press from Collinson (1990).

herbivory (spore feeding, piercing and sucking) occurred by the early Devonian. Borings containing coprolites, which occur in tissues of all major Upper Carboniferous swamp plants, represent detritivory by oribatid mites, an essential component of recycling of primary productivity in modern and ancient ecosystems (Labandeira *et al.* 1997). Feeding trails in Eocene palm flowers from Messel contain microlepidopteran coprolites full of palm pollen and clearly document insect pollen feeding (Schaarschmidt & Wilde 1986).

Small, hexagonally faceted, woody coprolites (Fig. 59.3b) are common in plant debris assemblages from the Wealden onwards (Collinson 1990). These are identical to coprolites found in termite nests (e.g. Boucot 1990, pp. 376–378) in fossil wood and they represent wood-feeding by dry wood termites with cellulose-digesting gut biota. The combination of body fossils (Jarzembowski 1981), nests and woody coprolites provides irrefutable evidence that this particular plant diet and feeding behaviour has a co-evolutionary history since the early Cretaceous and prior to angiosperm evolution.

Faecal material (dung) of larger vertebrate plant-eaters is often only loosely aggregated and lacks the high calcium content of carnivore coprolites and therefore has a low preservation potential except in dry conditions (Behrensmeyer *et al.* 1992; Hunt *et al.* 1994). It is also difficult to identify herbivore coprolite producers (Hunt *et al.* 1994). Chin & Gill (1996) and Chin & Kirkland (1998) reported Mesozoic herbivore coprolites and coniferous wood was documented in those probably produced by the dinosaur *Maiasaura*.

Caveats mentioned above concerning interpretation of gut contents also apply to coprolites. Furthermore the coprolite contains material which has successfully avoided digestion. It thus may indicate only part of the diet or may merely be a concentrate of unwanted or accidental food intake.

Trace fossils of animal feeding

Trace fossils may be studied by various techniques (LM, SEM, acetate peels, thin sections etc.) dependent largely on the preservation state of the host material. Trace fossils of plant feeding by arthropods are represented by bite marks, mines and galls preserved commonly on fossil leaves (see Chapter 58). Borings through tissues may indicate tissue-feeding (herbivory or detritivory) or use as shelter or dwelling (Boucot 1990, pp. 368–376; Labandeira *et al.* 1997). Borings in seeds may indicate seed predation by insect larvae or by adult insects with piercing mouthparts (Collinson 1990, 1998; Labandeira 1998; Hooker & Collinson in

press). In one Tertiary example, on Rutaceae seeds (Fig. 59.3a), host specificity is implied (Collinson 1998). Gnaw marks on fossil seeds (Fig. 59.3c) provide direct evidence of rodent seed-predation hence of rodent diet consisting of hard seeds or nuts (Collinson 1990, Collinson & Hooker 1991, Hooker & Collinson in press).

Food caches

Food caches indicate not only a particular diet but also distinctive feeding behaviour. Recognition of food caches must be in their field context. The oldest records are Miocene: a *Celtis*-filled heteromyid (kangaroo-rat) burrow and an accumulation of *Carya* nuts in a silicified tree stump (Collinson 1998). Cenozoic diffuse co-evolution between rodents and angiosperm families producing larger dry nuts (Collinson & Hooker 1991; Hooker & Collinson in press) suggests that food caching was probably a common behaviour, hence that fossil food caches should be more common than currently recorded.

Tooth morphology and microwear

Microwear is studied by SEM whilst teeth may be studied by SEM or LM using originals or casts (Collinson 1993; Chapter 12). The ability to mould and cast teeth or single wear facets enables study of a wide range of fossils with minimum impact on the specimens themselves. The dominant vertebrate plant-eaters of the Palaeozoic and Mesozoic probably fed on all parts of the plant with little dental specialization (Behrensmeyer *et al.* 1992). Complex dental batteries in hadrosaurs and other possible dietary adaptations in dinosaurs are discussed by Farlow (1987).

The Cenozoic fossil record of mammal teeth is highly informative regarding ancient diets (Collinson & Hooker 1987, 1991; Hooker & Collinson in press). Feeding on fruits or seeds requires pulping or crushing and involves vertical jaw movements. Leaf-feeding involves shearing and grinding and a dominantly horizontal jaw movement. Teeth of mammalian frugivores thus have blunt cusps with little cresting and multi-directional microwear concentrated on the cusp tips. In contrast, mammalian herbivores have strong cresting and distinct wear facets with unidirectional microwear (Fig. 59.4b). Intermediate states indicate mixed diets (Fig. 59.4a). Crown height indicates coarseness of diet (highest in herbivore grazers) and the semi-high crowned nature of *Thalerimys* (Fig. 59.4a) shows that it ate a relatively coarse diet. Microwear is influenced by variations in diet. For example, large, deep pits and gouges are super-

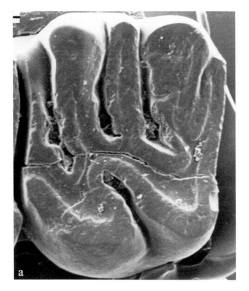 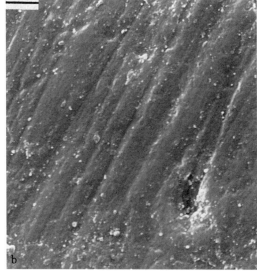

Fig. 59.4. SEM of casts (see Chapter 12) showing Cenozoic mammalian tooth morphology and microwear: (**a**) rodent tooth *Thalerimys*, with a mixed diet of herbivore browsing and frugivory, scale bar 100 µm; (**b**) unidirectional microwear on an artiodactyl tooth of *Dichodon*, indicating herbivore browsing, scale bar 10 µm. (a) and (b) both from the late Eocene, southern England.

imposed on (or may obscure) the unidirectional microwear scratches in herbivore grazers. These gouges are caused by silica phytoliths in grasses and their absence shows that *Dichodon* (Fig. 59.4b) was a herbivore browser, not a grazer. Dental features combined with locomotor adaptation and evidence from fossil floras, enable deduction of diffuse co-evolution between mammals and flowering plant-dominated vegetation, including diet and dispersal strategies, through the Cenozoic (Collinson & Hooker 1987, 1991; Hooker & Collinson in press).

$\delta^{13}C$ isotopic records

Discrimination against ^{13}C in favour of ^{12}C in plants results in characteristic carbon isotopic compositions reflecting the photosynthetic pathway (C_3, C_4 or crassulacean acid metabolism (CAM)).

These characteristics are conveyed to the carbon of animals feeding on plants. A diet with the C_4 plant signal has been recognized in shells of sub-Recent land snails (Goodfriend 1988) and in tooth enamel of Neogene mammals. A transition occurs in North American horses between a dominantly C_3 diet, a mixed diet and a C_4 diet at around 7 Ma (Wang *et al.* 1994; MacFadden & Cerling 1996). This effect has also been noted globally and amongst other grazing mammal groups (Cerling *et al.* 1993; MacFadden & Cerling 1996) and is taken to indicate the onset of a diet containing C_4 grasses. It post-dates the development of dental morphology of grazers (feeding presumably on C_3 grasses) by several million years. MacFadden (1998) extended the use of isotopic evidence to two sympatric fossil rhinos and inferred their niche differentiation as a browser and a mixed C_3/C_4 terrestrial grazer. Koch (1998) reviewed other examples.

Part Ten International Laws

60. International laws: collecting, transporting and ownership of fossils

Australia

JOHN G. DOUGLAS

Fossil collection in Australia is facilitated by public ownership of a great deal of the most prospective areas, notably the shoreline, stream frontages and road reserves. For example, the Canowindra, New South Wales Late Devonian fish site is in a road reserve, and Dinosaur Cove, with reptile and plant remains, is in the Otway National Park, Victoria, a coastal reserve. By and large anyone can collect fossils anywhere if they obtain approval from landowners or the authority with jurisdiction.

Legislated restriction on collecting and removing fossil specimens is confined to Heritage and Park Reserves and it is becoming increasingly difficult for amateur collectors to obtain legal access to sites in these areas. Accredited scientists can, however, almost always obtain approval to collect, without financial impost. This situation will be affected by future rulings under the recently enacted Native Titles Act whereby enormous areas, especially in the northern part of the continent, may pass out of public into Koori (Aboriginal) control.

A handful of sites outside National Park or equivalent reservation have been recognized under the Australian Heritage Commission Act, 1975, and registered as part of the National Estate. Status thus acquired, however, is largely theoretical, such recognition usually only occurring at the instigation of some concerned natural history group and it is left to the local Municipality or pertinent authority to identify and supervise. In any case there appears to be only three sites in this category, and it may be of interest that all contain fossil plant assemblages. Two of these, the Limestone Road Silurian *Baragwanathia longifolia* (primitive lycophyte) locality at Yea, and the Early Cretaceous Koonwarra Fish Beds with fish, plant, insect and other remains, including feathers, are in Victoria. The other is the Jurassic Talbragar Fish Beds near Gulgong, New South Wales.

Up to about ten years ago, apart from certain relatively easily evaded customs regulations, access to lucrative overseas markets was practically unrestricted, but blatant exploitation and vandalism by 'get-rich-quick' operators prompted the PROTECTION OF MOVABLE CULTURAL HERITAGE ACT 1986. This was amended in 1993, principally by removing a $A1000 valuation limit on palaeontological objects rendering all fossils, irrespective of value, subject to the Regulations and necessitating a Permit before export from Australia. This Act was designed not only to prevent the outflow of Australian cultural objects, but also to support the protection of those of other countries. The Act defines our movable cultural heritage as 'objects that are of importance to Australia, or to a particular part of Australia, for ethnological, archaeological, historical, literary, artistic, scientific or technological reasons'.

A 'palaeontological' object is therein defined as:

(a) a vertebrate or invertebrate fossil or plant fossil or trace fossil specimen, not being a fossil fuel or fossiliferous rock used or intended for any use relating to industry;

(b) a carving or a sculpture made from fossiliferous or fossilized material;

(c) any material, record or thing of scientific significance in relation to palaeontology; and;

(d) a precious opal replacement fossil of a vertebrate or invertebrate animal.

The particularly Australian character of (d) was given impetus by the prospect at the time of sale overseas of opalized pliosaur remains from Coober Pedy, South Australia. Persons convicted of unlawful export under the Act are subject to a fine not exceeding $A100,000 and/or imprisonment not exceeding 5 years.

The 1993 amendment also enlarged the reference to type species, including a definition of lectotype, neotype, paratype and syntype. An earlier amendment, contained in the Arts, Tourism and Territories Legislation Amendment Act 1990, allows a principal collecting institution (e.g. a public museum) 'to apply to the Minister for a permit to export a ... object that is accessioned into the collection for which the institute is responsible'. It should be emphasized that the Protection of Movable Cultural Heritage Act with amendments does not have any bearing on the collection or sale of Australian fossils within Australia. As is often the case with this type of legislation, there have been many complaints about its shortcomings. These include laxity of enforcement, and other aspects such as a requirement for specimen valuation on current Australian market value rather than on overseas market value, which may be up to ten times the local price.

As noted earlier there is little or no other specific State or Territory **legislation** covering fossil

International laws: collecting, transporting and ownership of fossils   323
In: JONES, T. P. & ROWE, N. P. (eds) *Fossil Plants and Spores: modern techniques.*
Geological Society, London, 323–338.

collecting except in the Northern Territory and Queensland, where recent legislation covering fossicking is pertinent. The Fossicking Act 1994 in Queensland separates fossicking activity from commercial mining. Fossicking is here defined as searching for and collection of gemstones, ornamental stones, minerals including alluvial gold nuggets, and 'some fossil specimens'. Meteorites and fossils of vertebrate animals are not included, and thus prohibited from collection under a Fossicking Licence. Again fossicking is not permitted in National Parks or State Reserves, except by special arrangement.

In the Northern Territory a Fossicker's Permit entitles search for 'rocks, minerals, crystals or fossils by hand or using hand-held implements to a depth of only one metre'.

I thank Mr Frank Holmes, for drawing attention to his comments in *The Fossil Collector* (Bulletin 36 of The Fossil Collectors Association of Australasia, ISSN 1037-2997) on the Protection of Movable Cultural Heritage Act 1986.

Belgium

PHILIPPE GERRIENNE

There is no specific legislation in Belgium concerning the collection of fossils but certain federal and regional laws protect valuable geological sites and thus may indirectly protect fossils. The Nature Conservation Act of 1973 (federal law) aims to safeguard 'the character, diversity and integrity of the natural environment through protective measures of the fauna and flora and their habitats' (Stein 1991). Although this law is especially intended for the protection of wildlife, it also provides protection for interesting geological or pedological sites (Jacobs 1997). The Federal Act of 1973 allowed the creation of nature reserves. Once a site has been classified, digging, drilling and any form of exploitation that might modify the soil or any aspect of the terrain is forbidden. The Monument and Landscape Conservation Act of 1931 recommends that both National monuments and the landscape can be protected through a procedure that regulates changes and may limit the activities of the owner (Jacobs 1997). According to this law, every Belgian citizen, organization or local authority may request the conservation and protection of a monument or site. Since the federalization of Belgium, which began in 1970, conservation has been transferred to both the Flemish and French Communities. Nevertheless, some aspects are still ruled by federal laws, that might be different from local decrees. In Flanders (north Belgium), the distinction is made between 'valuable geological objects' (i.e. small trans-

portable objects such as fossils) and 'valuable geological sites'. Unfortunately, no specific protection of the former exists. Under some conditions, the latter can be protected by the 1931 and/or 1973 Acts. In Wallonia (south Belgium), four laws/ decrees contribute to the protection of the geological heritage. The 1973 Federal Act is still valid today and permits the creation of nature reserves. The 1931 Act has been replaced by 'The Immovable Cultural Patrimony Protection Decree' of July, 1987 of the French Community. This decree aims to protect 'all immovable goods for historical, archaeological, scientific, artistic, social or technical reasons' (Franssen 1991) and also permits official 'classification' of a given site. As an example, the Vilaine Source cave and natural spring at Profondeville is protected for a range of scientific reasons in addition to its importance as an attractive part of the landscape (Jacobs 1997). According to the Quarry Decree of October 1988 of the Walloon Regional Council, the authorization of commercial exploitation includes recommendations on the planning and restoration of the site after exploitation. This procedure also includes regulations to protect the site on the basis of geological potential and not necessarily commercial value (Franssen 1991, Jacobs 1997). Article 40 of the Walloon Code for Land Management and Urbanisation authorizes partial revisions of regional or local development plans. Some of the latter have already been used to classify karst sites and other valuable geological locations termed 'natural areas'. It would thus be theoretically possible to protect fossil outcrops by including them within 'natural areas of scientific interest'. However, in order for them to be included in local mapped plans the regulations state, rather arbitrarily, that the site must have an area of at least 1 ha (Franssen 1991).

Information about the status and collectability of any site is available at the following addresses: (for sites situated in Wallonia) Ministère de la Région Wallonne, Direction générale des Ressources Naturelles et de l'Environnement, Service Conservation de la Nature et Espaces Verts, Avenue Prince de Liège 15, B-5100 Jambes; (for sites situated in Flanders) Ministerie van de Vlaamse Gemmeenschap, Administratie van Ruimtelijke Ordening en Leefmilieu, Bestuur Landinrichting, Dienst Natuurbehoud, Markiesstraat 1, B-1000 Brussels.

Canada

ROBERT R. OGILVIE

Canada is one of the largest countries in the world and has a rich and varied fossil resource. The

Canadian government does not regulate collection of fossils, since management of fossils is a provincial concern. Predictably, this leads to a wide variation in regulatory approach across the country. Over-collecting and associated problems have led to strict regulation in those provinces with the most significant resources.

Five of the six eastern provinces – Newfoundland, Prince Edward Island, New Brunswick, Quebec and Ontario – have no specific laws or regulations governing the collection, transportation or ownership of fossils. In Quebec, large-scale excavations may be controlled under the province's mining laws, but small-scale collecting is unregulated. As with most jurisdictions, parks and protected areas are not open for collecting and are usually subject to internal regulation.

Nova Scotia manages its fossil resources under the Special Places Protection Act, administered by the Nova Scotia Museum for the Department of Education and Culture. Sites of outstanding significance may be designated as Protected Sites, but all fossil exploration requires a Heritage Research Permit. Only qualified researchers are permitted to collect *in situ* material, though lengthy coastal exposures provide ample opportunities for finding loose fossils. All collected fossils belong to the government and must be submitted to the Nova Scotia Museum, which acts as the provincial repository for fossils and associated reports. As with most museums, that institution lends fossils for exhibition and research.

Manitoba manages its fossil resource through the Heritage Resources Act, administered by the Department of Culture, Heritage and Citizenship. Permits are required for all fossil exploration, and a provincial Export Permit is needed to take fossils across the provincial border. Again, all fossils belong to the province. Manitoba has a custody provision in place by which landowners may retain possession of fossils found on their land. Fossils found on Crown lands, the Canadian equivalent of public lands, may be placed in the custody of the finder. In both cases, ownership stays with the government and the fossils cannot be sold, lent, or moved across the border without permission.

Saskatchewan regulates its fossils under the Heritage Property Act, administered by the Department of Municipal Government. Permits are available for avocational and professional research. All macro and trace fossils belong to the provincial government, and no commercial collecting is allowed. Protected areas may be designated under the Act, but to date only one Heritage Property Site has been established.

Alberta is widely known for its dinosaur fossils. The Historical Resources Act, which is administered by the Department of Community Develop-

ment, regulates the collection of all fossils found in the province. Three types of permits are available: surface collection, excavation for research purposes, and excavation for commercial purposes. Only ammonites and ammonite shell for use in the jewellery industry, and fossil oyster shell used for animal feed, can be commercially excavated. A Disposition Certificate is required for this type of commercial operation. The province claims ownership of all fossils collected after 1978, which is when the Act was proclaimed. Moving fossils out of the province requires a Disposition Certificate and/or Provincial Export Permit except for approved institutions.

British Columbia has no specific laws for managing fossils, but the provisions of the Heritage Conservation Act are occasionally turned to that purpose. It is possible to designate significant fossil areas, and important fossils can be claimed for the government. Casual collecting on Crown land is allowed but excavation requires a license of occupancy, which is similar to a permit.

Though the federal government does not have specific laws governing the collection and ownership of fossils, it does have an interest in regulating the movement of fossils across its national borders. Fossils included in a Control List may not be exported from Canada without a Federal Export Permit approved by the Cultural Property Export Review Board. The Control List identifies those fossils that require a permit: type specimens, fossil amber, vertebrate and invertebrate fossil specimens valued at more than $Can250, bulk collections of vertebrate fossils or vertebrate trace fossils weighing more than 11.25 kg, or bulk collections of invertebrate fossils, plant fossils or fossiliferous rock weighing more than 22.5 kg. Permits are required both for loans and for material that is permanently leaving the country.

Laws and regulations are continually changing as jurisdictions examine the nature and value of their fossil resource. The wide range of regulatory regimes across Canada demonstrates the range of values placed on fossils and the difficulty of protecting them. Are they potentially important scientific specimens, valuable collectors' pieces, or merely curiosities and trinkets? The answers to these questions, when combined with the use or abuse of the resource, will continue to guide public policy in this area.

China

CHENG-SEN LI

There are many fossil plant sites in China where exceptional fossil material has been found and collected. However, only relatively few laws and regulations in China specifically relate to the protection of fossil sites and the collection and national export of fossils. The national 'Law for the Preservation of Antiquities of the People's Republic of China' (November 1982) states that fossil vertebrates and anthropological material of scientific importance are to be protected by the national government. This ruling is similar to that for cultural relics. The application for excavating fossils must be submitted to and approved by the Cultural Department Administration of the Chinese Government. Exportation of fossils must be declared to the customs and then verified and approved by the Cultural Department Administration. The legislation included in the 'Regulations for Nature Reserves of the People's Republic of China' (September 1994) includes geological sections, glacial structures, Karst areas, waterfalls and fossil locations. Such sites are listed and protected as Nature Reserves and collection of fossils is prohibited unless specifically permitted by the national or local governments.

Other legislation is more specifically related to geological and palaeontological material. The 'Provisions for the Protection and Administration of Geological Remains' (November 1994, Department of Geology and Mineral Resources) states that fossils and their locations relating to anthropology, vertebrates, invertebrates, micropalaeontology and palaeobotany should be protected. Collection of fossils under this legislation may be permitted by the national government administration.

Laws relating to fossils may also exist from local governments. An example includes a case concerning well preserved animal and plant fossils from the Miocene of Shanwang, Linqu county, Shandong Province, where the local Linqu County Government provided a public notice on September 4, 1995, stating that collection of fossils was prohibited unless permission was granted from the National Government for the purpose of scientific research.

The Chinese Academy of Sciences and its institutes such as the Institute of Botany (Beijing), and the Department of Geology and Mineral Resources, are authorities that can obtain permission to collect plant fossils for scientific research in Nature Reserves. Plant fossils may be exported outside of the country with the approval of the Chinese Academy of Sciences or other authoritative agencies.

France

JEAN GALTIER

In France the legal system concerning general Nature Conservation applies to the whole country without significant differences between one Région or Département and another. France has recently developed a number of laws concerning the protection of fossiliferous sites, but there are no clear regulations governing the collection, transport and ownership of fossils. Fossils are fundamentally the property of the landowner. Fossil collecting is strictly controlled or forbidden only in nature reserves and protected areas described below (Billet 1994, 1997).

On private land, permission must always be obtained from the owner. The same applies if the area is public, e.g. if it is a 'terrain communal', owned by a municipality. Any collecting activity undertaken without permission of the landowner is open to civil action in Court. Mention must be made of the recent 1995 law to 'reinforce the protection of the environment', which forbids the destruction of fossiliferous sites, as well as collecting fossils. An exception is made for collecting fossils for research or teaching activities. In the near future, this law will refer to a list of protected sites, but this list has yet to be published.

There is no direct control by the French government on the export of fossils out of the country.

Several laws have been designed to protect natural sites, including those of scientific interest. The 1930 law on the 'Protection of natural monuments and sites' was the first to mention site conservation of general interest to science. This law has been updated significantly by another ruling (July 1976) which allowed the creation of more than 100 nature reserves protecting, among others, geological and palaeontological sites. Ten of these reserves are strictly geological reserves. One example is the 'Réserve Géologique de Haute Provence' near Digne which was created in 1984 and is the largest geological reserve in Europe. It includes 18 different sites of geological and palaeontological interest (Martini 1994).

The original 'Réserve naturelle' only applied to publicly owned areas but this was modified in the 1976 law, which could apply to privately owned areas. On the request of the landowner, the agreement for a 'Réserve' can be delivered by the 'Préfet du Département' but 'Réserves' are generally for only individual sites rather than large-scale reserves. The procedure is relatively rapid and has been successfully applied to protect palaeontological sites where each site constitutes a 'Réserve naturelle volontaire'. Fossil collecting in Réserves naturelles is under the control of the Réserve Administration and Scientific Committee. A few palaeobotanical sites are included within existing Natural Reserves in France such as the Réserve Géologique de Haute Provence. Finally, legal ownership may be a matter for the local courts and, as such, might produce ambiguous legislation for palaeontological material. This was aptly demonstrated by a recent affair concerning a Plesiosaur skeleton which was first identified by a collector discovering a few vertebrae on privately owned land. The local court at Millau (central France) refused to consider the entire fossil as a national treasure and the collector – who was not the landowner – was declared the owner of the few vertebrae, but not the entire skeleton (Crochet 1994)!

The Netherlands

JOHANNA H. A. VAN KONIJNENBURG-VAN CITTERT

In the Netherlands there is a 'law for mining' which deals with everything concerning the subterranean search and exploitation of coal, oil, natural gas and salt. Permission from the Ministry of Economy is necessary for these economical aims, and representative samples of every boring etc. have to be presented to the Geological Survey for storage. Permission from the ministry is not needed for scientific research. The programme must include safety precautions and every project has to be announced to the ministry.

In the past many Carboniferous plant fossils were collected from underground mines and from spoil tips in the southern part of the Netherlands. A representative collection is kept at the Natural History Museum at Leiden (Naturalis). Nowadays, the mines are closed and there is only one spoil tip left where fossils can be collected with permission from the owners (see also below), but as this is more or less exhausted, collecting there no longer really occurs.

Boreholes for oil and gas yield mainly palynological samples which are studied and kept by either the Geological Survey or by oil companies who have the appropriate concession. Occasionally, the Laboratory for Palaeobotany and Palynology is included in such studies, the results of which are confidential.

For surface locations, such as quarries and spoil tips, only permission from the owners is needed to collect fossils, both in the loose lying material and *in situ*. There is no special law regarding the transport and ownership of these fossils, which means that anyone may possess and transport fossils which they have collected themselves (with permission from the owner of the locality). However, scientists working with fossils are only permitted to possess a private collection when the material is superfluous to the Institute's (Museum, Laboratory, Geological Survey) collection. There are no further rules for the ownership of fossils

which means that any owner of fossils can sell or present them to an institute or private persons.

There is one exception to these rules concerning the collecting of fossils from surface locations, and that is for Geological Monuments. To date, only one Geological Monument has been assigned (the 'Heymans Quarry' – the only place where Carboniferous sediments crop out in the Netherlands) but in the near future there will be approximately 25 Geological Monuments which will be controlled by the Foundation for the Conservation of Landscape Elements. In Geological Monuments it is (for the general public) forbidden to collect. For scientific purposes, a basic permission is necessary to collect from loose material, and a special permission to collect material *in situ*.

Spain

ANTONIO J. GONZÁLEZ-BARRIOS & ROBERT H. WAGNER

The conservation, protection and public use of geological sites containing important fossil localities, are topics that have come to the fore in recent years as a result of increased public awareness of the palaeontological heritage of Spain (Alcalá & Morales 1994). This awareness has been fuelled by newspaper articles on human fossil remains from Atapuerca and other sites, dinosaur footprints and other spectacular finds. Legal protection from destruction, commercial collectors and palaeontological tourism (trips organized on a commercial basis for private collectors of fossils), is coming into force, but is applied with varied degrees of stringency in different autonomous regions of Spain. Legal provisions applicable to palaeontological remains are generally partly an offshoot of the law protecting archaeological remains and partly a corollary to the general aspects of conservation of the natural environment and wildlife.

The most important law concerning the protection of fossil sites is the 'Ley de Patrimonio Histórico Español' (Spanish Historical Heritage Law, 16/1985, 25 June). Its first article establishes protection for '... fixed and movable objects of artistic, historical, palaeontological, archaeological, ethnographic, scientific or technical interest in the Spanish Historical Heritage'. This broad definition puts palaeontological material in the same category as archaeological and artistic objects, and opens the door to the same sort of conservation measures for palaeontology as archaeology. This could entail the obligation to halt any excavation that puts at risk the physical integrity of fossil remains of unusual interest. Whereas this obligation is reasonable in the case of human fossils in the archaeological context, it is less reasonable where mining operations uncover any other fossil remains. Strict application of the law may then become either unenforceable or lead to the wilful destruction of valuable fossil remains so as to avoid interference with excavations planned for industrial purposes. Indeed, the Spanish Historical Heritage Law requires the discovery of a palaeontological site to be notified within 24 hours. On the other hand, this law does not establish the ownership of fossils (as movable objects).

Geological heritage is also protected under a law that promotes the conservation of the Natural Environment and Wildlife (Law 4/89: Conservación de los Espacios Naturales, de la Flora y Fauna silvestres). This requires the site to be proposed and classed as either a 'Protected Area' or a 'Natural Monument' (Espacio Protegido, Monumento Natural). A 'Protected Area' implies the integrated planning of natural resources of the area involved, and thus can put restraints on mining, quarrying and any other exploitation.

With the gradual transfer of powers of government to the 17 autonomous regions of Spain, the majority have adopted National Heritage legislation which reproduces quite faithfully the laws enacted by the Spanish State. However, the workings of the law differ between regions and depend on the interest that has been taken: only a start has been made with the listing of sites in most regions.

The Historical Heritage Law dealing with the 'Patrimonio Histórico Español', mentions fossils as part of this heritage, but since it has been drawn up with a marked emphasis on archaeology it stresses the palaeontological and geological elements related to human endeavours and thus ignores the broader aspects of geological heritage.

Under Law 4/89 dealing with the Natural Environment and Wildlife, geological and palaeontological interests are subordinated to general environmental considerations. Article 16.2 envisages the declarations of 'Monumento Natural' for geological formations, fossil localities and others related to earth sciences, when they are of special interest because of their singularity and importance scientifically and with regard to the landscape. A total of 52 Monumentos Naturales have been recognized throughout Spain, but 50 of these are in the Canary Islands – half dealing specifically with volcanic formations. None of the Monumentos Naturales recognized thus far refer to sites of palaeontological interest. Article 26.4 prohibits the possession, trafficking and commerce of specimens of wild animals, dead or alive, or **their remains** (our emphasis); the latter may be construed as referring to fossils which may thus be regarded as falling under the prohibition of possession and commerce, even where there is no specific protection as conferred by a declaration of 'Monumento Natural'. This law is being used in various autonomous regions to prohibit digging for fossils without express permission. There have also been cases of commercial fossil collectors having their proceeds confiscated by the police.

Law 4/89, enacted for the protection of the Natural Environment and Wildlife in general, provides for the declaration of special areas for the protection of the natural environment (Planes de Ordenación de los Recursos Naturales de los Espacios Protegidos – PORN). The autonomous governments are competent to institute PORNs and do so with varying degrees of intensity in the various autonomous regions. Geological interests are paramount in only a small percentage of cases, and it is most common to find these interests alluded to vaguely in terms of a general recommendation to conserve. Geologists are only a small minority among the naturalists who are called upon to propose and defend PORNs, and the effectiveness of protection for sites of geological interest often depend in practice on local pressure groups who warn about destruction and exploitation, in which case, the law is activated because of social pressure.

Most of the autonomous regions have not yet enacted their own laws regarding their cultural and historical heritage, so it seems that we are only at the beginning of a long process which is to start with an inventory of what constitutes this heritage in any one of the regions. Indeed, some of the autonomous governments are moving in this direction, and this includes inventories of fossil sites of international repute. Only when it has been clearly established what needs to be preserved, will the most effective means emerge to protect and enact the requisite laws and ordinances. Until then, the loose wording of the existing laws, which were not specifically drawn up to protect and preserve the geological and palaeontological heritage of Spain and its constituent regions, will only allow protection in certain cases.

South Africa

JOHN M. ANDERSON

The winds of change are still blowing strongly through South Africa. Universal franchise came in 1994 and the newly written Constitution was signed in early 1997. In 1996 a white paper on the Arts, Culture and Heritage outlined a new policy and vision for heritage conservation in the country. In 1997 a draft National Heritage Bill was submitted to Parliament and is expected to be implemented as legislation in April 1998. Laws affecting 'palaeontological' collecting and collections currently fall under the National Monuments Act – in place since 1969 – and are monitored by the National Monuments Council.

We will first outline the essence of the draft National Heritage Bill as far as it pertains to palaeontology and then consider the principal differences between it and the present Act. Fossil plants and fossil animals are handled similarly in both the old and the new systems.

The draft National Heritage Bill

The new legislation and structures are designed to protect all heritage resources: defined as any place or object of cultural significance. Palaeontological sites and specimens fall within this ambit. 'Palaeontological' is defined in the draft Bill as 'any fossilized remains or fossil trace of animals or plants which lived in the geological past, other than fossil fuels or fossiliferous rock intended for industrial use and any site which contains such fossilized remains or trace'. A three-tiered management system – local, provincial and national – will operate.

Local

Accessibility and involvement are the key words. NGOs (non-governmental organizations, e.g. Mountain Club, Bird Society, Amateur Palaeontological Society) and local authorities are encouraged to identify heritage resources that are of significance to their communities, so that these can be protected.

Provincial

The province will be responsible for the management of heritage resources identified within their area and will keep a register of all (provincial heritage) places and objects.

National

A South African Heritage Agency (SAHA) will replace the current Head Office of the National Monuments Council and will be accountable to a National Heritage Resources Commission with seven to fifteen members appointed by the relevant minister. The SAHA will co-ordinate a national inventory of heritage resources, promote public awareness and heritage education, erect a financial assistance programme to promote and conserve heritage resources, liaise with foreign and international heritage organizations and observe conventions, control the export and import of heritage objects, and take care of heritage places.

Registered and declared places and objects are **formally protected**. All fossil sites (whether on private or public land) and specimens are, however, automatically protected by virtue of requiring a permit to excavate, collect and export. If a site is likely to be affected by certain categories of development, the provincial heritage authority may demand an impact assessment and mitigation.

From old Act to new Bill

The more significant changes affecting fossil plants in the new draft Bill include: involvement of local authorities and communities; all fossils are automatically the property of the State; fossils may not be collected or sold without a permit; all private collections must be registered with the SAHA or the provincial authority within two years of the Act being promulgated; mining, agricultural and engineering activities are no longer exempted from obtaining a permit to destroy, damage, alter, excavate or remove heritage resources; impact assessment studies must be carried out to ensure that heritage resources are minimally destroyed; conservation management plans for each protected site must be drawn up and made available to the public.

Legacy to the future

The spirit of the new Bill is to preserve the greatest possible part of the country's heritage resource, cultural and natural, extant and extinct. In that the drafting committee pored over numerous local submissions and studied heritage legislation of many countries in Africa and further afield, we can develop the sense of merging into a global heritage network for all future generations to cherish.

I wish to express my thanks to Janette Deacon, member of staff of the National Monuments Council, who supplied me with the information included in this article.

United Kingdom

CHRISTOPHER J. CLEAL

No laws in this country deal specifically with fossil collecting. However, there are various points of legislation concerned with property, land ownership and conservation that touch on the collection and ownership of fossils. The following is not a definitive statement of the legal position, which is, in many cases, ambiguous and has not been tested in the courts, but is a brief summary of the law as widely perceived (for more detailed reviews, see Taylor & Harte 1988, 1991). Separate legal systems exist in England and Wales, in Scotland and in Northern Ireland, but the law relating to fossil collecting is mostly the same throughout the country.

Fossil collecting

There is no right of access to any land in Britain unless that right is specifically granted by the occupier. Any activity undertaken without permission of the occupier is trespass and open to civil action in the courts. A trespasser damaging a site or taking anything from it can also be subject to action for criminal damage or theft. Even where access is permitted, it may not be for all activities. For instance, public rights of way are usually only for travel between two points; even just looking at a site is technically trespass, unless sight-seeing is specifically permitted. Such restrictions may not always be applied in practice. For instance, access to coastal exposures between high and low waters (usually owned by the Crown or the local authority) is only rarely restricted. On private land, however, permission must always be obtained from the occupier, not only to access a site, but also for whatever activity you intend to carry out (e.g. collecting).

An *in situ* fossil belongs to whoever owns the mineral rights for the site. These rights often only apply to a particular mineral: one person could own rights on coal and associated strata, while another owns rights on the ironstone. The owner of the relevant mineral rights must therefore give unequivocal permission to collect and keep any fossil found.

Fossils obtained from loose material have been effectively abandoned by the landowner, and in most of Britain are ownerless and cannot be 'stolen'. In Scotland, however, abandoned material reverts to the Crown and so technically should only be collected after obtaining permission from the Crown. This all assumes that the collector is not trespassing; trespassers forfeit all rights of ownership to collected material.

Conserved sites

The 1981 Wildlife and Countryside Act empowers English Nature, Scottish Natural Heritage and Countryside Council for Wales to designate major palaeontological localities as Sites of Special Scientific Interest (SSSI). This legislation is mainly designed to protect sites from developments requiring formal planning permission, such as building, road construction and quarrying (see Wimbledon 1988 for a summary of the legal position). However, the landowner is also given a list of other Potential Damaging Operations (PDO) which must not be undertaken without permission from the conservation agencies (or without three months notice). Most PDO are not directly relevant to collecting (e.g. agricultural development). PDO 25 specifically restricts fossil collecting but this has

been assigned to very few palaeobotanical sites. It is, anyway, the landowner and not the collector who must obtain permission for collecting to take place at such sites, and it is the landowner who will be penalized if he/she knowingly permits unsanctioned collecting.

Collecting from SSSI otherwise does not differ from collecting from other sites; permission must be obtained from the owner(s) of the land and mineral rights, and from the occupier.

The coverage of Earth science SSSI was revised in the 1970s and 1980s (Wimbledon et al. 1995). The 93 selected palaeobotanical sites are listed in Cleal (1988) and the detailed justification for the 42 Palaeozoic sites given by Cleal & Thomas (1995) (the Mesozoic and Tertiary sites are described in Cleal & Thomas in press).

Ownership of fossils

If a fossil has been legally collected, the collector normally has full legal right to it. Landowners can sometimes insist on the return of a fossil collected from their land, even if they gave prior permission to collect, but there are several restrictions on this. Landowners can be prevented from reclaiming a fossil if significant resources (time and/or money) were invested in excavating and preparing it. Landowners also cannot reclaim a legally collected fossil after six years (or after twelve years in Scotland). In certain parts of Britain (e.g. London) landowners also lose their claim to a fossil once it has been sold to a third party.

Assuming that full legal right of ownership can be confirmed, the collector can do with the specimen as (s)he wishes – to keep it, sell it, give it away, or even destroy it. No institution (e.g. museum, conservation agency) has any legal claim to a fossil unless the ownership has been voluntarily transferred to that institution.

Export and import of fossils

The UK government currently exerts little direct control on this (Taylor 1991). Only if the fossil is part of an artefact (e.g. jewellery) can there be some restrictions in law.

USA

ROBERT A. GASTALDO

The assortment of private, Native American, state, and Federal lands in the United States has generated a large number of legislative efforts to control just about every conceivable activity that may pertain to collection of geological samples on these lands. There are four basic types of land-ownership in the United States – privately owned, reservation, state-owned, and federally-owned land. Each has its own set of rules for the legal collection of fossils. In the case of privately-owned lands, fossils are owned by the person who legally owns the land from which they were collected. A collector must have permission from the landowner to be on the land, and the landowner should transfer ownership of the fossils if they are to be owned by someone besides the original landowner. Local laws that govern collection on private lands are usually based upon city or county ordinances and generally fall under trespass legislation. In its broadest sense, trespass refers to a wrongful entry upon the lands of another and, depending upon the pertinent local laws, may constitute either a misdemeanor or major felony. Trespass laws also apply to autonomous Native American lands, as well as individual state and federal properties (overseen by a number of agencies). Hence, as is true in most other parts of the world, it is always best to obtain written permission from the landowner(s) before attempting to excavate and recover materials for scientific study. It is also true, as in most other parts of the world, that typical property owners are co-operative and willing to give permission to professionals in pursuit of basic research.

In the case of reservation-, state-, and federally-owned lands, there are many different laws that pertain to the collection of palaeontological specimens. West (1991) summarized the state regulations for palaeontological collecting and, although not a completely satisfactory reference (Gastaldo 1997), a recent publication by Wolberg & Reinard (1997) attempts to outline the legal requirements and personal liabilities for collection of scientific specimens on Native American (reservation), state, and federal lands. These references have been used primarily as the basis for this section. It should be noted, though, that within the past decade legislation has been introduced in the US Senate (e.g. the Vertebrate Paleontological Resources Protection Act and the Paleontological Resource Act) and House of Representatives (e.g. Paleontological Resources Preservation Act) to govern fossil collection on federal lands. Although these particular bills were not passed by the House or Senate, attempts to regulate collection of palaeontological material continue. For example, the Fossil Preservation Act of 1996 was introduced by Rep. T. Johnson to provide for the collection of fossils on Federal lands. This bill was subsequently referred to the Committee on Resources and the Committees on Agriculture, Transportation, and Infrastructure. The bill was also referred to the Subcommittee on Resource Conservation, Research and Forestry. No action was taken on this proposal by any committee or subcommittee during the 104th Legislative Session. Bills of this nature, if passed and enacted, could severely limit collection of palaeontological resources on federally controlled lands. Individuals planning to develop a research programme on US Government-controlled lands should consult the US Federal Register (http://www.access.gpo.gov/su_docs/index.html) or the Library of Congress (http://lcweb.loc.gov/) for legislation that post-dates this section to determine if any of these bills, or modified versions thereof, have become law. In addition, consultation with the agencies listed here should provide the information necessary to determine if your proposed activity will be affected by any of the pertinent laws discussed herein.

Native American lands

According to most treaties signed by the United States government and Native American Nations, reservation lands are not part of the United States. They are autonomous, sovereign nations under the protectorate of the United States government. Collection of any material from reservation land, therefore, involves permission from the landowner, the Bureau of Indian Affairs, and the local Tribal Council. The Bureau of Indian Affairs (http://www. doi.gov/bureau-indian-affairs.html), an agency within the Department of the Interior, acts as the trustee for lands owned by Native Americans. There are 300 separate Native American reservations, home to more than 500 individual tribes. Permits for collection on these lands must be obtained from area offices of the Bureau of Indian Affairs (Table 60.1) before or after consultation with the appropriate Native American Nation.

The Navajo Nation is unique in maintaining that fossils found on their lands are their property. Either archaeological or environmental clearances may be required before palaeontological excavations can begin on these lands. The Tribal Minerals Department reviews requests for permits and it appears that only this governing body has the ability to grant or deny collecting requests on Navajo Nation lands. The Federal Bureau of Land Management does not have jurisdiction.

United States government lands

Current federal laws that govern the collection of fossils on government-controlled lands may be either broad or restrictive in their standards and, because the oversight of federal properties is maintained by many different government entities, there are several non-overlapping agencies that administer them. These include the Department of the Interior (Bureau of Land Management [http://

Table 60.1. *Native American (Reservation) lands*

State	Office address	Telephone number
Alaska	Juneau Area Office, Bureau of Indian Affairs, Federal Building, PO Box 3-8000, Juneau, AK 99802.	(907) 586-7177
Arizona, California, Idaho, Nevada, and Utah	Phoenix Area Office, Bureau of Indian Affairs, No. 1 North First St, PO Box 10, Phoenix, AZ 8500.	(602) 379-6600
Arizona, New Mexico (Navajo Reservation only)	Navajo Area Office, Bureau of Indian Affairs, PO Box M, Window Rock, AZ 86515.	(602) 871-5151
California	Sacramento Area Office, Bureau of Indian Affairs, 2800 Cottage Way, Sacramento, CA 94203.	(916) 978-4691
Colorado and New Mexico	Albuquerque Area Office, Bureau of Indian Affairs, 615 First Street NW, PO Box 26567, Albuquerque, NM 87125.	(505) 766-3170
Florida, Louisiana, Maine, Mississippi, New York, North Carolina	Eastern Area Office, Bureau of Indian Affairs, 1951 Constitution Ave. NW, Washington, DC 20245.	(703) 235-2571
Iowa, Michigan, Minnesota, and Wisconsin	Minneapolis Area Office, Bureau of Indian Affairs, Chamber of Commerce Bldg, 15 South Fifth St, 6th Floor, Minneapolis, MN 55402.	(612) 349-3631
Kansas and West Oklahoma	Anadarko Area Office, Bureau of Indian Affairs, WCD-Office Complex, PO Box 368, Anadarko, OK 73005.	(405) 247-6673
Montana and Wyoming	Billings Area Office, Bureau of Indian Affairs, 316 North 26th St, Billings, MT 59101.	(406) 657-6315
Nebraska, North Dakota, and South Dakota	Aberdeen Area Office, Bureau of Indian Affairs, 115 4th Avenue SE, Aberdeen, SD 37401.	(605) 226-7343
East Oklahoma	Muskogee Area Office, Bureau of Indian Affairs, Old Federal Building, Muskogee, OK 74401.	(918) 687-2296
Oregon and Washington	Portland Area Office, Bureau of Indian Affairs, 1425 Irving Street, PO Box 3785, Portland, OR 97232.	(503) 231-6702

Native American (Reservation) lands governed by the Bureau of Indian Affairs offices with pertinent addresses and telephone numbers for requesting permission to collect scientific samples on these properties. Distribution of Native American lands can be viewed at http://www.wes.army.mil/el/ccspt/natamap/usa_pg.html

www.blm.gov/] and the U.S. Geological Survey [http://www.usgs.gov/]) and Department of Agriculture (US Forest Service – http://www.fs.fed.us/). Federal laws that regulate the collection of fossils and protect them as national resources include the Antiquities Act of 1906, the Historic Sites Act of 1935, the Petrified Wood Act of 1962, the National Historic Preservation Act of 1966, the National Environmental Policy Act of 1969, the Federal Land Policy Management Act of 1976, and the National Forest Management Act (modified in 1986).

The Antiquities Act of 1906 prohibits the excavation, damage, or removal of any object of antiquity located on lands owned or controlled by the US government without permission from the federal land manager who oversees the property. Under the legislation, permits to 'gather objects of antiquity' may be granted to 'properly qualified' individuals whose purpose is undertaken for the benefit of 'reputable museums, universities, colleges, or other recognized scientific or educational institutions...' The cases that have been brought to court under this Act have involved the removal of Native American artefacts; the only case that has involved palaeontological collection on federal property resulted in dismissal upon the legal argument that 'antiquities' was overbroad when applied to fossils (Wolberg & Reinard 1997).

The Petrified Wood Act of 1962 allows individuals to collect permineralized wood samples without a permit from most federal lands. Quantities are limited to twenty-five pounds (11.4 kg) per day, with a maximum limit of 250 pounds (113.6 kg) per year. A specimen that weighs more than the yearly limit requires a permit before it can be removed. Exceptions to this Act include National Park Service (http://www.nps.gov/) lands (e.g. Petrified Forest National Monument [AZ], Fossil Cycad National Monument [SD], Yellowstone National Park [WY]) where any natural object (including fossils) is prohibited from collection within the park boundaries and removal from the site. The Organic Act of 1916 which established the National Park Service, an agency that controls approximately 11% of public lands, explicitly states that the agency's purpose is to 'conserve the scenery and the natural and historic objects...to provide for the enjoyment of the same in such a manner and by such means as will leave them unimpaired for the enjoyment of future generations.' Hence, a special permit is required from the National Park Service for collection of these specimens (legislation pertaining to the National Parks Service is available at http://www.nps.gov/legal/index.html). All specimens become the property of the National Park Service, to whom they must be returned after the completion of the research. This philosophy was extended under the Historic Sites Act of 1935 and the National Historic Preservation Act of 1966 requiring the National Park Service to set aside a palaeontological site as a national landmark under the National Natural Landmarks program if it is 'an outstanding representative example of the nation's national heritage, including geological features...or fossil evidence of the development of life on Earth.' It is possible that private and Native American lands may be designated as NNL sites; therefore, it may be necessary to request permission from the National Park Service even if the landowner grants permission for collecting.

The National Environmental Policy Act (NEPA) of 1969 was enacted to preserve important historical, cultural and natural attributes of our national heritage. This Act requires that an environmental impact statement (EIS) be prepared for any major federal action that impacts the natural and physical environment, which may include the change in a land-management agency's regulations. In general, this law does not apply to the scale of collection experienced by most palaeontologists, but where extensive excavation may occur, the NEPA may apply.

The Federal Land Policy Management Act of 1976 established jurisdiction for the Bureau of Land Management (BLM, Washington Office, Office of Public Affairs, 1849 C Street - Room 504-LS, Washington, DC 20240; http://www.blm.gov/), the largest federal land management agency, controlling more than one-eighth of all US lands. This is particularly true in Nevada, where BLM controls more than 80% of public land, and Colorado, Idaho, New Mexico, Utah and Wyoming, where this agency controls nearly 50%. The disturbance, removal, or destruction, without a written permit from BLM, of any 'scientific, cultural, archaeological or historic resource, natural object or area' from BLM-controlled lands is illegal. Wilful violation may result not only in a fine but also a prison sentence. The Bureau of Land Management has interpreted fossil resources as being scientifically valuable and, therefore, informally regulates collecting at the state-office level. Three types of permits are granted only to 'academic, scientific, governmental, or other qualified institutions or individuals or companies.' These permits are (1) non-collection reconnaissance permits for mapping and surveying, (2) collected and limited removal permits that allow for surface collection, and (3) permits for excavation. Although there is no formal set of regulations governing collection on BLM lands, each state agency should be consulted prior to collection of specimens on any public lands under BLM jurisdiction (http://www.blm.gov/StateOffices.html).

The US Forest Service (http://www.fs.fed.us/) controls approximately 25% of all public lands through the National Forest Management Act. There is no specific regulation against collection of fossils on these public lands because in 1986 this activity was deemed 'a legitimate scientific and education pursuit.' Nevertheless, land managers may issue closure orders to protect 'objects or areas of ... geological, or paleontological interest.' In general, collection of palaeobotanical specimens in 'open' lands does not require permission from this agency. But, if palaeobotanical assemblages are found associated with vertebrate remains, then a permit would be required because fossil vertebrates have 'traditionally been accorded special significance' subject to regulation. Violations are subject to fines, prison sentences, or both.

Applicable state laws

As might be expected in a country comprised of fifty individual states, laws governing the collection of palaeontological specimens on state properties range from non-existent to very specific, usually as the result of litigation that has transpired within that state's court system. Each state in the United States controls land and is responsible for establishing regulations for and monitoring its use. Paralleling federal land policies, the basic premise of states is that the contents of state lands are public property. Thus, public property must be deposited in a public repository once it has been removed from its site. Some states, such as Alabama, Arkansas, Florida and Louisiana (Fig. 60.1; Table 60.2) have enacted no legislation concerning the

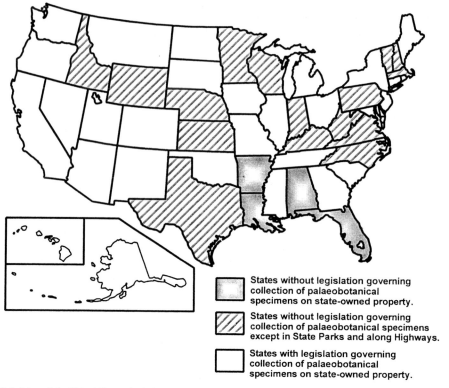

Fig. 60.1. Map of the United States depicting states in which there is no legislation regarding palaeontological collection on state-owned properties, where limited permitting is required to collect on specific state-owned lands, and states in which there is regulation of fossil collecting and the requirement for a collection permit.

collection of invertebrate and plant fossils on state properties. In some instances, though, laws have been enacted in these particular states to protect and preserve vertebrate palaeontological sites (e.g. Florida). In other states, the few laws governing collection of palaeontological specimens on state property are restricted to State Parks, Highways, and/or Forests (Table 60.2). Only a few states have enacted very restrictive laws governing fossil collection and, in many instances, these laws are enforced by the State Archaeologist (e.g. Alaska, Colorado, Georgia, Iowa, Massachusetts, Montana, South Carolina, Tennessee). In other cases, palaeontological collection on state-owned lands is overseen by the state's museum director. For example, Arizona requires a permit to be issued by the Director of the State Museum for excavation or collection of any 'paleontological or historical feature situated on lands owned or controlled by the state of Arizona, or any agency thereof.' Permits in Arizona are granted for a one-year duration. But, in most cases, a state's Department of Environmental or Natural Resources, Parks and Recreation,

Educational Lands and Funds, or Transportation is the agency controlling permitting. In only a very few instances is the state geological survey assigned the task of oversight (e.g. Mississippi, North Dakota, Utah). More states are increasingly reluctant to allow materials collected from their lands to be transported beyond state boundaries. Several states have now declared specific state museums as official repositories, and have dictated that materials collected on public lands be placed into that repository (Table 60.2).

Conclusions

Legislation concerning collection of palaeontological samples varies considerably from one government agency to another, ranging from complete indifference towards collection to severe restrictions on government-owned land. Land-use restrictions are more common in the southeastern and western United States because these areas are generally least vegetated, leaving their geological resources easily accessible. Additionally, these

Table 60.2. *State laws governing collection of fossil plants from State property*

State	Laws governing collection of fossil plants on State property	State Agency responsible for administering laws & granting permits
Alabama	NO	
Alaska	YES	Divison of Parks, Office of History & Archaeology, PO Box 107001, Anchorage, AK 99510 [1]
Arizona	YES	Arizona State Museum, University of Arizona, Tucson, AZ 85721 [2] (Note: Fossil plants are not specified in statutes, but State trespass statute is very broad.)
Arkansas	NO/YES	Director of State Parks, Arkansas State Parks, One Capitol Mall, Little Rock, AR 72201
California	YES	Department of Natural Resources, California State Lands Commission, 1807 13th Street, Sacramento, CA 95814
Colorado	YES	(1) Office of the State Archaeologist, 1300 Broadway, Denver, CO 80203 [2]; (2) Colorado Division of Parks and Outdoor Recreation, 1313 Sherman Street, Room 618, Denver, CO 80203; (3) Colorado Division of Wildlife, 6060 Broadway, Denver, CO 80216; (4) Colorado Department of Highways, 4201 East Arkansas Ave., Denver, CO 80222
Connecticut	YES	Department of Environmental Protection, Parks and Recreation Unit, State Office Building, Room 267, Hartford, CT 06106 [2]
Delaware	YES	Public Lands Commission, Department of Natural Resources and Environmental Control, Richardson Robbins Bldg., 89 Kings Highway , PO Box 1401, Dover, DE 19903
Florida,	NO	
Georgia	YES	State Archeologist, Department of Natural Resources, 270 Washington Street Southwest, Atlanta, GA 30334 [2]
Hawaii	YES	Department of Land and Natural Resources, 1151 Punchbowl Street, Honolulu, HI 96813[1]
Idaho	NO/YES	(1) Bureau of Minerals, Department of Lands, State House, Room 121, Boise, ID 83702; (2) Department of Parks and Recreation, 2177 Warm Springs Ave., Boise, ID 83720 [3, 4]
Illinois	YES	(1) Illinois State Museum, 1920 10th Street South, Springfield, IL 62704 [2]; (2) Illinois Department of Conservation, 524 South Second St., Springfield, IL 62706
Indiana	NO/YES	Indiana Department of Natural Resources, Government Center, 402 West Washington Street, Indianapolis, IN 46204 [5]
Iowa	YES	State Archaeologist, Eastlawn Building, University of Iowa, Iowa City, IA 52242 [6]
Kansas	NO/YES	Kansas Department of Wildlife and Parks, 900 Jackson - Room 502, Topeka, KS 66612
Kentucky	NO/YES	Kentucky Department of Parks, 10th Floor, Capital Plaza Tower, Frankfort, KY 40601
Louisiana,	NO	
Maine	YES	Maine Bureau of Public Lands, PO Box 327, Farmington, ME 04938
Maryland	YES	(1) Maryland Department of Natural Resources, Division of Mines and Mining, Annapolis, MD 21401; (2) Maryland Department of Natural Resources, Forests, Parks and Wilderness Service, Tawes State Office Building, Annapolis, MD 21401
Massachusetts	NO/YES	State Archaeologist, Massachusetts Historical Commission, 80 Boyleston Street, Boston, MA 021116
Michigan	YES	Michigan Parks Division and Forest Management Division, Department of Natural Resources, Box 30028, Lansing, MI 48919
Minnesota	NO/YES	Minnesota Department of Natural Resources, Division of Parks and Recreation, Box 39, 500 Lafayette Road, St. Paul, MN 55155
Mississippi	YES	Mississippi Bureau of Geology, PO Box 5348, Jackson, MS 39205 [7]
Missouri	YES	(1) Department of Natural Resources, Division of Parks, Recreation and Natural History, PO Box 176, Jefferson City, MO 65102; (2) Missouri Department of Conservation, Forestry Division, PO Box 180, Jefferson City, MO 65102
Montana	YES	State Historic Preservation Officer, Montana Historical Society, 225 North Roberts, Street, Helena, MT 59620 [1, 2, 8]

Table 60.2. *Continued*

State	Laws governing collection of fossil plants on State property	State Agency responsible for administering laws & granting permits
Nebraska	NO/YES	(1) Nebraska Board of Educational Lands and Funds, 555 North Cotner Blvd., Lincoln, NE 68505; (2) Nebraska Game and Parks Commission, 2200 North 33rd Street, PO Box 30370, Lincoln, NE 68503
Nevada	YES	(1) Director, Nevada State Museum, Capitol Complex, Carson City, NV 89710 [2]; (2) Nevada Division of State Parks, 1923 North Carson Street, Capitol Complex, Carson City, NV 89710
New Hampshire	NO/YES	(1) New Hampshire Department of Resources and Economic Development, Division of Forests and Lands, PO Box 856, Concord, NH 03301; (2) New Hampshire Department of Resources and Economic Development, Division of Parks and Recreation, Concord, NH 03301
New Jersey	YES	New Jersey State Division of Parks and Forests, PO Box 1420, Trenton, NJ 08625
New Mexico	YES	State Park and Recreation Division of New Mexico Department of Energy, Minerals and Natural Resources, 2040 South Pacheco, Santa Fe, NM 87501
New York	YES	(1) Director, New York State Museum, Empire State Plaza, CE 3140, Albany, NY 12230 [2]; (2) Division of Lands and Forests, New York State Department of Environmental Conservation, 50 Wolf Road, Albany, NY 12233 [2]
North Carolina	NO/YES	North Carolina Department of Natural Resources, Division of Parks and Recreation, PO Box 27387, Raleigh, NC 27611 [9]
North Dakota	YES	State Geologist, North Dakota Industrial Commission, University Station, Grand Forks, ND 58202 [10]
Ohio	YES	Ohio Department of Natural Resources, Division of Parks and Recreation & Division of Natural Areas and Preserves, Fountain Square Building F-1, Columbus, OH 43224 [11]
Oklahoma	YES	(1) Oklahoma Tourism and Recreation Department, Division of State Parks, 500 Will Rogers Building, Oklahoma City, OK 73105; (2) Oklahoma State Lands Department, 5801 North Broadway, Oklahoma City, OK 73105; (3) Oklahoma Department of Transportation, 200 NE 21st, Oklahoma City, OK 73105
Oregon	YES	(1) Oregon Division of State Lands, 1445 State Street, Salem, OR 97310 [12]; (2) State Parks and Recreation Department, 1115 Commercial Street NE, Salem, OR 97310
Pennsylvania	NO/YES	Pennsylvania Department of Environmental Resources, PO Box 8552, Harrisburg, PA 17105
Rhode Island	YES	Rhode Island State Properties Committee, Department of Environmental Management, 83 Park Street, Providence, RI 02903
South Carolina	YES	(1) South Carolina Department of Parks, Recreation and Tourism, 1205 Pendleton Street - Suite 113, Edgar Brown Building, Columbia, SC 29201; (2) Institute for Archeology and Anthropology, University of South Carolina, Columbia, SC 29208 [13]
South Dakota	YES	(1) Commissioner of School and Public Lands, 500 East Capital Ave, Pierre, SD 57501; (2) South Dakota Department of Game, Fish and Parks, Foss Building, Pierre, SD 57501
Tennessee	YES	(1) Commissioner, Department of Environment and Conservation (and State Archaeologist, Division of Archaeology), 701 Broadway, Nashville, TN 37219; (2) Tennessee Division of Parks and Recreation, 701 Broadway, Nashville, TN 37219
Texas	NO/YES	Texas State Paks and Wildlife Department, 4200 Smith School Road, Austin, TX 78744
Utah	YES	(1) State Archeologist, Utah Division of State History, Antiquities Section, 300 Rio Grande, Salt Lake City, UT 84101; (2) School and Trust Lands Administration, 675 East 500 South, Salt Lake City, UT 84102 [14]; (3) Utah Geological Survey, 1594 West North Temple, Suite 300, Salt Lake City, UT 84114-6100 [14]

Table 60.2. *Continued*

State	Laws governing collection of fossil plants on State property	State Agency responsible for administering laws & granting permits
Vermont	YES	Vermont Agency of Natural Resources, Department of Forest, Parks, and Recreation, 103 South Main Street, Center Building, Waterbury, VT 05676
Virginia	NO/YES	(1) Department of Conservation and Recreation, 203 Governor Street - Suite 302, Richmond, VA 23219; (2) Virginia Department of Forestry, PO Box 3758, Alderman and McCormick Road, Charlottesville, VA 22903; (3) Virginia Division of State Parks, 203 Governor Street - Suite 306, Richmond, VA 23219
Washington	YES	Washington Department of Natural Resources, Division of Lands and Minerals, Olympia, WA 98504
West Virginia	NO/YES	(1) West Virginia Department of Natural Resources, Office of Real Estate Management, Building 3 - Room 643, 1900 Kanawha Boulevard East, Charleston, WV 25305; (2) West Virginia Department of Parks and Recreation, Department of Commerce, Capital Complex, Charleston, WV 25305
Wisconsin	NO/YES	Department of Natural Resources, PO Box 7921, Madison, WI 53707
Wyoming	NO/YES	(1) Wyoming Recreation Commission, State Parks Division, Herschler Building, 122 West 25th Street, Cheyenne, WY 82202 [2]; (2) Wyoming State Board of Land Commissioners, Herschler Building, 122 West 25th Street, Cheyenne, WY 82202 [15]

[1] Results of permitted investigations must be made available to general public through institutions and museums, and specimens must be deposited within an appropriate state repository

[2] Specimens and records must be placed into a state repository, and the state owns all collections

[3] Although there is no statute governing collection, the general criminal code applies. The repository is designated by the Idaho State Historical Society

[4] Collection within State Parks must be approved by the Park Manager

[5] Fossils on most state lands are governed by the agency responsible for maintenance of the property (e.g. Division of Nature Preserves, Division of Fish and Wildlife, Division of Forestry, and Division of Parks)

[6] Permits given on a case-by-case basis

[7] Permits sanctioned by official immediately in charge of state land

[8] Both palaeontological and archaeological artefacts are considered "antiquities" and require permits for collection. In 1991, there was a moratorium on issuance of collecting permits

[9] School class collecting and hobby collecting is not allowed on state lands.

[10] A permit for exploratory purposes is required before a permit for excavation can be requested

[11] The Department of Transportation should be consulted for roadside collecting

[12] Permineralized wood may be collected on state lands without a permit when valued at less than $US500

[13] Submerged palaeontological materials (including river banks and beaches below the MLT) require a permit; a 'hobby licence' may be obtained for $US10 (non-residents), but a 'data recovery licence' may be needed for extensive excavations

[14] Fossil collections can only be removed from the state with permission from these agencies

[15] Written permission is required for fossil collection in state parks, recreation and other areas. Unless released by the Board of Land Commissioners, fossils cannot be removed from the state. The state routinely allows fossils to go to *bona fide* scientific institutions on permanent loan

areas have lower population densities and a higher proportion of state and federally owned lands than elsewhere.

Because of the frequently high monetary value placed on Native American objects, states have sought anthropological/archaeological expertise in the offices of land management. As West (1991) notes, this has often led to resource administration being managed by archaeologists with little or no ability, or interest, in palaeontology or geology. This has caused difficulties in fossil-rich states where permitting for fossil collection has been left to these managers. Overall, common sense must prevail when beginning a research programme on private, reservation, or government-owned lands. All parties involved with the land use must be consulted prior to the initiation of collection, and written agreement concerning the disposition of the fossil material should be acquired to avoid later repercussions.

Glossary of terms

US Federal Register
  (http://www.access.gpo.gov/su_docs/index.html)
US Library of Congress (http://lcweb.loc.gov/)
US Bureau of Indian Affairs
  (http://www.doi.gov/bureau-indian-affairs.html)
US Department of the Interior: Bureau of Land
  Management (http://www.blm.gov/)
US Department of the Interior: US Geological
  Survey (http://www.usgs.gov/)
US Department of Agriculture: US Forest Service
  (http://www.fs.fed.us/)
United States Antiquities Act of 1906
United States Historic Sites Act of 1935
United States Petrified Wood Act of 1962
United States National Historic Preservation Act
  of 1966
United States Federal Land Policy Management
  Act of 1976
United States National Forest Management Act

References

ABAD, A. R., CEASE, K. R. & BLANCHETTE, R. A. 1988. A rapid technique using epoxy resin Quetol 651 to prepare woody plant tissues for ultrastructural study. *Canadian Journal of Botany*, **66**, 677–682.

AHARON, P. 1991. Recorders of reef environment histories – stable isotopes in corals, giant clams, and calcareous algae. *Coral Reefs*, **10**, 71–90.

AITKEN, M. J. 1990. *Science–based dating in archaeology*. Longman, London and New York.

ALCALÁ, L. & MORALES, J. 1994. Towards a definition of the Spanish palaeontological heritage. *In:* O'HALLORAN, D., GREEN, C., HARLEY, M., STANLEY, M. & KNILL, J. (eds) *Geological and Landscape Conservation* . Geological Society, London, 57–61.

ALEMANY, L. B., GRANT, D. M., ALGER, T. D. & PUGMIRE, R. J. 1983. Cross polarization and magic angle sample spinning NMR spectra of model organic compounds. 3. Effect of the 13C-1H dipolar interaction on cross polarization and carbon–proton dephasing. *Journal of American Chemical Society*, **105**, 6697–6704.

ALEXANDERSSON, E. T. & MILLIMAN, J. D. 1981. Intragranular Mg–calcite cement in Halimeda plates from the Brazilian continental shelf. *Journal of Sedimentary Petrology*, **51**(4), 1309–1314.

ALLEN, J. R. L. 1985. *Principles of Physical Sedimentology*. Unwin–Hyam, London.

—— 1992. Trees and their response to wind: Mid–Flandrian strong winds, Severn Estuary and inner Bristol Channel, southwest Britain. *Philosophical Transactions of the Royal Society of London B*, **338**, 335–364.

ALVIN, K. L. 1974. Leaf anatomy of *Weichselia* based on fusainized material. *Palaeontology*, **17**, 587–598.

AMMONS, R., FRITZ, W. J., AMMONS, R. B. & AMMONS, A. 1987. Cross–identification of ring signatures in Eocene trees (*Sequoia magnifica*) from the Specimen Ridge locality of the Yellowstone Fossil Forests. *Palaeogeography, Palaeoclimatology, Palaeoecology*, **60**, 97–108.

ANDERSON, T. F. & ARTHUR, M. A. 1983. Stable isotopes of oxygen and carbon and their application to sedimentologic and palaeoenvironmental problems. *In: Stable isotopes in sedimentary geology*, SEPM Short Course Notes, No. **10**. Society of Economic Palaeontologists and Mineralogists, Tulsa.

—— & STEINMETZ, J. C. 1981. Isotopic and biostratigraphical records of calcareous nanno-fossils in a Pleistocene core. *Nature*, **294**, 740–744.

ANDREWS, H. N. 1970. Index of generic names of fossil plants, 1820–1965. *Bulletin of the United States Geological Survey*, **1300**, 1–354.

ANDREWS, J. E., RIDING, R. & DENNIS, P. F. 1993. Stable isotopic compositions of Recent freshwater cyanobacterial carbonates from the British isles: local and regional environmental controls. *Sedimentology*, **40**, 303–314.

ARCHANGELSKY, A., ANDREIS, R. R., ARCHANGELSKY, S. & ARTABE, A. 1995. Cuticular characters adapted to volcanic stress in a new Cretaceous cycad leaf from Patagonia, Argentina. Considerations on the stratigraphy and depositional history of the Baquero Formation. *Review of Palaeobotany and Palynology*, **89**, 213–233.

—— & DEL FUEYO, G. 1989. *Squamastrobus* gen. n., a fertile podocarp from the early Cretaceous of Patagonia, Argentina. *Review of Palaeobotany and Palynology*, **59**, 109–126.

—— & TAYLOR, T. N. 1986. Ultrastructural studies of fossil plant cuticles. II. *Tarphyderma* gen. n., a Cretaceous conifer from Argentina. *American Journal of Botany*, **73**, 1577–1587.

——, —— & KURMANN, M. H. 1986. Ultrastructural studies of fossil plant cuticles: *Ticoa harrisii* from the early Cretaceous of Argentina. *Botanical Journal of the Linnean Society*, **92**, 101–116.

ARCHER, A. W. & MAPLES, C. G. 1987. Monte Carlo simulation of selected binomial similarity coefficients (I): Effect of number of variables. *Palaios*, **2**, 609–617.

ARCHER, K. J. & COLE, A. L. J. 1986. Cuticle, cell wall ultrastructure and disease resistance in maidenhair fern. *New Phytologist*, **103**, 341–348.

ASH, S. R. 1980. Upper Triassic floral zones of North America. *In:* DILCHER, D. L. & TAYLOR, T. N. (eds) *Biostratigraphy of Fossil Plants*. Dowden, Hutchinson & Ross, Stroudsburg PA, 153–170.

—— & CREBER, G. T. 1992. Palaeoclimatic interpretation of the wood structures in the Chinle Formation (Upper Triassic), Petrified Forest National Park, Arizona, USA. *Palaeogeography, Palaeo-climatology, Palaeoecology*, **96**, 299–317.

ASSMAN, E. 1970. *The Principles of Forest Yield Study*. Pergamon Press, Oxford.

AUSTIN, J. J., ROSS, A. J., SMITH, A. B., FORTEY, R. A. & THOMAS, R. H. 1997. Problems of reproducibility – does geologically ancient DNA survive in amber-preserved insects? *Proceedings of the Royal Society of London, Series B, Biological Sciences*, **264**, 467–474.

AVERY, B. W. & BASCOMB, C. L. (eds) 1974. *Soil Survey Laboratory Methods*. Soil Survey of England and Wales Technical Monograph **6**, Harpenden.

BAILEY, I. W. & SINNOTT, E. W. 1915. A botanical index of Cretaceous and Tertiary climates. *Science*, **41**, 831–834.

—— & —— 1916. The climatic distribution of certain types of angiosperm leaves. *American Journal of Botany*, **3**, 24–39.

BAILEY, J. F., RICHARDS, M. B., MACAULEY, V. A. *ET AL.* 1996. Ancient DNA suggests a recent expansion of European cattle from a diverse wild progenitor species. *Proceedings of the Royal Society of London*, **B263**, 1467–1473.

339

BAILLIE, M. G. L. 1982. *Tree-ring dating and archaeology*. Croom-Helm, London.

—— 1995. *A slice through time: dendrochronology and precision dating*. Batsford, London.

—— 1996. Extreme environmental events and the linking of the tree–ring and ice–core records. *In*: DEAN, J. S., MEKO, D. M. & SWETNAM, T. W. (eds) *Tree rings, environment and humanity: Proceedings of the International Conference, Tucson, Arizona, 17–21 May 1994*. Tucson, Radiocarbon (publisher), 703–711.

—— & MUNRO, M. A. R. 1988. Irish tree–rings, Santorini and volcanic dust veils. *Nature*, **332**, 344–346.

—— & PILCHER, J. R. 1973. A simple cross–dating program for tree–ring research, *Tree-Ring Bulletin*, **33**, 7–14.

BAKKER, J. C. 1991. Effects of humidity on stomatal density and its relation to leaf conductance. *Scientia Horticulrae*, **48**, 205–212.

BALME, B. E. 1995. Fossil in situ spores and pollen grains: an annotated catalogue. *Review of Palaeobotany and Palynology*, **87**, 81–323.

BANG, B. S. 1994. Framboidal pyrite and associated organic matrices: a risky composite for preservation of fossils. *In*: KEJSAR, U. B. (ed.) *Surface treatment: cleaning, stabilization and coatings*. IIC Nordic Group, Danish Section, XIII Congress, Copenhagen, 65–82.

BANKS, H. P. 1980. Floral assemblages in the Siluro–Devonian. *In*: DILCHER, D. L. & TAYLOR, T. N. (eds) *Biostratigraphy of fossil plants*. Dowden, Hutchinson & Ross, Stroudsburg PA, 1–24.

——, LECLERCQ, S. & HUEBER, F. M. 1975. Anatomy and morphology of *Psilophyton dawsonii*, sp. n.. from the late Lower Devonian of Quebec (Gaspé), and Ontario, Canada. *Palaeontographica Americana*, **8**, 77–127.

BARALE, G. & BALDONI, A. 1993. L'ultrastructure de la cuticle de quelques Bennettitales du Crétacé inférieur d'Argentine. *Compte Rendu de Academie des Sciences Paris*, **316**, Série II, 1171–1177.

BARRIE, A. & PROSSER, S. J. 1996. Automated analysis of light–element stable isotopes by isotope ratio mass spectrometry. *In*: BOUTTON, T. W. & YAMASAKI, S. (eds) *Mass Spectrometry of Soils*: Marcel Dekker Inc., 1–46.

BARSS, M. S. & WILLIAMS, G. L. 1973. Palynology and nannofossil processing techniques. *Geological Survey of Cananda, Department of Energy, Mines and Resources, Papers* **73–26**, 1–26.

BARTHEL, M. 1997. Epidermal structures of sphenophylls. *Review of Palaeobotany and Palynology*, **96**, 115–127.

BARTRAM, K. 1987. Lycopod succession in coals: an example from the Low Barnsley Seam (Westphalian B), Yorkshire, England. *In*: SCOTT, A. C. (ed.) *Coal and Coal-bearing Strata: Recent Advances*. Geological Society, London, Special Publications, **32**, 187–200.

BARTUSKA, V. J., MACIEL, G. E., SCHAEFER, J. & STEJSKAL, E. O. 1977. Prospects for carbon-13 nuclear magnetic resonance analysis of solid fossil-fuel materials. *Fuel*, **56**, 354–358.

BASCOMB, C. L. 1961. A calcimeter for routine use on soil samples. *Chemistry in Industry*, 1826–1827.

BASINGER, J. F. & CHRISTOPHEL, D. C. 1985. Fossil flowers and leaves of the Ebenaceae from the Eocene of southern Australia. *Canadian Journal of Botany*, **63**, 1825–1843.

BASSETT, M. G. 1990. Zone fossils. *In*: BRIGGS, D. E. G. & CROWTHER, P. R. (eds) *Palaeobiology. A synthesis*. Blackwell, Oxford, 466–467.

BATEMAN, R. M. 1990. Fabric analysis and ICP: Under-used geoanalytical techniques of value for plant biostratigraphy, provenance and palaeoecology. *American Journal of Botany*, **77** (abstracts supplement), 210.

—— 1991. Palaeoecology. *In*: CLEAL, C. J. (ed.) *Plant Fossils In Geological Investigation. The Palaeozoic*. Ellis Horwood Ltd., Chichester, 34–116.

—— 1995. Bulk geochemical data as an aid to correlating key palaeobotanical specimens and horizons. *American Journal of Botany*, **82** (abstracts supplement), 83.

—— & MORTON, N. 1994. New petrified Middle Jurassic floras from nearshore marine sediments at Bearreraig, Skye, W. Scotland. *American Journal of Botany*, **81** (abstracts supplement), 88.

—— & ROTHWELL, G. W. 1990. A reappraisal of the Dinantian floras at Oxroad Bay, East Lothian, Scotland. 1. Floristics and the development of whole–plant concepts. *Transactions of the Royal Society of Edinburgh*, **B81**, 127–159.

—— & SCOTT, A. C. 1990. A reappraisal of the Dinantian floras at Oxroad Bay, East Lothian, Scotland. 2. Volcanicity, palaeoecology and palaeoenvironments. *Transactions of the Royal Society of Edinburgh*, **B81**, 161–194.

——, MORTON, N. & DOWER, B. L. 1999. Early Middle Jurassic plant communities in northwest Scotland: paleoecological and paleoclimatic significance. *In*: HALL, R., SMITH, P. & POULTON, T. (eds) *Proceedings of the Fifth International Symposium on the Jurassic System*.

BATES, C. D., COXON, P. & GIBBARD, P. L. 1978. A new method for the preparation of clay-rich sediment samples for palynological investigation. *New Phytologist*, **81**, 459–463.

BATTEN, D. J. 1969. Some British Wealden megaspores and their facies distribution. *Palaeontology*, **12**, 333–350.

—— 1973. Use of palynologic assemblage–types in Wealden correlation. *Palaeontology*, **16**, 1–40.

—— 1992. Stratigraphic and palaeoenvironmental analyses continue to demand the inclusion of high quality palaeontological data. *Cretaceous Research*, **13**, 591–595.

—— 1996c. Upper Jurassic and Cretaceous miospores. *In*: JANSONIUS, J. & MCGREGOR, D. C. (eds) *Palynology: Principles and Applications*. American Association of Stratigraphic Palynologists Foundation, **2**, 807–830.

—— 1996a. Palynofacies and palaeoenvironmental interpretation. *In*: JANSONIUS, J. & MCGREGOR, D. G. (eds) *Palynology: Principles and Applications*.

American Association of Stratigraphic Palynologists Foundation, Dallas, **3**, 1011–1064.

—— 1996*b*. Palynofacies and petroleum potential. *In:* JANSONIUS, J. & MCGREGOR, D. G. (eds) *Palynology: Principles and Applications.* American Association of Stratigraphic Palynologists Foundation, Dallas, **3**, 1065–1084.

——, COLLINSON, M. E. & BRAIN, A. P. R. 1998. Ultrastructural interpretation of the Late Cretaceous megaspore *Glomerisporites pupus* and its associated microspores. *American Journal of Botany*, **85**, 724–735.

—— & KOVACH W. L. 1990. *Catalog of Mesozoic and Tertiary Megaspores.* Contribution Series – American Association of Stratigraphic Palynologists, **24**. Houston TX, USA.

—— & MORRISON, L. 1983. Methods of palynological preparation for palaeoenvironmental, source potential and organic maturation studies. *In:* COSTA, L. I. (ed.) Palynology – Micropalaeontology: Laboratories, Equipment and Methods. *Norwegian Petroleum Directorate, Bulletin,* **2**, 35–53.

BECK, A. L., LABANDEIRA, C. C. & MAMAY, S. H. 1996. Host spectrum and intensity of insect herbivory on a Lower Permian riparian flora: implications for the early sequestering of vascular plant tissues. *Geological Society of America, Abstracts with Programs,* **28**, 105.

BECK, C. B., GALTIER, J. & STEIN, W. E. 1992. A reinvestigation of *Diichnia* Read from the New Albany Shale of Kentucky. *Review of Palaeobotany and Palynology*, **75**, 1–32.

——, SCHMID, R. & ROTHWELL, G. W. 1982. Stelar morphology of the primary vascular system of seed plants. *Botanical Review,* **48**, 691–815.

BECKER, B. 1993. An 11 000-Year German Oak and Pine Dendrochronology for Radiocarbon Calibration. *Radiocarbon*, **35**, 201–213.

—— & SCHMIDT, B. 1982. Verlangerung der Mitteleuropäischen Eichenjahrringchronologie in das Zweite Vorchristliche Jahrtausand (bis 1462 vor Chr.). *Archäologisches Korrespondenblatt,* **12**, 101–106.

BEERLING, D. J. 1997. Interpreting environmental and biological signals from the stable carbon isotope composition of fossilized organic and inorganic carbon. *Journal of the Geological Society, London,* **154**, 303–309.

——, BIRKS, H. H. & WOODWARD, F. I. 1995. Rapid late–glacial atmospheric CO_2 changes reconstructed from the stomatal density record of fossil leaves. *Journal of Quaternary Science,* **10**, 379–384.

—— & CHALONER, W. G. 1992. Stomatal density as an indicator of atmospheric CO_2 concentration. *The Holocene,* **2**, 71–78.

—— & —— 1994. Atmospheric CO_2 changes since the last glacial maximum: evidence from the stomatal density of fossil leaves. *Review of Palaeobotany and Palynology,* **81**, 11–17.

—— & KELLY, C. K. 1997. Stomatal density responses of temperate woodland plants over the past seven decades of CO_2 increase: a comparison of Salisbury (1927) with contemporary data. *American Journal of Botany*, in press.

—— & WOODWARD, F. I. 1996. Stomatal density responses to global environmental change. *Advances in Bioclimatology*, **4**, 171–221.

—— & —— 1997. Changes in land plant function over the Phanerozoic: reconstructions based on the fossil record. *Botanical Journal of the Linnean Society,* **124**, 137–153.

BEHAR, F. & HATCHER, P. G. 1995. Artificial coalification of a fossil wood from brown coal by confined system pyrolysis. *Energy and Fuel*, **9**, 984–994.

BEHRENSMEYER, A. K., BADGLEY, C. *ET AL.* 1992. Paleoenvironmental contexts and taphonomic modes. *In:* BEHRENSMEYER, A. K. *ET AL.* (eds) *Terrestrial Ecosystems Through Time.* Chicago University Press, Chicago, 14–136.

——, DAMUTH, J. D., DIMICHELE, W. A., POTTS, R., SUES, H.-D. & WING, S. (eds) 1992. *Terrestrial ecosystems through time. Evolutionary paleoecology of terrestrial plants and animals.* Chicago Press, Chicago.

BELL, M. 1988. Artefacts in staining procedures. *In*: CRANG, R. P. F. & KLOMPARENS, K. L. (eds) *Artefacts in biological electron microscopy.* Plenum Publishing, 81–106.

BENNER, B., HATCHER, P. G. & HEDGES, J. I. 1990. Early diagenesis of mangrove leaves in a tropical estuary: Bulk chemical characterization using solid-state 13C NMR and elemental snalyses. *Geochimica et Cosmochimica Acta,* **54**, 2003–2013.

BENTON, M. 1993 (ed.) *The Fossil Record 2.* Chapman & Hall, London.

BERGER, J. P. 1990. Floral changes in the Molasse of western Switzerland (Oligo–miocene) palaeoclimatic implications. *In:* KNOBLOCH, E. & KVACEK, Z. (eds) *Proceedings of the Symposium 'Paleofloristic and Palaeoclimatic Changes in the Cretaceous and Tertiary' 1989.* Geological Survey, Prague.

BERGLUND, B. E. & RALSKA–JASIEWICZOWA, M. 1986. Pollen analysis and pollen diagrams. *In:* BERGLUND, B. E. (ed.). *Handbook of Holocene Palaeoecology and Palaeohydrology,* J. Wiley & Sons, Chichester, 455–484.

BERNER, R. A. 1984. Sedimentary pyrite formation: an update. *Geochimica and Cosmochimica Acta,* **48**, 605–615.

—— 1994. GEOCARB II: a revised model of atmospheric CO_2 over Phanerozoic time. *American Journal of Science*, **294**, 56–91.

BERRY, C. M. & EDWARDS, D. 1995. New species of the lycophyte *Colpodexylon* Banks from the Devonian of Venezuela. *Palaeontographica*, **B137**, 59–74.

—— & FAIRON-DEMARET, M. 1997. A reinvestigation of the cladoxylopsid *Pseudosporochnus nodosus* Leclercq et Banks from the Middle Devonian of Goé, Belgium. *International Journal of Plant Sciences*, **158**, 350–372.

BÉRUBÉ, K. A., JONES, T. P. & WILLIAMSON, B. J. 1997. Electron Microscopy of Urban Airborne Particulate Matter. *Microscopy and Analysis*, September, 11–13.

BEVERLUIS, J. R. 1943. De micrografische Identificatie van conifere Houtsoorten. *Meded. Landbouwhoogesschool,* **D.47, 2**, Wageningen.

BILLET, P. 1994. L'émergence d'un droit du patrimoine géologique en France. Mémoire Société Géologique de France, **165**, 17–19.

—— 1997. La protection juridique du patrimoine géologique en France: bilan (provisoire) d'un siècle de protection. La lettre des Réserves Naturelles, **44–45**, 43–53.

BIRKELAND, P. W. 1984. *Soils and Geomorphology.* Oxford University Press, New York.

BIRKS, H. H. 1973. Modern macrofossil assemblages in lake sediments in Minnesota. *In:* BIRKS, H. J. B. & WEST, R. G. (eds) *Quaternary Plant Ecology.* Blackwells, Oxford, 173–189.

BIRKS, H. J. B. & BIRKS, H. H. 1980. *Quaternary palaeoecology.* Edward Arnold, London.

—— 1981. The use of pollen analysis in the reconstruction of past climates: A review. *In:* WIGLEY, T. *ET AL.* (eds) *Climate and History.* Cambridge University Press, Cambridge, 111–138.

—— 1986. Numerical zonation, comparison and correlation of Quaternary pollen–stratigraphical data. *In:* BERGLUND, B. E. (ed.) *Handbook of Holocene Palaeoecology and Palaeohydrology.* Wiley, Chichester, 743–774.

BISH, D. L. & POST, J. E. 1989. Modern powder diffraction. *Mineralogical Society of America, Reviews in mineralogy*, **20**, 73–99.

BLACKITH, R. & REYMENT, R. A. 1971. *Multivariate Morphometrics.* Academic Press, New York.

BLAZER, A. M. 1975. Index of generic names of fossil plants, 1966–1973. *Bulletin of the United States Geological Survey,* **1396**, 1–54.

BLOKKER, P., SCHOUTEN, S., VAN DEN ENDE, H. DE LEEUW, J. W., HATCHER, P.G. & SINNINGHE DAMSTE, J. S. 1997. Chemical structure of algaenans from the fresh water alage *Tetraedron minimum, Scenedesmus communis* and *Pedlastrum boryanum. Marine Biogeochemie,* In press.

BOARDMAN, N. K. 1977. Comparative photosynthesis of sun and shade plants. *Annual Review of Plant Physiology*, **28**, 355–377.

BOCHERENS, H., FRIIS, E. M., MARIOTTI, A. & PEDERSEN, K. R. 1994. Carbon isotopic abundances in Mesozoic and Cenozoic fossil plants: Palaeoecological implications. *Lethaia*, **26**, 347–358.

BOCKELIE, J. F. 1994. Plant roots in core. *In:* DONOVAN, S.K. (ed.) *The Palaeobiology of Trace Fossils.* Johns Hopkins University Press, Baltimore and John Wiley and Sons, Chichester, 177–199.

BONNEFILLE, R. 1994. Palynology and paleoenvironment of East African hominid sites. *In:* CORRUCHINI, R. S. & CIOCHON, C. L. (eds) *Integrative Paths to the Past.* Prentice-Hall, Englewood Cliffs, New Jersey, 415–427.

BOOKSTEIN, F. L. 1991. *Mophometric Tools for Landmark Data.* Cambridge University Press, Cambridge.

BOON, J. J. 1992. Analytical pyrolysis mass spectrometry: new vistas opened by temperature-resolved in-source PYMS. *International Journal of Mass Spectrometry and Ion Processes*, **118/119**, 755–787.

——, STOUT, S. A., GENUIT, W. & SPACKMAN, W. 1989 Molecular paleobotany of *Nyssa* endocarps. *Acta Botanica Neerlandica*, **38**, 391–404.

BORNEMANN, G. 1856. *Über organische Reste der Lettenkohlengruppe Thüringens. Ein Beitrag zur Flora und Fauna dieser Formation besonders über fossile Cycadeen, nebst vergleichenden Untersuchungen über die Blattstruktur der jetztweltigen Cycadeengattungen.* Engelmann, Leipzig.

BOUCOT, A. J. 1990. Evolutionary palaeobiology of behaviour and coevolution. Elsevier, Amsterdam.

BOULTER, M. C. 1984. Palaeobotanical evidence for land–surface temperature in the European Palaeogene. *In:* BRENCHLEY, P. (ed.) *Fossils and Climate.* Wiley, New York, NY, 35–47.

——, BENFIELD, J. N., FISHER, H. C., GEE, D. A. & LHOTAK, M. 1996. The evolution and global migration of the Aceraceae. *Philosophical Transactions of the Royal Society of London,* **B351**, 589–603.

BOWMAN, S. 1990. *Radiocarbon Dating.* British Museum, London.

BOYD, A. 1991. Fossil leaves and fruits as indicators of paleotransport in a Miocene lake from northern Idaho. *Journal of Sedimentary Petrology,* **61**, 269–279.

BRACK-HANES, S. D. & VAUGHN, J. C. 1978. Evidence of Paleozoic chromosomes from lycopod microgametophytes. *Science,* **200**, 1383–1385.

BRADSHAW, R. H. W. & WEBB, T., III. 1985. Relationships between contemporary pollen and vegetation data from Wisconsin and Michigan, USA. *Ecology,* **66**, 721–737.

BRAGA, J. C., MARTIN, J. M. & RIDING, R. 1996. Internal structure of segment reefs: *Halimeda* algal mounds in the Mediterranean Miocene. *Geology,* **24**, 35–38.

BRAND, W. A. 1996. High precision isotope ratio monitoring techniques in mass spectrometry. *Journal of Mass Spectrometry,* **31,** 225–235.

BRENNER, G. J. 1963. The spores and pollen of the Potomac Group of Maryland. *Maryland Department of Geology, Mines, and Water Resources Bulletin,* **27**, 1–215.

BRETT, C. & WALDRON, K. 1990. *Physiology and biochemistry of plant cell walls.* Topics in plant physiology, **2**. Unwin Hyman.

BREWER, R. 1976. *Fabric and Mineral Analysis of Soils,* (2nd edn). Krieger, New York.

BRIFFA, K. R. 1994. Mid and late Holocene climate change: evidence from tree-growth in northern Fennoscandia. *In:* FUNNELL, B. M & KAY, R. L. F. (eds) *Palaeoclimate of the Last Glacial/Interglacial Cycle.* Special Publication **94/2**, NERC, London, 61–65.

BRIGGS, D. 1977. *Sources and Methods in Geography: Sediments.* Butterworths, London.

BRIGGS, D. E. G. 1990. Flattening. *In:* BRIGGS, D. E. G. & CROWTHER, P. R. (eds) *Palaeobiology, a synthesis.* Blackwell, Oxford, 244–247.

——, RAISWELL, R., BOTTRELL, S. H., HATFIELD, D. & BARTELS, C. 1996. Controls on the pyritization of exceptionally preserved fossils: an analysis of the Lower Devonian Hunsrück Slate of Germany. *American Journal of Science,* **296**, 633–663.

—— & WILLIAMS, S. H. 1981. The restoration of flattened fossils. *Lethaia,* **14,** 157–164.

BRIMHALL, G. H., CHADWICK, O. A., LEWIS, C. J., COMPSTON, W., WILLIAMS, I. S., DANTI, K. J., DIETRICH, W. E. ET AL. 1991. Deformational mass transport and invasive processes in soil evolution. *Science*, **255**, 695–702.

BRONK RAMSEY, C. 1995. Radiocarbon calibration and analysis of stratigraphy: the OxCal program. Proceedings of the 15th International ^{14}C conference. *Radiocarbon,* **37**(2)**,** 425–430.

BROOKS, J. & ELSIK, W. C. 1974. Chemical oxidation (using ozone) of the spore wall of *Lycopodium clavatum*. *Grana*, **14**(2–3), 85–91.

—— & SHAW G. 1978. Sporopollenin: A review of its chemistry, palaeobiochemistry and geochemistry. *Grana*, **17**, 91–97.

BROWN, S. M. 1992.Fossil species of modern plant genera: a first list for vascular plants. *IOP Circular*, **10**, p. 23.

BROWN, T. A., ALLABY, R. G., BROWN, K. A., O'DONOGHUE, K. & SOLLARES, R. 1994. DNA in Wheat Seeds from European Archeological Sites. *In:* ADAMS, R. P. MILLER, J. S. GOLENBERG, E. M. & ADAMS, J. E. (eds) *Conservation of Plant Genes II: Intellectual Property Rights and DNA Utilization* . St Louis, MO, Missouri Botanical Gardens, 37–46.

BRUMMITT, R. K. 1992. *Vascular plant families and genera.* Royal Botanic Gardens, Kew.

—— 1996. In defence of paraphyletic taxa. *In:* VAN DER MAESEN, L. J. G. ET AL. (eds) *The Biodiversity of African Plants.* Kluwer, Netherlands, 371–384.

BRUSH, G. S. & BRUSH, L. M. 1972. Transport of pollen in a sediment laden channel: a laboratory study. *American Journal of Science*, **272**, 359–381.

BUNTLEY, G. J. & WESTIN, F. C. 1985. A comparative study of developmental color in a Chestnut-Chernozem-Brunizem soil climosequence. *Proceedings of the Soil Science Society of America*, **29**, 579–582.

BURNHAM, R. J. 1988. A large-diameter coring device for use in shallow water and soft sediments. *Journal of Paleontology*, **62**, 477–478.

—— 1993. Reconstructing richness in the plant fossil record. *Palaios*, **8**, 376–384.

—— 1994. Patterns in tropical leaf litter and implications for angiosperm paleobotany. *Review of Palaeobotany and Palynology*, **81**, 99–113.

——, WING, S. L. & PARKER, G. G. 1992. The reflection of deciduous forest communities in leaf litter: implications for autochthonous litter assemblages from the fossil record. *Paleobiology*, **18**, 30–49.

BUTTERWORTH, M. A & WILLIAMS, G. L. 1954. Descriptions of nine species of small spores from the British coal measures. *Annals and magazine of natural history, zoology, botany and geology*, **7**(**82**), 753–764.

CALDER, J. H., GIBLING, M. R., EBLE, C. F., SCOTT, A. C. & MACNEIL, D. J. 1996. The Westphalian D fossil lepidodendrid forest at Table Head, Sydney Basin, Nova Scotia; sedimentology, paleoecology and response to changing edaphic conditions. *In:* HOWER, J. C. & EBLE, C. F. (eds) Geology and Petrology of Appalacian Coals; a selection of papers from the Symposium. *International Journal of Coal Geology*, **31**(**1–4**), 277–313.

CANFIELD, D. E. & RAISWELL, R. 1991. Pyrite formation and fossil preservation. *In:* ALLISON, P. A. & BRIGGS, D. E. G. (eds) *Pyrite Formation and Fossil Preservation.* Plenum Press, New York, 337–387.

CANNY, M. J. 1984. Translocation of nutrients and hormones. *In:* WILKINS, M. (ed.) *Advanced Plant Physiology.* Longman, London, 277–296

CANO, R. J., POINAR, H. & POINAR, G. O., JR. 1992. Isolation and partial characterisation of DNA from the bee *Proplebeia dominicana* (Apidae: Hymenoptera) in 25–40 million year old amber. *Medical Sciences Research*, **20**, 249–251.

CARATINI, C. 1994. *Palynofacies of some recent marine sediments: the role of transportation. In:* TRAVERSE, A. (ed.) *Sedimentation of Organic Particles.* Cambridge University Press, UK, 129–139.

CASTELLETTI, L. 1975. Una nuova tecnica per lo studio dei carboni in archeologia. *Istituto Lombardo, Accademia di Scienze e Lettere, Rendiconti, Cl. Lettere,* **109**, 100–111.

CERLING, T. E. 1991. Carbon dioxide in the atmosphere: evidence from Cenozoic and Mesozoic paleosols. *American Journal of Science*, **291**, 377–400.

—— 1992a. Development of grasslands and savannas in East Africa during the Neogene. *Palaeogeography, Palaeoclimatology, Palaeoecology, Global and Planetary Change Section*, **97**, 241–247.

—— 1992b. Further comments on using carbon isotopes in paleosols to estimate the CO_2 content of the palaeoatmosphere. *Journal of the Geological Society of London*, **149**, 673–676.

—— 1992c. Use of carbon isotopes in paleosols as an indicator of the $p(CO_2)$ of the paleoatmosphere. *Global Biogeochemical Cycles*, **6**, 307–314.

——, HARRIS, J. M., AMBROSE, S. H., LEAKEY, M. G. & SOLOUNIAS, N. 1997. Dietary and environmental reconstruction with stable isotope analysis of herbivore tooth enamel from the Miocene locality of Fort Ternan, Kenya. *Journal of Human Evolution*, **33**, 635–650.

——, QUADE, J., WANG, Y., & BOWMAN, J. R. 1989. Carbon isotopes in soils and paleosols as paleoecological indicators. *Nature,* **341**, 138–139.

——, WANG, Y. & QUADE, J. 1993. Global ecological change in the late Miocene: expansion of C4 ecosystems. *Nature*, **361**, 344–345.

CHABAL, L. 1997. Forêts et sociétés en Languedoc (Néolithique final, Antiquité tardive). L'anthracologie, méthode et paléoécologie. DAF, CNRS, Paris.

CHALONER, W. G. 1953. On the megaspores of *Sigillaria*. *Annals and Magazine of Natural History, Series 12*, **6**, 881–897.

—— 1968. The paleoecology of fossil spores. *In:* DRAKE, E. T. (ed.) *Evolution and Environment.* Yale University Press, New Haven, 125–138.

—— 1986. Reassembling the whole fossil plant, and naming it. *In:* SPICER, R. A. & THOMAS, B. A. (eds) Systematic and Taxonomic Approaches in Palaeobotany. *Systematics Association Special Volume*, **31**, 67–78.

—— & COLLINSON, M. E. 1975a. Application of SEM to

a sigillarian impression fossil. *Review of Palaeobotany and Palynology,* **20**, 85–101.

—— & —— 1975*b*. An illustrated key to the commoner British Upper Carboniferous plant compression fossils. *Proceedings of the Geologists' Association,* **86**, 1–44.

——, HARPER, J. L. & LAWTON, J. L. (eds) 1991. The evolutionary interactions of animals and plants. *Philosophical Transactions of the Royal Society of London,* **B333**, 177–305.

——, HILL, A. & ROGERSON, E. C. W. 1978. Early Devonian plant fossils from a Southern England borehole. *Palaeontology,* **21**, 693–707.

—— & GAY, M. M. 1972. Scanning electron microscopy of latex casts of fossil plant impressions. *Palaeontology,* **16**, 654–659.

CHANDRA, S. & SURANGE, K. R. 1979. Revision of the Indian species of *Glossopteris. Birbal Sahni Institute of Palaeobotany Monograph,* **2**, 1–291.

CHARMAN, D. J. 1992. The effects of acetylation on fossil *Pinus* pollen and *Sphagnum* spores discovered during routine pollen analysis. *Review of Palaeobotany and Palynology,* **72**, 159–164.

CHESWORTH, W. 1992. Weathering systems. *In:* MARTINI, I. P. & CHESWORTH, W. (eds) *Weathering, Soils and Paleosols.* Elsevier, Amsterdam, 19–40.

CHIN, K. & GILL, B. D. 1996. Dinosaurs, dung beetles, and conifers: Participants in a Cretaceous food web. *Palaios,* **11**, 280–285.

—— & KIRKLAND, J. I. 1998. Probable herbivore coprolites from the Upper Jurassic Mygatt-Moore Quarry, Western Colorado. *Modern Geology,* **23**, 249–276.

CHITALEY, S. 1985. A new technique for thin sections of pyritized permineralizations. *Review of Palaeobotany and Palynology,* **45**, 301–306.

CHRISTOPHEL, D. C & GREENWOOD, D. R. 1988. A comparison of Australian tropical rainforest and Tertiary fossil leaf beds. *In:* KITCHING, R. (ed.) *The ecology of Australia's wet tropics. Proceedings of the Ecological Society of Australia,* **15**, 139–148.

CHRISTOPHER, R. A. & GOODMAN, D. K. 1996. Chapter 15: Introduction to biostratigraphy and time scales. *In:* JANSONIUS, J. & MCGREGOR, D. C. (eds) *Palynology: Principles and Applications.* American Association of Stratigraphic Palynologists Foundation, **2**, 463–492.

CLARK, J. S. 1988*a*. Particle motion and the theory of charcoal analysis: source area, transport, deposition, and sampling. *Quaternary Research,* **30**, 67–80.

—— 1988*b*. Stratigraphic charcoal analysis on petrographic thin sections: application to fire history in northwestern Minnesota. *Quaternary Research,* **30**, 81–91.

—— & ROYALL, P. D. 1995. Particle-size evidence for source areas of charcoal accumulation in Late Holocene sediments of eastern North American lakes. *Quaternary Research,* **43**, 80–89.

CLAYTON, G. 1972. Compression structures in the Lower Carboniferous miospore *Dictyotriletes admirabilis* Playford. *Palaeontology,* **15**, 121–124.

CLEAL, C. J. 1978. Floral biostratigraphy of the upper Silesian Pennant Measures of South Wales. *Geological Journal,* **13**, 165–194.

—— 1984. The Westphalian D floral biostratigraphy of Saarland (Fed. Rep. Germany) and a comparison with that of South Wales. *Geological Journal,* **19**, 327–351.

—— 1988. British palaeobotanical sites. *In:* CROWTHER, P. R. & WIMBLEDON, W. A. (eds) The use and conservation of palaeontological sites. *Special Papers in Palaeontology,* **40**, 57–71.

—— 1991. *Plant fossils in geological investigation: the Palaeozoic.* Ellis Horwood, Chichester.

—— 1993. Pteridophyta. Gymnospermophyta *In:* BENTON, M. J. (ed.) *The Fossil Record 2.* Chapman & Hall, London, 779–808.

—— & SHUTE, C. H. 1995. A synopsis of neuropteroid foliage from the Carboniferous and Lower Permian of Europe. *Bulletin of the Natural History Museum, London, Geology Series,* **51**, 1–52.

—— & THOMAS, B. A. 1994. *Plant fossils of the British Coal Measures.* Palaeontological Association, London.

—— &—— 1995. *Palaeozoic palaeobotany of Great Britain.* Geological Conservation Review Series, 9. Chapman & Hall, London.

—— & —— in press. *Mesozoic and Tertiary Palaeobotany of Great Britain.* JNCC, Peterbrough.

CLEMENT–WESTERHOF, J. A. 1984. Aspects of Permian palaeobotany and palynology. IV. The conifer *Ortiseia* Florin from the Val Gardena Formation of the Dolomites and the Vicentinian Alps (Italy) with special reference to a revised concept of the Walchiaceae (Göppert) Schimper. *Review of Palaeobotany and Palynology,* **41**, 51–166.

CLIFFORD, D. J. & HATCHER, P. G. 1995. Structural transformations of polylabdanoid resinites during maturation. *Organic Geochemistry,* **23**, 407–418.

CLIFFORD, S. C., BLACK, C. R., ROBERTS, J. A., STRONACH, I. M., SINGLETON–JONES, P. R, MOHAMED, A. D. & AZAM–ALI, S. N. 1995. The effect of elevated atmospheric CO_2 and drought on stomatal frequency in groundnut (*Arachis hypogaea* L.). *Journal of Experimental Botany,* **46**, 847–852.

COHEN, A. D., RAYMOND, R. R., RAMIREZ, C., MORALES, C. & PONCE, F. 1990. The Chanquinola peat deposit of north-western Panama: a tropical domed back barrier coal-forming environment. *International Journal of Coal Geology,* **16**, 139–142.

—— & SPACKMAN, W. 1980. Phytogenic organic sediments and sedimentary environments in the Everglades-mangrove complex of Florida. *Palaeontographica Abt. B,* **172**, 125–149.

——, —— & RAYMOND, R. JR. 1987. Interpreting the characteristics of coal seams from chemical, physical and petrographic studies of peat deposits. *In:* SCOTT, A. C. (ed) *Coal and Coal-bearing Strata: Recent Advances.* Geological Society, London, Special Publications, **32**, 107–125.

COLBATH, G. K. 1985. A comparison of palynological extraction techniques using samples from the Silurian Bainbridge Formation, Missouri, USA. *Review of Palaeobotany and Palynology,* **44**, 153–164.

COLES, J. M. (ed.) (annual publication since 1975) *The Somerset Levels Papers.* The Somerset Levels Project, Dept. of History, University of Exeter .

COLLINS, A. 1990. The 1–10 Spore Colour Index (SCI): a universally applicable colour maturation scale, based on graded, picked palynomorphs. *Mededelingen Rijks Geologische Dienst*, **45**, 39–47.

COLLINSON, M. E. 1980. Freshwater Macrophytes in Palaeolimnology. *Palaeogeography, Palaeo-climatology, Palaeoecology*, **62**, 317–342.

—— 1983a. accumulations of fruits and seeds in three small sedimentary environments in southern England and their palaeoecological significance. *Annals of Botany*, **52**, 583–592.

—— 1983b. Fossil Plants of the London Clay. *Palaeontological Association Field Guide to Fossils*, **1**.

—— 1986. Use of modern generic names for plant fossils. *In:* SPICER, R. A. & THOMAS, B. A. (eds) Systematic and Taxonomic Approaches in Palaeobotany. *Systematics Association Special Volume*, **31**, 91–104.

—— 1987. Special problems in the conservation of palaeobotanical material. *Geological Curator*, **4**, 439–445.

—— 1988. The special significance of the Middle Eocene fruit and seed flora from Messel, West Germany. *Courier Forschungsinstitut Senckenberg*, **107**, 187–197.

—— 1990. Plant evolution and ecology during the early Cainozoic diversification. *Advances in Botanical Research*, **17**, 1–98.

—— 1993. Microscopy and land palaeobiology. *Microscopy and Analysis*, March, 19–21.

—— 1995. Conservation and care of palaeobotanical material. *In:* COLLINS, C. (ed.) *The Care and Conservation of Palaeontological Material*, 31–46.

—— 1996. Plant macrofossils from the Bracklesham group (Early and Middle Eocene), Bracklesham Bay, West Sussex, England: review and significance in the context of coeval British Tertiary floras. *Tertiary Research*, **16**, 175–202.

—— 1998. Evolution of angiosperm fruit and seed morphology and associated functional biology: status in the Late Cretaceous and Palaeogene. *In:* KURMANN, M. H. & HEMSLEY, A. R. (eds) *Evolution of Plant Architecture*. Royal Botanic Gardens, Kew.

——, BATTEN, D. J., SCOTT, A. C. & AYONGHEA, S. 1985. Palaeozoic, Mesozoic and contemporaneous megaspores from the Tertiary of Southern England; indicators of sedimentary provenance and ancient vegetation. *Journal of the Geological Society, London*, **142,** 375–395.

——, BOULTER, M. C. & HOLMES, P. L. 1993. Magnoliophyta ('Angiospermae'). *In:* BENTON, M. J. (ed.) *The Fossil Record 2*. Chapman & Hall, London, 809–842.

—— & HOOKER, J. J. 1987. Vegetational and mammalian faunal changes in the early Tertiary of southern England. *In:* FRIIS, E. M., CHALONER, W. G. & CRANE, P. R. (eds) *The Origins of Angiosperms and their Biological Consequences*. Cambridge University Press, Cambridge, 259–303.

—— & —— 1991. Fossil evidence of interactions between plants and plant-eating mammals. *Philosophical Transactions of the Royal Society of London*, **B333**, 197–208.

——, MÖSLE, B. M., FINCH, P., SCOTT, A. C. & WILSON, R. The preservation of plant cuticle in the fossil record: a chemical and microscopical investigation. *Ancient Biomolecules*, **2**, 251–265.

——, VAN BERGEN, P. F., SCOTT, A. C. & DE LEEUW, J. W. 1994. The oil-generating potential of plants from coal and coal-bearing strata through time: a review with new evidence from Carboniferous plants. *In:* SCOTT, A. C. & FLEET, A. J. (eds) *Coal and Coal–bearing Strata as Oil-prone Source Rocks?* Geological Society, London, Special Publications, **77**, 31–70.

COMBOURIEU, N. & GALTIER, J. 1985. Nouvelles observations sur *Polypterospermum, Polylophospermum, Colpospermum et Codonospermum*, ovules de Pteridospermales du Carbonifère supérieur français. *Palaeontographica B*, **196**, 1–29.

COOK, E. R., BIRD, T., PETERSON, M., BARBETTI, M., BUCKLEY, B., D'ARRIGO, R., FRANCEY, R. & TANS, P. 1991. Climate change in Tasmania inferred from a 1089-year tree-ring chronology of huon pine. *Science*, **253**, 1266–1268.

COOPER, A., RHYMER, J., JAMES, H. F. *ET AL.* 1996. Ancient DNA and island endemics. *Nature*, **381**, 484.

COPE, M. J. 1985. *Some studies on the origin, nature and occurrence of charcoalified plant fossils*. PhD thesis, University of London.

—— 1993. A preliminary study of charcoalified plant fossils from the middle Jurassic Scalby Formation of North Yorkshire. *Special Papers in Palaeontology*, **49**, 101–111.

COURTINAT, B. 1993. The significance of palynofacies fluctuations in the Greenhorn Formation (Cenomanian–Turonian) of the Western Interior Basin, USA. *Marine Micropalaeontology*, **21**, 249–257.

COUSINS, W. J. 1975. Optical microscopy of charcoal. *Journal of Microscopy*, **105**, 15–18.

COUVERT, M. 1970. *Etude de charbons préhistoriques. Préparation des coupes minces et analyse des structures*. Centre de Recherches Anthropologiques, Préhistoriques et Ethnographiques, Algeria.

COXON, P. & WALDREN, S. 1997. Flora and vegetation of the Quaternary temperate stages of NW Europe: Evidence for large-scale range changes. *In:* HUNTLEY, B., CRAMER, W., MORGAN, A. V., PRENTICE, H. C. & ALLEN, J. R. M. (eds) *Past and Future Rapid Environmental Changes: The Spatial and Evolutionary Responses of Terrestrial Biota*. NATO ASI Series. Series I, Global Environment Change, Volume **47**. Springer Verlag. 103–117.

CRAIG, H. 1953. The geochemistry of stable carbon isotopes. *Geochimica et Cosmochimica Acta*, **3**, 53–92.

—— 1957. Isotopic standards for carbon and oxygen and correction factors for mass spectrometric analysis of carbon dioxide. *Geochimica et Cosmochimica Acta*, **12**, 133–149.

CRANE, P. R., FRIIS, E. M. & PEDERSEN, K. R. 1995. The origin and early diversification of angiosperms. *Nature*, **374**, 27–33.

—— & HERENDEEN, P. S. 1996. Cretaceous floras containing angiosperm flowers and fruits from eastern North America. *Review of Palaeobotany and Palynology*, **90**, 319–337.

——, MANCHESTER, S. R. & DILCHER, D. L. 1990. A preliminary survey of fossil leaves and well-preserved reproductive structures from the Sentinel Butte Formation (Paleocene) near Almont, North Dakota. *Fieldiana Geology*, **1418**, 1–63.

CREBER, G. T. 1977. Tree rings: A natural data-storage system. *Biological Reviews*, **52**, 349–383.

—— & CHALONER, W. G. 1984. Climatic implications from growth rings in fossil woods. *In:* BRENCHLEY, P. (ed.) *Fossils and Climate*, 49–74.

—— & FRANCIS, J. E. 1987. Productivity in fossil forests. *In:* JACOBY, G. C. (ed.) *Proceedings of the International Symposium on Ecological Aspects of Tree-ring Analysis*. US Department of Energy, Washington, DC, 319–326.

CRELLING, J. C., PUGMIRE, R. J., MEUZELAAR, H. L. C., McCLENNON, W. H., HUAI, H. & KARAS, J. 1991. Chemical structure and petrology of resinite from the Hiawatha 'B' coal seam. *Energy & Fuels*, **5**, 688–694.

CREPET, W. L. 1974. Investigations of North American cycadeoids: the reproductive biology of *Cycadeoidea. Palaeontographica*, **148B**, 144–169.

——, FRIIS, E. M. & NIXON, K. 1991. Fossil evidence for the evolution of biotic pollination. *Philosophical Transactions of the Royal Society*, **B333**, 187–195.

CRESSEY, G. & SCHOFIELD, P. F. 1996. Rapid whole-pattern profile-stripping method for the quantification of multiphase samples. *Powder Diffraction*, **11**, 35–39.

CROCHET, J.-Y. 1994. Un plésiosaure devant le tribunal de Millau (Aveyron, France). *Mémoire de la Société Géologique de France*, **165**, 45–46.

CROOKALL, R. 1929. *Coal Measure Plants*. Edward Arnold, London.

CUNNINGHAM, A., GAY, I. D., OEHSCHLANGER, A. C. & LANGENHEIM, J. H. 1983. ^{13}C NMR and IR analyses of the structure, aging and botanical origin of Dominican and Mexican ambers. *Phytochemistry*, **22**, 965–968.

CUTLER, D. F., ALVIN, K. L. & PRICE, C. E. 1982. *The Plant Cuticle*. Academic Press, London.

CWYNAR, L. C., BURDEN, E. & McANDREWS, J. H. 1979. An inexpensive sieving method for concentrating pollen and spores from fine-grained sediments. *Canadian Journal of Earth Sciences*, **16**, 1115–1120.

DAGHLIAN, C. P. 1983. A simple method for combined light, scanning and transmission electron microscope observation of single pollen grains from dispersed pollen samples. *Pollen et Spores*, **24**, 537–545.

—— & TAYLOR, T. N. 1979. A new method for isolating pollen and spores from acetate peels for scanning electron microscopy. *Review of Palaeobotany and Palynology*, **27**, 85–89.

DAHLQVIST, R. L. & KNOLL, J. W. 1978. Inductively-coupled plasma–atomic emission spectrometry analysis of biological materials and soils for major, trace and ultra-trace elements. *Applied Spectroscopy*, **32**, 1–30.

DARRAH, W. C. 1936. The peel method in paleobotany.

Botanical Museum Leaflets. Harvard University, **4**, 69–83.

DAVIS, J. C. 1986. *Statistics and Data Analysis in Geology* (2nd edn). John Wiley & Sons, New York.

DAVIS, P. H. 1971. Distribution Patterns in Anatolia with Particular Reference to Endemism. *In:* DAVIS, P. H. *et al.* (eds) *Plant Life of South-West Asia*. Botanical Society of Edinburgh, 15–27.

DELCOURT, P. A. 1987. *Long-term forest dynamics of the temperate zone: a case study of late-Quaternary forests in eastern North America*. Springer, New York.

—— & DELCOURT, H. R. 1981. Vegetation maps for eastern North America: 40,000 yr B.P. to the present. *In:* ROMANS, R. C. (ed.) *Geobotany II*. Plenum Press, New York, 123–165.

DEMAERSCHALK, J. P. & KOZAK, A. 1977. The whole–bole system: a conditioned dual-equation system for precise prediction of tree profiles. *Canadian Journal of Forest Research*, **7**, 488–497.

DeNIRO, M. J. & HASTORF, C. A. 1985. Alteration of $^{15}N/^{14}N$ and $^{13}C/^{12}C$ ratios of plant matter during the initial stages of diagenesis: Studies utilizing archaeological specimens from Peru. *Geochimica et Cosmochimica Acta*, **49**, 97–115.

DERENNE, S., LARGEAU, C., & HATCHER, P. G. 1992. Structure of *Chlorella fusca* algaenan – Relationships with ultralaminae in lacustrine kerogens. Species and environment-dependent variation in the composition of fossil ultralaminae. *Organic Geochemistry*, **18**, 417–422.

DESALLE, R. 1994. Implications of ancient DNA for phylogenetic studies. *Experientia*, **50**, 543–550.

——, GATESY, J., WHEELER, W. & GRIMALDI, D. 1992. DNA sequences from a fossil termite in Oligo-Miocene amber and their phylogenetic implications. *Science*, **257**, 1933–1936.

DÉTIENNE, P. & JACQUET, P. 1983. *Atlas d'identification des bois de l'Amazonie et des régions voisines*. Centre Technique Forestier Tropical, Noguent-sur-Marne.

DETTMANN, M. E. 1963. Upper microfloras from South-eastern Australia. *Proceedings of the Royal Society of Victoria*, **77**(1), 1–148.

—— 1965. Techniques used in the Study of Megaspores. *In:* KUMMEL, B. & RAUP, D. (eds) *Handbook of paleontological techniques*. San Francisco, Freeman, 699–706.

DIGBY, P. G. N. & KEMPTON, R. A. 1987. *Multivariate Analysis of Ecological Communities*. Chapman & Hall, London.

DILCHER, D. L. 1974 Approaches to the identification of angiosperm leaf remains. *The Botanical Review*, **40**, 157.

—— & TAYLOR, T. N. (eds) 1980. *Biostratigraphy of Fossil Plants*. Dowden, Hutchinson & Ross, Stroudsburg PA.

DiMICHELE, W. A. & DeMARIS, P. J. 1987. Structure and dynamics of a Pennsylvanian-age *Lepidodendron* forest: Colonizers of a disturbed swamp habitat in the Herrin (No. 6) Coal of Illinois. *Palaios*, **2**, 146–157.

—— & PHILLIPS, T. L. 1988. Paleoecology of the Middle Pennsylvanian-age Herrin coal swamp (Illinois) near a contemporaneous river system, the Walshville paleochannel. *Review of Palaeobotany and Palynology*, **56**, 151–176.

——, —— & MCBRINN, G. E. 1991. Quantitative analysis and paleoecology of the Secor coal and roof-shale floras (Middle Pennsylvanian, Oklahoma). *Palaios*, **6**, 390–409.

——, RISCHBIETER, M. O., EGGERT, D. L. & GASTALDO, R. A. 1984. Stem and leaf cuticle of *Karinopteris*: source of cuticles from the Indiana 'paper' coal. *American Journal of Botany*, **71**, 626–637.

DIX, E. 1934. The sequence of floras in the Upper Carboniferous, with special reference to South Wales. *Transactions of the Royal Society of Edinburgh*, **57**, 789–838.

DIXON, W. T. 1982. Spinning-sideband-free and spinning-sideband only NMR spectra in spinning samples. *Journal of Chemical Physics*, **77**, 1800–1809.

DOBRUSKINA, I. A. 1982. [Triassic flora of Eurasia]. *Trudy Akademii Nauk SSSR, Seria geologicheskaya*, **365**, 1–195 [in Russian].

DODSWORTH, P. 1995. A note of caution concerning the application of quantitative palynological data from oxidized preparations. *Journal of Micropalaeontology*, **14**, 6.

DOHER, L. I. 1980. *Palynomorph preparation procedures currently used in the paleontology and stratigraphy laboratories, U. S. Geological Survey*. United States Geological Survey, Circular, **830**.

DORAN, J. B. 1980. A new species of *Psilophyton* from the Lower Devonian of northern New Brunswick, Canada. *Canadian Journal of Botany*, **58**, 2241–2262.

DOUGLASS, A. E. 1928. *Climatic cycles and tree growth*. Carnegie Institution of Washington Publication, **289, II**. Carnegie Institution, Washington.

DOWDESWELL, J. A. & SHARP, M. J. 1986. Characterization of pebble fabrics in modern terrestrial glacigenic sediments. *Sedimentology*, **33**, 699–710.

DOYLE, J. A., HOTTON, C. L. & WARD, J. V. 1990. Early Cretaceous tetrads, zonasulcate pollen, and Winteraceae. I. Taxonomy, morphology, and ultrastructure. *American Journal of Botany*, **77**, 1544–1557.

——, VAN CAMPO, M. & LUGARDON, B. 1975. Observations on exine structure in *Eucommiidites* and Lower Cretaceous angiosperm pollen. *Pollen et Spores*, **17**, 429–486.

DOYLE, P., BENNETT, M. R. & BAXTER, A. N. 1994. *The Key to Earth History. An introduction to stratigraphy*. Wiley, Chichester.

DRIESE, S. G. & FOREMAN, J. L. 1992. Paleopedology and paleoclimatic implications of Late Ordovician vertic paleosols, Juniata Formation, southern Appalachians. *Journal of Sedimentary Petrology*, **62**, 71–83.

——, MORA, C. I., COTTER, E. & FOREMAN, J. L. 1992. Paleopedology and stable isotope chemistry of Late Silurian vertic paleosols, Bloomsburg Formation, central Pennsylvania. *Journal of Sedimentary Petrology*, **62**, 825–841.

DRINNAN, A. N., CRANE, P. R., FRIIS, E. M. & PEDERSEN, K. R. 1990. Lauraceous flowers from the Potomac Group (mid-Cretaceous) of eastern North America. *Botanical Gazette*, **151**, 370–384.

DUGAS, D. P & RETALLACK, G. J. 1993. Middle Miocene fossil grasses from Fort Ternan, Kenya. *Journal of Paleontology*, **67**, 113–128.

DUNAY, R. E. & HAILWOOD, E. A. 1995. *Non-biostratigraphical Methods of Dating and Correlation*. Geological Society, London, Special Publications, **89**.

DUNWIDDIE, P. W. 1987. Macrofossil and pollen representation of coniferous trees in modern sediments from Washington. *Ecology*, **68**, 1–11.

EBLE, C. F. & GRADY, W. C. 1993. Paleoecological interpretation of a middle Pennslyvanian coal bed from the central Appalachian basin, U.S.A. *International Journal of Coal Geology*, **16**, 255–286.

—— & —— 1993. Palynologic and petrographic characteristics of two Middle Pennsylvanian coal beds and a probable modern analogue. *Geological Society of America Special Paper*, **286**, 119–138.

EDER–KOVAR, J. 1990. Typen der Geologisch-Palaontologischen Abteilung Palaobotanik. *Katalogue Band 8 der Wissenschaftlichen Sammlungen des Naturhistorischen Museums in Wien PALAEOBOTANIK Heft 1.*

EDWARDS, D. 1996. New insights into early land ecosystems: a glimpse of a Lilliputian world. *Review of Palaeobotany and Palynology*, **90**, 159–174.

——, ABBOTT, G. D. & RAVEN, J. A. 1996a. Cuticles of early land plants: a palaeoecophysiological evaluation. *In:* KERSTIENS, G. (ed.) *Plant Cuticles*. Bios Scientific publishers, Oxford, 1–31.

——, DAVIES, K. L., RICHARDSON, J. B. & AXE, L. 1995a. The ultrastructure of spores of *Cooksonia pertoni*. *Palaeontology*, **38**, 153–168.

——, ——, RICHARDSON, J. B., WELLMAN, C. H. & AXE, L. 1996b. Ultrastructure of *Synorisporites downtonensis* and *Retusotriletes* cf. *coronadus* in spore masses from the Pridoli of the Welsh Borderland. *Palaeontology*, **39**, 783–800.

——, FANNING, U. & RICHARDSON, J. B. 1994. Lower Devonian coalified sporangia from Shropshire: *Salopella* Edwards and Richardson and *Tortilicaulis* Edwards. *Botanical Journal of the Linnean Society*, **116**, 89–110.

——, KERP, H. & HASS, H. 1998. Stomata in early land plants: an anatomical and ecophysiological approach. *Journal of Experimental Botany*, **49**, 255–278.

——, SELDEN, P. A., RICHARDSON, J. B. & AXE, L. 1995b. Coprolites as evidence for plant–animal interaction in Siluro-Devonian terrestrial ecosystems. *Nature*, **377**, 177–288.

EDWARDS, D. S. 1980. Evidence for the sporophytic status of the Lower Devonian plant *Rhynia gwynne-vaughanii* Kidston. *Review of Palaeobotany and Palynology*, **29**, 177–188.

EHLERINGER, J. R. 1991. $^{13}C/^{12}C$ fractionation and its utility in terrestrial plant studies. *In:* COLEMAN, D. C. & FRY, B. (eds) *Carbon Isotope Techniques*. Academic Press, New York, 187–200.

EHRLICH, W. W. & HALL, J. W. 1959. The ultrastructure of Eocene pollen. *Grana Palynologica*, **2**, 32–35.

EKLUND, H., FRIIS, E. M. & PEDERSEN, K. J. 1997. Chloranthaceous floral structures from the Late Cretaceous of Sweden. *Plant Systematics and Evolution*, **207**, 13–42.

ELDREDGE, N. 1996. Hierarchies in macroevolution. *In:* JABLONSKI, D., ERWIN, D. H. & LIPPS, J. H. (eds) *Evolutionary Paleobiology*. University of Chicago Press, 42–61.

ENDRESJ, P. K. & FRIIS, E. M. (eds). 1994. *Early Evolution of Flowers*. Plant Systematics and Evolution, Supplement 8, Springer, New York.

ERDTMAN, G. 1956. 'LO analysis' and 'Welcker's rule'. A centenary. *Svensk Botanisk Tidskrift*, **54**, 135–141.

——, PRAGLOWSKI, J. & NILSSON, S. 1963. *An Introduction to a Scandinavian Pollen Flora*. II. Almqvist and Wiksell, Stockholm.

ERSLEV, E. A. 1988. Normalized center-to-center strain analysis of packed aggregates. *Journal of Structural Geology*, **10**, 201–209.

—— 1989. *Instrain, an integrated fabric analysis program for the Macintosh*. Rockware, Inc., Wheat Ridge, Colorado.

ESHET, Y. & HOEK, R. 1996. Palynological processing of organic-rich rocks, or: How many times have you called a palyniferous sample 'barren'? *Review of Palaeobotany and Palynology*, **94**, 101–109.

ESPINOZA de PERNIA, N. & MILLER, R. B. 1991. Adapting the IAWA list of microscopic features for hardwood identification to DELTA. *International Association of Wood Anatomists Bull.* n.s., **12**(1), 34–50.

ESTERLE, T. S., FERM, J. C. & YAU-LIONG, T. 1989. A test for the analogy of tropical domed peat deposits to 'dulling up' sequences in coal beds: preliminary results. *Journal of Organic Chemistry*, **14**, 333–342.

ESWARAN, H. 1968. Point-count analysis as applied to soil micromorphology. *Pedologie (Ghent)*, **18**, 238–252.

ETHERIDGE, R. & MCCULLOCH, A. R. 1916. Sub-fossil crustaceans from the coasts of Australia. *Records of the Australian Museum*, **11**, 1–14.

EVANS, J. R., SHARKEY, T. D., BERRY, J. A. & FARQUHAR, G. D. 1986. Carbon isotope discrimination measured concurrently with gas exchange to investigate CO_2 diffusion in leaves of higher plants. *Australian Journal of Plant Physiology*, **13**, 281–292.

EVITT, W. R. 1984. Some techniques for preparing, manipulating and mounting dinoflagellates. *Journal of Micropalaeontology*, **3**, 11–18.

—— 1985. *Sporopollenin Dinoflagellate Cysts: their Morphology and Interpretation*. American Association of Stratigraphic Palynologists Foundation, Dallas.

EWBANK, G., EDWARDS, D. & ABBOTT G. D. 1997. Chemical characterization of Lower Devonian vascular plants. *Organic Geochemistry*, **25**, 461–473.

FÆGRI, K. 1956. Recent trends in palynology. *Botanical Review*, **22**, 639–664.

—— & IVERSEN, J. 1950. *Textbook of modern pollen analysis*. Ejnar Munksgaard, Copenhagen.

—— & —— 1975. *Textbook of Pollen Analysis* (revised K. FÆGRI). Blackwell, Oxford.

—— & —— 1989. *Textbook of Pollen Analysis* (4th edn K. FÆGRI, P. E. KALAND & K. KRZYWINSKI). J. Wiley & Sons, Chichester.

FAIRON-DEMARET, M. 1978. *Estinnophyton gracile* gen. et sp. nov., a new name for specimens previously determined *Protolepidodendron wahnbachense* Kr. et W. from the Siegenian of Belgium. *Bulletin de l'Académie royale de Belgique*, Classe des Sciences, 5ème sér., **64**, 579–610.

FAO, 1974. *Soil map of the world. Vol. I. Legend*. UNESCO, Paris.

FARLEY, M. B. 1990. Vegetation distribution across the early Eocene depositional landscape from palynological analysis. *Palaeogeography, Palaeoclimatology, Palaeoecology*, **79**, 11–27.

FARLOW, J. O. 1987. Speculations about the diet and digestive physiology of herbivorous dinosaurs. *Paleobiology*, **13**, 60–72.

FARQUHAR, G. D., O'LEARY, M. H. & BERRY, J. H. 1982. On the relationship between carbon isotope discrimination and the intercellular carbon dioxide concentration in leaves. *Australian Journal of Plant Physiology*, **9**, 121–137.

FARR, K. M. 1989. Palynomorph and palynodebris distributions in modern British and Irish estuarine sediments. *In:* BATTEN, D. J. & KEEN, M. J. (eds) *Northwest European Micropalaeontology and Palynology*. Ellis Horwood Ltd, Chichester, 265–285.

FARRINGTON, O. S. & BATEMAN, R. M. 1992. A holistic approach to the analysis of archaeological deposits, illustrated using a Late Roman urban sequence from northwest Europe. *In:* VANDIVER, P. B., DRUZIK, J. R., WHEELER, G. S. & FREESTONE, I. C. (eds) *Materials Issues in Art and Archaeology III*. Materials Research Society Symposium Proceedings 267 (San Francisco), 179–192.

FAURE, G. 1986. *Principles of isotope geology* (2nd edn). John Wiley & Sons, Chichester.

FENG, B.-C. 1989. Paleoecology of an upper Middle Pennsylvanian coal swamp from western Pennsylvania, U.S.A. *Review of Palaeobotany and Palynology*, **57**, 299–312.

FERGUSON, C. W. 1969. A 7104-year annual tree-ring chronology for bristlecone pine, *Pinus Aristata*, from the White Mountains, California. *Tree-Ring Bulletin*, **29**, 2–29.

FERGUSON, D. K. 1970. *The Miocene flora of Kreuzau, Western Germany*. North–Holland Publishing Company, Amsterdam/London.

—— 1971. The Miocene Flora of Kreuzau, Western Germany, I. The Leaf Remains. *Verhandelingen der Koninklijke Nederlandse Akademie van Wetenschappen*. **II, 60, 1**. North Holland Publ., Amsterdam, 297.

—— 1985. The origin of leaf assemblages, new light on an old problem. *Review of Palaeobotany and Palynology*, **47**, 117–188.

—— 1993. Plant taphonomic studies with special reference to Messel. *In:* SSCHRENK, F. & ERNST, K. (eds) *Monument Grube Messel – Perspectives and Relationships. Kaupia*, **2**, 117–126.

—— 1995. Plant part processing and community

reconstruction. *Eclogae geologicae Helvetiae,* **88**, 627–641.

——, van der BURGH, J., CLAUSING, A. *et al.* 1996. Actuopalaeobotany – a taphonomic peep-show ? – Summary of workshop discussions. *Neues Jahrbuch für Geologie und Paläontologie, Abhandlungen,* **202**, 149–158.

FIGUEIRAL, I., MOSBRUGGER, V., ROWE, N. P., ASHRAF, A. R., UTESCHER, T. & JONES, T. P. 1998. The Miocene peat-forming vegetation of northwestern Germany: An analysis of wood remains and comparison with previous palynological interpretations. *Review of Palaeobotany and Palynology,* in press.

FISHER, M. J., BARNARD, P. C. & COOPER, B. S. 1980. Organic maturation and hydrocarbon generation in the Mesozoic sediments of the Sverdrup Basin, Arctic Canada. *Proceedings IV International Palynological Conference, Lucknow (1976–77),* **2**, 581–588.

FISSUNENKO, O. P. & LAVEINE, J.-P. 1984. Comparaison entre la distribution des principales espèces-guides végétales du Carbonifère moyen dans le bassin du Donetz (URSS) et les bassins du Nord-Pas-de-Calais et de Lorraine (France). *Compte rendu 9e Congrès de Stratigraphie et de Géologie du Carbonifère (Washington & Urbana, 1979),* **1**, 95–100.

FOREST, C. E., MOLNAR, P. & EMANUEL, K. A. 1995. Palaeoaltimetry from energy conservation principles. *Nature,* **374**, 347–350.

FORMAN, R. T. T. & GODRON, M. 1986. *Landscape Ecology.* Wiley, New York.

FOWELL, S. J., CORNET, B. & OLSEN, P. E. 1992. Late Triassic palynofloral evolution and climate cyclicity, eastern North America. *International Union of Geological Sciences Global Sedimentary Geology Program, Project Pangea Workshop,* Lawrence, Kansas, USA, 17.

FRANCIS, J. E. 1984. The seasonal environment of the Purbeck (Upper Jurassic) fossil forests. *Palaeogeography, Palaeoclimatology, Palaeoecology,* **48**, 285–307.

—— 1986. Growth rings in Cretaceous and Tertiary wood from Antarctica and their palaeoclimatic implications. *Palaeontology,* **29**, 665–684.

—— 1988. A 50-million-year-old fossil forest from Strathcona Fiord, Ellesmere Island, Arctic Canada: Evidence for a warm polar climate. *Arctic,* **41**, 314–318.

——, WOLFE, K. J., ARNOTT, M. J. & BARRETT, P. J. 1994. Permian climates of the southern margins of Pangea: evidence from fossil wood in Antarctica. *Canadian Society of Petroleum Geologists Memoir,* **17**, 275–282.

FRANCEY, R. J., GIFFORD, R. M., SHARKEY, T. D. & WEIR, B. 1985. Physiological influences on carbon isotope discrimination in huon pine (*Lagorostrobus franklini*). *Oecolgia (Berlin),* **66**, 211–218.

FRANSSEN, L. 1991. Legal provisions for the valorisation of the geological heritage in the Walloon region. *Bulletin de la Société belge de Géologie,* **100**, 285–286.

FREEMAN, K. H. & HAYES, J. M. 1992. Fractionation of carbon isotopes by phytoplankton and estimates of ancient CO_2 levels. *Global Biogeochemical Cycles,* **6**, 185–198.

FRENZEL, B. 1968. *Grundzüge der pleistozänen Vegetationsgeschichte Nord-Eurasiens. (Outline of the Pleistocene vegetation history of Northern Eurasia)* Steiner, Wiesbaden.

——, PÉCSI, M. & VELICHKO, A. A. (eds) 1992. *Atlas of paleoclimats and paleoenvironments of the Northern Hemisphere. Late Pleistocene – Holocene.* Fischer, Stuttgart.

FRIEDMAN, G. R. & JOHNSON, M. R. 1996. Thin section grain size analysis revisited: discussion and reply. *Sedimentology,* **43**, 189–191.

FRIELINGSDORF, J. 1992. *Klimamarken in Neogenen Hölzern vom Niederrhein.* PhD thesis, Geological Institute, University of Cologne, **86**, ISSN 0069-5874.

FRIIS, E. M. 1984. Preliminary report of upper Cretaceous angiosperm reproductive organs from Sweden and their level of organisation. *Annals of the Missouri Botanical Garden,* **71**, 403–418.

—— 1985. *Actinocalyx* gen. nov., sympetalous angiosperm flowers from the Upper Cretaceous of Southern Sweden. *Review of Palaeobotany and Palynology,* **45**, 171–183.

——, CRANE, P. R. & PEDERSEN, K. R. 1988. Reproductive structures of Cretaceous Platanaceae. *Det Kongelige Danske Videnskabernes Selskab Biologiske Skrifter,* **31**, 1–55.

——, PEDERSEN, K. R. & CRANE, P. R. 1995. *Appomattoxia ancistrophora* gen. et sp. nov., a new early Cretaceous plant with similarities to *Circaeaster* and extant Magnoliidae. *American Journal of Botany,* **82**, 933–943.

—— & SKARBY, A. 1981. Structurally preserved angiosperm flowers from the Upper Cretaceous of Southern Sweden. *Nature,* **291**, 485–486.

FRÜND, R. & LÜDEMANN, H.-D. 1994. Characterization of soil organic matter with high-speed CP-MAS-NMR-spectroscopy. *In:* SENESI, N. & MIANO, T. M. (eds) *Humic Substances in the Global Environment and Implications on Human Health.* Elsevier Science, 161–166.

FRY, N. 1979. Random point distributions and strain measurement in rocks. *Tectonophysics,* **60**, 806–807.

FUNKHOUSER, J. W. & EVITT, W. E. 1959. Preparation techniques for acid-insoluble microfossils. *Micropaleontology,* **5**(3), 369–375.

GALE, S. J. & HOARE, P. G. 1991. *Quaternary Sediments.* Belhaven, London.

GALEHOUSE, J. S. 1971. Point counting. *In:* CARVER, R. E. (ed.) *Procedures in sedimentary petrology.* John Wiley, New York, 385–407.

GALTIER, J. 1997. Coal-ball floras of the Namurian–Westphalian of Europe. *Review of Palaeobotany and Palynology,* **95**, 51–72.

GANDOLFO, M. A., NIXON, K. C. & CREPET, W. L. 1998. A new fossil flower from the Turonian of New Jersey: *Dressiantha bicarpellata* gen.et sp. nov. (Capparales). *American Journal of Botany,* **85**, 964–974.

GASTALDO, R. A. 1988. A Conspectus of Phytotaphonomy. *In:* DIMICHELE, W. A. & WING, S.

L. (eds) *Methods and Applications of Plant Paleoecology: Notes for a Short Course.* Paleontological Society Special Publication, **3**, 14–28.

—— (ed.) 1989. Special Issue on Plant Taphonomy. *Review of Palaeobotany and Palynology,* **58**, 1–94.

—— 1990. The paleobotanical character of log assemblages necessary to differentiate blow-downs resulting from cyclonic winds. *Palaios,* **5**, 472–478.

—— 1992. Taphonomic considerations for plant evolutionary investigations. *The Palaeobotanist,* **41**, 211–223.

—— 1997. (Book Review): Collecting the Natural World – Legal Requirements & Personal Liability for Collecting Plants, Animals, Rocks, Minerals & Fossils. *Palaios,* **12**, 501.

——, BEARCE, S. C., DEGGES, C. *et al.* 1989. Biostratinomy of a Holocene oxbow lake: a backswamp to mid-channel transect. *Review of Palaeobotany and Palynology,* **58**, 47–60.

——, FENG, W. & STAUB, J. R. 1996. Palynofacies patterns in channel deposits of the Rajang River and Delta, Sarawak, East Malaysia. *Palaios,* **11**, 266–279.

—— & HUC, A. Y. 1992. Sediment facies, depositional environments, and distribution of phytoclasts in the Recent Mahakam River delta, Kalimantan, Indonesia. *Palaios,* **7**, 574–591.

—— & STAUB, J. R. 1999. A Mechanism to Explain the Preservation of Leaf Litters Lenses in Coals Derived from Raised Mires. *Palaeogeography, Palaeoclimatology, Palaeoecology,* in press.

GAUCH, JR., H. G. 1982. Multivariate analysis in community ecology. *In:* BECK, E., BIRKS, H. J. B. & CONNOR, E. F. (eds) *Cambridge studies in ecology.* Cambridge University Press, New York.

GELIN, F., BOOGERS, I., NOORDELOOS, A. A. M., SINNINGHE DAMSTÉ, J. S., RIEGMAN, R. & DE LEEUW, J. W. 1997. Resistant biomacromolecules in marine microalgae of the classes Eustigmatopgyceae and Chlorophyceae: Geochemical implications. *Organic Geochemistry,* **26**, 659–675.

GENSEL, P. G. 1980. Devonian in situ spores: a survey and discussion. *Review of Palaeobotany and Palynology,* **30**, 101–132.

GERRIENNE, P. & STREEL, M. 1994. A biostratigraphic method based on a quantification of the characters of Devonian tracheophytes. *Paleobiology,* **20**, 208–214.

GILL, R. C. O. 1996. *Modern Analytical Geochemistry.* Longman.

GILLESPIE, R. 1984. *Radiocarbon User's Handbook.* Oxford University Committee for Archaeology, Oxford.

GIRARDIN, C. & MARIOTTI, A. 1991. Analyse isotopique du ^{13}C en abondance naturelle dans le carbone organique : un système automatique avec robot préparateur. *Cahiers de l'Orstom, série Pédologie,* **26**, 371–380.

GIVULESCU, R. 1984. Pathological elements on fossil leaves from Chiuzbaia (galls, mines and other insect traces). *Dari de Seama ale Sedintelor,* **69** (for 1981), 123–133.

GIVNISH, T. J. 1979. On the adaptive significance of leaf form. *In:* SOLBRIG, O. T., JAIN, S. & RAVEN, P. H. (eds) *Topics in Plant Population Biology.* Columbia University Press, New York, 375–407.

—— (ed.) 1986.*On the Economy of Plant Form and Function.* Cambridge University Press, Cambridge.

—— & VERMEIJ, G. 1976. Sizes and shapes of liane leaves. *American Naturalist,* **110**, 743–776.

GOLENBERG, E. M. 1991. Amplification and analysis of Miocene plant fossil DNA. *Philosophical Transactions of the Royal Society of London,* **B333**, 419–427.

—— 1993. Fossil samples. *In:* HERRMANN, B. & HUMMEL, S. (eds) *Ancient DNA.* New York, Springer Verlag, 237–256.

—— 1994. Uncertainty in the analysis of fossil DNA sequences. *In:* ADAMS, R. P., MILLER, J. S. GOLENBERG, E. M. & ADAMS, J. E. (eds) *Conservation of Plant Genes II: Intellectual Property Rights and DNA Utilization.* Missouri Botanical Gardens, St. Louis, MO, 15–26.

——, BICKEL, A. & WIEHS, P. 1996. Effects of highly fragmented DNA on PCR. *Nucleic Acids Research,* **24**, 5026–5033.

——, GIANNASSI, D. E., CLEGG, M. T. ET AL. 1990. Chloroplast DNA sequence from a Miocene *Magnolia* species. *Nature,* **344**, 656–658.

GOÑI, M. A., NELSON, B., BLANCHETTE, R. A. & HEDGES, J. I. 1993. Fungal degradation of wood lignins: Geochemical perspectives from CuO-derived phenolic dimers and monomers. *Geochimica et Cosmochimica Acta,* **57**, 3985–4002.

GOODALL, D. W. (ed.) 1986. *Ecosystems of the World.* Elsevier, Amsterdam.

GOODARZI, F. & SWAINE, D. J. 1994. The influence of geological factors on the concentration of boron in Australian and Canadian coals. *Chemical Geology,* **118** (1–4), 301–318.

GOODFRIEND, G. A. 1988. Mid–Holocene rainfall in the Negev Desert from ^{13}C of land snail shell organic matter. *Nature,* **333**, 757–760.

GOODMAN, D. K. 1979. Dinoflagellate 'communities' from the Lower Eocene Nanjemoy Formation of Maryland, U.S.A. *Palynology,* **3**, 169–190.

GOULDING, C. J. & MURREY, J. C. 1976. Polynomial taper equations that are compatible with tree volume equations. *New Zealand Journal of Forestry Science,* **5**, 313–322.

GOWER, J. C. 1971. A general coefficient of similarity and some of its properties. *Biometrics,* **27**, 857–872.

—— & DIGBY, P. G. N. 1981. Expressing complex relationships in two dimensions. *In:* BARNETT, V. (ed.) *Interpreting Multivariate Data.* Wiley, New York, 83–118.

—— & ROSS, G. J. S. 1969. Minimum spanning trees and single linkage cluster analysis. *Applied Statistics,* **18**, 54–64.

GRAY, H. R. 1956. *The form and taper of forest–tree stems.* Imperial Forestry Institute, Oxford, Paper **32**, 1–74.

GRAY, J. 1965. Techniques in palynology: extraction techniques. *In:* KUMMEL, B. & RAUP, D. (eds) *Handbook of Paleontological Techniques.* W. H. Freeman & Co., San Francisco, 530–587.

GRAYSON, J. F. 1975. Relationship of palynomorph translucency to carbon and hydrocarbons in clastic sediments. *In*: ALPERN, B. (ed.) *Pétrographie de la matière organique des sédiments, relations avec la paléotemperature et le potential pétrolier.* Centre National de la Recherche Scientifique, Paris, 261–273.

GREEN, J. W. 1963. Methods of carbohydrate chemistry, II. *In:* WHISTLER, R. L. (ed.) Academic Press, New York, 9–21.

GREENWOOD, D. R. 1991. The taphonomy of plant macrofossils. *In*: DONOVAN, S. K. (ed.) *The Processes of Fossilization.* Belhaven Press, London, 141–169.

—— 1992. Taphonomic constraints on foliar physiognomic intepretations of Late Cretaceous and Tertiary paleoclimates. *Review of Palaeobotany and Palynology*, **71**, 149–190.

GREGOR, J. 1989. Versuch eines neuen Klima–Modells für die Zeit der Oberen Meeres– und Süßwassermolasse in Bayern. (Attempt at a new climate model for the Upper Marine and Freshwater Molasse in Bavaria). *Documenta naturae*, **46**, 34–47.

GREGUSS, P. 1955. *Identification of living gymnosperms on the basis of xylotomy.* Kiadó, Budapest.

—— 1959. *Holzanatomie der Europäischen Laubhölzer und Sträucher.* Kiadó, Budapest.

GREIG, J. 1989. *Handbook for Archaeologists*, 4, *Archaeobotany.* European Science Foundation.

GREUTER, W., BARRIE, F. R. BURDET, H. M. *ET AL.* (eds) 1994. *International Code of Botanical Nomenclature (Tokyo Code).* Koeltz Scientific Books, Koenigstein.

GRIERSON, J. D. 1976. *Leclercqia complexa* (Lycopsida, Middle Devonian): its anatomy, and the interpretation of pyrite petrifactions. *American Journal of Botany*, **63**, 1184–1202.

GRÖCKE, D. R. 1997. Carbon-isotope stratigraphy of terrestrial plant fragments in the early Cretaceous from South-Eastern Australia. *In:* WOLBERG, D. L., STUMP, E. & ROSENBERG, G. R. (eds) *Dinofest™ International.* The Academy of Natural Sciences, Philadelphia, 457–461.

GROSSMAN, E. L. & KU, T–L. 1986. Oxygen and carbon isotope fractionation in biogenic aragonite: temperature effects. *Chemical Geology (Isotope Geoscience Section)*, **59**, 59–74.

GUENNEL, G. K. 1952. Fossil spores of the Alleghenian coals in Indiana. *Report Progress Indiana Department Conservation Geological Survey*, **4**, 1–40.

GUILFORD, W. J., SCHNEIDER, D. M., LABOVITZ, J. & OPELLA, S. J. 1988. High resolution solid state 13C NMR spectroscopy of sporopollenins from different plant taxa. *Plant Physiology*, **86**, 134–136.

GUIOT, J. 1994. Statistical analyses of biospherical variability. *In:* DUPLESSY, J.-C. & SPYRIDAKIS, M.-T. (eds) *Long-term climatic variations.* NATO ASI Series, **122**, 299–334.

——, REILLE, M., BEAULIEU, J. L. DE & PONS, A. 1992. Calibration of the climatic signal in a new pollen sequence from La Grande Pile. *Climate Dynamics*, **6**, 259–264.

GUTJAHR, C. C. M. 1966. Carbonization of pollen grains and spores and their application. *Leidse Geologische Medelingen*, **38**, 1–30.

GUY-OHLSON, D., OHLSON, N. G. & LINDQUIST, B. 1988. Fossil palynomorph deformation and its relationship to sedimentary deposition. *Geologiska Foreningens i Stockholm Forhandlingar*, **110**, 111–119.

HABIB, D., ESHET, Y. & VAN PELT, R. 1994. Palynology of sedimentary cycles. *In:* TRAVERSE, A. (ed.) *Sedimentation of Organic Particles.* Cambridge University Press, UK, 311–335.

HAGELBERG, E. & CLEGG, J. B. 1991. Isolation and characterization of DNA from archaeological bone. *Proceedings of the Royal Society, London,* **B244**, 45–50.

HAMILTON, G. J. & CHRISTIE, J. M. 1971. *Forest management tables (metric).* Forestry Commission, Her Majesty's Stationery Office, London.

HAMILTON WATERS, P. 1983. A review of the moulding and casting materials and techniques in use at the Palaeontology Laboratory, British Museum (Natural History). *The Conservator*, **7**, 37–43.

HANDT, O., HÖSS, M., KRINGS, M. & PÄÄBO, S. 1994a. Ancient DNA: methodological challenges. *Experientia*, **50**, 524–529.

——, RICHARDS, M., TROMMSDORFF, M. *ET AL.* 1994b. Molecular genetic analyses of the Tyrolean Ice Man. *Science*, **264**, 1775–1778.

HÄNNI, C., LAUDET, V., STEHELIN, D. & TABERLET, P. 1994. Tracking the origins of the cave bear (*Ursus spelaeus*) by mitochondrial DNA sequencing. *Proceedings of the National Academy of Science, USA*, **91**, 12 336–12 340.

HANSEN, B. S. & CUSHING, E. J. 1973. Identification of *Pinus* pollen of Quaternary age from the Chuska Mountains, New Mexico. *Geological Society of America Bulletin,* **84**, 1181–1200.

HARLAND, W. B. *ET AL.* 1989. *A Geological Time Scale.* Cambridge University Press.

HARMS, J. C., SOUTHARD, J., SPEARING, D. R. & WALKER, R. G. 1975. *Depositional environments as interpreted from primary sedimentary and stratification sequences.* Lecture Notes, Society of Economic Palaeontologists and Mineralogists, Short Course 2, Dallas, Texas.

HARRIS, T. M. 1926. Note on a new method for the investigation of fossil plants. *The New Phytologist*, **25**, 58–60.

—— 1937. The fossil flora of Scoresby Sound, East Greenland. Part 5. The stratigraphic relations of the plant beds. *Meddelelser om Grønland*, **112**, 1–114.

—— 1964. *The Yorkshire Jurassic flora II. Caytoniales, Cycadales & pteridosperms.* British Museum (Natural History), London.

—— 1969. *The Yorkshire Jurassic flora III. Bennettitales.* British Museum (Natural History), London.

—— 1974. *Williamsoniella lignieri*: its pollen and the compression of spherical pollen grains. *Palaeontology*, **17**, 125–148.

HART, G. F. 1970. The biostratigraphy of Permian palynofloras. *Geoscience and Man*, **1**, 89–131.

—— 1994. Maceral palynofacies of the Louisiana deltaic plain in terms of organic constituents and hydrocarbon potential. *In:* TRAVERSE, A. (ed.)

Sedimentation of Organic Particles. Cambridge University Press, UK, 141–176.

HARVEY, P. H. & PAGEL, M. D. 1991. *The Comparative Method in Evolutionary Biology*. Oxford University Press, Oxford.

HASE, J. & IWAUCHI, A. 1985. Late Cenozoic vegetation and paleoenvironment of Northern and Central Kyushu, Japan. *Journal of the Geological Society of Japan*, **19**, 753–770.

HASIOTIS, S. & BOWN, T. M. 1992. Invertebrate trace fossils: the backbone of continental ichnology. *In:* MAPLES, C. G. & WEST, R. R. (eds) *Trace fossils.* Paleontological Society Short Course in Paleontology, **5**, 65–104.

HATCHER, P. G. 1988. Dipolar-dephasing 13C NMR studies of decomposed and coalified xylem tissue: Evidence for chemical structural changes associated with defunctionalization of lignin structural units during coalification. *Energy and Fuels*, **2**, 48–58.

——, LERCH, H. E. III & VERHEYEN, T. V. 1989. Organic geochemical studies of the transformation of gymnosperm xylem during peatification and coalification to subbituminous coal. *International Journal of Coal Geology*, **13**, 65–97.

——, LYONS, P. C., THOMPSON, C. L., BROWN, F. W. & MACIEL, G. E. 1982. Organic matter in a coal ball: Peat or coal? *Science*, **217**, 831–833.

——, WENZEL, K. A. & CODY, G. D. 1994. The coalification reactions of vitrinite derived from coalified wood: Transformations to the rank of bituminous coal. *In:* MUKHOPADHYAY, P. K. & DOW, W. G. (eds) *Vitrinite Reflections as a Maturity Parameter.* American Chemical Society, Washington, DC, 112–135.

HAWKSWORTH, D. L. (ed.) 1994. *A draft glossary of terms used in bionomenclature.* IUBS Monograph **9**. 1–74. Paris, IUBS.

—— (ed.) 1996. *Draft BioCode – The Prospective International Rules for the Scientific Names of Organisms.* International Union of Biological Sciences, Paris.

——, MCNEIL, J. SNEATH, P. H. A.,TREHANE, R. P. & TUBBS, P. K. (eds) 1994. Towards a Harmonized Bionomenclature for Life on Earth. *Biology International Special Issues*, **30**, 1–44. International Union of Biological Sciences, Paris.

HAYATSU, R., BOTTO, R. E., MCBETH, R. L., SCOTT, R. G. & WINANS, R. E. 1988. Chemical alteration of a biological polymer 'sporopollenin' during coalification: Origin, formation, and transformation of the coal maceral sporinite. *Energy & Fuels*, **2**, 843–847.

HAYS, P. D. & GROSSMAN, E. L. 1991. Oxygen isotopes in meteoric calcite cements as indicators of continental paleoclimate. *Geology*, **19**, 441–444.

HEER, O. 1855–1859. *Flora Tertiaria Helvetiae* (3 vols). Winterthur.

HEINZ, C. 1990. Dynamique des végétations holocènes en méditerranée nord-occidentale d'après l'anthracoanalyse de sites préhistoriques: méthodologie et paléoecologie. *Paleobiologie Continentale*, **16** (2), Montpellier.

HELENTJARIS, T. 1988. Does RFLP analysis of ancient Anasazi samples suggest that they utilized hybrid maize? *Maize Genetics Cooperative News Letter*, **62**, 104–105.

HELSON, S., DAVID, P. & FERMONT, W. J. J. 1995. Calibration of conodont colour alteration using color image analysis. *Journal of Geology*, **103**, 257–267.

HEMSLEY, A. R., BARRIE, P. J., SCOTT, A. C. & CHALONER, W. G. 1994a. Studies of fossil and modern spore and pollen wall biomacromolecules using 13C solid state NMR. *Biomolecular Palaeontology*, **1**, 15–19.

——, CLAYTON, G. & GALTIER, J. 1994b. Further studies on a late Tournaisian (Lower Carboniferous) flora from Loch Humphrey Burn, Scotland: spore taxonomy and ultrastructure. *Review of Palaeobotany and Palynology*, **81**, 213–231.

——, JENKINS, P. D., COLLINSON, M. E. & VINCENT, B. 1996a. Experimental modelling of exine self-assembly. *Botanical Journal of the Linnean Society*, **121**, 177–187.

—— & SCOTT, A. C. 1991. Ultrastructure and relationships of Upper Carboniferous spores from Thorpe Brickworks, West Yorkshire, UK. *Review of Palaeobotany and Palynology*, **69**, 337–351.

——, —— & COLLINSON, M. E. 1998. Megaspore Architecture: diversity and function in freely dispersed forms. *In:* KURMANN, M. H. & HEMSLEY, A. R. (eds) *Evolution of Plant Architecture.* Royal Botanic Gardens, Kew.

——, ——, BARRIE, P. J. & CHALONER. W. G. 1996b. Studies of fossil and modern spore wall biomacromolecules using C-13 solid state NMR. *Annals of Botany*, **78**, 83–94.

HERENDEEN, P. S. 1991. Charcoalified angiosperm wood from the Cretaceous of eastern North America and Europe. *Review of Palaeobotany and Palynology*, **70**, 225–239.

——, CRANE, P. R. & DRINNAN, A. N. 1995. Fagaceous flowers, fruits, and cupules from the Campanian (late Cretaceous) of Central Georgia, USA. *International Journal of Plant Science*, **156**, 93–116.

——, KONOPKA, A. S., SMITH MERRILL, G. L. & CRANE, P. R. 1996. Three–dimensionally preserved moss sporophytes and gametophytes from the Late Cretaceous. International organization of palaeobotany meeting 1996: abstracts and programme, 41.

HERMAN, A. B. & SPICER, R. A. 1996. Palaeobotanical evidence for a warm Cretaceous Arctic Ocean. *Nature*, **381**, 330–333.

HESSE, M. & WAHA, M. 1989. A new look at the acetolysis method. *Plant Systematics and Evolution*, **163**, 147–152.

HESSELBO, S. P. & PARKINSON, D. N. (eds) 1996. *Sequence Stratigraphy in British Geology.* Geological Society, London, Special Publications, **103**.

HIBBERT, F. A. 1967. The use of scanning electron microscopy in the study of Carboniferous miospores. *New Phytologist*, **66**, 825–826.

HICKEY, L. J. & WOLFE, J. A. 1975. The bases of angiosperm phylogeny: vegetative morphology. *Annals of the Missouri Botanical Gardens*, **62**, 538–589.

HIGGS, K., CLAYTON, G. & KEEGAN, J. B. 1988. Stratigraphic and Systematic Palynology of the Tournaisian Rocks of Ireland. *Geological Survey of Ireland, Special Paper,* **7**, 93.

—— & SCOTT, A. C. 1982. Megaspores from the uppermost Devonian (Strunian) of Hook Head, County Wexford, Ireland. *Palaeontographica,* **B181**, 79–108.

HIGHTON, P. J. C., PEARSON, A. & SCOTT, A. C. 1991. Palynofacies and palynodebris and their use in Coal Measure palaeoecology and palaeoenvironmental analysis. *Neues Jahrbuch für Geologie und Paläontologie Abhandlungen,* **183**(1–3), 135–169.

HILL, C. R. 1990. Scanning electron microscopy in palaeobotany. *In:* CLAUGHER, D. (ed.) *Scanning Electron Microscopy in Taxonomy and Functional Morphology.* Systematics Association Special Volume, **41**, 193–234.

HILL, M. O. 1979. Correspondence analysis: a neglected multivariate method. *Applied Statistics,* **23**, 340–354.

HILL, R. S. & GIBSON, N. 1986. Distribution of potential macrofossils in Lake Dobson, south central Tasmania, Australia. *Journal of Ecology,* **74**, 373–384.

HILL, S. A., WATERHOUSE, J. S., FIELD, E. M., SWITSUR, V. R. & REES, T. 1995. Rapid recycling of triose phosphates in oak stem tissue. *Plant Cell and Environment,* **18**, 931–936.

HILLAM, J., GROVES, C. M., BROWN, D. M., BAILLIE, M. G. L., COLES, J. M. & COLES, B. J. 1990. Dendrochronology of the English Neolithic. *Antiquity,* **64**, 210–20.

HILLIER, S. J. & MARSHALL, J. 1988. A rapid technique to make polished thin sections of sedimentary organic matter concentrates. *Journal of Sedimentary Petrology,* **58**, 754–755.

HILLMAN, G. 1986. Plant foods in ancient diet: the archaeological role of palaeofaeces in general and Lindow man's gut contents in particular. *In:* STEAD, I., BOURKE J. & BROTHWELL, D. (eds) *Lindow Man. The body in the bog.* British Museum, London.

——, WALES, S., MCLAREN, F., EVANS, J. & BUTLER, A. 1993. Identifying problematic remains of ancient plant foods: a comparison of the role of chemical, histological and morphological criteria. *World Archaeology,* **25**, 94–121.

HILTON, J. & EDWARDS, D. 1996. A new Late Devonian acupulate preovule from the Taff Gorge, South Wales. *Review of Palaeobotany and Palynology,* **93**, 235–252.

HOLLAND, C. H., AUDLEY-CHARLES, M. G., BASSETT, M. G. ET AL. 1978. *A Guide to Stratigraphical Procedure.* Geological Society, London, Special Report, **10**.

HOLLAND, H. D. 1984. *The Chemical Evolution of the Atmosphere and Oceans.* Princeton University Press, Princeton.

HOLLOWAY, P. J. 1982. Structure and histochemistry of plant cuticular membranes: an overview. *In:* CUTLER, D. F., ALVIN, K. L. & PRICE, C. E. (eds) *The Plant Cuticle.* Academic Press, London, 1–32.

—— 1984. Cutins and suberins, the polymeric plant lipids. *In:* MANGOLD, H. K. (ed.) *CRC Handbook of Chromatography, Lipids, Vol. 1.* CRC Press, Boca Raton, FL, 321–346.

HOLLSTEIN, E. 1980. MittelEuropäische Eichenchronologi, Trierer dendrochronologische forschungen zur archäologie und Kunstgeschichte. *Trierer Grabungen und Forschungen,* **11**. Phillip Von Zabern, Mainz am Rhein.

HOLMES, J. C. 1977. The Carboniferous fern *Psalixochlaena cylindrica* as found in Westphalian A coal-balls from England. Part I. Structure and development of the cauline system. *Palaeontographica B,* **164**, 33–75.

—— & LOPEZ, J. 1986. The Disappearing Peel Technique: an improved method for studying permineralized plant tissues. *Palaeontology,* **29**, 787–808.

HOLMES, P. L. 1994. the sorting of spores and pollen by water: experimental and field evidence. *In:* TRAVERSE, A. (ed.) *Sedimentation of organic particles.* Cambridge University Press, 9–32.

HOLMES, R. L. 1983 Computer assisted quality control in tree-ring dating and measurement. *Tree-Ring Bulletin,* **43**, 69–75.

HOOGHIEMSTRA, H., STALLING, H., AGWU, C. O. C. & DUPONT, L. M. 1992. Vegetational and climatic changes at the northern fringe of the Sahara 250,000–5000 years BP: evidence from 4 marine pollen records located between Portugal and the Canary Islands. *Review of Palaeobotany and Palynology,* **74**, 1–53.

HOOKER, J. J. & COLLINSON, M. E. Plant–animal interactions – dispersal. *In:* BRIGGS, D. E. G. & CROWTHER, P. (eds) *Palaeobiology II.* Blackwell Scientific Publications, Oxford, in press.

——, ——, VAN BERGEN, P. F., SINGER, R. L., DE LEEUW, J. W. & JONES, T. P. 1995. Reconstruction of land and freshwater palaeoenvironments near the Eocene–Oligocene boundary, southern England. *Journal of the Geological Society, London,* **152**, 449–468.

HORAI, S., KONDO, R., MURAYAMA, K. ET AL. 1991. Phylogenetic affiliation of ancient and contemporary humans inferred from mitochondrial DNA. *Philosophical Transactions of the Royal Society of London,* **B333**, 409–417.

HORELL, M. 1991. Phytogeography and paleoclimate interpretation on the Maestrichtian. *Palaeogeography, Palaeoclimatology, Palaeoecology,* **86**, 87–138.

HÖSS, M., DILLING, A., CURRANT, A. & PÄÄBO, S. 1996a. Molecular phylogeny of the extinct ground sloth *Mylodon darwinii. Proceedings of the National Academy of Science, USA,* **93**, 181–185.

——, JARUGA, P., ZASTAWNY, T., DIZDOROGLU, M. & PÄÄBO, S. 1996b. DNA-damage and DNA-sequence retrieval from ancient tissues. *Nucleic Acids Research,* **24**, 1304–1307.

——, PÄÄBO, S. & VERESHCHAGIN, N. K. 1994. Mammoth DNA sequences. *Nature,* **370**, 333.

HOTTON, C. L. & STEIN, W. E. 1994. An ontogenetic model for the Mississippian seed plant family Calamopityaceae. *International Journal of Plant Sciences,* **155**, 119–142.

HOWARTH, R. W. 1979. Pyrite: its rapid formation in a salt marsh and its importance in ecosystem metabolism. *Science*, **203**, 49–51.

HOWIE, F. M. P. 1979. Museum climatology and the conservation of palaeontological material. *In:* BASSET, M. G. (ed.) *Curation of Palaeontological Collections.* Special Papers in Palaeontology, **22**, 103–125.

HOYT, W. H., & DeMAREST, J. M. III. 1981. *Vibracoring in Coastal Environments: the R.V. Phryne II Barge and Associated Coring Methods.* Sea Grant College Program, DEL.SG.**01.81**, 33.

HUGHES, M. K., TOUCHAN, R. & BROWN, P. M. 1996. A multimillennian network of giant sequoia chronologies for dendroclimatology. *In:* DEAN, J. S., MEKO, D. M. & SWETNAM, T. W. (eds) *Tree rings, environment and humanity: Proceedings of the International Conference, Tucson, Arizona, 17–21 May 1994.* Radiocarbon, Tucson, 225–234.

HUGHES, N. F. 1986. The problems of data-handling for early angiosperm-like pollen. *In:* SPICER, R. A. & THOMAS, B. A. (eds) Systematic and Taxonomic Approaches in Palaeobotany. *Systematics Association Special Volume,* **31**, 233–251.

—— 1989. *Fossils as Information.* Cambridge University Press, Cambridge.

—— 1994. *The enigma of angiosperm origins.* Cambridge University Paleobiology Series no.1, Cambridge University Press, Cambridge.

—— & MOODY-STUART, J. C. 1967. Palynological facies and correlation in the English Wealden. *Review of Palaeobotany and Palynology,* **1**, 259–268.

HUMPHRIES, D. W. 1992. *The preparation of thin sections of rocks, minerals, and ceramics.* Royal Microscopical Society Microscopy Handbooks, **24**, Oxford Science Publications.

HUNER, N. P. A., PALTA, J. P., LI, H. & CARTER, J. V. 1981. Anatomical changes in leaves of puma rye in response to growth at cold-hardening temperatures. *Botanical Gazette,* **142**, 55–62.

HUNT, A. P., CHIN, K. & LOCKLEY, M. G. 1994. The palaeobiology of vertebrate coprolites. *In:* DONOVAN, S. K. (ed.) *The Palaeobiology of Trace Fossils.* John Wiley & Sons, Chichester, 221–240.

HUNTLEY, B. & BIRKS, H. J. B. 1983. *An atlas of past and present pollen maps for Europe, 0–13,000 years ago.* Cambridge University Press, UK.

—— & PRENTICE, I. C. 1988. July temperatures in Europe from pollen data, 6000 years before present. *Science,* **241**, 687–690.

IAWA COMMITTEE, 1989. IAWA list of microscopic features for hardwood identification. *IAWA Bulletin,* **10**, 219–332.

IGARASHI, K., NAKASHIMA, R. & NAYA, T. 1991. Microwave sample digestion of coals for trace-element analysis. *Bunseki Kagaku,* **40**, T 71–T 75.

IGERSHEIM, A. & CICHOCKI, O. 1996. A simple method for microtome sectioning of prehistoric charcoal specimens, embedded in 2-hydroxyethyl methacrylate (HEMA). *Review of Palaeobotany and Palynology,* **92**, 389–393.

ILIC, J. 1987. The CSIRO family key for hardwood identification. CSIRO Division Chemical and Wood Technology Technical Paper n° 8.

INTERNATIONAL ORGANISATION FOR STANDARDISATION (ISO) 7404/2. 1985. *Methods for the petrographic analysis of bituminous coal and anthracite - part 2: methods of preparing coal samples.* Centre National de la Recherche Scientifique, 15, quai Anatole-France, F-75007 Paris, France.

—— 7404/5. 1984. *Methods for the petrographic analysis of bituminous coal and anthracite - part 5: methods of determining microscopically the reflectance of vitrinite.* Centre National de la Recherche Scientifique, 15 quai Anatole-France, F-75007, Paris, France.

IRWIN, W. J. 1993. Pyrolysis techniques. *In:* WINEFORDNER, J. D. (ed.) *Treatise on Analytical Chemistry, Part 1, Volume 13* (2nd edn) *Thermal Methods.* John Wiley & Sons, Inc., 309–353.

IVERSEN, J. & TROELS-SMITH, J. 1950. *Pollenmorfologiske Definitioner og Typer.* Danmarks Geologiske Undersøgelse, **4**, (3).

JACKSON, S. T. 1989. *Postglacial Vegetational Changes Along an Elevational Gradient in the Adirondack Mountains (New York): A Study of Plant Macrofossils.* New York State Museum Bulletin, **465.**

—— 1994. Pollen and spores in Quaternary lake sediments as sensors of vegetation composition: theoretical models and empirical evidence. *In:* TRAVERSE, A. (ed). *Sedimentation of Organic Particles.* Cambridge University Press, Cambridge, 253–286.

——, OVERPECK, J. T., WEBB, T., III, KEATTCH, S. E. & ANDERSON, K. H. 1997. Mapped plant-macrofossil and pollen records of Late Quaternary vegetation change in eastern North America. *Quaternary Science Reviews,* **16**, 1–70.

——, WEBB, T. III, PRENTICE, I. C. & HANSEN, J. E. 1995. Exploration and calibration of pollen/vegetation relationships: a PC program for the extended *R*-value models. *Review of Palaeobotany and Palynology,* **84**, 365–374.

JACOBS, B. F. & A. L. DEINO, A. L. 1996. Test of climate–leaf physiognomy regression models, their application to two Miocene floras from Kenya, and $^{40}Ar/^{39}Ar$ dating of the Late Miocene Kapturo site. *Palaeogeography, Palaeoclimatology, Palaeo-ecology,* **123**, 259–271.

JACOBS, P. 1997. Conservation of the geological heritage in Belgium. *In:* GONGGRIJP G. (ed.) *Geoconservation Manual.* Instituut voor Bos- en Natuuronderzoek, Wageningen, The Netherlands.

JACOBSON, R. E., RAY, S. F., ATTRIDGE, G. G. & AXFORD, N. R. 1979. *The manual of photography.* Focal Press, London & Boston.

JACOMET, S., BROMBACHER, C. & DICK, M. 1989. *Berichte der Zürcher Denkmalpflege Monographien 7.* Zürich.

JACQUIOT, C. 1955. *Atlas d'Anatomie des bois des Conifères.* Centre Technique du Bois, Paris.

——, TRENARD, Y. & DIROL, D. 1973. *Atlas d'anatomie des bois des Angiosperms.* Centre Technique du Bois, Paris.

JANSONIUS, J. & HILLS, L. V. 1976. *Genera file of fossil spores and pollen.* Special Publication of the

Department of Geology, University of Calgary, Calgary, Canada.

—— & McGregor, D. C. 1996. Introduction. *In:* Jansonius, J. & McGregor, D. C. (eds) *Palynology: principles and applications.* American Association of Stratigraphic Palynologists Foundation, **1**, 1–10.

Jarvis, K. E., Gray, A. L. & Houk, R. S. 1992. *Handbook of Inductively Coupled Plasma Mass Spectrometry.* Blackie, Glasgow.

Jarzembowski, E. A 1981. An early Cretaceous termite from southern England (Isoptera: Hodotermitidae). *Systematic Entomology,* **6**, 91–96.

—— 1990. A boring beetle from the Wealden of the Weald. *In:* Boucot, A. J. (ed.) *Evolutionary paleobiology of behaviour and coevolution.* Elsevier, Amsterdam, 373–376.

—— 1995. Fossil cockroaches or pinnule insects? *Proceedings of the Geologists' Association,* **105**, 305–311.

Jarzen, D. M. & Nichols, D. J. 1996. Pollen. *In:* Jansonius, J. & McGregor, D. C. (eds) *Palynology: principles and applications.* American Association of Stratigraphic Palynologists Foundation, **1**, 261–291.

Jefferson, T. H. 1982. Fossil forests from the Lower Cretaceous of Alexander Island, Antarctica. *Palaeontology,* **25**, 681–708.

Jeffery, C. 1989. *Biological Nomenclature* (3rd edn.). Edward Arnold, London.

Jeram, A. J. 1994. Carboniferous Orthosterni and their relationship to living scorpions. *Palaeontology,* **37**, 513–550.

Johnson, N. G. & Gensel, P. G. 1992. A reinterpretation of the Early Devonian land plant, *Bitelaria* Istchenko and Istchenko, 1979, based on new material from New Brunswick, Canada. *Review of Palaeobotany and Palynology,* **74**, 109–138.

Johnson, R. A. & Wichern, D. W. 1988. *Applied Multivariate Statistical Analysis* (2nd edn.). Prentice Hall, Englewood Cliffs, NJ.

Jones, A., Reed, R. & Weyers, J. 1996. *Practical skills in biology.* Longman, UK.

Jones, G. 1991 Numerical analysis in archaeobotany. *In:* Van Zeist, W., Wasylikowa, K. & Behre, K-E. (eds) *Progress in Old World Palaeoethnobotany.* Balkema, Rotterdam, 63–80.

——, Charles, M., Colledge, S. & Halstead, P. 1995. Towards the archaeobotanical recognition of winter-cereal irrigation: An investigation of modern weed ecology in northern Spain. *In: Res archaeo-botanicae: Proceedings of the ninth Symposium of the international workgroup for palaeoethnobotany.* Verlag, Kiel.

Jones, H. G. 1992. *Plants and Microclimate. A Quantitative Approach to Environmental Plant Physiology.* Cambridge University Press, Cambridge.

Jones, J. B. 1991. *Kjeldahl Method for Nitrogen (N) Determination.* Macro-micro, Athens, Georgia.

Jones, M. K. 1991. Sampling in palaeoethnobotany. *In:* Van Zeist, W., Wasylikowa, K. & Behre, K-B. (eds) *Progress in Old World Palaeoethnobotany.* Balkema, Rotterdam, 53–62.

Jones, R. A. 1994. The application of microwave technology to the oxidation of kerogen for use in palynology. *Review of Palaeobotany and Palynology,* **80**, 333–338.

—— & Ellin, S. J. 1998. Improved palynological sample preparation using an automated focused microwave digestion system. *In:* Bryant, V. & Wrenn, J. (eds) *New Developments in Palynomorph Sampling, Extraction and Analysis.* American Association of Stratigraphic Palynologists Contribution Series, **33**, 23–28.

Jones, T. P. 1993. New morphological and chemical evidence for a wildfire origin for fusain from comparisons with modern charcoal. *Special Papers in Palaeontology,* **49**, 113–123.

—— 1994. ^{13}C enriched Lower Carboniferous fossil plants from Donegal, Ireland: Carbon isotope constraints on taphonomy, diagenesis and palaeoenvironment. *Review of Palaeobotany and Palynology,* **81**, 53–64.

—— & Chaloner, W. G. 1991. Fossil charcoal, its recognition and palaeoatmopheric significance. *Palaeogeography, Palaeoclimatology, Palaeo-ecology (Global and Planetary Change Section),* **97**, 39–50.

——, Fortier, S. M., Pentecost, A. & Collinson, M. E. 1996. Stable carbon and oxygen isotopic compositions of Recent charophyte oosporangia and water from Malham Tarn, U.K.: palaeontological implications. *Biogeochemistry,* **34**, 99–112.

Josten, K.-H. & Laveine, J.-P. 1984. Paläobotanisch-stratigraphische Untersuchungen im Westfal C- D von Nordfrankreich und Nordwestdeutschland. *Fortschritte Geologie Rheinland und Westfalen,* **32**, 89–117.

—— 1962. *Neuropteris semireticulata,* eine neue Art als Bindeglied zwischen den Gattungen *Neuropteris* und *Reticulopteris. Paläontologische Zeitschrift,* **36**, 33–45.

Jowsey, P. C. 1966. An improved peat sampler. *New Phytologist,* **65**, 245–248.

Joy, K. W., Willis, A. J. & Lacey, W. S. 1956. A rapid cellulose peel technique in palaeobotany. *Annals of Botany,* **20**, 635–637.

Jupp, P. E., Spurr, B., Nichols, G. J. & Hurst, J. P. P. 1987. Statistical determination of the apex of a sediment distribution system from palaeocurrent data. *Mathematical Geology,* **19**, 319–333.

Kawase, M. & Takahashi, M. 1995. Chemical composition of sporopollenin in *Magnolia grandiflora* (Magnoliaceae) and *Hibiscus syracus* (Malvaceae). *Grana,* **34**, 242–245.

Kearsley, J. B. & Jackson, S. T. 1997. History of a *Pinus strobus*–dominated stand in northern New York. *Journal of Vegetation Science,* **8**, in press.

Keddie, J. L., Meredith, P., Jones, R. A. L. & Donald, A. M. 1996. Film formation of acrylic latices with varying concentrations of non-film-forming latex particles. *Langmuir,* **12**, 3793–3801.

Kelly, C. K. & Beerling, D. J. 1995. Plant life form, stomatal density and taxonomic relatedness: a reanalysis of Salisbury (1927). *Functional Ecology,* **9**, 422–432.

KELMAN, Z. & MORAN, L. 1996. Degradation of ancient DNA. *Current Biology,* **6**, 223.

KEMPF, E. K. 1971. Electron microscopy of Mesozoic megaspores from Denmark. *Grana,* **11**, 151–163.

KENRICK, P. & CRANE, P. 1991 Water-conducting cells in early fossil land plants: implications for the early evolution of tracheophytes. *Botanical Gazette,* **152**, 335–356.

—— & —— 1997. *The Origin and Early Diversification of Land Plants.* Smithsonian Institution Press, Washington, DC.

—— & EDWARDS, D. 1988. The anatomy of Lower Devonian *Gosslingia breconensis* Heard based on pyritized axes, with some comments on the permineralization process. *Botanical Journal of the Linnean Society,* **97**, 95–123.

——, —— & DALES, R. C. 1991. Novel ultrastructure in water-conducting cells of the Lower Devonian plant *Sennicaulis hippocrepiformis. Palaeontology,* **34**, 751–766.

KENT, M. & COKER, P. 1992. *Vegetation Description and Analysis.* Belhaven Press, London, 363.

KERKAR, V. 1994. Mineralogical studies on calcareous algae. *Current Science,* **66**, 381–382.

—— & UNTAWALE, A. G. 1995. Studies on structure and organization of calcium–carbonate deposits in algae. *Current Science,* **68**, 843–845.

KERP, H. 1990. The study of fossil gymnosperms by means of cuticular analysis. *Palaios,* **5**, 548–569.

—— & BARTHEL, M. 1993. Problems of cuticular analysis of pteridosperms. *Review of Palaeobotany and Palynology,* **78**, 1–18.

KERP, J. H. F. & HAUBOLD, H. 1988. Towards a reclassification of the West- and Central- European species of the form-genus *Callipteris* Brongniart 1849. *Zeitschrift geologische Wissenschaft,* **16**, 865–876.

——, POORT, R. J., SWINKELS, H. A. J. M. & VERWER, R. 1990. Aspects of Permian Palaeobotany and Palynology. IX. Conifer-dominated Rotliegend floras from the Saar-Nahe Basin (?Late Carbon-iferous – Early Permian; SW-Germany) with special reference to the reproductive biology of the earliest conifers. *Review of Palaeobotany and Palynology,* **62**, 205–248.

KERSTIENS, G. 1996. Signalling across the divide: a wider perspective of cuticular structure-function relation-ships. *Trends Plant Science,* **1**, 125–129.

KICKINGER, V. 1997. *Pflanzen als Klimaindikatoren.* Mag. Thesis, University of Vienna.

KISLEV, M. 1988. Nahal Hemar cave: Desiccated plant remains: An interim report. *Atiqot,* **18**, 76–81.

KLOK, J., BAAS, M., COX, H. C., DE LEEUW, J. W., RIJPSTRA, W. I. C. & SCHENCK, P. A. 1984. Qualitative and quantitative characterization of the total organic matter in a recent marine sediment (Part II). *Organic Geochemistry,* **6**, 265–278.

KLOMPARENS, K. L. (ed.) *Artefacts in biological electron microscopy.* Plenum Publishing, 81–106.

KLUTE, A. (ed.) 1986. *Methods of soil analysis. Part 1. Physical and mineralogical methods.* American Society of Agronomy Monograph, **9**, 363–375.

KNIGHT, J. D., MATUS, A. M., VAN KESSEL, C., PARRY, G. R. & SLINKARD, A. E. 1994. Comparison of a dual-inlet gas isotope ratio mass spectrometry system and an automated single-inlet mass spectrometry system for $d^{13}C$ analysis. *Communications in Soil Science and Plant Analysis,* **25**, 447–454.

KNOLL, A. H. 1985. Exceptional preservation of photosynthetic organisms in silicified carbonates and silicified peats. *Philosophical Transactions of the Royal Society of London,* **B311**, 111–122.

KOCH, P. L. 1998. Isotopic reconstructions of past continental environments. *Annual Review of Earth and Planetary Sciences,* **26**, 573–613.

KÖGEL-KNABNER, I., DE LEEUW, J. W., TEGELAAR. E. W., HATCHER, P. G. & KERP, H. 1994. A lignin-like polymer in the cuticle of spruce needles: implications for the humification of spruce litter. *Organic Geochemistry,* **21**, 1219–1228.

KÖHLER, J. The Upper Oligocene flora from Enspel (Westerwald). *Courier Forschungsinstitut Senckenberg,* in press.

KOSANKE, R. M. 1950. Pennsylvanian spores of Illinois and their use in correlation. *Illinois Geological Survey Bulletin,* **74**.

KOVACH, W. L. 1989. Comparisons of multivariate analytical techniques for use in pre-Quaternary plant paleoecology. *Review of Palaeobotany and Palynology,* **60**, 255–282.

—— & BATTEN, D. J. 1994. Association of palynomorphs and palynodebris with depositional environments: quantitative approaches. *In:* TRAVERSE, A. (ed.) *Sedimentation of Organic Particles.* Cambridge University Press, Cambridge, 391–407.

KRASSILOV, V. A. 1981. Changes of Mesozoic vegetation and the extinction of dinosaurs. *Palaeogeography, Palaeoclimatology, Palaeoecology,* **34**, 207–224.

KRÄUSEL, R. 1949. Die Koniferen-Hölzer, II teil. Kritische Untersuchungen zur Diagnostic lebender und fossiler Koniferen-Hölzer. *Paleontographica* B, **89**, 82–203.

KRINGS, K. & KERP, H. 1997*a.* Cuticles of *Lescuropteris genuina* from the Stephanian (Upper Carboniferous) of Central France - evidence for a climbing growth habit. *Botanical Journal of the Linnean Society London,* **123**, 73–89.

—— &—— 1997*b.* An improved method for obtaining large pteridosperm cuticles. *Review of Palaeobotany and Palynology,* **96**, 453–456.

KRINGS, M., STONE, A., SCHMITZ, R. W. *ET AL.* 1997. Neandertal DNA sequences and the origin of modern humans. *Cell,* **90**, 19–30.

KRÜGER, H., VAN RENSBURG, L. & PEACOCK, J. 1996. Cuticular membrane fine structure of *Nicotiana tabacum* L. Leaves. *Annals of Botany,* **77**, 11–16.

KUBÍNOVÁ, L. 1994. Recent stereological methods for the measurement of leaf anatomical characteristics: estimation of volume density, volume and surface area. *Journal of Experimental Botany,* **44**, 165–174.

KÜRSCHNER, W. M. 1996. Leaf stomata as biosensors of palaeoatmospheric CO_2 levels. *LPP Contributions Series,* **5**, 1–153.

—— 1997. The anatomical diversity of recent and fossil leaves of the durmast oak (*Quercus petraea* Lieblein / *Q. pseudocastanea* Goeppert) – impli-cations for their use as biosensors of palaeoatmospheric CO_2 levels. *Review of Palaeobotany and Palynology,* **96**, 1–30.

——, VAN DER BURGH, J., VISSCHER, H. & DILCHER, D. L. 1996. Fossil oak leaves as biosensors of Late Neogene to early Pleistocene paleoatmospheric CO_2 concentrations. *In:* POORE, R. & SLOAN, L. (eds) Climates and Climatic Variability in the Pliocene. *Marine Micropaleontology,* **27**, 299–312.

——, WAGNER, F., VISSCHER, E. H. & VISSCHER, H. 1997. Predicting the stomatal frequency response to a future CO_2 enriched atmosphere – constraints from historical observations. *Geologische Rundschau,* **86**, 512–517.

KVACEK, Z. & WALTHER, H. 1978. Anisophylly and leaf homeomorphy in some Tertiary plants. *Courier Forschungsinstitut Senckenberg* **30**, 84–94.

LABANDEIRA, C. C. 1997. Insect mouthparts: Ascertaining the paleobiology of insect feeding strategies. *Annual Review of Ecology and Systematics,* **28**, 153–193.

—— 1998. Early history of arthropod and vascular plant associations. *Annual Review of Earth and Planetary Sciences,* **26**, 329–377.

—— & BEALL, B. S. 1990. Arthropod terrestriality. *In:* MIKULIC, D. (ed.) *Arthropod Paleobiology.* Short courses in Paleontology, **3**, 215–255. University of Tennessee Press, Knoxville.

——, DILCHER, D. L., DAVIS, D. R. & WAGNER, D. L. 1994. Ninety-seven million years of angiosperm–insect association: Palaeobiological insights into the meaning of coevolution. *Proceedings of the National Accademy of Science,* **91**, 12 278–12 282.

——, NUFIO, C., WING, S. & DAVIS, D. 1995. Insect feeding strategies from the Late Cretaceous Big Cedar Ridge Flora: Comparing the diversity and intensity of Mesozoic Herbivory with the Present. *Geological Society of America, Abstracts with Programs,* **27** (**6**), A447.

—— & PHILLIPS, T. L. 1996*a*. Insect fluid-feeding on Upper Pennsylvanian tree ferns (Palaeodictyoptera, Marattiales) and the early history of the piercing-and-sucking functional feeding group. *Annals of the Entomological Society of America,* **89**, 157–183.

——&—— 1996*b*. A late Carboniferous petiole gall and the early history of the Holometabola. *Proceedings of the National Academy of Science,* **93**, 8470–8474.

——, —— & NORTON, R. A. 1997. Oribatid mites and the decomposition of plant tissues in Paleozoic coal-swamp forests. *Palaios,* **12**, 319–353.

LACEY, W. S. 1963. Palaeobotanical techniques. *In:* CARTHY, J. D. & DUDDINGTON C. L. (eds) *Viewpoints in Biology* (vol. 2). Butterworths, London, 202–243.

LAMARCHE, V. C. JR. & HARLAN, T. P. 1973. Accuracy of tree-ring dating of bristlecone pine for calibration of the radiocarbon time scale. *Journal of Geophysical Research,* **78**, 8849–8858.

LAMB, M. A. 1923. Leaflets of Cycadaceae. *Botanical Gazette,* **76**, 185–202.

LAMBERT, J. B. & FRYE, J. S. 1982. Carbon functionalities in amber. *Science,* **217**, 55–57.

——, —— & POINAR, G. O. 1985. Amber from the Dominican republic: Analysis by nuclear magnetic resonance spectroscopy. *Geoarchaeology,* **5**, 43–52.

LANDSBERG, J. & OHMART, C. 1989. Levels of insect defoliation in forests: patterns and concepts. *Trends in Ecology and Evolution,* **4**, 96–100.

LANG, G. 1994. *Quartäre Vegetationsgeschichte Europas. Methoden und Ergebnisse.* (Quaternary vegetation history of Europe). Fischer, Jena.

LANG, P. J., SCOTT, A. C. & STEPHENSON, J. 1995. Evidence of plant–arthropod interactions from the Eocene Branksome Sand Formation, Bournemouth, England: Introduction and description of leaf mines. *Tertiary Research,* **15**, 145–172.

LAPASHA, C. A. 1986. General unknown entry and search system: a program package for computer-assisted identification. *North-Carolina Agricultural Research Service Bulletin,* **474A**, Raleigh.

—— & WHEELER, E. A. 1987. A microcomputer based system for computer-aided wood identification . *IAWA Bulletin,* **8**, 347–354.

LARA, A. & VILLALBA, R. 1993. A 3620-Year temperature record from *Fitzroya cupressoides* tree rings in southern South America. *Science,* **260**, 1104–1106.

LAREW, H. G. 1986. The fossil gall record: A brief summary. *Proceedings of the Entomological Society Washington,* **88** (20), 385–388.

—— 1992. Fossil galls. *In:* SHORTHOUSE, J. D. & ROHFRITSCH, O. (eds) *Biology of insect-induced galls.* Oxford University Press, New York, 50–59.

LARTER, S. R. & HORSFIELD, B. 1993. Determination of structural components of kerogens by the use of analytical pyrolysis methods. *In:* ENGEL, M. H. & MACKO, S. A. (eds) *Organic Geochemistry.* Plenum Press, New York, 271–287.

LAVEINE, J.-P. 1977. Report on the Westphalian D. *In:* HOLUB, V. M. & WAGNER, R. H. (eds) *Symposium on Carboniferous Stratigraphy.* Geological Survey, Prague, 71–83.

——, LEMOIGNE, Y. & ZHANG S. 1993. General characteristics and paleobiogeography of the Parispermaceae (genera *Paripteris* Gothan and *Linopteris* Presl), pteridosperms from the Carboniferous. *Palaeontographica, Abteilung B,* **230**, 81–139.

——, ZHANG, S. & LEMOIGNE, Y. 1989. Global paleobotany, as exemplified by some Upper Carboniferous pteridosperms. *Bulletin de la Société belge de Géologie,* **98**, 115–125.

LAWLOR, D. A., DICKEL, C. D., HAUSWIRTH, W. W. & PARHAM, P. 1991. Ancient *HLA* genes from 7,500-year-old archaeological remains. *Nature,* **349**, 785–788.

LEAVITT, S. W. & DANZER, S. R. 1993. A method for the batch processing of small wood samples to holocellulose for stable carbon isotope analysis. *Analytical Chemistry,* **65**, 87–89.

—— & LONG, A. 1982. Stable carbon isotopes as a potential supplemental tool in dendrochronology. *Tree Ring Bulletin,* **42**, 49–55.

—— & —— 1986. Stable carbon isotope variability in tree foliage and wood. *Ecology,* **67**, 1002–1010.

—— & —— 1991. Seasonal stable carbon isotope variability in tree rings: possible paleoenviron-mental signals. *Chemical Geology (Isotope Geoscience Section)* **87**, 59–70.

LECLERCQ, S. 1951. Etude morphologique et anatomique d'une fougère du Dévonien supérieur, le

Rhacophyton zygopteroides nov. sp. *Annales de la Société géologique de Belgique.*, Mémoire in 4°, **9**, 1–62.

—— 1960. Refendage d'une roche fossilifère et dégagement de ses fossiles sous binoculaire. *Senckenbergiana lethaea*, **41**, 483–487.

—— & ANDREWS, H. N. 1960. *Calamophyton bicephalum*, a new species from the Middle Devonian of Belgium. *Annales of the Missouri Botanical Garden*, **47**, 1–23.

LEEDER, M. R. 1982. *Sedimentology: Process and Product.* Allen & Unwin, London.

LEITCH, A. R. 1991. Calcification of the Charophyte Oosporangium. *In:* RIDING, R. (ed.) *Calcareous algae and stromatolites.* Springer-Verlag, Berlin.

LENTIN, J. K. & WILLIAMS, G. L. 1980. Dinoflagellate provincialism with emphasis on Campanian peridiniaceans. *American Association of Stratigraphic Palynologists, Contribution Series*, **7**.

LEPAGE, B. A. & BASINGER, J. F. 1993. The use of lacquer (nitrocellulose) for the coating and preservation of fossil leaf impressions. *Journal of Paleontology*, **67**, 128–134.

—— &—— 1994. Additional note on the use of lacquer (nitrocellulose) for the coating and preservation of fossil leaf compressions. *Journal of Paleontology*, **68**, 1164.

LEROI-GOURHAN, A. 1975. The flowers found with Shanidar IV, a Neanderthal burial in Iraq. *Science*, **190**, 562–564.

LEUSCHNER, H. H. & DELORME, A. 1984. Verlangerung der Göttingen Eichenjahrringchronologien fur Nord- und Suddeutschland bis zum Jahr 4008 v. Chr. *Forstarchiv*, **55**, 1–4.

LEVY, J. K. 1987. The natural history of the degradation of wood. *Philosophical Transactions of the Royal Society of London,* **A 321**, 423–433.

LHOTAK, M. & BOULTER, M. C. 1995. Towards the creation of an international database of palaeontology. *In:* GILES, J. R. A. (ed.) *Geological Data Management.* Geological Society, London, Special Publications, **97**, 55–64.

LICHTENTHALER, H. K. 1985. Differences in morphology and chemical composition of leaves grown at different light intensities and qualities. *In:* BAKER, R. N., DAVIES, W. J. & ONG, C. K. (eds) *Control of Leaf Growth.* Cambridge University Press, Cambridge, 201–221.

LICKISS, P. D. & MCGRATH, V. E. 1996. Breaking the sound barrier. *Chemistry in Britain*, **32**, (3), 47–50.

LIDGARD, S. & CRANE, P. R. 1990. Angiosperm diversification and Cretaceous floristic trends a comparison of palynofloras and leaf macrofloras. *Paleobiology*, **16**, 77–93.

LIPHSHITZ, N. & WEISEL, Y. 1973. Dendroarchaeological investigations in Israel (Tel Beersheba and Arad in the Northern and Eastern Negev). *Israel Expl. Journal*, **23**, 30–37.

LIPMAN, P. W. & MULLINEAUX, D. R. (eds) 1983. The 1980 eruptions of Mount St. Helens, Washington State. *United States Geological Survey Professional Paper 1250*, 379–400. University of Washington Press.

LO, H. B. 1988. Photometric methods for measuring the thermal maturity on strew slides. *Organic Geochemistry*, **12**, 303–307.

LOADER, N. J., ROBERTSON, I., BARKER, A. C., SWITSUR, V. R. & WATERHOUSE, J. S. 1997. An improved technique for the batch processing of small wholewood samples to a-cellulose. *Chemical Geology*, **136**, 313–317.

——, SWITSUR, V. R. & FIELD, E. M. 1995. High resolution stable isotope analysis of tree rings: implications of 'microdendroclimatology' for palaeoenvironmental research. *Holocene,* **5**, 457–460.

LOGAN, K. J. & THOMAS, B. A. 1987. The distribution of lignin derivatives in fossil plants. *New Phytologist*, **105**, 157–173.

LOHMANN, G. P. & SCHWEITZER, P. N. 1990. On Eigenshape analysis. *In:* ROHLF, F. J. & BOOKSTEIN, F. L. (eds) *Proceedings of the Michigan Morphometrics Workshop.* Special Publication Number 2, The University of Michigan Museum of Zoology, Ann Arbor, 147–166.

LONG, A., DAVIS, O. K. & DE LANOIS, J. 1992. Separation and ^{14}C dating of pure pollen from lake sediments: nanofossil AMS dating. Proceedings of the 14th International ^{14}C conference. *Radiocarbon,* **34, 3**, 557–560.

LONGO MARZIANI, G. P. & IANNONE, A. 1986. A new method for cutting thin sections from prehistoric charcoal specimen. *Review of Palaeobotany and Palynology*, **48**, 295–301.

LORENTE, M. R. 1990. Digital image analysis: an approach for quantitative characterisation of organic facies and palynofacies. *Mededelingen, Rijks Geologische Dienst*, **45**, 103–109.

LOTTES, A. L. & ZIEGLER, A. M. 1994. World peat occurrence and the seasonality of climate and vegetation. *Palaeogeography, Palaeoclimatology, Palaeoecology*, **106**, 23–37.

LOVE, L. G., COLEMAN, M. L. & CURTIS, C. D. 1983. Diagenetic pyrite formation and sulphur isotope fractionation associated with a Westphalian marine incursion, northern England. *Transactions of the Royal Society of Edinburgh, Earth Sciences*, **74**, 165–182.

LOWE, J. J. & WALKER, M. J. C. 1984. *Reconstructing Quaternary Environments.* Longman, London.

—— & —— 1997. *Reconstructing Quaternary Environments* (2nd edn). Longman, London.

LUGARDON, B. & DELCAMBRE, C. B. 1994. Exospore ultrastructure in Carboniferous sphenopsids. *In:* KURMANN, M. H. & DOYLE, J. A. (eds) *Ultrastructure of fossil spores and pollen.* Royal Botanic Gardens, Kew, 53–66.

LYONS, P. C. & DARRAH, W. C. 1989. Earliest conifers of North America: upland and/or paleoclimatic indicators? *Palaios*, **4**, 480–486.

——, OREM, W. H., MASTALERZ, M., ZODROW, E. L., VIETH-REDEMANN, A. & BUSTIN, R. M. 1995. ^{13}C NMR, micro-FTIR and fluorescence spectra, and pyrolysis-gas chromatograms of coalified foliage of late Carboniferous medullosan seed ferns, Nova Scotia, Canada: Implications for coalification and chemotaxonomy. *International Journal of Coal Geology*, **27**, 227–248.

MacDonald, G. M. 1996. Non-aquatic Quaternary. *In:* Jansonius, J. & McGregor, D. C. (eds) *Palynology: principles and applications.* American Association of Stratigraphic Palynologists Foundation, **2**, 879–910.

MacFadden, B. J. 1998. Tale of two rhinos: isotopic ecology, paleodiet, and niche differentiation of Aphelops and Teleoceras from the Florida Neogene. *Paleobiology,* **24**, 274–286.

—— & Cerling, T. E. 1996. Mammalian herbivore communities, ancient feeding ecology, and carbon isotopes: A 10 million-year sequence from the Neogene of Florida. *Journal of Vertebrate Paleontology,* **16**, 103–115.

Mack, G. H., Cole, D. R., Giordano, T. H., Schaal, W. C. & Barcelos, J. H. 1991. Paleoclimatic controls on stable oxygen and carbon isotopes in caliche of the Abo Formation (Permian), south-central New Mexico, USA. *Journal of Sedimentary Petrology,* **61**, 458–472.

Mackereth, F. J. H. 1958. A portable core-sampler for lake deposits. *Limnology and Oceanography,* **3**, 181–191.

Mahaffy, J. F. 1985. Profile patterns of coal and peat palynology in the Herrin (No. 6) Coal Member, Carbondale Formation, Middle Pennsylvanian of southern Illinois. *Proceedings 9th International Congress of Carboniferous Stratigraphy and Geology,* **5**, 155–59.

Maher, L. J. 1981. Statistics for microfossil concentration measurements employing samples spiked with marker grains. *Review of Palaeobotany and Palynology,* **32**, 153–191.

Maheshwari, H. K. & Bajpai, U. 1996. Ultrastructure of the 'cuticular membrane' in two Late Triassic corystospermaceous taxa from India. *Palaeobotanist,* **45**, 41–49.

Mai, D. H. 1991. Palaeofloristic changes in Europe and the confirmation of the arctotertiary-palaeotropical geofloral concept. *Review of Palaeobotany and Palynology,* **68**, 29–36.

—— 1995. *Tertiäre Vegetationsgeschichte Mitteleuropas.(Tertiary vegetation history of central Europe).* Springer, Stuttgart, Heidelberg, New York.

Maisey, J. G. (ed.) 1991. *Santana Fossils: an Illustrated Atlas.* T.F.H., Neptune City, New Jersey.

Malone, S. R., Mayeux, H. S., Johnson, H. B. & Polley, H. W. 1993. Stomatal density and aperture length in four plant species grown across a subambient CO_2 gradient. *American Journal of Botany,* **80**, 1413–1418.

Mamay, S. H. 1992. *Sphenopteridium* and *Telangiopsis* in a *Diplopteridium*-like association from the Virgilian (Upper Pennsylvanian) of New Mexico. *American Journal of Botany,* **79**, 1092–1101.

—— & Bateman, R. M. 1991. *Archaeocalamites lazarii,* sp. nov.: the range of Archaeocalamitaceae extended from the lowermost Pennsylvanian to the mid–Lower Permian. *American Journal of Botany,* **78**, 489–496.

—— & Mapes, G. 1992. Early Virgilian plant megafossils from the Kinney Brick Company Quarry, Manzanita Mountains, New Mexico. *Bulletin of the New Mexico Bureau of Mines & Mineral Resources,* **138**, 61–85.

Manchester, S. R. 1988. Fruits and seeds of *Tapiscia* (Staphyleaceae) from the middle Eocene of Oregon, USA. *Tertiary Research,* **9**, 59–66.

—— 1992. Flowers, fruits, and pollen of *Florissantia,* an extinct malvalean genus from the Eocene and Oligocene of western North America. *American Journal of Botany,* **79**, 996–1008.

—— & Crane, P. R. 1983. Attached leaves, inflorescences, and fruits of *Fagopsis,* an extinct genus of fagaceous affinity from the Oligocene Florissant flora of Colorado, USA. *American Journal of Botany,* **70**, 1147–1164.

Marčenko, E., Srdoc, D., Golubic, S., Pezdic, J. & Head, M. J. 1989. Carbon uptake in aquatic plants deduced from their natural ^{13}C and ^{14}C content. *In:* Long, A., Kra, R. S. & Srdoc, D. (eds) Proceedings of the 13th International ^{14}C conference. *Radiocarbon,* **31** (3), 785–794.

Marcus, L. F. 1990. Traditional morphometrics. *In:* Rohlf, F. J. & Bookstein, F. L. 1990. *Proceedings of the Michigan Morphometrics Workshop.* Special Publication Number 2, The University of Michigan Museum of Zoology, Ann Arbor, 77–122.

Maricq, M. & Waugh, J. S. 1979. NMR in rotating solid. *Journal of Chemical Physics,* **70**, 3300–3316.

Marino, B. D. & McElroy, M. 1991. Isotopic composition of atmospheric CO_2 inferred from carbon in C_4 plant cellulose. *Nature,* **349**, 127–131.

Marshall, D. J. 1988. *Cathodoluminescence of geological materials.* Unwin Hyman, Boston, London, England.

Marshall, J. E. A. 1991. Quantitative spore colour. *Journal of the Geological Society,* **148**, 223–233.

Marshall, K. L. & Batten, D. J. 1988. Dinoflagellate cyst associations in Cenomanian–Turonian 'black shale' sequences of northern Europe. *Review of Palaeobotany and Palynology,* **54**, 85–103.

Martini, G. 1994. Bilan général de la protection du patrimoine géologique en France. *Mémoire de la Société Géologique de France,* **165**, 111–118.

Marziani, G. P. L. & Iannone, A. 1986. A new method for cutting thin sections from prehistoric charcoal specimen. *Review of Palaeobotany and Palynology,* **48**, 295–301.

Matten, L. C. 1966. Improved technique for preparing iron hydroxide plant petrifactions. *Journal of Paleontology,* **40**, 225–226.

—— 1973. Preparation of pyritized plant petrifactions: 'a plea for pyrite'. *Review of Palaeobotany and Palynology,* **16**, 165–173.

Maynard, J. B. 1992. Chemistry of modern soils as a guide to interpreting Precambrian paleosols. *Journal of Geology,* **100**, 279–289.

McCormac, F. G., Baillie, M. G. L., Pilcher, J. R. & Kalin, R. M. 1995. Location-dependent differences in the 14-C content of wood. *Radiocarbon,* **37**, 395–407.

McElwain, J. C. 1998. Do fossil plants signal palaeo-atmospheric CO_2 concentrations in the geological past ? *Philosophical Transactions of the Royal Society,* **B353**, in press.

—— & CHALONER, W. G. 1995. Stomatal density and index of fossil plants track atmospheric carbon dioxide in the Palaeozoic. *Annals of Botany,* **76,** 389–395.

—— &—— 1996. The fossil cuticle as a skeletal record of environmental change. *Palaios,* **11,** 376–388.

McGINNES, E. A. JR., KANDEEL, S. A. & SZOPA, P. S. 1971. Some structural changes observed in the transformation of wood into charcoal. *Wood and Fibre,* **3 (2),** 77–83.

McKINNEY, D. E., BORTIATYNSKI, J. M., CARSON, D. M., CLIFFORD, D. J., DE LEEUW, J. W. & HATCHER, P. G. 1996. Tetramethylammonium hydroxide (TMAH) thermochemolysis of the aliphatic biopolymer cutan: Insights to its chemical structure. *Organic Geochemistry,* **24,** 641–650.

——, CARSON, D. M., CLIFFORD, D. J., MINARD, R. D. & HATCHER, P. G. 1995. Off-line thermochemolysis versus flash pyrolysis for the *in situ* methylation of lignin: Is pyrolysis necessary ? *Journal of Analytical and Applied Pyrolysis,* **34,** 41–46.

MEDAKOVIC, D., POPOVIC, S., ZAVODNIK, N., GRZETA, B. & PLAZONIC, M. 1995. X-ray-diffraction study of mineral components in calcareous algae (Corallinaceae, Rhodophyta*).* *Marine Biology,* **122,** 479–485.

MEDINA, E. & MINCHIN, P. 1985. Stratification of d^{13}C values of leaves in Amazonian rain forests. *Oecologia,* **45,** 377–378.

METZ, G., WU, X. & SMITH, S. O. 1994. Ramped-amplitude cross polarization in magic-angle-spinning NMR. *Journal of Magnetic Resonance, Series A,* **110,** 219–227.

MEYEN, S. V. 1969. New data on relationship between Angara and Gondwana Late Paleozoic floras. *In: Gondwana Stratigraphy. IUGS Symposium, Buenos Aires, 1967.* UNESCO, Paris, 141–157.

—— 1973. Plant morphology and its nomothetical aspects. *Botanical Review,* **39,** 205–260.

—— 1987. *Fundamentals of Palaeobotany.* Chapman & Hall, London.

MEYER, H. W. 1992. Lapse rates and other variables applied to estimating paleoaltitudes from fossil floras. *Palaeogeography, Palaeoclimatology, Palaeoecology,* **99,** 71–99.

MIDDLETON, B. A. 1995. Sampling devices for the measurement of seed rain and hydrochory in rivers. *Bulletin of the Torrey Botanical Club,* **122,** 152–155.

MILLAY, M. A. & EGGERT, D. A. 1974. Microgametophyte development in the Paleozoic seed fern family Callistophytaceae. *American Journal of Botany,* **61,** 1067–1075.

MILLSPAUGH, S. H. & WHITLOCK, C. 1995. A 750-year fire history based on lake sediment records in central Yellowstone National Park, USA. *The Holocene,* **5,** 283–292.

MILTON, J. A. 1993. *The application of quantitative spore colour measurement to thermal maturity studies.* PhD thesis, University of Southampton.

MONK, C. D. 1966. An ecological significance in evergreenness. *Ecology,* **47,** 504–505.

MOOK, W. M., KOOPMANS, M., CARTER, A. F. & KEELING, C. D. 1983. Seasonal latitudinal and secular variations in the abundance of the isotope ratios of atmospheric carbon dioxide. 1. Results form land stations. *Journal of Geophysical Research,* **88,** 10 915–10 933.

—— & WATERBOLK, H. T. 1985. *Radiocarbon dating.* European Science Foundation Handbooks for Archaeologists No.3, Strasbourg.

MOORE, P. D., WEBB, J. A. & COLLINSON, M. E. 1991. *Pollen Analysis* (2nd edn). Blackwell Scientific Publications, London.

MORA, C., DRIESE, S. G. & SEAGAR, P. G. 1991. Carbon dioxide in the Paleozoic atmosphere: evidence from carbon-isotope composition of pedogenic carbonate. *Geology,* **19,** 1017–1020.

MORGAN, A. J. 1985. *X-ray microanalysis in electron microscopy for biologists.* Royal Microscopy Society Handbooks 05, Oxford University Press.

MORTON, N. 1990. Bearreraig (Isle of Skye, NW Scotland) as Boundary Stratotype for the base of the Bajocian Stage. *Memorie Descrittive della Carta Geologica d'Italia,* **40,** 23–48.

MOSBRUGGER, V. 1990. *The tree habit in land plants.* Lecture Notes in Earth Sciences, **28,** Springer, Berlin.

—— 1995. New methods and approaches in Tertiary palaeoenvironmental research. *Abhandlungen Museum Mineralogie Geologie Dresden,* **41,** 41–52.

——, GEE, C. T., BELZ, G. & ASHRAF, A.-R. 1994. Three-dimensional reconstruction of an *in situ* Miocene peat forest from the Lower Rhine Embayment, northwestern Germany new methods in palaeovegetation analysis. *Palaeogeography, Palaeoclimatology, Palaeoecology,* **110,** 295–317.

—— & ROTH, A. 1996. Biomechanics in fossil plant biology. *Review of Palaeobotany and Palynology,* **90,** 195–207.

—— & SCHILLING, H.-D. 1992. Terrestrial palaeoclimatology in the Tertiary: a methodological critique. *Palaeogeography, Palaeoclimatology, Palaeoecology,* **99,** 17–29.

—— & UTESCHER, T. 1997. The coexistence approach – a method for quantitative reconstructions of Tertiary terrestrial palaeoclimate data using plant fossils. *Palaeogeography, Palaeoclimatology, Palaeoecology,* **134,** 61–86.

MOSHIER, S. O. & KIRKLAND, B. L. 1993. Identification and diagenesis of a Phylloid alga, Archaeolithophyllum from the Pennsylvanian Providence Limestone, western Kentucky. *Journal of Sedimentary Petrology,* **63** (1), 1032–1041.

MURCHISON, D. G., COOK, A. C. & RAYMOND, A. C. 1985. Optical properties of organic matter in relation to thermal gradients and structural deformation. *Philosophical. Tranactions of the Royal Society of Lond*on, **A315,** 157–186.

MURPHY, C. P. 1983. Point counting pores and illuvial clay in thin section. *Geoderma,* **31,** 133–150.

MURRAY, M. G. & THOMPSON, W. F. 1990. Rapid isolation of high-molecular-weight plant DNA. *Nucleic Acids Research,* **8,** 4321.

MYERS, R. L. & EWEL, J. J. (eds) 1992. *Ecosystems of Florida.* University of Central Florida Press, Orlando.

NAKASHIMA, S., STURGEON, R. E., WILLIE, S. M. &

BERMAN, S. S. 1988. Acid digestion of marine samples for trace element analysis using microwave heating. *Analysist*, **113**, 159–163.

NAMBUDIRI, E. M. V., TIDWELL, W. D., SMITH, B. N. & HEBBERT, N. P. 1978. A C$_4$ plant from the Pliocene. *Nature*, **276**, 816–817.

NAUGOLNYKH. S. V. & KERP, H. 1996. Aspects of Permian Palaeobotany and Palynology. XV. On the oldest known peltasperms with radially symmetrical ovuliferous discs from the Kungurian (uppermost Lower Permian) of the Fore–Urals (Russia). *Review of Palaeobotany and Palynology*, **91**, 35–62.

NEALE, J. L. & WALKER, D. 1996. Sampling sediment under warm deep water. *Quaternary Science Reviews*, **15**, 581–590.

NEEDHAM, J. G., FROST, S. W. & TOOTHILL, B.H. 1928. *Leaf-mining insects*. Balliere, Tindall & Cox, London.

NEILSON, R. P. 1995. A model for predicting continental-scale vegetation distribution and water balance. *Ecological Applications*, **5**, 362–385.

NELSON, G. & ROSEN, D. E. 1981. *Vicariant Biogeography*. Columbia University Press.

NESBITT, M. & GREIG, J. 1989. A bibliography for the archaeobotanical identification of seeds from Europe and the Near East. *Circaea*, **7** (1), 11–30.

NEUMANN, K. 1992. The contribution of anthracology to the study of the late Quaternary vegetation history of the Mediterranean region and Africa. *Bulletin de la Société Botanique de France*, **139**, *Actualités botaniques* (2/3/4), 421–440.

NEVES, R. & OWENS, B. 1966. Some Namurian camerate spores from the English Pennines. *Pollen et Spores*, **8** (2), 337–360.

NEWMAN, A. 1998. Pyrite oxidation and museum collections: a review of theory and conservation treatments. *The Geological Curator*, **6**(10), 363–371.

NIER, A. O. & GULBRANSEN, E. A. 1939. Variations in the relative abundances of carbon isotopes. *Journal of the American Chemistry Society*, **61**, 697.

NIKLAS, K. J. 1977. Branching patterns and mechanical design in Paleozoic plants: a theoretic assessment. *Annals of Botany*, **42**, 33–39.

—— 1990. Biomechanics of *Psilotum nudum* and some early Paleozoic vascular sporophytes. *American Journal of Botany*, **77**, 590–606.

—— 1992. *Plant biomechanics – an engineering approach to plant form and funcion*. University of Chicago Press, Chicago.

—— 1994. Predicting the height of fossil plant remains: an allometric approach to an old problem. *American Journal of Botany*, **81**, 1235–1242.

—— 1997. Adaptive walks through fitness landscapes for early vascular land plants. *American Journal of Botany*, **84**, 16–25.

——, BROWN, R. M., JR., SANTOS, R. & VAIN, B. 1978. Ultrastructure and cytochemistry of Miocene angiosperm leaf tissues. *Proceedings of the National Academy of Sciences, USA*, **75**, 3263–3267.

—— & KERCHNER, V. 1984. Mechanical and photosynthetic constraints on the evolution of plant shape. *Paleobiology*, **10**, 79–101.

NIKLAUS, T. R., BONANI, G., SIMONIUS, M., SUTER, M. & WÖLFLI, W. 1992. CalibETH: an interactive computer program for the calibration of radiocarbon dates. Proceedings of the 14th International ^{14}C conference. *Radiocarbon,* **34 (3)**, 483–492.

NIP, M., DE LEEUW, J. W., SCHENCK, P. A., WINDIG, W., MEUZELAAR, H. L. C. & CRELLING, J. C. 1989. A flash pyrolysis and petrographic study of cutinite from the Indiana paper coal. *Geochimica et Cosmochimica Acta,* **53**, 671–683.

——, TEGELAAR, E., DE LEEUW, J. W., SCHENCK, P. A. & HOLLOWAY, P. J. 1986. A new highly aliphatic and resistant biopolymer in plant cuticles: evidence from analytical pyrolysis and ^{13}C-NMR of present day and fossil plants. *Naturwissenschaften,* **73**, 579–585.

OANA, S. & DEEVEY, E. S. 1960. Carbon 13 in lake waters and its possible bearing on paleolimnology. *American Journal of Science*, **258A**, 253–272.

OBOH-IKUENOBE, F. E. 1996. Correlating palynofacies assemblages with sequence stratigraphy in Upper Cretaceous (Campanian) sedimentary rocks of the Book Cliffs, east-central Utah. *Geological Society of America Bulletin*, **108**, 1275–1294.

OGLE, N. & MCCORMAC, F. G. 1994. High resolution d^{13}C measurements of oak show a previously unobserved spring depletion. *Geophyical Research Letters*, **21**, 2373–2375.

OLDHAM, T. C. B. 1976. Flora of the Wealden plant debris beds of England. *Palaeontology*, **19**, 437–502.

ORCEL, A., ORCEL, C., DANÉROL, A. & RAMSEYER, D. 1992. Contribution to the study of the Neolithic forest dynamic. The example of Delley/Portalban II (CH) *Lundqua,* **34**, 242–246.

OSBORN, J. M. & TAYLOR, T. N. 1993. Pollen morphology and ultrastructure of the Corystospermales: permineralized *in situ* grains from the Triassic of Antarctica. *Review of Palaeobotany and Palynology,* **79**, 205–219.

——, —— & CRANE, P. R. 1991. The ultrastructure of *Sahnia* pollen (Pentoxylales). *American Journal of Botany,* **78**, 1560–1569.

OVERPECK, J. T., WEBB T. III & PRENTICE, I. C. 1985. Quantitative interpretation of fossil pollen spectra: dissimilarity coefficients and the method of modern analogs. *Quaternary Research,* **23**, 87–108.

OVINGTON, J. D. 1961. Some aspects of energy flow in plantations of *Pinus sylvestris* L. *Annals of Botany, New Series,* **25**,12–20.

PÄÄBO, S. 1989. Ancient DNA: Extraction, characterization, molecular cloning, and enzymatic amplification. *Proceedings of the National Academy of Science, USA,* **86**, 1939–1943.

—— 1990. Amplifying ancient DNA. *In:* INNIS, M. A., GELFAND, D. H., SNINSKY, J. J. & WHITE, T. J. (eds) *PCR Protocols: A Guide to Methods and Applications,* Academic Press, Inc., 159–166.

——, IRWIN, D. M. & WILSON, A. C. 1990. DNA damage promotes jumping between templates during enzymatic ampification. *Journal of Biological Chemistry,* **265**, 4718–4721.

PACINI, E., FRANCHI, G. G. & HESS, M. 1985. The tapetum: its form, function, and possible phylogeny in Embryophyta. *Plant Systematics and Evolution*, **149**, 155–185.

PAGE, A. L. (ed.) 1982. *Methods of soil analysis, Part 2, Chemical and microbiological properties*. American Society of Agronomy Monograph, **9**, 13–27.

PANEK, J. A. & WARING, R. H. 1995. Carbon isotope variation in Douglas Fir foliage: improving the d^{13}C-climate relationship. *Tree Physiology*, **15**, 657–663.

PARKHURST, D. & LOUCKS, O. 1972. Optimal leaf size in relation to environment. *Journal of Ecology*, **60**, 505–537.

PATTERSON, W. A. III, EDWARDS, K. J. & MAGUIRE, D. J. 1987. Microscopic charcoal as a fossil indicator of fire. *Quaternary Science Reviews*, **6**, 2–23.

PAYNE, R. W., LANE, P. W., DIGBY, P. G. N. *ET AL.* 1993. *Genstat 5.3*. Clarendon Press, Oxford.

PEARSALL, D. 1989. *Paleoethnobotany: A handbook of Procedures*. Academic Press, San Diego.

PEARSON, D. L. 1982. Approaching a pollen/spore color standard. *Palynology*, **6**, 289.

—— 1984. *Pollen/spore color 'standard'*. Phillips Petroleum Company Exploration Projects Section. (a propriety spore colour comparator).

PEARSON, G. W., BECKER, B. & QUA, F. 1993. High-precision ^{14}C measurement of German and Irish oaks to show the natural ^{14}C variations from 7890–5000 BC, *Radiocarbon*, **35**, 93–104.

——, PILCHER, J. R., BAILLIE, M. G. L., CORBETT, D. M., & QUA, F. 1986. High-precision ^{14}C measurement of Irish oaks to show the natural ^{14}C variations from AD 1848–5210 BC. *In:* STUIVER, M. & KRA, R. S. (eds) Calibration issue. Proceedings of the 12th International ^{14}C conference. *Radiocarbon*, **28**, **2B**, 911–934.

—— & STUIVER, M. 1986. High-precision calibration of the radiocarbon time scale, 500–2500 BC. *In:* STUIVER, M. & KRA, R. S. (eds) Calibration issue. Proceedings of the 12th International ^{14}C conference. *Radiocarbon*, **28**, **2B**, 839–862.

PEARSON, M., DAVIES, W. J. & MANSFIELD, T. A. 1995. Asymmetric responses of adaxial and abaxial stomata to elevated CO_2: impacts on the control of gas exchange by leaves. *Plant, Cell and Environment*, **18**, 837–843.

PEAT, H. J. & FITTER, A. H. 1994. Comparative analyses of ecological characteristics of British Angiosperms. *Biological Reviews*, **69**, 95–115.

PEERSEN, O. B., WU, X., KUSTANOVICH, I. & SMITH, S. O. 1993. Variable-amplitude cross-ploarization MAS NMR. *Journal of Magnetic Resonance, Series A*, **104**, 334–339.

PEIRCE, A. S. 1936. Anatomical interrelationships of the Taxodiaceae. *Tropical Woods*, **46**, New Haven, Conn., 1–15.

PENNY, J. H. J. 1986. *Early Cretaceous angiosperm pollen from Egypt*. PhD thesis, University of Cambridge.

PETTITT, J. M. 1966. Exine structure in some fossil and recent spores and pollen as revealed by light and electron microscopy. *Bulletin of the British Museum (Natural History) Geology*, **13**, 221–257.

PFEFFERKORN, H. W & FUCHS, K. 1991. A field classification of fossil plant-substrate interaction.

Neues Jahrbuch für Geologie und Paläontologie Abhandlungen, **183**, 17–36.

——, MUSTAFA, H. & HASS, H. 1975. Quantitative Charakterisierung ober-karboner Abdruckfloren: *Neues Jahrbuch für Geologie und Paläontologie Abhandlungen*, **150**, 253–269.

PHILLIPS, E. W. J. 1966 . Identification of softwoods by their microscopic structure. *Forest Products Research, Bulletin*, **22**. HMSO, London.

PHILLIPS, T. L., AVCIN, M. J. & BERGGREN, D. 1976. Fossil peat from the Illinois Basin. A guide to the study of coal-balls of Pennsylvanian age. *Illinois State Geological Survey Educational Series*, **11**, 1–39.

——, KUNZ, A. B. & MICKISH, D. J. 1977. Paleobotany of permineralized peat (coal balls) from the Herrin (No.6) Coal Member of the Illinois Basin. *In:* GIVEN, P. N. & COHEN, A. D. (eds) *Interdisciplinary Studies of Peat and Coal Origins*. Geological Society of America, Microform Publication, **7**, 18–49.

—— & DIMICHELE, W. A. 1981. Paleoecology of Middle Pennsylvanian age coal swamps in southern Illinois – Herrin Coal Member at Sahara Mine No. 6. *In:* NIKLAS, K. J. (ed.) *Paleobotany, Paleoecology and Evolution*. Praeger Scientific Publishers, New York, Vol. 1, 231–285.

——&—— 1998. A transect through a clastic-swamp to peat-swamp ecotone in the Springfield Coal, Middle Pennsylvanian age of Indiana, USA. *Palaios*, **13**, 113–128.

—— & PEPPERS, R. A. 1984. Changing patterns of Pennsylvanian coal-swamp vegetation and implications of climatic control on coal occurrence. *International Journal of Coal Geology*, **3**, 205–255.

——, —— & DIMICHELE, W. A. 1985. Stratigraphic and interregional changes in Pennsylvanian-age coal-swamp vegetation: environmental inferences. *International Journal of Coal Geology*, **5**, 43–109.

——, ——, AVCIN, M. J. & LAUGHNAN, P. F. 1974. Fossil plants and coal: Patterns of change in Pennsylvanian coal swamps of the Illinois Basin. *Science*, **187**, 1367–1369.

PHIPPS, D. & PLAYFORD, G. 1984. Laboratory techniques for extraction of palynomorphs from sediments. *Department of Geology, University of Queensland, Papers*, **11** (1), 1–23.

——&—— 1985. Laboratory Techniques for Extraction of Palynomorphs from Sediments. *Department of Geology, University of Queensland, Papers*, **11,** (1), 1–23.

PICKFORD, M. 1986. Sedimentation and fossil preservation in the Nyanza Rift system, Kenya. *In:* FROSTICK, L. E., RENAUT, R. W., REID, I. & TIERCELIN, J. J. (eds) *Sedimentation in the African Rifts*. Geological Society, London, Special Paper, **25**, 345–362.

—— 1995. Fossil land snails of East Africa and their paleoecological significance. *Journal of African Earth Science*, **20**, 167–226.

PILCHER, J. R., BAILLIE, M. G. L., BROWN, D. M., MACSWEENY, P. B. & MCLAWRENCE, A. 1995. Dendrochronology of sub-fossil pine in the North of Ireland. *Journal of Ecology*, **83**, 665–671.

——, ——, SCHMIDT, B. & BECKER, B. 1984. A 7272-

year tree-ring chronology for western Europe. *Nature*, **312**, 150–52

PINES, A., GIBBY, M. G. & WAUGH, J. S. 1972. Proton enhanced nuclear induction spectroscopy. A method for high resolution NMR of dilute spins in solids. *Journal of Chemical Physics*, **56**, 1776–1777.

PLU, A. 1979. Identification des macro-restes végétaux. *In:* ROUBET, C. (ed.) *Economie pastorale préagricole en Algérie orientale. Le Néolithique de tradition Capsienne.* Example: l'Aurès. Paris, 426–438.

POCOCK, S. A. J. & VASANTHY, G. 1988. *Cornetipollis reticulata*, a new pollen with angiospermid features from Upper Triassic (Carnian) sediments of Arizona (USA), with notes on *Equisetosporites. Review of Palaeobotany and Palynology*, **55**, 337–356.

POINAR, H. N., CANO, R. J. & POINAR, G. O., JR. 1993. DNA from an extinct plant. *Nature*, **363**, 677.

——, HÖSS, M., BADA, J. L. & PÄÄBO, S. 1996. Amino acid racemization and the preservation of ancient DNA. *Science*, **272**, 864–866.

POOLE, I., WEYERS, J. D. B., LAWSON, T. & RAVEN, J. A. 1996. Variations in stomatal density and index: implications for palaeoclimatic reconstructions. *Plant, Cell and Environment*, **19**, 705–712.

POTONIE, R. 1962. Regeln nach denen sich die Sekundarfalten der Sporen bilden. *Palaontologisches Zeitschrift*, **36**, 46–54.

—— & KREMP, G. 1954. Die Gattungen der palaozoischen sporae dispersae und ihre Stratigraphie. *Geologisches Jahrbuch,* **69,** 11–194.

POTTS, P. J. 1987. *A Handbook of Silicate Rock Analysis* (2nd edn). Blackie, Glasgow.

—— 1994. *A Handbook of Silicate Rock Analysis.* Blackie, Glasgow.

POULSON, N. E., GUDMUNDSON, L., HANSEN, J. M. & HUSFELDT, Y. 1990. Palynological preparation techniques, a new maceration tank-method and other modifications. *Geological Survey of Denmark, Series C,* **10**, 1–23.

POVEY, D. A. R., SPICER, R. A. & ENGLAND, P. C. 1994. Palaeobotanical investigation of early Tertiary palaeoelevations in northeastern Nevada: initial results. *Review of Palaeobotany & Palynology,* **81**, 1–10.

POWELL, A. J., BRINKHUIS, H. & BUJAK, J. P. 1996. Upper Paleocene–Lower Eocene dinoflagellate cyst sequence biostratigraphy of southeast England. *In:* KNOX, R. W. O'B., CORFIELD, R. M. & DUNAY, R. E. (eds) *Correlation of the Early Paleogene in Northwest Europe.* Geological Society, London, Special Publications, **101**, 145–183.

——, DODGE, J. D. & LEWIS, J. 1990. Late Neogene to Pleistocene palynological facies of the Peruvian continental margin upwelling, Leg 112. *Proceedings of the Ocean Drilling Program, Scientific Results,* **112**, 297–321.

PRENTICE, I. C. 1980. Multidimensional scaling as a research tool in Quaternary palynology: A review of theory and methods. *Review of Palaeobotany and Palynology*, **31**, 71–104.

—— 1985. Pollen representation, source area, and basin size: toward a unified theory of pollen analysis. *Quaternary Research*, **23**, 76–86.

—— 1988. Records of vegetation in space and time: the principles of pollen analysis. *In:* HUNTLEY, B. & WEBB, T., III (eds) *Vegetation History*. Kluwer, The Hague, 17–42.

——, CRAMER, W., HARRISON, S. P., LEEMANS, R., MONSERUD, R. A. & SOLOMON, A. M. 1992. A global biome model based on plant physiology and dominance, soil properties and climate. *Journal of Biogeography*, **19**, 117–134.

—— & WEBB, T., III. 1986. Pollen percentages, tree abundances and the Fagerlind effect. *Journal of Quaternary Science*, **1**, 35–43.

PROSS, J., SCHIEBEL, A. A., MOSBRUGGER, V. & KVACEK, Z. Tertiary pollen and spores as a tool for quantitative paleoclimate reconstructions: the Oligocene of Central Europe. *Proceedings IX International Palynological Congress*, in press.

PRYOR, J. S. 1988. Sampling methods for quantitative analysis of coal-ball plants. *Palaeogeography, Palaeoclimatology, Palaeoecology*, **63**, 313–326.

—— 1996. The Upper Pennsylvanian Duquesne Coal of Ohio (USA): Evidence for a dynamic peat-accumulating swamp community. *International Journal of Coal Geology*, **29**, 119–146.

PUNT, W., BLACKMORE, S., NILSSON, S. & LE THOMAS, A. 1994. Glossary of pollen and spore terminology. *LPP Contributions Series No.* **1**, LPP Foundation, Utrecht.

RAFTERY, B. 1990. *Trackways through time: archaeological investigations on Irish bog roads, 1985–1989.* Headline, Dublin.

RAISTRICK, A. & SIMPSON, J. 1933. The microspores of some Northumberland coals and their use in the correlation of coal seams. *Transactions of the Institute of Mining Engineers (London),* **85**, 225–235.

RAMSAY, J. G. & HUBER, M. I. 1983. *Techniques of Modern Structural Geology. Vol. 1. Strain Analysis.* Academic Press, London.

RAUP, D. M. 1966. Geometric analysis of shell coiling: general problems. *Journal of Paleontology,* **40**, 1178–1190.

RAVEN, J. A. 1984. Physiological correlates to the morphology of early vascular plants. *Botanical Journal of the Linnean Society*, **88**, 105–126.

RAYMO, M. E., GRANT, B., HOROWITZ, M. & RAU, G. H. 1996. Mid-Pliocene warmth: stronger greenhouse and conveyor. *Marine Micropaleontology*, **27**, 312–326.

RAYMOND, A. 1987. Paleogeographic distribution of Early Devonian plant traits. *Palaios*, **2**, 113–132.

—— 1988. The paleoecology of a coal-ball deposit from the Middle Pennsylvanian of Iowa dominated by cordaitean gymnosperms. *Review of Palaeobotany and Palynology*, **53**, 233–250.

—— & PHILLIPS, T. L. 1983. Evidence of an Upper Carboniferous mangrove community. *In:* TEAS, H. J. (ed.) *Tasks for Vegetation Science,* **8**, 19–30.

RAYNAUD, D., JOUZEL, J., BARNOLA, J. M., CHAPPELLAZ, J., DELMAS, R. J. & LORIUS, C. 1993. The ice record of greenhouse gases. *Science*, **259**, 926–934.

READ, C. B. & MAMAY, S. H. 1964. Upper Paleozoic floral zones and floral provinces of the United

States. *Professional Papers of the United States Geological Survey*, **454-K**, 1–35.

READING, H. G. (ed.) 1996. *Sedimentary Environments: processes, facies and stratigraphy*. Blackwell Scientific Publications, Oxford, 623.

REED, S. J. B. 1996. *Electron microprobe analysis and scanning electron microscopy in geology*. Cambridge University Press.

REES, P. M., ZIEGLER, A. M. & VALDES, P. J. Jurassic phytogeography and climates: New data and model comparisons. *In:* HUBER, B. T., MACLEOD, K. G. & WING, S. L. (eds) *Warm climates in earth history*. Cambridge University Press, in Press.

REID, E. & CHANDLER, M. E. J. 1933. *The Flora of the London Clay*. British Museum, Natural History, London.

REILLE, M. 1992. *Pollen et Spores d'Europe et d'Afrique du Nord*. Laboratoire de Botanique Historique et Palynologie, Marseille.

—— & DE BEAULIEU, J. L. 1995. Long Pleistocene pollen records from the Praclaux crater, south-central France. *Quaternary Research*, **44**, 205–215.

REITSMA, T. 1970. Suggestions towards unification of descriptive terminology of angiosperm pollen grains. *Review of Palaeobotany and Palynology*, **10**, 39–60.

REMY, W., TAYLOR, T. N. & HASS, H. 1994. Early Devonian fungi: a blastocladealean fungus with sexual reproduction. *American Journal of Botany*, **81**, 690–702.

RETALLACK, G. J. 1984. Completeness of the rock and fossil records: some estimates using fossil soils. *Paleobiology*, **10**, 59–78.

—— 1986. The Hitchcox limey peat soil as a modern analog for Pennsylvanian coals bearing coal balls. *Abstracts with Programs of the 99th Annual Meeting of the Geological Society of America, San Antonio, Texas*, **18**, 728.

—— 1988. Field recognition of paleosols. *In:* REINHARDT, J. & SIGLEO, W. R. (ed.) *Paleosols and Weathering through Geologic Time: Techniques and Applications*. Geological Society of America, Special Paper, **216**, 1–20.

—— 1991a. *Miocene Paleosols and Ape Habitats of Pakistan and Kenya*. Oxford University Press, New York.

—— 1991b. Untangling the effects of burial alteration and ancient soil formation. *Annual Reviews of Earth and Planetary Sciences*, **19**, 183–206.

—— 1992a. Middle Miocene fossil plants from Fort Ternan (Kenya) and evolution of African grasslands. *Paleobiology*, **18**, 383–400.

—— 1992b. Comment on the paleoenvironment of *Kenyapithecus* at Fort Ternan. *Journal of Human Evolution*, **23**, 363–369.

—— 1994a. A pedotype approach to latest Cretaceous and early Paleocene paleosols in eastern Montana. *Geological Society of America Bulletin*, **106**, 1377–1397.

—— 1994b. The environmental factor approach to the interpretation of paleosols. *In:* AMUNDSON, R., HARDEN, J. & SINGER, M. (eds) *Factors of Soil Formation: a Fiftieth Anniversary Retrospective.*

Soil Science Society of America, Special Paper, **33**, 31–64.

—— 1997. *A Colour Guide to Paleosols*. John Wiley & Sons, Chichester.

—— 1998. Fossil soils and completeness of the rock and fossil record. *In:* DONOVAN, S. K. & PAUL, C. R. C. (eds) *The Adequacy of the Fossil Record*. John Wiley & Sons, Chichester, 131–162.

——, DUGAS, D. P. & BESTLAND, E. A. 1990. Fossil soils and grasses of a Middle Miocene East African grassland. *Science*, **247**, 1325–1328.

—— & KRINSLEY, D. H. 1993. Metamorphic alteration of a Precambrian (2.2 Ga) paleosol from South Africa revealed by back scatter imaging. *Precambrian Research*, **63**, 27–41.

REX, G. M. 1985. A laboratory flume tank investigation of the formation of fossil stem fills. *Sedimentology*, **32**, 245–255.

—— 1986a. Further experimental investigations on the formation of plant compression fossils. *Lethaia*, **19** 143–159.

—— 1986b. Experimental modelling as an aid to interpreting the original three–dimensional structures of compressions.*In:* SPICER, R. A. & THOMAS, B. A. (eds) *Systematic and taxonomic approaches in palaeobotany*. *Systematics Association Special Volume*, **31**, 17–38.

—— & CHALONER, W. G. 1983. The experimental formation of plant compression fossils. *Palaeontology*, **26**, 231–252.

REYNOLDS, E. S. 1963. The use of lead citrate at high pH as an electron opaque stain in electron microscopy. *Journal of Cell Biology*, **17**, 208–212.

RICE, C. M., ASHCROFT, W. A., BATTEN, D. J. ET AL. 1995. A Devonian auriferous hot spring, Rhynie, Scotland. *Journal of the Geological Society of London*, **152**, 229–250.

RICHARDSON, F. & HALL, V. A. 1994. Pollen concentrate preparation from highly organic Holocene peat and lake deposits for AMS dating. *Radiocarbon*, **36 (3)**, 407–412.

RICHARDSON, J. B. 1996. Lower and Middle Palaeozoic records of terrestrial palynomorphs. *In:* JANSONIUS, J. & McGREGOR, D. C. (eds) *Palynology: principles and applications*. American Association of Stratigraphic Palynologists Foundation, **2**, 555–574.

RIDING, R. (ed.) 1991. . *Calcareous algae and stromatolites*. Springer-Verlag.

RIGBY, D., BATTS, B. D. & SMITH, J. W. 1981. The effect of maturation on the isotopic compositon of fossil fuels. *Organic Geochemistry*, **3**, 29–36.

ROBERTSON, A. I. & DUKE, N. C. 1987. Insect herbivory on mangrove leaves in North Queensland. *Australian Journal of Ecology*, **12**, 1–7.

ROCK, N. M. S. & WATERHOUSE, K. 1986. Value of chemostratigraphical correlation in metamorphic terrains: an illustration from the Shinness and Armadale marbles, Sutherland, Scotland. *Proceedings of the Geologists' Association*, **97**, 347–356.

ROGERS, S. O. 1994. Phylogenetic and taxonomic information from herbarium and mummified DNA. *In:* ADAMS, R. P., MILLER, J. S., GOLENBERG, E. M. & ADAMS, J. E. (eds) *Conservation of Plant Genes*

II: Intellectual Property Rights and DNA Utilization. Missouri Botanical Gardens, St. Louis, MO, 47–67.

—— & BENDICH, A. J. 1985. Extraction of DNA from milligram amounts of fresh, herbarium and mummified plant tissues. *Plant Molecular Biology,* 5, 69–76.

ROGERSON, E. C. W., EDWARDS, D., DAVIES, K. L. & RICHARDSON, J. B. 1993. Identification of *in situ* spores in a Silurian *Cooksonia* from the Welsh Borderland. *Special Papers in Palaeontology,* 49, 17–30.

ROLLINSON, H. 1993. *Using geochemical data: evaluation, presentation, interpretation.* Longman Scientific & Technical, Essex, England.

RONDON, M. A. & THOMAS, R. J. 1994. A piston-ball mill for the rapid preparation of plant and soil samples for the automated analysis of nitrogen (^{15}N) and carbon (^{13}C). *Communications in Soil Science and Plant Analysis,* 25, 435–445.

ROSE, J. 1974. Small-scale spatial variability of some sedimentary properties of lodgement till and slumped till. *Proceedings of the Geologists' Association,* 85, 239–258.

ROTH, J. L. & DILCHER, D. L. 1978. Some considerations in leaf size and leaf margin analysis of fossil leaves. *Courier Forschungsinstitut Senckenberg,* 30, 165–171.

ROWE, N. P. 1992. The gymnosperm *Archaeopteridium tschermakii* and an assocoated glandular fructification from the Upper Visean Drybrook Sandstone of Great Britain. *Palaeontology,* 35, 875–900.

—— & SPECK, T. 1997. Biomechanics of *Lycopodiella cernua* and *Huperzia squarrosa*: implications for inferring growth habits of fossil small-bodied Lycopsids. *Mededelingen Nederlands Instituut voor Geowetenschappen TNO,* 58, 293–302.

——— &—— 1998. Biomechanics of plant growth forms: The trouble with fossil plants. *Review of Palaeobotany and Palynology,* 102, 43–62.

——, —— & GALTIER, J. 1993. Biomechanical analysis of a Palaeozoic gymnosperm stem. *Proceedings of the Royal Society London,* B252, 19–28.

ROWLEY, J. C. & MORAN, D. T. 1975. A simple procedure for mounting wrinkle-free sections on formvar-coated slot grids. *Ultramicroscopy,* 1, 151–1155.

RUPPERT, L. F., STANTON, R. W., CECIL, C. B., EBLE, C. F. & DULONG, F. T. 1991. Effects of detrital influx in the Pennsylvanian Upper Freeport peat swamp. *International Journal of Coal Geology,* 17, (2), 95–116.

SAIZ-JIMENEZ, C. 1994. Analytical pyrolysis of humic substances: Pitfalls, limitations, and possible solutions. *Environmental Science & Technology,* 28, 1773–1780.

—— & DE LEEUW, J. W. 1986. Lignin pyrolysis products: Their structures and their significance as biomarkers. *Organic Geochemistry,* 10, 869–876.

SALISBURY, E. J. 1927. On the causes and ecological significance of stomatal frequency, with special reference to the woodland flora. *Philosophical Transactions of the Royal Society (London),* B216, 1–65.

SALVADOR, A. (ed.) 1994. *International stratigraphic guide. A guide to stratigraphic classification, terminology, and proceedure* (2nd edn). IUGS and Geological Society of America.

SANDER, P. M. 1987. Taphonomy of the Lower Permian Geraldine Bonebed in Archer County, Texas. *Palaeogeography Palaeoclimatology Palaeoecology,* 61, 221–236.

—— & GEE, C. T. 1990. Fossil charcoal: techniques and applications. *Review of Palaeobotany and Palynology,* 63, 269–279.

SANDERSON, J. B. 1994. *Biological Microtechnique.* Royal Society Microscopy Handbooks, 28, Bios Scientific Publishers, Oxford.

SARDASHTI, M. & MACIEL, G. E. 1987. Effects of sample spinning on cross polarization. *Journal of Magnetic Resonance,* 72, 467–474.

SAVAGE, N. M. 1988. The use of sodium polytungstate for conodont separations. *Journal of Micropalaeontology,* 7, 39–40.

SCHAAL, S. & ZIEGLER, W. (eds) 1992. *Messel – An insight into the history of life and of the earth.* Clarendon Press, Oxford.

SCHAARSCHMIDT, F. 1982. Präparation und Untersuchung der Eozänen Pflanzenfossilien von Messel bei Darmstadt. *Courier Forschungsinstitut Senckenberg,* 56, 59–77.

—— & WILDE, V. 1986. Palmenblüten und -blätter aus dem Eozän von Messel. *Courier Forschungsinstitut Senckenberg,* 86, 177–202.

SCHAEFER, J. & STEJSKAL, E. O. 1976. Carbon-13 nuclear magnetic resonance of polymers spinning at the magic angle. *Journal of American Chemical Society,* 98, 1031–1032.

SCHEIHING, M. H. & PFEFFERKORN, H. W. 1984. The taphonomy of land plants in the Orinoco Delta: A model for the incorporation of plant parts in clastic sediments of Upper Carboniferous age in Euramerica. *Review of Palaeobotany and Palynology,* 41, 205–240.

SCHIØLER, P., BRINKHUIS, H., RONCAGLIA, L. & WILSON, G. J. 1997. Dinoflagellate biostratigraphy and sequence stratigraphy of the type Maastrichtian (Upper Cretaceous), ENCI Quarry, The Netherlands. *Marine Micropalaeontology,* 31, 65–95.

SCHLESER, G. H. 1990. Investigations of the d^{13}C Pattern in Leaves of *Fagus sylvatica* L. *Journal of Experimental Botany,* 41, 565–572.

—— 1992. d^{13}C Pattern in a Forest Tree as an Indicator of Carbon Transfer in Trees. *Ecology,* 73, 1922–1925.

—— & JAYASEKERA, R. 1985. D^{13}C variations of leaves in forests as an indication of reassimilated CO_2 from the soil. *Oecologia,* 65, 536–542.

SCHMID, R. 1967. Electron microscopy of wood of Callixylon and Cordaites. *American Journal of Botany,* 54, 720–729.

SCHOCH, P. G., ZINSOU, C. & MONIQUE, S. 1980. Dependence of the stomatal index on environmental factors during stomatal differentiation in leaves of *Vigna sinensis* L. *Journal of Experimental Botany,* 31, 1211–1216.

SCHÖNFELD, C. & STORCH, D. 1979. Einsatz des Auflichtmikroskopes Vertival in der paläobotanischen Arbeit. *Jenaer Rundschau*, **24**, 242–245.

SCHOPF, J. M. 1975. Modes of fossil preservation. *Review of Palaeobotany and Palynology*, **20**, 27–53.

SCHWEINGRUBER, F. 1978. *Mikroskopische holzanatomie*. Zurcher AG, Zug.

—— 1990. *Anatomie europäischer Hölzer. Ein Atlas zur Bestimmung europäischer Baum-, Strauch- und Zwergstrauchhölzer*. Haupt, Stuttgart.

SCOTT, A. C. 1974. The earliest conifer. *Nature*, **251**, 707–7C8.

—— 1978. Sedimentological and ecological control of Westphalian B plant assemblages from West Yorkshire. *Proceedings of the Yorkshire Geological Society*, **41**, 461–508.

—— 1989a. Geological applications of Laser Scanning Microscopy. *Microscopy and Analysis*, **10**, 17–19.

—— 1989b. Observations on the nature and origin of fusain. *International Journal of Coal Geology*, **12**, 443–475.

—— 1992. Trace fossils of plant–arthropod interaction. *In:* MAPLES, C. G. & WEST, R. R. (eds) *Trace Fossils*. Short Courses in Paleontology **5**. Paleontological Society, University of Tennessee, Knoxville, 197–223.

—— & COLLINSON, M. E. 1983. Investigating fossil plant beds. *Geology Teaching*, **7**, 114–122 & **8**, 12–26.

——, STEPHENSON, J. & COLLINSON, M. E. 1994. The fossil record of leaves with plant galls. *Systematics Association Special Volume*, **49**, 447–470.

——,—— & CHALONER, W. G. 1992. Interaction and coevolution of plants and arthropods during the Palaeozoic and Mesozoic. *Philosophical Transactions of the Royal Society of London*, **B335**, 129–165.

—— & TAYLOR, T. N. 1983. Plant/animal interactions during the Upper Carboniferous. *Botanical Review*, **49**, 259–307.

SELA, J. 1977. Removal of gold from SEM specimens for sequential treatment. *Scanning Electron Microscopy*, 620.

—— & BOYDE, A. 1977. Cyanide removal of gold from SEM specimens. *Journal of the Royal Microscopical Society*, **3**, 229–231.

SENFTLE, J. T., LANDIS, C. R. & MCLAUGHLIN, R. L. 1993. Organic petrographic approach to kerogen characterization. *In:* ENGEL, M. H. & MACKO, S. A. (eds) *Organic Geochemistry*. Plenum Press NY, 355–374.

SHACKLEY, M. L. 1981a. *Environmental Archaeology*. Allen & Unwin, London.

—— 1981b. *Archaeological sediments*. Butterworth, London.

SHI, G. R. 1993. Multivariate data analysis in palaeoecology and palaeobiogeography – A review. *Palaeogeography, Palaeoclimatology, Palaeoecology*, **105**, 199–234.

SHUTE, C. H. 1986. Suggestions on the designation and terminology of palaeobotanical type material. *In:* SPICER, R. A. & THOMAS, B. A. (eds) Systematic and taxonomic Approaches in Palaeobotany. *Special Papers in Palaeontology*, **31**, 275–282.

—— & CLEAL, C. J. 1987. Palaeobotany in museums. *Geological Curator*, **4**, 553–559.

—— & EDWARDS, D. 1989. A new rhyniopsid with novel sporangium organization from the Lower Devonian of South Wales. *Botanical Journal of the Linnean Society*, **100**, 111–137.

SIDOW, A., WILSON, A. C. & PÄÄBO, S. 1991. Bacterial DNA in *Clarkia* fossils. *Philosophical Transactions of the Royal Society, London*, **B333**, 429–433.

SIMONEIT, B. R. T., GRIMALT, J. O., WANG, T. G., COX, R. E., HATCHER, P. G. & NISSENBAUM, A. 1986. Cylic terpenoids of contemporary resinous plant detritus and of fossil woods, ambers and coals. *In:* LEYTHAEUSER, D. & RULLKOTTER, J. (eds) *Advances in Organic Geochemistry, 1985 Organic Geochemistry*, **10**, 877–889.

SIMS, H., HERENDEEN, P. S. & CRANE, P. R. 1998. New genus of fossil Fagaceae from the Santonian (Late Cretaceous) of Central Georgia, USA. *International Journal of Plant Science*, **159**, 391–404.

SLAVIN, M. 1978. *Atomic Absorption Spectroscopy* (2nd edn). John Wiley & Sons.

SMART, P. & TOVEY, N. K. 1981. *Electron Microscopy of Soils and Sediments: Examples*. Clarendon Press, Oxford.

SMART, T. L. & HOFFMANN, E. S. 1988. Environmental interpretation of archaeological charcoal. *In:* HASTORF, C. A. & POPPER, V. (eds) *Current Paleoethnobotany*. University of Chicago Press, Chicago.

SMITH, A. G., SMITH, D. G. & FUNNELL, B. M. 1994. *Atlas of Mesozoic and Cenozoic coastlines*. Cambridge University Press.

SMITH, A. H. V. & BUTTERWORTH, M. A. 1967. Miospores in the coal seams of the Carboniferous of Great Britain. *Special Papers in Palaeontology*, **1**, 1–324.

SMITH, F. H. & GANNON, B. L. 1973. Sectioning of charcoals and dry ancient woods. *American Antiquity*. **38**, 468–472.

SMOOT, E. L. & TAYLOR, T. N. 1978. Sieve areas in fossil phloem. *Science*, **202**, 1081–1083.

—— &—— 1984 The fine structure of fossil plant cell walls. *Science*, **225**, 621–623.

SNAPE, C. E., AXELSON, D. E., BOTTO, R. E., DELPUECH, J. J., TEKELY, P., GERSTEIN, B. C., PRUSKI, M., MACIEL, G. E. & WILSON, M. A. 1989. Quantitative reliability of aromaticity and related measurements on coals by 13C n.m.r. A debate. *Fuel*, **68**, 547–560.

SOIL SURVEY STAFF. 1997. *Keys to soil taxonomy*. Pocahontas Press, Blacksburg, Virginia.

SOKAL, R. R. & ROHLF, F. J. 1981. *Biometry* (2nd edn. Freeman, San Francisco.

—— &—— 1995. *Biometry: the Principals and Practice of Biological Research* (3rd edn). W. H. Freeman and Co., San Francisco.

SOLTIS, P. S., SOLTIS, D. E. & SMILEY, C. J. 1992. An *rbcL* sequence from a Miocene *Taxodium* (bald cypress). *Proceedings of the National Academy of Science USA*, **89**, 449–451.

SOLUM, M. S., PUGMIRE, R. J. & GRANT, R. J. 1989. 13C solid-state NMR of Argonne coals. *Energy Fuels*, **3**, 187–193.

SORAUF, J. E. & STEIN, W. E. 1993. Biological fabric and the study of growth in the Devonian tabulate coral genera *Lecfedites* and *Favosites*. *Courier Forschungsinstitut Senckenberg*, **164**, 159–168.

SPATZ, H. -Ch., ROWE, N. P., SPECK, T. & DAVIERO, V. 1998. To have or not to have secondary xylem: Biomechanics of hollow stemmed Sphenopsids. *Review of Palaeobotany and Palynology*, **102**, 63–77.

SPECK, T. 1994a. A biomechanical method to distinguish between self-supporting and non self-supporting plants. *Review of Palaeobotany and Palynology*, **81**, 65–82.

—— 1994b. Bending stability of plant stems: ontogenetical, ecological, and phylogenetical aspects. *Biomimetics*, **2**, 109–128.

—— & ROWE, N. P. 1994. Biomechanical analysis of *Pitus dayi*: early seed plant vegetative morphology and its implications on growth habit. *Journal of Plant Research*, **107**, 443–460.

——&—— 1998. A quantitative approach to analytically defining size, form and habit in living and fossil plants. *In:* HEMSLEY, A. R. & KURMANN, M. (eds) *The Evolution of Plant Architecture*. Linnean Society London and Royal Botanic Gardens Kew.

——, ——, BRÜCHERT, F., HABERER, W., GALLENMÜLLER, F. & SPATZ, H.-Ch. 1996. How plants adjust the 'material properties' of their stems according to differing mechanical constraints during growth – an example of smart design in nature. *In:* ENGIN, A. E. (ed.) *Bioengineering*. PD-Volume 77, Proceedings of the 1996 Engineering Systems Design and Analysis Conference, Volume 5, ASME 1996, 233–241.

——, SPATZ, H.-Ch. & VOGELLEHNER, D. 1990. Contributions to the Biomechanics of Plants. I. Stabilities of Plant Stems with Strengthening Elements of Different Cross-Sections Against Weight and Wind Forces. *Botanica Acta*, **103**, 111–122.

—— & VOGELLEHNER, D. 1988a. Biophysical Examinations of the Bending Stability of Various Stele Types and the Upright Axes of Early 'Vascular' Land Plants. *Botanica Acta*, **101**, 262–268.

—— &—— 1988b. Biophysikalische Untersuchungen zur Mechanostabilität verschiedener Stelentypen und zur Art des Festigungssystems früher 'Gefäß'-Landpflanzen. *Palaeontographica B*, **210**, 91–126.

—— & —— 1992a. Fossile Bäume, Spreizklimmer und Lianen. Versuch einer biomechanischen Analyse der Stammstruktur. *Courier Forschungs–Institut Senckenberg*, **147**, 31–54.

—— &—— 1992b. Biomechanics and maximum height of some Devonian land plants. *In:* KOVAR-EDER, J. (ed.) *Palaeovegetational development in Europe and regions relevant to its palaeofloristic evolution*. Museum of Natural History, Vienna, 413–422.

—— &—— 1994. Devonische Landpflanzen mit und ohne hypodermales Sterom. Eine biomechanische Analyse mit Überlegungen zur Frühevolution des Leit-und Festigungssystems. *Palaeontographica B*, **233**, 157–227.

SPICER, R. A. 1981. The sorting and deposition of allochthonous plant material in a modern environment at Silwood Lake, Silwood Park, Berkshire, England. *US Geological Survey Professional Paper*, **1143**, 1–77.

—— 1986. Computerised palaeobotanical databases: the way forward ? *In:* SPICER R. A. & THOMAS, B. A. (eds) *Systematic and Taxonomic Approaches in Palaeobotany*. Systematic Association Special Volumes, **31**, 283–295.

—— 1989a. Physiological characteristics of land plants in relation to climate through time. *Transactions of the Royal Society of Edinburgh*, **80**, 321–329.

—— 1989b. The formation and interpretation of plant fossil assemblages. *Advances in Botanical Research*, **16**, 95–191.

—— 1998 Leaf physiognomy and climate change. *In:* CULVER, S. J. & RAWSON, P. (eds) *Biotic Response to Global Change: The Last 145 Million Years*. Kluwer, Dordrecht, in press.

—— & GREER, A. G. 1986. Plant Taphonomy in Fluvial and Lacustrine Systems. *University of Tennessee, Department of Geological Sciences, Studies in Geology*, **15**, 10–26.

—— & HILL, C. R. 1979. Principal component and correspondence analyses of quantitative data from a Jurassic plant bed. *Review of Palaeobotany and Palynology*, **28**, 273–299.

——, REES, P. M. & CHAPMAN, J. L. 1994. Cretaceous phytogeography and climate signals. *In:* ALLEN, J. R. L., HOSKINS, B. J., SELLWOOD, B. W., SPICER, R. A. & VALDES, P. J. (eds) *Palaeoclimates and their modelling: with special reference to the Mesozoic Era*. Chapman & Hall, London, 69–78.

——, —— & HERMAN, A. B. 1996. The Cretaceous vegetation and climate of Asia: Some insights. *In:* SAHNI, A. (ed.) *Cretaceous stratigraphy and palaeoenvironments*. Geological Society of India, Memoirs, **37**, 405–433.

—— & THOMAS, B. A. (eds) 1986. *Systematic and Taxonomic Approaches in Palaeobotany*. Systematics Association Special Volumes, **31**.

SPURR, A. R. 1969. A low viscosity resin embedding medium for electron microscopy. *Journal of Ultrastructural Research*, **26**, 31–43.

STACH, E., MACKOWSKY, M- TH., TEICHMÜLLER, M., TAYLOR, G. H., CHANDRA, D. & TEICHMÜLLER, R. 1975. *Stach's textbook of coal petrology* (2nd edn). Gebrueder Borntraeger Berlin-Stuttgart.

——, ——, ——, ——, —— &—— 1982. *Stach's textbook of coal petrology* (3rd edn). Gebrueder Borntraeger Berlin-Stuttgart.

STAPLIN, F. L. 1982. Determination of thermal maturation index from color of exinite (pollen, spores). *In:* STAPLIN, F. L. (ed.). *How to assess maturation and paleotemperatures*. SEPM Short Course, **7**, 7–11.

STEIN, J. 1991. Legislation in Wallonia. *Bulletin de la Société belge de Géologie*, **100**, 287–291.

STEIN, W. E. 1993. Modeling the evolution of stelar architecture in vascular plants. *International Journal of Plant Sciences*, **154**, 229–263.

—— 1998. Developmental logic – establishing a relationship between developmental process and phylogenetic pattern in primitive vascular plants. *Review of Palaeobotany and Palynology*, **102**, 15–42.

——, WIGHT, D. C. & BECK, C. B. 1982. Techniques for preparation of pyrite and limonite permineralizations. *Review of Palaeobotany and Palynology*, **36**, 185–194.

STEJSKAL, E. O., SCHAEFER, J. & WAUGH, J. S. 1977. Magic-angle spinning and polarization transfer in proton-enhanced NMR. *Journal of Magnetic Resonance,* **28**, 105–112.

STEPHENSON, J. 1991. *Evidence of plant/insect interactions in the Late Cretaceous and Early Tertiary*. PhD thesis, University of London.

—— & SCOTT, A. C. 1992. The geological history of insect-related plant damage. *Terra Nova,* **4**, 542–552.

STEWART, W. N. & TAYLOR, T. N. 1965. The Peel Technique. *In:* KUMMEL, B. & RAUP, D. (eds) *Handbook of Paleontological Techniques*. Freeman & Co, San Francisco, 224–232.

STIEBER, J. 1967. A Magyaroszági Felsöpleisztocén vegetáció története az anthrakotómiai eredmények Tükreben. *Földtani Közlony*, **97**, 308–317.

STOUT, S. A. & BOON, J. J. 1994. Structural characterization of the organic polymers comprising a lignite's matrix and megafossils. *Organic Geochemistry*, **21**, 953–970.

—— & HOWER, J. C. (eds) 1993. Collected papers from the ninth annual meeting of the Society for Organic Petrology. *Organic Geochemistry*, **20**.

STRANKS, L. & ENGLAND, P. 1997. The use of a resemblance function in the measurement of climatic parameters from the physiognomy of woody dicotyledons, *Palaeogeography, Palaeoclimatology, Palaeoecology*, **131**, 15–28.

STRONG, D. R., LAWTON, J. H. & SOUTHWOOD, T. R. E. 1984. *Insects on plants: community patterns and mechanisms*. Blackwell Scientific Publications, Oxford.

STUIVER, M. 1970. Oxygen and carbon isotope ratios of freshwater carbonates as climatic indicators. *Journal of Geophysical Research*, **75**, 5247–5257.

—— & BECKER, B. 1993, High-precision decadal calibration of the radiocarbon timescale, AD 1950–6000 BC. *Radiocarbon*, **35**, 35–65.

—— & BRAZIUNAS, T. F. 1993. [14]C ages of marine samples to 10,000 BC. *In:* STUIVER, M., LONG, A. & KRA, R. S. (eds) Calibration 1993. *Radiocarbon*, **35** (1) 137–189.

—— & KRA, R. S. (eds) 1986. Calibration issue, Proceedings of the 12th International ^{14}C conference. *Radiocarbon,* **28** (**2B**), 805–1030.

——, LONG, A. & KRA, R. S. (eds) 1993. Calibration 1993. *Radiocarbon*, **35** (**1**), 1–244.

—— & PEARSON, G. W. 1986. High–precision calibration of the radiocarbon time scale, AD 1950–500 BC, *In:* STUIVER, M., LONG, A. & KRA, R. S. (eds) Calibration issue. Proceedings of the 12th International ^{14}C conference. *Radiocarbon,* **28** (**2B**), 805–838.

—— & REIMER, P. J. 1993. Extended ^{14}C data base and revised CALIB 3.0 [14]C Age calibration program. *Radiocarbon*, **35** (**1**), 215–230.

SUC, J. -P. 1984. Origin and evolution of the Mediterranean vegetation and climate in Europe. *Nature*, **307**, 429–432.

SUDO, T., SHIMODA, S., YOTSUMOTO, H. & AITA, S. 1981. *Electron Micrographs of Clay Minerals*. Elsevier, Amsterdam.

SUESS, H. E. 1970. Bristlecone pine calibration of the radiocarbon timescale from 5200 BC to the present, *In:* OLSSON, I. U. (ed.) *Radiocarbon variations and absolute chronology*. John Wiley and Sons, New York, 303–309.

SUGITA, S. 1994. Pollen representation of vegetation in Quaternary sediments: theory and methods in patchy vegetation. *Journal of Ecology*, **82**, 881–897.

SWAN, A. R. H. & SANDILANDS, M. 1995. *Introduction to Geological Data Analysis*. Blackwell Science, Oxford, 446.

SWERHONE, G. D. W., HOBSON, K. A., VAN KESSEL, C. & BOUTTON, T. W. 1991. An economical method for the preparation of plant and animal tissue for d[13]C analysis. *Communications in Soil Science and Plant Analysis*, **22**, 177–190.

SYTSMA, K. J. 1994. DNA extraction from recalcitrant plants: Long, pure, and simple? *In:* ADAMS, R. P., MILLER, J. S., GOLENBERG, E. M. & ADAMS, J. E. (eds) *Conservation of Plant Genes II: Intellectual Property Rights and DNA Utilization*. Missouri Botanical Gardens, St. Louis, MO, 69–81.

TALBOT, M. R. 1990. A review of the palaeohydrological interpretation of carbon and oxygen isotopic ratios in primary lacustrine carbonates. *Chemical Geology (Isotope Geoscience Section)*, **80**, 261–279.

TANS, P. T. & MOOK, W. G. 1980. Past atmospheric CO_2 levels and the ^{13}C/^{12}C ratios in tree rings. *Tellus*, **32**, 268–283.

TATE, T. A. & RETALLACK, G. J. 1995. Thin sections of paleosols. *Journal of Sedimentary Research*, **A65**, 579–580.

TAYLOR, G. H., TEICHMÜLLER, M., DAVIS, A., DIESSEL, C. F. K., LITTKE, R. & ROBERT, P. (with contributions from: GLICK, D. C., SMYTH, M., SWAINE, D. J., VANDERBROUCKE, M. & ESPITALIÉ, J.) 1998. *Organic petrology*. Gebrüder borntraeger. Berlin. Stuttgart.

TAYLOR, M. A. 1981. *Wood in Archaeology*. Shire Archaeology, Aylesbury.

—— 1991*a*. The local geologist 1: exporting your heritage? *Geology Today*, **7**, 32–36.

—— 1991*b*. The local geologist 4: fossils, minerals and the law. *Geology Today*, **7**, 189–193.

—— & HARTE, J. D. C. 1988. Palaeontological site conservation and the law in Britain. *In:* CROWTHER, P. R. & WIMBLEDON, W. A. (eds) The use and conservation of palaeontological sites. *Special Papers in Palaeontology*, **40**, 21–39.

TAYLOR, P. D. 1986. Scanning electron microscopy of uncoated fossils. *Palaeontology*, **29**, 685–690.

TAYLOR, T. N. 1968. Application of scanning electron microscopy in paleobotany. *Transactions of the American Microscopical Society*, **87**, 510–515.

—— 1976. The ultrastructure of *Schopfipollenites*: orbicules and tapetal membranes. *American Journal of Botany*, **63**, 857–862.

—— 1990. Microsporogenesis in fossil plants. *In:* BLACKMORE, S. & KNOX, R. B. (eds) *Microspores – evolution and ontogeny*. Academic Press Ltd., Great Britain, 121–145.

—— & ALVIN, K. L. 1984. Ultrastructure and development of Mesozoic pollen: *Classopollis*. *American Journal of Botany*, **71**, 575–587.

—— & GRAUVOGEL–STAMM, L. 1995. The ultrastructure of voltzialean pollen. *Review of Palaeobotany and Palynology*, **84**, 281–303.

—— & MILLAY, M. A. 1977. Structurally preserved fossil cell contents. *Transactions of the American Microscopical Society*, **96**, 390–393.

——, OSBORN, J. M. & TAYLOR, E. L. 1996. The importance of *in situ* pollen and spores in understanding the biology and evolution of fossil plants. *In:* JANSONIUS, J. & McGREGOR, D. C. (eds) *Palynology: principles and applications.* American Association of Stratigraphic Palynologists Foundation, **1**, 427–441.

—— & ROTHWELL, G. W. 1982. Studies of seed fern pollen: development of the exine in *Monoletes* (Medullosales). *American Journal of Botany*, **69**, 570–578.

TAYLOR, W. A. 1990. Comparative analysis of megaspore ultrastructure in Pennsylvanian lycophytes. *Review of Palaeobotany and Palynology*, **62**, 65–78.

——, TAYLOR, T. N., & ARCHANGELSKY, S. 1989. Comparative ultrastructure of fossil and living gymnosperm cuticles. *Review of Palaeobotany and Palynology*, **59**, 145–151.

TEGELAAR, E. W., DE LEEUW, J. W., LARGEAU, C., DERENNE, S., SCHULTEN, H. -R., MÜLLER, R., BOON, J. J., NIP, M. & SPRENKELS, J. C. M. 1989. Scope and limitations of several pyrolysis methods in the structural elucidation of a macromolecular plant constituent in the leaf cuticle of *Agave americana* L. *Journal of Analytical and Applied Pyrolysis*, **15**, 29–54.

——, KERP, J. H. F., VISSCHER, H., SCHENCK, P. A. & DE LEEUW, J. W. 1991. Bias of the paleobotanical record as a consequence of variations in the chemical composition of higher vascular plant cuticles. *Paleobiology*, **17**, 133–144.

——, WATTENDORFF, J. & DE LEEUW, J. W. 1993. Possible effects of chemical heterogeneity in higher land plant cuticles on the preservation of its ultrastructure upon fossilization. *Review of Palaeobotany and Palynology*, **77**, 149–170.

TER BRAAK, C. J. F. 1986. Correspondence analysis of incidence and abundance data: properties in terms of unimodal response model. *Ecology*, **67**, 1167–1179.

—— 1987–1992. *CANOCO — a FORTRAN program for Canonical Correspondence Ordination.* Microcomputer Power, Ithaca, New York.

—— & PRENTICE, I. C. 1988. A theory of gradient analysis. *Advances in Ecological Research*, **18**, 271–317.

THINON, M. 1988. Utilisation de la microscopie épiscopique interférentielle pour l'identification botanique des charbons de bois. *In:* HACKENS T, MUNOT, A. V. & TILL, C. (eds) Bois et Archéologie, Actes du Symp. Europ., Louvain–la–Neuve, Oct. 1987, *PACT* 22, 179–188.

THOMAS, B. A. 1974. The lepidodendroid stoma. *Palaeontology*, **17**, 525–539.

THOMAS, K. W. 1964. A new design for a peat sampler. *New Phytologist*, **63**, 422.

THOMPSON, M. & WALSH J. N. 1983. A handbook of inductively coupled plasma spectrometry. *Blackie*, Glasgow, Scotland.

THOMPSON, T. A., MILLER, C. S., DOSS, P. K., THOMPSON, L. D. P. & BAEDKE, S. J. 1991. Land-based vibracoring and vibracore analysis: Tips, tricks and traps. Indiana Geological Survey Occasional Paper, **58**, 1–13.

THORNE, R. F. 1992. An updated classification of the flowering plants. *The Botanical Review*, **58**, 225–348.

THROUGHTON, J. H., WELLS, P. V. & MOONEY, H. A. 1974. Photosynthetic mechanisms and paleoecology from carbon isotope ratios in ancient specimens of C4 and CAM plants. *Science*, **185**, 610–612.

TICHÁ, I. 1982. Photosynthetic characteristics during ontogenesis of leaves. 7. Stomatal density and sizes. *Photosynthetica*, **16**, 375–471.

TIESZEN, L. L. 1991. Natural variations in the carbon isotope values of plants: Implications for archaeology, ecology, and paleoecology. *Journal of Archaeological Science*, **18**, 227–248.

TIFFNEY, B. H. 1991. The collection and study of dispersed angiosperm fruits and seeds. *Palaios*, **5**, 499–519.

TILL, R. 1974. *Statistical Methods for the Earth Scientist.* Macmillan, London.

TOLONEN, K. 1986. Charred particle analysis. *In:* BERGLUND, B. E. (ed.) *Handbook of Holocene Palaeoecology and Palaeohydrology.* J. Wiley & Sons, Chichester, 485–496.

TOOLIN, L. J. & EASTOE, C. J. 1993. Late Pleistocene–recent atmospheric d^{13}C record in C4 grasses. *Radiocarbon*, **35**, 263–269.

TOTLAND, M., JARVIS, I. & JARVIS, K. E. 1993. Determination of the platinum-group elements and gold in solid samples by slurry nebulization ICP-MS. *Chemical Geology*, **104 (1–4)**, 175–188.

TRAVERSE, A. 1978. Palynological analysis of DSDP Leg 42B (1975) cores from the Black Sea. *In:* ROSS, D. A. *ET AL.* (eds) *Reports of the Deep Sea Drilling Project*, **62** (2), 993–1015.

—— 1982. Response of world vegetation to Neogene tectonic and climatic events. *Alcheringa*, **6**, 197–209.

—— 1988. *Paleopalynology.* Unwin & Hyman, London.

—— 1990. Studies of pollen and spores in rivers and other bodies of water, in terms of source-vegetation and sedimentation, with special reference to Trinity River and Bay, Texas. *Review of Palaeobotany and Palynology*, **64**, 297–303.

—— 1992. Organic Fluvial Sediment: Palynomorphs and 'Palynodebris' in the Lower Trinity River, Texas. *Annals of the Missouri Botanical Garden*, **79**, 110–125.

—— 1994. Sedimentation of palynomorphs and palynodebris: an introduction. *In:* TRAVERSE, A. (ed.) *Sedimentation of Organic Particles.* Cambridge University Press, UK, 1–8.

—— 1996. Nomenclature and taxonomy: systematics. *In:* JANSONIUS, J. & McGREGOR, D. C. (eds) *Palynology: Principles and Applications.* American

Association of Stratigraphic Palynologists Foundation, **1**, 11–28.

—— & GINSBURG. R. N. 1966. Palynology of the surface sediments of Great Bahama Bank, as related to water movement and sedimentation. *Marine Geology*, **4**, 417–459.

TUCKER, M. E. 1981. *Sedimentary Petrology*. Blackwell Scientific Publications, Oxford.

TURNER, C. & WEST, R. G. 1968. The subdivision and zonation of interglacial periods. *Eiszeitalter und Gegenwurt*, **19**, 93–101.

TYSON, R. V. 1989. Late Jurassic palynofacies trends, Piper and Kimmeridge Clay Formations, UK onshore and northern North Sea. *In:* BATTEN, D. J. & KEEN, M. C. (eds) *Northwest European Micropalaeontology and Palynology*. Ellis Horwood Ltd., Chichester, 135–172.

—— 1995. *Sedimentary Organic Matter. Organic Facies and Palynofacies*. Chapman & Hall, London.

—— 1996. Sequence-stratigraphical interpretation of organic facies variations in marine siliciclastic systems: general principles and application to onshore Kimmeridge Clay Formation, UK. *In:* HESSELBO, S. P. & PARKINSON, D. N. (eds) *Sequence Stratigraphy in British Geology*. Geological Society, London, Special Publications, **103**, 75–96.

UPCHURCH, G. R. JR. 1995. Dispersed angiosperm cuticles: their history, preparation, and application to the rise of angiosperms in Cretaceous and Paleocene coals, south western interior of North America. *International Journal of Coal Geology*, **28**, 161–227.

VAKHRAMEEV, V. A. 1991. *Jurassic and Cretaceous floras and climates of the Earth*. Cambridge University Press, Cambridge.

——, DOBRUSKINA, I. A., MEYEN, S. V. & ZAKLINSKAYA, E. D. 1978. *Paläozoische und mesozoische Floren Eurasiens und die Phytogeographie dieser Zeit*. (Paleozoic and Mesozoic flora from Eurasia, and their Recent phytogeography). VEB Gustav Fischer Verlag, Jena.

VAN BERGEN, P. F. 1994. *Palaeobotany of Propagules: An Investigation combining Microscopy and Chemistry*. PhD thesis, University of London, UK.

——, COLLINSON, M. E., BRIGGS, D. E. G., DE LEEUW, J. W., SCOTT, A. C., EVERSHED, R. P. & FINCH, P. 1995. Resistant biomacromolecules in the fossil record. *Acta Botanica Neerlandica*, **44**, 319–342.

——, —— & DE LEEUW, J. W. 1993. Chemical composition and ultrastructure of salvinialean microspore massulae and megaspores. *Grana*, **suppl. 1**, 18–30.

——, ——, HATCHER, P. G. & DE LEEUW, J. W. 1994a. Lithological control on the state of preservation of fossil seed coats of water plants. *Organic Geochemistry*, **22**, 683–702.

——, GOÑI, M., COLLINSON, M. E., BARRIE, P. J., SINNINGHE DAMSTÉ, J. S. & DE LEEUW, J. W. 1994b. Chemical and microscopic characterization of outer seed coats of fossil and extant water plants. *Geochimica et Cosmochimica Acta*, **58**, 3823–3844.

——, SCOTT, A. C., BARRIE, P. J., DE LEEUW, J. W. & COLLINSON, M. E. 1994c. The chemical composition of upper Carboniferous pteridosperm cuticles. *Organic Geochemistry*, **21**, 107–112.

VAN DE WATER, P. K., LEAVITT, S. W. & BETANCOURT, J. L. 1994. Trends in stomatal density and $^{13}C/^{12}C$ ratios of *Pinus flexilis* needles during last glacial–interglacial cycle. *Science*, **264**, 239–243.

VAN DEN HOEK, C., MANN, D. G. & JAHNS, H. M. 1995. *Algae: an introduction to phycology*. Cambridge University Press.

VAN DER BURGH, J. 1973. Hölzer der Niederrheinischen Braunkohlenformation. II. (Fossil woods from the Lower Rhine Brown Coal Formation. II.) *Review of Palaeobotany and Palynology*, **15**, 73–275.

——, VISSCHER, H., DILCHER, D. L. & KÜRSCHNER, W. M. 1993. Atmospheric signatures in Neogene fossil leaves. *Science*, **260**, 1788–1790.

VAN DER EEM, J. G. L. A. 1983. Aspects of Middle and Late Triassic palynology. 6. Palynological investigations in the Ladinian and lower Karnian of the western Dolomites, Italy. *Review of Palaeobotany and Palynology*, **16**, 1–122.

VAN DER HEIJDEN, E. & BOON, J. J. 1994. A combined pyrolysis mass spectrometric and light microscopic study of peatified *Caluna* wood isolated from raised bog peat deposits. *Organic Geochemistry*, **22**, 903–919.

VAN DER PLICHT, J. & MOOK, W. G. 1989. Calibration of radiocarbon ages by computer. *In:* LONG, A., KRA, R. S. & SRDOC, D. (eds) Proceedings of the 13th International ^{14}C conference. *Radiocarbon,* **31 (3)**, 805–816.

VAN GIJZEL, P. 1979. Manual of the techniques and some geological applications of fluorescence microscopy. *American Association of Stratigraphic Palynologists. 12. Annual Meeting, Dallas 1979*, 55 pp.

—— 1990. Transmittance colour index (TCI) of amorphous organic matter: a new thermal maturity indicator for hydrocarbon source rocks, and its correlation with mean vitrinite reflectance and thermal alteration index (TAI). *Mededelingen Rijks Geologische Dienst*, **45**, 49–64.

VAN ZEIST, W., WASYLIKOWA, K. & K. BEHRE, K-E. (eds) 1991. *Progress in Old World Palaeoethnobotany*. Balkema, Rotterdam.

VAUGHAN, A. & NICHOLS, G. J. 1995. Controls on the deposition of charcoal: implications for sedimentary accumulations of fusain. *Journal of Sedimentary Research*, **A65**, 129–135.

VERNET, J. L. 1973. Etude sur l'histoire de la végétation du sud-est de la France au Quaternaire d'après les charbons de bois principalement. *Paléobiologie Continentale*, **4** (1), Montpellier, 1–90.

VINCENT, J. F. V. & JERONIMIDIS, G. 1992. The mechanical design of fossil plants. *In:* RAYNER, J. M. V. & WOOTTON, R. J. (eds) *Biomechanics in evolution*, Cambridge University Press, Cambridge, 21–36.

VOGEL, J. C. 1978. Recycling of carbon in a forest environment. *Oecologia Plantarum,* **13**, 89–94.

VOGEL, J. S. 1995. Report on the AMS sample preparation workshop, Saturday 13 August 1994. Proceedings of the 15th International ^{14}C conference. *Radiocarbon,* **37** (2), 815–817.

VOGT, C. 1994. Speciation of the inorganic components in

brown–coal. *Fresenius Journal of Analytical Chemistry*, **350 (1–2)**, 89–92.

VONHOF, H. B. & WESSELINGH, F. P. 1997. A three component water mixing system recorded in a Miocene Fresh-brackish water mollusc fauna from the Andean Foreland Basin (Pebas FM Columbia): evidence from O, C and Sr isotopes. *Abstract, European Union of Geosciences 9*, (**82/2B**), 685.

WAGNER, F., BELOW, R., DE KLERK, P., DILCHER, D. L., JOOSTEN, H., KÜRSCHNER, W. M. & VISSCHER, H. 1996. A natural experiment on plant acclimation: lifetime stomatal frequency response of an individual tree to annual CO_2 increase. *Proceedings of the National Acadamy of Science USA*, **93**, 11705–11708.

WAGNER, R. H. 1984. Megafloral zones of the Carboniferous. *Compte rendu 9e Congrès International de la Stratigraphie et de Géologie du Carbonifère*, **2**, 109–134.

WALKER, J. W. & WALKER, A. G. 1984. Ultrastructure of Lower Cretaceous angiosperm pollen and the origin and early evolution of flowering plants. *Annals of the Missouri Botanical Garden*, **71**, 464–521.

WALKER, R. G. & JAMES, N. P. (eds) 1992. *Facies Models: response to sea level change*. Geological Association of Canada, St Johns, Newfoundland.

WALTER, H. & LIETH, H. 1967. *Klimadiagramm-Weltatlas*. Fischer, Jena.

—— 1985. *Vegetation of the earth and ecological systems of the geo–biosphere* (3rd edn). Springer-Verlag, New York.

WALTON, J. 1928. A method for preparing fossil plants. *Nature*, **122**, 571.

—— 1936. On the factors which influence the external form of fossil plants: with descriptions of the foliage of some species of the Palaeozoic Equisetalean genus *Annularia* Sternberg. *Philosophical Transactions of the Royal Society*, **2**, 219–237.

WANG, C. -W. 1961. The forests of China with a survey of grassland and desert vegetation. *Maria Moors Cabot Foundation Public, Cambridge, USA*, **5**, 313.

WANG, Y., CERLING, T. E. & MACFADDEN, B. J. 1994. Fossil horses and carbon isotopes: new evidence for Cenozoic dietary, habitat and ecosystem changes in North America. *Palaeogeography, Palaeoclimatology, Palaeoecology*, **107**, 269–279

WARNER, R. B. 1990. A proposed adjustment for the 'old-wood effect'. Proceedings of the 2nd International symposium on ^{14}C and archaeology. *PACT*, **29**, 159–172.

WASYLIKOWA, K. 1986. Analysis of fossil seeds and fruits. In: BERGLUND, B. E. (ed.) *Handbook of Holocene Palaeoecology and Palaeohydrology*. John Wiley, Chichester and New York, 571–590.

WATERBOLK, H. T. 1971. Working with radiocarbon dates. *Proceedings of the Prehistoric Society*, **37** (**2**), 15–33.

WATERHOUSE, H. K. 1995. High-resolution palynofacies investigation of Kimmeridgian sedimentary cycles. In: HOUSE, M. R. & GALE, A. S. (eds) *Orbital Forcing Timescales and Cyclostratigraphy*. Geological Society, London, Special Publications, **85**, 75–114.

WATSON, L. & DALLWITZ, M. J. 1994. *The Families of Flowering Plants*. CSIRO, Melbourne (CD–ROM).

WATT, A. D. 1982. Index of generic names of fossil plants, 1974–1978. *Bulletin of the United States Geological Survey*, **1517**, 1–63.

WEBB III, T. 1987. The appearance and disappearance of major vegetational assemblages: long term vegetational dynamics in eastern North America. *Vegetation*, **69**, 177–187.

—— & BRYSON, R. A. 1972. Late and Postglacial climatic change in the northern Midwest, USA: quantitative estimates derived from fossil pollen spectra by multivariate statistical analysis. *Quaternary Research*, **2**, 70–115.

WELLMAN, C. H., EDWARDS, D. & AXE, L. 1996. Curation of exceptionally preserved early land plant fossils: problems and solutions. *Curator*, **39**, 209–216.

——, —— &—— 1998. Ultrastructure of laevigate hilate cryptospores from sporangia and spore masses from the Late Silurian and Early Devonian of the Welsh Borderland. *Philosophical Transactions of the Royal Society, London*, **B353**, 1983–2004.

WESSEL, P. & WEBER, O. 1855. Neuer Beitrag zur Tertiärflora der niederrheinischen Braunkohlenformation. *Palaeontographica*, **4**, 111–178.

WEST, R. G. 1981. Palaeobotany and Pleistocene stratigraphy in Britain. *New Phytologist*, **87**, 127–137.

WEST, R. M. 1991. *State Regulation of Geological, Paleontological, and Archaeological Collecting – 1991*. The American Museum of Natural History, New York, 30.

WEST, R. R. (ed.) Trace Fossils. *Short Courses in Paleontology*, **5**.

WESTERN, A. C. 1963. Wood and Charcoal in Archaeology. In: BROTHWELL, D. & HIGGS, E. (eds) *Science in Archaeology*, Thames and Hudson. London, 150–160.

WEYERS, J. D. B. & LAWSON, T. 1997. Heterogeneity in stomatal characters. *Advances in Botanical Research*, **26**, 317–352.

—— & MEIDNER, H. 1990. *Methods in Stomatal Research*. Longman Scientific and Technical, Harlow.

WHEELER, E. A., PEARSON, R. G., LAPASHA, C. A., ZACK T. & HATLEY, W. 1986. Computer-aided wood identification, Reference manual. *North Carolina Agriculture Research Service Bulletin*, 474.

WHITAKER, M. F., GILES, M. R. & CANNON, S. J. C. 1992. Palynological review of the Brent Group, UK sector, North Sea. In: MORTON, A. C., HASZELDINE, R. S., GILES, M. R. & BROWN, S. (eds) *Geology of the Brent Group*. Geological Society, London, Special Publications, **61**, 169–202.

WHITE, J. M., AGER, T. A., ADAM, D. P., LEOPOLD, E. B., LIU, G., JETTÉ, H. & SCHWEGER, C. E. 1997. An 18 million year record of vegetation and climate change in northwestern Canada and Alaska: tectonic and global climatic correlates. *Palaeogeography, Palaeoclimatology, Palaeoecology*, **140**, 293–306.

WHITE, J. W. C., CIAIS, P., FIGGE, R. A., KENNY, R. & MARKGRAF, V. 1994. A high-resolution record of atmospheric CO₂ content from carbon isotopes in peat. *Nature*, **367**, 153–156.

WHITHAM, A. G. 1986. Pumice. *Bulletin of Volcanology*, **48**, 209–223.

WHITLOCK, C. & MILLSPAUGH, S. H. 1996. Testing the assumptions of fire-history studies: an examination of modern charcoal accumulation in Yellowstone National Park, USA. *The Holocene*, **6**, 7–15.

WILLARD, D. A. & PHILLIPS, T. L. 1993. Paleobotany and palynology of the Bristol Hill Coal Member (Bond Formation) and Friendsville Coal Member (Mattoon Formation) of the Illinois Basin (Upper Pennsylvanian). *Palaios*, **8**, 574–586.

——, DiMICHELE, W. A., EGGERT, D. L., HOWER, J. C., REXROAD, C. B. & SCOTT, A. C. 1995. Paleoecology of the Springfield Coal Member (Desmoinesian, Illinois Basin) near the Leslie Cemetary paleochannel, southwestern Indiana. *International Journal of Coal Geology*, **27**, **1**, 59–98.

WILLCOX, G. 1977. Exotic Plants from Roman water-logged sites in London *Journal of Archaeological Science*, **4**, 269–282.

WILLIAMS, D. M. 1973. Flotation at Siraf. *Antiquity*, **47**, 288–292.

——, HARKIN, J. & HIGGS, K. T. 1996. Implications of new microfloral evidence from the Clew Bay Complex for Silurian relationships in the western Irish Caledonides. *Journal of the Geological Society, London*, **153**, 771–777.

WILLMER, C. M. & FRICKER, M. 1996. *Stomata* (2nd edn). Chapman & Hall, London.

WILSON, J. 1979. Macroscopic features of wind damage to leaves of *Acer pseudoplatanus* L. and its relationship with season, leaf age and windspeed. *Annals of Botany*, **46**, 303–311.

WILSON, M. A. 1987. *NMR techniques and applications in geochemistry and soil chemistry*, Pergamon Press, Oxford, 353.

——, BATTS, B. D. & HATCHER, P. G. 1988. Molecular composition and mobility of torbanite precursors: Implications for the structure of coal. *Energy & Fuels*, **2**, 668–672.

——, COLLIN, P. J., VASSALLO, A. M. & RUSSEL, N. J. 1984. The nature of olefins and carboxyl groups in an Australian brown coal resin. *Organic Geochemistry*, **7**, 161–168.

WIMBLEDON, W. A. 1988. Palaeontological site conservation in Britain: facts, form, function, and efficacy. *In:* CROWTHER, P. R. & WIMBLEDON, W. A. (eds) The use and conservation of palaeontological sites. *Special Papers in Palaeontology*, **40**, 41–55.

——, BENTON, M. J., BEVINS, R. E., BLACK, G. P., BRIDGLAND, D. R., CLEAL, C. J., COOPER, R. G. & MAY, V. C. 1995. The development of a methodology for the selection of British geological sites for conservation: Part 1. *Modern Geology*, **20**, 159–202.

WING, S. L. & DiMICHELE, W. A. 1995. Conflict between local and global changes in plant diversity through geologic time. *Palaios*, **10**, 551–564.

WINSTON, R. B. 1988. Paleoecology of Middle Pennsylvanian-age peat-swamp plants in Herrin coal, Kentucky, U.S.A. *International Journal of Coal Geology*, **10**, 203–238.

WINT, G. R. W. 1983. Leaf damage in tropical rain forest canopies. *In:* SUTTON, S. L., WHITMORE, C. & CHADWICK, A. C. (eds) *Tropical Rain Forest: Ecology and Management*. Blackwell Scientific Publications, Boston, 229–239.

WNUK, C. & PFEFFERKORN, H. W. 1987. A Pennsylvanian-age terrestrial storm deposit: Using plant fossils to characterize the history and process of sediment accumulation. *Journal of Sedimentary Petrology*, **57**, 212–221.

WOILLARD, G. M. 1978. Grande Pile peat bog: A continuous pollen record for the last 140,000 years. *Quaternary Research*, **9**, 2–21.

WOLBERG, D. & REINARD, P. 1997. *Collecting the Natural World – Legal Requirements & Personal Liability for Collecting Plants, Animals, Rocks, Minerals & Fossils*. Geoscience Press, Inc., Tucson, Arizona, 330.

WOLFE, J. A. 1979. *Temperature parameters of humid to mesic forests of eastern Asia and their relation to forests of other regions of the Northern Hemisphere and Australasia*. U.S. Geological Survey Professional Paper, **1106**, 1–37.

—— 1985. Distribution of major vegetational types during the Tertiary. *In:* SUNDQUIAT, E. T. & BROECKER, W. S. (eds) *The carbon cycle and atmospheric CO₂*. American Geophysical Union Monograph, **32**, 357–375.

—— 1990. Palaeobotanical evidence for a marked temperature increase following the Cretaceous/Tertiary boundary. *Nature*, **343**, 153–156.

—— 1993. A method of obtaining climatic parameters from leaf assemblages. *U.S. Geological Survey Bulletin*, **2040**, 1–73.

—— 1994a. Tertiary climatic changes at middle latitudes of western North America. *Palaeogeography, Palaeoclimatology, Palaeoecology*, **108**, 195–205.

—— 1994b. An analysis of Neogene climates in Beringia. *Palaeogeography, Palaeoclimatology, Palaeoecology*, **108**, 207–216.

—— 1995. Paleoclimatic estimates from Tertiary leaf assemblages. *Annual Review of Earth & Planetary Sciences*, **23**, 119–142.

——, FOREST, C. E. & MOLNAR, P. 1998. Paleobotanical evidence of Eocene and Oligocene paleoaltitudes at midlatitude western North America. *Geological Society of America Bulletin*, **110**, 664–678.

——, SCHORN, H. E., FOREST, C. E. & MOLNAR, P. 1997. Paleobotanical evidence for high altitudes in Nevada during the Miocene. *Science*, **276**, 1672–1675.

WOLFENBARGER, D. O. 1946. Dispersion of Small Organisms. *The American Midland Naturalist*, **35**, 1–152.

WOOD, G. D., GABRIEL, A. M. & LAWSON, J. C. 1996. Palynological techniques – processing and microscopy. *In:* JANSONIUS, J. & McGREGOR, D. C. (eds) *Palynology: Principles and Applications*. American Association of Stratigraphic Palynologists Foundation, **1**, 29–50.

WOODLAND, B. G. & STENSTROM, R. C. 1979. The occurrence and origin of siderite concretions in Francis Creek Shale (Pennslyvanian) of northeastern Illinois. *In* NITECKI, M. H. (ed.) *Mazon*

Creek Fossils. Academic Press, New York, 69–103.

WOODWARD, F. I. 1987. Stomatal numbers are sensitive to increases in CO_2 from the pre–industrial levels. *Nature*, **327**, 617–618.

—— & BAZZAZ, F. A. 1988. The responses of stomatal density to CO_2 partial pressure. *Journal of Experimental Botany*, **39**, 1771–1781.

—— & KELLY, C. K. 1995. The influence of CO_2 concentration on stomatal density. *New Phytologist*, **131**, 311–327.

WRIGHT, H. E., JR. 1980. Cores of soft lake sediments. *Boreas*, **9**, 107–114.

—— 1991. Coring tips. *Journal of Paleolimnology*, **6**, 37–49.

——, MANN, D. H. & GLASER, P. H. 1984. Piston corers for peat and lake sediments. *Ecology*, **65**, 657–659.

WRIGHT, V. P. & VANSTONE, S. D. 1991. Assessing the carbon dioxide content of ancient atmospheres using paleo-calcretes: theoretical and empirical constraints. *Journal of the Geological Society, London*, **148**, 945–947.

XIAHONG, F. & EPSTEIN, S. 1995. Carbon isotopes of trees from arid environments and implications for reconstructing atmospheric CO_2 concentration. *Geochimica et Cosmochimica Acta*, **59**, 2599–2608.

YAMAGUCHI, D. K. & ALLEN, G. L. 1992. A new computer program for estimating the statistical significance of cross-dating positions for 'floating' tree-ring series. *Canadian Journal of Forestry Research*, **22**, 1215–1221.

YANG, H., GOLENBERG, E. M. & SHOSHANI, J. 1997*a*. A blind testing design for authenticating ancient DNA sequences. *Molecular Phylogenetics and Evolution*, **7**, 261–265.

——, —— &—— 1997*b*. Proboscidean DNA from museum and fossil specimens: An assessment of ancient DNA extraction and amplification techniques. *Biochemical Genetics*, **35**, 165–179.

YOUNKER, J. L. & EHRLICH, R. 1977. Fourier biometrics: harmonic amplitudes as multivariate shape descriptors. *Systematic Zoology*, **26**, 336–342.

YULE, B. L., ROBERTS, S. & MARSHALL, J. E. A. 1995. Spores under the spotlight. *Microscopy News*, September 1995.

——, ——, —— & MILTON, J. A. 1998. Quantitative spore colour measurement using colour image analysis. *Organic Geochemistry*, **28**, 139–149.

ZAGWIJN, W. & HAGER, H. 1987. Correlation of continental and marine Neogene deposits in the South-eastern Netherlands and the Lower Rhine district. *Mededelingen van de Werkgroep voor Tertiaire en Kwartaire Geologie*, **24**, 1–2, 59–78.

ZELIBOR, J. L., JR, ROMANKIW, L., HATCHER, P. G. & COLWELL, R. R. 1988. Comparative analysis of the chemical composition of mixed and pure cultures of green algae and their decomposed residues using ^{13}C nuclear magnetic resonance. *Journal of Applied and Environmental Microbiology*, **54**, 1051–1060.

ZETSCHE, F. 1932. Kork und cuticularsubstanzen. *In:* KLEIN, G. (ed.) *Handbuch der Pflanzeranalyse*. Springer-Verlag, Berlin, 205–215.

—— & KÄLIN, O. 1932. Eine Methode zur Isolierung des Polymerbitumendds (Sporenmembranen, Kutikulen usw.) aus Kohlen. *Braunkohle*, Halle, **31**, 345–351.

—— & VICARI, H. 1931. Untersuchungen über die Membran der Sporen und Pollen III. 2. *Picea orientalis, Pinus silvestris* L., *Corylus avellana* L. *Helvetica Chimica Acta*, **14**, 62–67.

ZHANG, M. & MACIEL, G. E. 1989. Large-volume MAS system for improved signal-to-noise ratio. *Journal of Magnetic Resonance*, **85**, 156–161.

ZIEGLER, A. M. 1990. Phytogeographic patterns and continental configurations during the Permian Period. *In:* MCKERROW, W. S. & SCOTESE, C. R. (eds) *Palaeozoic Palaeogeography and Biogeography*. Geological Society, London, Memoir, **12**, 363–379.

——, PARRISH, J. M., YAO, J. P. *ET AL.* 1994. Early Mesozoic phytogeography and climate. *In:* ALLEN, J. R. L., HOSKINS, B. J., SELLWOOD, B. W., SPICER, R. A. & VALDES, P. J. (eds) *Palaeoclimates and their modelling: with special reference to the Mesozoic Era*. Chapman & Hall, London, 89–97.

——, REES, P. M., ROWLEY, D. B., BEKKER, A., QING LI & HULVER, M. L. 1996. Mesozoic assembly of Asia: constraints from fossil floras, tectonics and paleomagnetism. *In:* YIN, A. & HARRISON, M. (eds) *The tectonic evolution of Asia*. Cambridge University Press, Cambridge, 371–400.

ZIELINSKI, G. A., MAYEWSKI, P. A., MEEKER, L. D. *ET AL.* 1994. Record of volcanism since 7000 B.C. from the GISP2 Greenland ice core and implications for the volcano–climate system. *Science*, **264**, 948–952.

ZODROW, E. L. & CLEAL, C. J. 1985. Phyto- and chronostratigraphical correlations between the late Pennsylvanian Morien Group (Sydney, Nova Scotia) and the Silesian Pennant Measures (south Wales). *Canadian Journal of Earth Sciences*, **22**, 1465–1473.

—— &—— 1993. The epidermal structure of the Carboniferous gymnosperm frond *Reticulopteris*. *Palaeontology*, **36**, 65–79.

ZOHARY, D. & HOPF, M. 1993. *Domestication of plants in the Old World, the origins and spread of cultivated plants in West Asia, and the Nile Valley* (2nd edn). Oxford University Press.

Glossary of terms

A horizon: surface horizon of a soil, commonly including organic matter.

AA or AAS: atomic absorption spectrometry. A method of chemical analysis using light absorption wavelengths of flaming aerosol of sample.

Abundance, isotopic: the ratio of the number of an isotope to the total number of atoms within the mixture of isotopes of an element.

Acetolysis: a chemical reaction in which cellulose and other organic components are depolymerized by replacing hydroxyl groups with acetyl groups, forming cellulose triacetate which is soluble with glacial acetic acid.

Acidic: with a low pH (<7), and abundance of hydronium ion (H^+) in solution.

Adpression: a fossil formed when the original organism or fragment has been compressed in the sediment. If the coalified plant tissue is still preserved, it is a compression; if the coalified plant tissue has been lost, it is an impression.

Age offset: sample where the zero age at death assumption does not apply. Typical example is heartwood from a long-lived tree where atmospheric carbon exchange ceased long before the time of felling. Also known as the 'old wood effect'.

Alfisol: fertile forest soil, with subsurface clayey horizon.

Aliphatic constituents: organic compounds that do not include benzene rings in their structure. Examples include alkanes, alkenes, alkanols, fatty acids.

Alkali elements: sodium (Na) and potassium (K).

Alkaline earth elements: calcium (Ca) and magnesium (Mg).

Alluvium: sedimentary deposits of rivers.

Alumina: aluminum oxide (Al_2O_3).

Amphistomatous: having stomata on both the upper and lower surfaces of the leaf.

AMS ^{14}C dating: undertaken using an accelerator mass spectrometer. Directly measures the ratio of ^{14}C to ^{12}C atoms. Requires a smaller sample than does conventional dating.

AOM (amorphous organic matter): a visibly unstructured kerogen component comprising heterogeneous 'fluffy' material. It is characteristic of organic-rich dark-coloured mudrocks and forms under reducing conditions from the diagenetic repolymerization of the decomposition products of primarily algal precursors. It is normally associated with pyrite, both framboids and cubes. It contains inclusions of structured plant debris and other organic walled microfossils. It frequently is the dominant kerogen component and if mudrocks have a high organic content it will be the dominant material. At appropriate maturity levels (below a vitrinite reflectivity of about 1%) it shows clear fluorescence in UV excitation. In reflected light terminology it is the bituminite maceral but not the oil generation product, bitumen. Geochemically a type I or II kerogen. Material similar to AOM can form from the extreme degradation of structured plant debris within an anoxic environment.

Archaeological wood: structurally preserved wood from archaeological horizons, generally either desiccated or waterlogged, constituting built structures or artefacts or scattered in sedimentological horizons.

Arctotertiary: largely deciduous floral elements assumed or shown to have originated in the circumpolar region in the early Tertiary.

Aridisol: desert soil, usually thin profiles, commonly with calcareous nodules or salt crystals within a metre of the surface.

Aromatic constituents: organic compounds that do include benzene rings in their structure. Examples include phenols, methoxyphenols, benzenes, naphthalene.

Axial second moment of area (m^4): geometrical parameter used in biomechanical studies describing the cross-sectional area and cross-sectional shape. Tissues that are arranged more peripherally in the stem show higher contributions to the axial second moment of area than tissues closer to the centre.

Azonal: those communities governed by the microclimate and/or edaphic factors, e.g. riparian and littoral communities.

B horizon: subsurface horizon of soil, often enriched in clay or carbonate.

Background: criterion which determines the maximum (oldest) limit for ^{14}C dating. Represents the lowest (smallest) detectable ^{14}C level.

Bases: principal cations of soil solutions (Ca^{2+}, Mg^{2+}, Na^+, K^+).

Binomial: the combination of two names which designate a species: these are the generic name (the name of the genus – e.g. *Lepidodendron*) and the specific epithet (e.g. *acutum*). The generic name plus epithet constitute the binomial

374

(*Lepidodendron acutum*), the formal Latinized name of the organism.

Biocode: an international code designed to cover the nomenclature of all groups of organisms, drawn up (in draft only) by a committee of the International Union of Biological Sciences. See Hawksworth, 1996.

Biocoenosis: a community of living organisms.

Biohorizon: a stratigraphical level where there is distinctive change in the palaeontological content. The change may be reflected in the appearance or extinction of one or more taxa, or of a marked change in abundance.

Biome: a large and climatically uniform region of the Earth defined by certain ranges of temperature and precipitation through the annual cycle (e.g. cool temperate biome).

Biostratigraphy: the division of rock sequences based on their palaeontological content. The standard biostratigraphical division is the biozone.

Biostratinomy: the transport, deposition and burial of an organism as part of the fossilization process.

Biozone: a body of strata defined by its distinctive palaeontological content; it includes range zones and interval zones.

Bisaccate pollen: pollen grain with two separate bladders (sacci) projecting from the body of the grain.

Bk horizon: B horizon with accumulation of carbonates, usually calcite nodules.

Blotch mine: a leaf mine in which the feeding takes place in a single expanding area as the lava grows.

Bt horizon: B horizon with accumulation of clay.

Bulk density: a measure of mass in a given volume (grams per cubic centimetre or g cm^{-3}); usually indicated by symbol r. The density of a whole body including gaps and pores filled with air.

Bulk maceration: maceration of larger quantities of material, usually larger pieces of rock, which may contain cuticles of several species.

C horizon: subsurface soil horizon, excluding bedrock, slightly more weathered than the material from which the soil formed or is presumed to have formed. Lacks properties of A and B horizons, but includes weathering as shown by mineral oxidation, accumulation of silica, carbonates or more soluble salts, and gleying.

Calcareous: consisting largely of calcite.

Calcification: soil-building process of the accumulation of carbonate, usually as nodules in subsurface horizons.

Calcite: carbonate mineral of dry soils ($CaCO_3$).

Calibration: method for correcting raw radio-carbon ages for time dependent variations in ^{14}C production. Makes use of master curves constructed from long dendrochronological sequences. Produces dates (or date ranges) in calendar years.

Carbonaceous: with abundant organic matter.

Carbonate: common anion (CO_3^{2-}) in soil solution and component of carbonate minerals such as calcite and siderite.

Carbonatite: igneous rock composed primarily of carbonate minerals.

Cathode ray: stream of electrons released into a vacuum within a cathode ray tube.

Cellulose: a linear polysaccharide consisting of glucose units. Together with hemicelluloses, cellulose forms the main part of the cell walls of plants.

Charcoal: carbonaceous remains of plant material formed after exposure to high temperatures with limited oxygen.

Chelating agent: a compound which 'locks up' unwanted ions (usually metal) by forming a closed ring of atoms around the unwanted ion.

Chemolysis: breakdown of large (macro)molecules using specific chemical reagents. Affecting only certain chemical bonds.

Chemosystematic: systematic information based on chemical compounds or a distinct chemical composition .

Chitin: a CHNO compound with structure very similar to cellulose but with acetamide side groups. Chitin hydrolyses to chitobiose units, just as cellulose does to cellobiose units. Occurs in the walls of many parts of fungi, including many spore types, as well as in exoskeletons of arthropods, mouth parts of certain annelid worms, and in other protist and animal parts.

Chronology: a long year-by-year record of mean ring width, or indices of mean ring width, for a site or region.

Chronostratigraphy: the division of rock sequences based on time. The body of rock deposited between time planes is classified according to a hierarchical set of units, the main ones being (in descending order of rank) erathem, system, series and stage. The time itself is classified according to an equivalent set of units, the main ones being (in descending order of rank) era, period, epoch and age.

Chronozone: the lowest ranking division in the hierarchy of chronostratigraphical terms (Holland *et al.* 1978).

Clay skin: coating of clay formed on cracks within soil.

Cleat fracture: a joint set confined within coalified material and arranged subnormal to bed boundaries. This term is used independently of the scale of the fracture set and may vary from a scale of microns (μm) to mm.

Coalification: the development of coal from peat by increasing chemical and physical alteration of organic matter without geothermal influence, mainly by reduction of the O/C-ratio.

Colluvium: deposits of landslides, soil creep and other mass wasting.

Community: a recurring assemblage of plants and animals adapted to a specific set of local environmental conditions (e.g. swamp community).

Concurrent range biozone: a body of strata characterized by the overlapping ranges of specified taxa (Holland *et al.* 1978).

Conventional ^{14}C dating: also known as radiometric ^{14}C dating. Relies on the detection of beta decay particle emissions which can be done by gas or liquid scintillation counting. Requires a larger sample than AMS.

Coprolite: fossil faeces / fecal pellet.

Corestone: spheroidally weathered remnant of parent material, least weathered toward the centre, and usually within the C horizon of deep weathering profiles.

Corpus: the central body of a saccate pollen grain.

Critical buckling length (m): term used in biomechanical studies describing the maximum height an upright column or stem can reach before it fails due to global buckling caused by its own weight (including weight of additional apical loads).

Cross-bedding: sedimentary layering that is inclined to regional layering, commonly due to the formation of dunes with slip-faces at an angle to the ground surface.

Cross-field pitting: pits occurring between radial faces of longitudinal tracheids and the radial faces of ray parenchyma. These are often very diagnostic for wood identification.

CTAB: hexadecyltrimethyl-ammonium Bromide.

Cutan: surface within a soil modified by enrichment, bleaching, coating or other alteration; formed at the surface of a ped, channel, grain or other feature of the soil.

Cuticle: the outer non-cellular layer covering the epidermis of most aerial parts of higher plants. This layer is continuous and interrupted only by stomata and lenticels and protects the underlying tissues, mainly against excessive water loss. The cuticle forms a natural cast of the underlying epidermis and in many cases this pattern is diagnostic and can therefore be used in taxonomic studies. Moreover, fossil cuticles may provide important information on palaeoecology and palaeoclimate.

Cutin: a lipid mainly found in the cuticule of plants

as a water-repellent and protective coating on the outer cell walls.

Death dates: the year in which a tree last grew, died or was felled, as distinct from the last ring of a sample which may be many years before the death of the tree from which it came.

DEDTCA: (also known as DETC) diethyl-dithiocarbamic acid.

Dégagement: technique of removing sediment surrounding a plant fossil using sharpened needles. The forces are applied by lightly striking the needle with a hammer or manipulating the needle by hand.

Delta ^{13}C/δ^{13}C(%): the convention by which stable isotopes are given. It is defined by the expression $δ(\%) = (R_s/R_{ref} - 1) \times 1000$ in which R is the ratio of $^{13}C/^{12}C$ and the subscripts denote the sample (s) and standard (ref), respectively.

Dendrochronology: the use of tree rings as a method of dating. Relies on the fact that many temperate trees lay down distinct annual growth rings whose width varies depending on the ambient climate during the growing season. Measuring the ^{14}C content gives rise to the calibration curve.

Depth function: a plot with depth from the surface of the profile as vertical axis (y) and measured soil feature as horizontal axis (x), a common graphical presentation of chemical and petrographic data on soils and palaeosols.

Diachronous: describes an event that occurred at different times in different places.

Diagenesis: the chemical, physical and biological changes that may affect sedimentary deposits and the fossils therein after deposition.

Dinoflagellates: one-celled organisms with complex life cycle, usually including a vegetative, thecal stage and a sexually generated cyst stage. In some dinoflagellates the thecal stage has cellulosic plates arranged in patterns characteristic of the species, and a cyst wall of similarly arranged sporopollenin plates. Fossil dinoflagellates are apparently all cysts of such forms.

Discrimination, isotopic: denoted as Δ expresses the isotope shift between air, R_a and tree material, R_t, and is roughly given by $Δ \cong (δ^{13}C_a - δ^{13}C_t)$.

Disjunct distribution: marked by a separation of a generally continuous geographical distribution.

EDAX: Energy Dispersive Analysis X-ray.

EDTA: ethylenediaminetetraacetic acid.

Eh: electrode potential (usually in millivolts): for soils a measure of the degree of oxidation. Oxidized soils have high positive Eh. Reduced soils have low negative Eh.

Endemic, endemism: restricted to, or native to, a particular region.

Endocarp: interior woody part of a seed or fruit coat of plants, also known as a pit or stone, as in cherries and peaches.

Endoreticulations: ornamentation on the inner surface of the saccus wall in certain pollen grains.

Epitype: a specimen intended to supplement the role of the holotype (see 'Holotype') and assist in its interpretation. Designated only when the holotype is demonstrably ambiguous or obscure.

Error term: composite measure or estimate of the experimental error in determining the ^{14}C content of a sample. Usually described as normal (i.e. Gaussian). Always includes the Poisson (counting) statistics and sometimes other factors.

Eusaccate: a pollen grain that possesses a true saccus with endoreticulations.

Eutaxon (pl., -taxa): A term coined by Meyen (1987) for taxa of whole plants, especially living ones, or those few fossil taxa where the structure of the whole organism is preserved (cf. 'Parataxa').

Event dates: the dates of significant environmental events which show up in tree-ring records.

Exoexine: the outer wall layer in a visibly (light microscopy) two-layered spore. A neutral term applied to fossil material where the homology of the wall layers with extant spores is unknown. Usually paler in colour than the intexine.

Fabric analysis: determining the orientations relative to (1) magnetic north and (2) the gravitational vertical of elongate macroscopic clasts within a sediment, in order to infer the hydraulic conditions prevalent at the time of clast deposition.

Ferric iron: iron in the Fe^{3+} valence state, usually within red or yellow minerals or compounds.

Ferrous iron: iron in the Fe^{2+} valence state, usually within grey to green minerals or compounds.

Flash pyrolysis: pyrolysis technique in which the final set pyrolysis temperature is reached instantaneously. Examples are Curie-point pyrolysis and filament pyrolysis.

Flexural stiffness (Nm^2): biologically tangible value describing the bending stiffness of a plant stem; calculated as the product of the axial second moment of area and the structural Young's modulus of the stem.

Flot: plant and other remains which float during sieving of archaeological sediments.

Flotation: system for recovery of materials from archaeological sediments which float, always combined with a wet-sieve.

Form-genus: a genus of fossil plants based on a detached organ which, because of the limited characters shown, cannot be assigned to a family, although it may be possible to assign it to a higher taxonomic level. The 'artifical' nature of such a genus is illustrated by the several instances where we have one form-genus in which different species may closely resemble members of two or more different families.

Fossil-fuel (or Suess) effect: the effect of burning coal, oil and other fossil fuels has been to significantly lower the ^{14}C content of the atmosphere since the first half of the twentieth century.

Fractionation: isotopes of an element have slightly different chemical properties which results in small differences of their corresponding reaction rates. Furthermore, they show somewhat different distributions in different chemical phases which leads to isotopic exchange reactions. All such changes in isotope compositions caused by physico-chemical processes within a system are termed isotope fractionations.

Frass: a concentration of fecal pellets associated with a plant structure, such as in galleries bored in wood or within a leaf mine.

Functionalized polar pyrolysis products: organic compounds formed upon pyrolysis that possess distinct regions of partial positive and negative charge. For example, these include fatty acids and long chain alkanols.

Gall: these are produced as a result of a physiological reaction in the host plant tissues immediately surrounding an invasive parasite, usually an insect. The gall develops not only as a protective layer but also as a food and water connecting system to the plant.

Gaussian: usual form of the error term of an uncalibrated ^{14}C measurement. It has a normal (i.e. dumb-bell shaped) probability distribution.

Germination site: region on pollen grain or spore wall where pollen tube or gametophyte emerges.

Gleization: process of gley formation.

Gley: soil that is blue-grey or green-grey coloured, strongly mottled or with abundant iron–manganese nodules, usually due to waterlogging, but sometimes produced by burial.

Global buckling (or Euler buckling): tall, slender poles or stems will deflect from the vertical and finally fail mechanically due to applied axial compressive loads caused by their own weight and/or additional apical loads if they have reached or exceeded a critical length. This type of mechanical failure is called global buckling and may occur long before the critical compressive strength of the material constituting the pole is reached.

Goniometer: mechanical device which allows the

orientation of a sample to be rotated and tilted to the precise orientation required for sawing and sectioning.

Grana stacks: membrane-bound discs within chloroplasts that contain the chlorophyll and accessory pigments.

Granular ped: a form of ped or clod that is small and rounded.

Growth form: describing shape, posture and structure of a plant based on quantitative data of the ontogenetic variations of mechanical stem properties and the underlying structural variations; three broadly defined types of growth forms are distinguished among woody plants: (1) 'self-supporting' shrubs and trees, (2) 'semi-self-supporting' (leaning) plants ('Spreizklimmer'), (3) 'non-self-supporting lianas'. The term 'growth form' as used here does not follow the concept of a plant's architecture which is based on a description of overall distribution and relative positioning of component modules.

Haematite (hematite – American sp.): red iron oxide mineral (Fe_2O_3).

Halogenation: the introduction of halogen atoms (e.g. Br) into an organic molecule either by substitution or addition.

Hardwater effect: bias often, although not invariably, associated with the presence of calcium ions in aquatic environments resulting from the dissolution of 'infinite-age' calcium carbonate. The geological ^{14}C-depleted carbon dilutes the atmospheric content in the water making samples which take their carbon from such sources appear too old.

Harmomegathy: the way in which a pollen grain or spore changes in size and/or shape in response to changes hydration.

Hash: mechanically fragmented organic material.

Hemicelluloses: a group of polysaccharides consisting of different sugar units. Together with cellulose, hemicelluloses form the main part of the cell walls.

Holotype: a specimen designated by the author of a species or higher taxon as that with which the name is permanently associated (also referred to as simply 'the type').

Homotaxy: a similarity in the serial arrangement of biozones in spatially separated stratigraphical sections. The resulting homotaxial correlations do not define time-planes between the sequences, but merely mark the relative levels of change in the sequences.

Hue: colour, such as red, yellow or green, independent of murkiness (chroma) or lightness (value) of the colour, in the Munsell system of colour classification.

Humic acids: a generic term for humic compounds in organic sediments that can be extracted by alkali treatment.

Humus: a generic term for products resulting from the anaerobic decomposition of organic matter.

Hydrolysis: common weathering reaction in soil solutions, converting aluminosilicate minerals to clay and cations in solution.

Hydronium: hydrogen ion (H^+).

Hydroperiod: that part of the year in which the biotope is flooded.

Hyperstomatous: having stomata only on the upper surface of the leaf.

Hypostomatous: having stomata only on the lower surface of the leaf.

ICP: inductively coupled plasma emission spectrometry. A method of chemical analysis using wavelengths of light emitted from atomized sample introduced into an argon plasma.

INAA: instrumental neutron activation analysis.

Inaperturate: pollen or spore with no marked ridges and without furrows (colpi) or pores (pori).

Inceptisol: soil with some weathering and incipient development of a variety of different kinds of horizons, but none well-enough developed that the soil could be identified with another order.

Infection pegs: specialized hyphal structures of fungi that are capable of penetrating the cuticle of a host plant.

Interval Zone: a body of strata between two specified biohorizons (see 'Biohorizon').

Intexine: the inner wall layer in a visibly (light microscopy) two-layered spore. A neutral term applied to fossil material where the homology of the wall layers with extant spores is unknown. Usually darker in colour than the exoexine.

Intine: the inner part of the wall of pollen grains or vascular plant spores, consisting of cellulose.

IRMS: Isotope Ratio Mass Spectrometer, a dual viscous flow inlet mass spectrometer for the comparative measurement of a sample with a standard.

Isotopes: atoms of the same chemical element having different mass numbers but the same atomic number, i.e. same number of protons but different numbers of neutrons.

Items: term used in archaeobotanical terminology for a 'Unit of identification', e.g. seed, glume, spikelet fork etc.

Kerogen: sedimentary organic matter insoluble in normal organic solvents (i.e. hexane, methanol, dichloromethane). Kerogen is macromolecular in composition.

Kjeldahl titration: wet chemical method for determining nitrogen content of soils and rocks.

Labile minerals: minerals, such as olivine and pyroxene, that are relatively easily weathered.

Lamellae: general term for thin layer in pollen or spore wall.

Lammas: a second generation of shoots made by a number of tree species (e.g. oaks) that are formed in late June or early July. They are slender twigs which exceed the first generation, or the spring shoots, in length.

Leaching: depletion of a chemical element from a soil by dissolution in water or other solvent.

Leaf mine: a feeding trace made between the upper and lower leaf cuticles, generally by the larval stage of an insect who feeds on the mesophyll tissue.

Lectotype: a substitute for the holotype (see 'Holotype'), designated, ideally from among the original specimens, when an author failed to designate a holotype.

Libby half-life: measure of the rate of radioactive decay of ^{14}C when it was first measured by American chemist, Willard Libby. Accepted value is 5568 years. Now known to be incorrect as the more accurate age is 5730 years. Despite this, the Libby half-life is still used for consistency. A correction is made when a measurement is calibrated.

Lignin: amorphous biopolymers exclusively occurring in cell walls. Lignin provides most of the structural rigidity in plants. It is very resistant to microbial degradation and can only be destroyed by white-rot fungi under aerobic conditions. Thus lignin and lignin-related complexes exhibit a high potential for preservation.

Lignite: Brown coal, low rank coal, which has undergone moderate coalification (between peat and bituminous coal in rank).

Linear mine: a leaf mine in which the feeding trail is tunnel-like, forming a straight or sinuous trail.

Lipids analysis: chemical analysis of solvent soluble organic compounds mostly studied using chromatography.

Lipids, lipoids: generic terms for oils, fats, waxes and related products found in living tissues.

Maceration: method by which sedimentary rocks are disintegrated using physical and chemical techniques, the purpose being to extract acid-insoluble microfossils; these include palyno-morphs.

Macromolecule: large molecule containing randomly arranged chemical (sub)units. This is as opposed to polymer, which is a large molecule composed of regularly arranged repeating chemical units.

Magnesia: magnesium oxide (MgO).

Marginal trace: a simple form of feeding trace on a leaf margin comprising simple single, multiple or continuous bite marks.

Mesofossil: a fossil, intermediate in size between a microfossil and megafossil, visible in the field, but requiring microscopic study.

Metamorphism: alteration of rocks during deep burial and heating, generally to more than 200°C or greater than 7 km, whichever comes first.

Microsporogenesis: the complete set of developmental processes leading to the formation of microspores in plants.

Moderately developed soil or palaeosol: with surface rooted zone and obvious subsurface clayey, sesquioxidic, humic or calcareous or surface organic horizons, qualifying as argillic, spodic or calcic horizons or Histosol and developed at least to the extent of nodules for calcic horizons.

Mole: mass in grams of Avogadro's number (6.022×10^{23}) of atoms or molecules of an element or compound, calculated by dividing weight percent of analysed element or compound by its atomic weight.

Molecular weathering ratio: ratio of chemical constituents in moles, calculated in order to understand changing chemical proportions due to weathering.

Mollisol: grassland soil with a mollic epipedon at least 18 cm thick.

Monosaccate pollen: pollen grain with a single bladder (saccus) projecting from the body of the grain.

Neotype: a type specimen designated to replace the holotype (see 'Holotype') when it has been lost or destroyed.

Nephelinite: igneous rock with common nepheline, and iron and magnesium rich minerals, such as olivine and pyroxene, and little if any quartz.

Neutral line: a term used in biomechanical studies calculated by using the structural Young's modulus of the youngest ontogenetic stage (E_{OS1}) as a slope (neutral line = $E_{OS1} \times I$); for constant contributions of each stem tissue towards the axial second moment of area and for a constant Young's modulus of the stem tissues during ontogeny; values of structural Young's modulus for the stem would remain constant during ontogeny and data of flexural stiffness would lie along the neutral line.

Neutral plane: plane of zero fibre stress in a rod or stem subject to bending. The fibres in the stem part windward to the neutral plane are extended, the fibres in the leeward side compressed.

Neutron activation analysis: method of chemical analysis using radiation induced after neutron irradiation in a nuclear reactor.

Nicols: polarizing light filters on a petrographic microscope.

Nodule: hard, cemented lumps of soil material with an undifferentiated, massive internal fabric.

Nomenclature: the application of names to objects or concepts. Terminology.

Nomogram: graph that consists of lines marked in such a way that needed and unknown values can be obtained from measured or known values.

Non-marginal trace: feeding traces not affecting the leaf margin, such as hole within the leaf.

Ontogenetic stage: term employed in bio-mechanical studies of plant growth forms representing a stage of axial development in the entire ontogenetic trajectory of a plant; distal axes, young plant stems such as saplings and new reiterative branches represent young ontogenetic stages; older and more basal axes represent older ontogenetic stages.

Opaque: impervious to light, and so black when viewed by transmitted light in a petrographic thin section.

Orbicules: small, spherical structures formed by a secretory tapetum in some vascular plants, and often having the same ornamentation as the pollen grain or spore wall surface.

Orbital forcing: the control of the Earth's climate by external (orbital) factors which are described by the astronomical variables that alter the amount of radiation received at the Earth's surface and the distribution of that radiation spatially.

Organ-genus: a genus based on only part (an organ or organs) of a fossil plant, showing a sufficient range of distinctive characters that it may reasonably be assigned to a family. An organ-genus is regarded as 'natural', in the sense that its constituent species are believed to have the same close relationship as those of a living genus. However, an organ-genus differs from a genus of living plants in that only fossils of the same organ, showing the same type of characters, can be assigned to it (e.g. fossil lauraceous leaves cannot be assigned to *Laurocarpum*, an organ-genus of fossil lauraceous fruit).

Oryctocoenosis: that part of a fossil assemblage that has been sampled.

Oxalic acid standard: the internationally recognized standard held by the US NIST against which all ^{14}C measurements are made. The activity of this material is that of a wood sample grown in AD 1950 minus the fossil-fuel effect.

Oxisol: deeply weathered soils with kaolinitic clays, quartz and few weatherable minerals.

Palaeopalynology: the study of fossil spores and pollen.

Palaeosol: soil of a landscape of the past: a past surficial region of a planet or similar body altered in place by biological, chemical or physical processes, or a combination of these. (Note that paleosol rather than palaeosol or paleosoil) has been formally adopted by the INQUA-ISSS Palaeopedology Commission.

Palynodebris: all of the (mostly plant) organic debris found in palynological preparations along with palynomorphs. This includes such things as wood in various stages of degradation, leaf cuticles, other plant cells and tissue fragments, fungal hyphae, algal filaments, and more or less amorphous degraded organic matter of diverse origin.

Palynofacies: in a limited sense, the palynoflora associated with a particular sedimentary environment, or represented in a rock horizon. In a broader sense, the palynoflora, together with the palynodebris of such an environment or rock level.

Palynoflora: the total of all palynomorphs present in a subject rock or sediment sample or group of samples.

Palynology: the study of pollen.

Palynomorph: fossil spores and pollen (= sporomorphs), fungal spores, dinoflagellate cysts, and other resistant (sporopollenin or chitin) fossils found in palynological preparations and having an approximate size of between 5 mm and 500 mm.

Parataxon; (pl.,-taxa): a taxonomic unit, principally used of fossils, based on only part of an organism or part of its life cycle. For some authors this term includes the names of ichnofossils (trace fossils), based on fossil trails, footprints and burrows of various animals.

Parietal tapetum: another term for secretory tapetum; type of tapetum in which orbicules are produced.

Partial range biozone: a body of strata within the range of a particular fossil group, above the last appearance of the preceding fossil group and below the first appearance of the next succeeding fossil group (Holland *et al.* 1978).

PDB: internationally adopted reference for the stable carbon isotopes. The material is a fossil belemnite from the Pee Dee formation, Upper Cretaceous, of South Carolina, USA. It is no longer available. A substitute is available nowadays from the IAEA in Vienna as V-PDB (see 'Reference standards' and 'Carbon isotopic standard' in the Appendix).

Peatification: the formation of peat from dead vegetation by microbial and chemical alteration of organic matter, mainly by reduction of the O/C-ratio.

Ped: natural aggregate of soil; that is, stable lumps

or clods of soil between roots, burrows, cracks or other planes of weakness.

Pedotype: reference profile for definition of a soil or palaeosol mapping unit.

Permineralization: or cellular permineralization (currently but less accurately termed 'petrifaction'): early infiltration and permeation of tissues (not 'replacement') by mineral-charged water with intracellular and interstitial precipitation of colloidal or microcrystalline mineral matter; several types: siliceous, calcareous, pyritic, limonitic, phosphatic, etc. (Schopf 1975; Bateman 1991).

Petrifaction: permeation, but not replacement, of cells and interstices by mineral matrix at or very soon after deposition. Synonymous with permineralization.

Petrography: description of rocks, usually including study in thin section.

pH: negative logarithm of the activity of the hydronium ion (H^+): for soils a measure of acidity. Acidic soils have a low pH (<7) and alkaline soils have a high pH (>7), with a total observed range in nature of 3–11, from a theoretical 1–14.

Phonolite: mafic volcanic rock with alkali feldspar and a feldspathoid such as nepheline, lacking quartz.

Phytochorion: a geographical area defined for a particular time interval by its distinctive palaeobotany. There is a hierarchy of phytochoria, in descending order of rank: palaeokingdom, palaeoarea, palaeoprovince, palaeodistrict, palaeoregion. The palaeo- prefix is important as it does not just show that it is an ancient phytogeographical division, but that it is based on the very partial view of the original vegetation provided by the fossil record.

Phytolith: mineral particle made by a plant, such as opal bodies of grasses.

Plasmodesmata: thin tube of protoplasm that connects protoplasts of adjacent cells.

pMC / % Modern: percent modern carbon. Measurements where the ^{14}C activity is greater than the modern activity at AD 1950, as defined by the oxalic acid standard.

Podzolization: soil-building process of acidic leaching leading to a subsurface accumulation of sesquioxides, organic matter or combinations of these.

Point-counting: systematic search and record of grain type or size made to determine mineral composition or grain size of palaeosols.

Pollen assemblage biozone (pab): a body of strata characterized by a certain assemblage of pollen taxa without rigorous regard to their individual ranges outside of the biozone in question (Holland *et al.* 1978). Frequently used synony-

mously in Quaternary literature with *pollen assemblage zone (paz)* and given local and regional significance.

Pollen-analysis = pollen statistics: the assembling and presentation of data from successive levels in cored sediment of the percentage composition of species of pollen and spores. The spectrum of spore/pollen composition, usually presented as a percentage of total pollen or of a select group of pollen, tends to be uniform over wide areas at a given level. This enables palynologists to predict probable vegetation composition at these levels and to suggest the probable climatic conditions indicated. The data also permit relative dating of the levels.

Potash: potassium oxide (K_2O).

Primary replication: where a number of tree-ring patterns have been cross-matched to provide internal checking of a length of chronology, forming a site or regional chronology.

Protist: a one-celled eukaryotic organism, including diverse forms such as dinoflagellates, which have been regarded as plants (Algae), and foraminifera, which have been treated as animals (Protozoa).

Protosaccate: saccate pollen grain in which continuous threads of sporopollenin extend from the inner surface of the saccus to the outer surface of the corpus.

Pseudomorph: one mineral occurring in the crystal form of another.

PVP: polyvinylpyrrolidone.

Pyrolysis: breakdown of large (macro)molecules using thermal energy in an inert atmosphere, or in vacuo. The type of chemical bonds broken will depend on the amount of thermal energy used (i.e. higher temperatures will break more stable chemical bonds).

Quartz: common mineral of soils (SiO_2).

Range Zone: a body of strata defined by the presence of a taxon (Taxon Range Zone) or of an assemblage of taxa (Assemblage Range Zone).

Realm: continent-scale region with a distinctive flora and fauna that has evolved through geographic isolation from other continents (e.g. Australian realm).

Reference standards: various reference gases for isotopes are in use with mass spectrometers for measuring relative isotope ratios, i.e. determination of d-values. It is common practice that every laboratory uses its own standard which is calibrated against international reference standards.

Release: a rapid burst of enhanced growth, indicated by notably wider growth rings, following, for example, the removal of competition or fertilization.

Relict, relictual: a persistent remnant of a previously diverse flora or fauna.

Reservoir effect: most commonly associated with samples which assimilate carbon from the marine environment (in which case known as the 'marine reservoir effect'). although can apply to other situations. Caused by the fact that ^{14}C mixing takes so long that radioactive decay becomes an appreciable factor. As mixing is not a straightforward process the magnitude of the effect can vary geographically.

Ring pattern: the measured ring widths of successive growth rings in a sample, from the centre to the outside of a tree.

Riparian: adapted to life on the margins of a natural water body, such as a river or lake.

Ripple mark: sedimentary structure of small-scale undulations of a bedding plane; miniature dune-like forms produced by wind or water currents.

Saccus wall: wing-like extension of the pollen wall formed by a separation of the exine.

Salinization: process of salt accumulation.

Saltation: the transport of particles as bedload in a series of ballistic jumps.

Sapwood: the living, normally unconsolidated, outer wood of a tree occurring immediately beneath the bark.

Schistosity: degree of development of planes of fissility and foliation characteristic of fine-grained metamorphic rocks.

Schulze's reagent: a mixture of nitric acid (HNO_3) and potassium chlorate ($KClO_3$) for clearing fossil cuticles and palynomorphs by oxidation. There are two types of Schulze's reagent, i.e. 'dry Schulze' and 'wet Schulze'. The dry 'Schulze' is made by adding a few crystals of potassium chlorate, whereas the 'wet' variant by adding a saturated potassium chlorate solution. The concentration of the nitric acid depends on the nature of the material and has to be determined empirically.

Scour-and-fill: sedimentary structure with a bowl-shaped depression filled with concordant sedimentary layers.

Secondary replication: where a number of site chronologies have been cross-matched to provide external checking of each constituent chronology.

SEM: Scanning electron microscopy.

Sesquioxides: alumina (Al_2O_3) and ferric iron (Fe_2O_3).

Siderite: carbonate mineral of waterlogged and organic-rich soils ($FeCO_3$).

Silica: silicon dioxide (SiO_2).

Silt: a category of clastic sedimentary particle finer than sand, coarser than clay (i. e. 4–62.5 mm).

Sink: the depositional site of the organic matter.

Siraf machine: flotation tank used extensively on archaeological sites (Williams 1973).

Skeletonization: the veins of the leaves are not removed (even secondary and tertiary veins) whereas the tissues between are eaten or decayed.

Skeletonized leaf: plant leaf decayed in such a way that cuticle and soft tissues have been removed to reveal the woody vascular traces or veins.

Slide: small glass pane used for supporting thin section of rock or soil.

Slurry: material, mainly mineral matter, which passes through a wet-sieve from archaeological material.

Soil horizons: gradational changes in texture or mineral content down into parent material of a soil or palaeosol from the truncated land surface.

Solvent insoluble: insoluble in organic solvents mainly macromolecular in nature. Kerogen is solvent insoluble.

Source: the locality from which the organic matter was derived.

Soxhlet extraction: an extraction procedure using organic solvent and a soxhlet apparatus. The organic solvent extracts the solvent-soluble fraction (mainly lipids) and leave an insoluble residue. The residue comprises kerogen and, if present, minerals.

Spodosol: acidic sandy soil with B horizons enriched in organic matter, iron and aluminum or combinations of these, but not clay.

Sporoderm: the general term for the entire wall of a pollen grain or spore.

Sporomorph: a palynomorph that is either a pollen grain, or the spore of an embryo-producing plant.

Sporopollenin: a very tough CHO biopolymer of large molecular size, variously regarded as isoprene-like, or carotenoid-like. Chemically extremely stable and can only be destroyed by oxidation, thus giving pollen and spores a high potential of preservation. Comprises the wall of most pollen grains and spores of embryo-producing plants.

Spot dates: an independently derived date for a specimen which can be inserted into the stratigraphy in which it occurs.

Steppe: a natural environment, usually of middle latitudes, characteristic of colder parts of the Pleistocene, dominated by low temperatures and low precipitation (= cold and dry). Areas with this environment are characterized by vegetation consisting of grasses and other xerophytic (dry-tolerant) herbs, and xerophytic shrubs such as *Artemisia* and *Atriplex*.

Strongly developed soil or palaeosol: with

especially thick (2–3 m), red, clayey or humic subsurface (B) horizons or surface organic horizons (coal or lignites) or especially well developed soil structure or calcic horizons as a continuous layer.

Structural moieties = Structural building blocks: chemical groups/building blocks which are characteristic in a large macromolecule. Often specific for certain distinct macromolecules. For example aromatic compounds such as 2-methoxyphenols are characteristic for lignin, the structural component in wood, and aliphatic components such as certain hydroxy fatty acids (i.e. 9-hydroxyhexadecanoic acid), are characteristic for the biopolyester cutin in cuticles.

Structural Young's modulus (Pa) = (N/ m^{-2}): mechanical parameter describing the material properties of an inhomogeneous composite material, such as a plant stem, in bending. The structural Young's modulus is calculated by dividing the experimentally determined flexural stiffness by the mean axial second moment of area of the tested stem (see 'Young's modulus').

Suberin: a lipid found in some plant cells, especially cork, as a water-repellent protective coating on the inner cell walls.

Systematics: the process of classifying objects. More or less synonymous with taxonomy (see 'Taxonomy')

Tapetal membranes: series of membranes formed during microsporogenesis.

Taphocoenosis: an assemblage of fossils brought together by sedimentary processes. A fossil assemblage embedded in sediment.

Taphonomy: the natural history of fossils, following the death of the organic matter from which the fossil is derived. This includes sedimentary processes, as well as processes occurring after sedimentation, during and after formation of rock.

Taxon (pl., taxa): a unit within a classification, e.g. a species, a family. The latter is a 'higher order' taxon than the species.

Taxonomy: more or less synonymous with systematics, although some authors see taxonomy as devising a single classification, while systematics considers the science of the process of classifying on a broader basis. For some authors, systematics also includes the handling of nomenclature.

Temperature-resolved pyrolysis: pyrolysis technique using a probe. The thermal energy is applied to the sample using a resistively-heated filament which is temperature ramped from c. 200°C to 800°C with a speed ranging from 20 K s^{-1} to 1 K s^{-1}.

Tertiary replication: where independent chronologies constructed by different workers provide an external check on each other.

Thanatocoenosis: an assemblage not yet embedded in sediment.

Thermoplastic mounting media: adhesive, mounting resins, such as 'Lakeside', which become liquid on heating and harden when cold.

Thin section: transparent, thin (10–30 mm) slice of rock or soil mounted between glass covers, used for microscopic examination.

Time width: total growth and exchange period represented. Results in an average measure of the ^{14}C activity. An example would be a block of wood with 50 growth rings.

Transported mass fraction: proportion of the mass of a chemical element lost or gained during soil formation or burial.

Trichome: hair.

Tris: (also known as THAM) Tris[hydroxymethyl]-aminomethane.

Tuff: compacted pyroclastic deposit of volcanic ash, dust or lapilli.

Ubisch bodies: (see 'Orbicules').

Ultisol: acidic, deeply weathered forest soil, with clayey, ferric, aluminous or humic subsurface horizon.

Ultrathin section: especially thin section cut with ultramicrotome, thickness often determined by interference colours.

Very strongly developed: with unusually thick (>3 m) subsurface (B) horizons or surface horizons (coal or lignites); such a degree of development is found mainly at major geological unconformities.

Very weakly developed soil or palaeosol: with little evidence of soil development apart from root traces and abundant sedimentary, metamorphic or igneous textures remaining from parent material.

Walkley–Black method: wet chemical titration method for the determination of abundance (weight percent) of soil organic carbon.

Weakly developed soil or palaeosol: with a surface rooted zone (A horizon), as well as incipient subsurface clayey, calcareous, sesquioxidic or humic or surface organic horizons, but none of these developed to the extent that they would qualify as argillic, spodic or calcic horizons or histic epipedons.

Weathering: processes related to the chemical action of water, air and organisms. Weathering is often accompanied by biodegradation and oxidation.

Wet-sieve: sieve immersed in water used for sieving archaeological sediments.

XRF: X-ray fluorescence spectrometry. A method of chemical analysis using wavelengths of secondary radiation induced by bombardment of sample with X-rays.

Young's modulus (Pa) = (N m^{-2}): mechanical parameter describing the stiffness of a (macroscopically homogeneous) material in bending; the bending stiffness of each plant stem tissue in bending is characterized by a value of Young's modulus.

Appendix: list of chemicals, equipment and suppliers

Ampersand Systems Ltd: (supplier of database software used for curation of Palaeobotany collections in NHM, London, see Chapter 35): St George's Hall, Easton-in-Gordano, Bristol BS20 0PX, UK

Buehler-met® Metallographic grinding papers: Buehler UK Ltd, Science Park, University of Warwick, Coventry CV4 7HS (web: http://www.buehlerltd.com/).

Butvar: (Polyvinyl butryl – specimen conservation, see Chapter 35): Conservation Resources (UK) Ltd, Units 1,2,& 4, Pony Rd, Horsepath Industrial Estate, Cowley, Oxfordshire OX4 2RD, UK.

CANOCO program: (for Macintosh or PC) can be purchased from: Microcomputer Power, 111 Clover Lane, Ithaca, NY 14850, USA.

Canada balsam: mounting medium for microscopy. SIGMA Chemical Co.

Carbon isotopic standard: a reference in use for carbon isotopes is the V-PDB-reference standard which is available form the International Atomic Energy Agency, PO 100, Wagramer Straße 5, A-1400 Wien, Austria.

Carbowax: (Polyethylene glycol) for embedding prior to microtome sectioning. SIGMA Chemical Co.

Cellulose acetate sheet: A.Warne & Co, 11 Nelson Trading Estate, The Path, Morden Road, London SW19 3BL, UK. (Fax 44 (0)181 543 6089).

Clearcol: (mounting medium, palynology) available from Marblehead Testing Laboratories, Marblehead, MA 01905, USA).

Coltène President light body Polyvinylsiloxane dental moulding material: Coltène UK Ltd, 8A Teknol House, Victoria Road, Burgess Hill, West Sussex RH15 9LF, UK.

Comparitor Microscope: for example, two Leica DM LB microscopes linked with a comparison bridge. Supplier: Leica Imaging Systems Ltd., Clifton Road, Cambridge CB1 3QH, UK.

Computer ^{14}C calibration programs can be obtained from:
Calib: Quaternary Research Center, AK60, University of Washington, Seattle, WA 98195, USA.
Groningen: Center for Isotope Research, University of Groningen, Nijenborgh 4, 9747 AG Groningen, The Netherlands.
CalibETH: Institute für Mittelenergiephysik, ETH-Hönggerberg, CH-8093 Zürich, Switzerland.

OxCal: Research Laboratory for Archaeology and the History of Art, Oxford University, 6 Keble Road, Oxford OX1 3QJ, UK.

Deltagraph Professional: Deltapoint Inc., California, 1991.

Diamond polish paste: Agar Scientific Ltd, 66a Cambridge Road, Stansted, Essex CM24 8DA, UK (Tel. 44 279 813519, fax. 44 279 815106).

Diamond wire saw: Agar Scientific Ltd, 66a Cambridge Road, Stansted, Essex CM24 8DA, UK (Tel. 44 279 813519, fax. 44 279 815106).

DNA products: Qiagen GmbH. Max-Volmer-Straße 4, 40724 Hilden, Germany; Promega Corporation, 2800 Woods Hollow Road, Madison, WI 53711-5399 USA; Gibco BRL Life Technologies, Gaithersburg, MD USA; Amersham Life Science. 2636 South Clearbrook Drive, Arlington Heights, IL 60005 USA; Molecular Research Center, Inc. 5645 Montgomery Rd, Cincinnati, OH 45212 USA; Sigma Chemical Company, PO Box 14508, St. Louis, MO 63178, USA.

DPX, Euparal, Canada Balsam (mounting media): Agar Scientific Ltd, 66a Cambridge Road, Stansted, Essex CM24 8DA, UK (Tel. 44 279 813519, fax. 44 279 815106).

Elvacite: Cold-setting epoxy resin with excellent optical properties including non-fluorescence in UV. Supplier: Charles Tennant & Co. (London) Ltd, 69 Grosvenor Street, London W1X OBP, UK.

EM suppliers, USA: Ted Pella Inc., 4595 Mountain Lakes Blvd, Redding, CA 96003 (tel. (916) 243 2200). Electron Microscopy Sciences, 321 Morris Rd, Box 251, Fort Washington, PA 19034 (tel. 1 800 523 5874). Diatome, PO Box 125, 321 Morris Rd, Fort Washington, PA 19034 (tel. (215) 646 1478).

England Finder Slide: a precision-marked glass slide used to assign unique coordinates to pollen and spores on a slide. This enables location of the specimens on any other microscope regardless of make and type (nb: not useful for silicone oil mounts where specimens can move freely within the mounting medium). Supplier: Graticules Ltd, Sovereign Way, Tonbridge, Kent, UK.

Epotek: Resin for mounting thin sections and wafers. 'Intertronics', Unit 9, Station Field Industrial Estate, Banbury Rd, Kidlington, Oxfordshire OX5 IJD, UK; see also in USA: Epoxy Technology Inc., 14 Fortune Drive,

Billerica, MA 01821-3972, USA (tel. 1 508 667 3805, fax 1 508 663 9782, http://www.epotek.com/).

Estwing manufacturing Co. Inc.: Purveyors of geological hammers and chisels (tel. USA (815) 397 9558, fax (815) 397 8665; web: http://www.estwing.com).

Euparal: Agar Scientific Ltd, 66a Cambridge Road, Stanstead, Essex CM24 8DA, UK (tel. 44 279 813519, fax 44 279 815106).

Fine-mesh nylon screen: TEKTO, 333 S. Highland Avenue, Briarcliff Manor, NY 10510, USA. (tel. 914 941 7767).

Genstat for Windows 5.4: Numerical Algorithms Group, Oxford, 1997.

Grab sampler: Van Veen grabs, Eijkelkamp Agriresearch Equipment, PO Box 4, Giesbeek, The Netherlands.

Histoknife: (disposable steel microtome blades, and holder): Heraeus Kulzer GmbH, Philipp-Reis-Strasse 8/13, D-61273 Wehrheim, Postfach 1242, D-61273 Wehrheim, Germany (tel. 49 6081 959 0, fax. 49 6081 959 304).

Instron: Instron-Wolpert GmbH, Ludwigshafen, Germany.

Isomet® diamond wafering blades: Buehler UK Ltd, Science Park, University of Warwick, Coventry CV4 7HS; http://www.buehlerltd.com/

Lakeside: (No. 70C Lakeside Brand) thermoplastic resin for mounting thin sections. Hugh Courtright & Co. Ltd, 6333 West 65th Street Chicago, Ill 60638, USA.

Leather-working needles: (the best, most resistant) are manufactured by GERHARD WEYLAND Ltd, Iserlohn, Germany. They can be found at shoemakers and leather crafts outlets, at least in European countries. Supplied in Belgium from: 'FIRME CALLOT',KMO Zone 'Blauwe Steen', Neerveld 6, B - 25550 Koentich, Belgium (tel: (32) 34575820, fax: (32) 34575820).

Leica Quantimet / LIDA (Image Analysis and Archiving System): a typical advanced image analysis and electronic image storage system. Supplier: Leica Imaging Systems Ltd, Clifton Road, Cambridge CB1 3QH, UK.

Low speed diamond saw: Agar Scientific Ltd, 66a Cambridge Road, Stansted, Essex CM24 8DA, UK (tel. 44 279 813519, fax 44 279 815106).

Lycopodium **marker tablets:** B. E. Berglund & T. Persson, Department of Quaternary Geology, Lund University, Tornavägan 13, S-223 63 Lund, Sweden (fax: +46 46 2224830).

Microslice 2: small cutting and wafering saw. Malvern Instruments Ltd., Spring Lane South, Malvern, Worcestershire WR14 1AT, UK.

Nylon and Polypropylene sieve meshes: NORMESH, Northern Mesh and technical fabrics, 18–20 Miles Street, Oldham, Greater Manchester OL1 3NU, UK.

Nylon & Selvyt cloth (for polishing): Agar Scientific Ltd, 66a Cambridge Road, Stansted, Essex CM24 8DA, UK (tel. 44 279 813519, fax. 44 279 815106).

Optimas Corporation: 8911 North Creek Parkway, Bothell, WA 98011 USA (tel: (425) 402 8888 / (800) 635 7226, fax: (425) 402 8844, email: optimas@optimas.com,web: http://www.optimas.com/).

Paleo-Bond: (stabilizing and gluing material in the field) Uncommon Conglomerates Inc., 400 Western Avenue North, St. Paul, MN 55103, USA (tel: (800) 323 4545, fax: (USA) 612 227 6526; web: http://www.global-expos.com/paleo-bond.html).

Paleoclimate Databases (pollen, macrofossil, lake-level, etc.): John Keltner, NOAA Paleo-climatology Program, 325 Broadway, NGDC E/GC, Boulder, CO 80303, USA (email: jkeltner@ngdc.noaa.gov; web:http://www.ngdc.noaa.gov/paleo/paleo.html).

Paper-bonded silicone carbide (manual grinding): Agar Scientific Ltd, 66a Cambridge Road, Stansted, Essex CM24 8DA, UK (tel. 44 279 813519, fax 44 279 815106).

Paraloid Acrylic polymer: (suppliers of product 'code B 27', soluble in Acetone, Toluene and Cellulosolve). From: CONSERVATION RESOURCES (UK) LTD, Unit 1 Pony Road, Horse path Industrial Estate, Cowley, Oxford, OX4 2RD, UK (tel: 44 0 1865 747755, fax 44 0 1865 747035).

Paraloid B72: (for specimen repair and consolidation, see Chapter 35): Conservation Resources (UK) Ltd, Units 1,2,4, Pony Rd, Horsepath Industrial Estate, Cowley, Oxfordshire OX4 RD, UK.

Piston corers and rods: Greenfield Machine Works, John Erdman, Box 457 Greenfield Road Costigan, ME 04423 USA (tel. 207 827 5557, fax 207 827 4105; email: jperdman@aol.com). Dr D. R. Engstrom, St Croix Watershed Research Station, Science Museum of Minnesota, Marine on St Croix, MN 55047, USA (email:dre@maroon.tc.umn.edu).

Plastazote: (foam plastic for storage/curation, see Chapter 35): Wilford Manufacturing Co., Unit 5, Greaves Way, Stanbridge Rd, Leighton Buzzard, Beds LU7 8UB, UK.

Polyester filtration mesh: (available in numerous mesh sizes) – Precision Textiles Limited, Bury Business Centre, Kay Street, Bury, Lancs BL9 6BU, UK.

Polypropylene sieve mesh: Henry Simon Special Products Division, PO Box 31, Stockport, Cheshire SK3 0RT, UK.

Resins, adhesives, etc., suppliers include:

Agar Scientific Ltd, 66a Cambridge Road, Stansted, Essex CM24 8DA, UK (tel. 44 1279 813519, fax 44 1279 815106).

CIBA Polymers, Duxford, Cambridge CB2 4QA, UK (tel. 44 1223 832121, fax 44 1223 493322) (including the Araldite 2000 range).

Loctite UK Limited, Watchmead, Welwyn Garden City, Hertfordshire AL7 1JB, UK (tel. 44 1707 821000, fax 44 1707 821200).

TAAB laboratories equipment Ltd, 3 Minerva House, Calleva Park, Aldermaston, Berks RG7 8NA, UK (tel. 44 118 9817775, fax 44 118 9817881).

RockWare, Inc.: The RockWare Building, 2221 East St, Suite 101, Golden, CO 80401, USA (tel. (303) 278 3534 / (800) 775 6745, fax (303) 278 4099; web: http://www.aescon.com/rockware/).

Safranin: general stain, SIGMA Chemical Co.

Sampling devices can be obtained from:

Ben Meadows Co. (http://www.benmeadows.com)

Munsell Soil Color Charts (Cat. No. 22190), Extendible Eijkelkamp Peat Sampler (Cat. No. 290218), Piston Sampler Set (for sampling to 5 m depth; Cat. No. 290222), Van Dorn-style Bottle Water Column Sampler (Cat. No. 224250), Stainless Steel Sampling Dredge (Cat. No. 224211), Modified Birge-Ekman-style Box Sediment Sampler (Cat. No. 224202) Model AM-22 Water Pollution Field Detection Kit (Cat. No. 221540).

OZTEC Industries Inc., 65 Channel Drive, Port Washington, NY 11050, USA (tel. 516 883 8857).

Portable Concrete Vibrator GV-5W, Robin-Engine Backpack Vibrator (w/o head & shaft), 2″ × 14″ vibrator head, 21 ft. flexible shaft, Ball-bearing connector.

STOW Manufacturing Co., Brandywine Highway, PO Box 490, Binghamton, NY 13902, USA (tel. 607 723 6411). 18050-551 500G – 5 HP Briggs & Stratton Engine, 16301-501 2100-2 1/8″ × 13″ Lg. Head, 13829-521 382V-21 – $^{3}/_{8}$″ × 21′ Lg. Shaft.

Dreyer Vibrator Co., Inc. 1610 N. Colorado, San Antonio, TX 78201 210-734-4261, USA. Model 'CG' 14218 (with 14′ shaft and 2 $^{1}/_{8}$″ Head), 14′ CG Extension Shaft.

SEM accessories: including stubs, stub boxes, carbon adhesive discs (carbon pads), sticky tabs (double-sided sellotape pads), double-sided sellotape roll, stub adapters, single stub storage/transport tubes, Silver Dag, W100 Wax (Apiezon – carbon putty). Agar Scientific Ltd, 66a Cambridge Road, Stanstead, Essex CM24 8DA, UK. (tel. 44 279 813519, fax 44 279 815106).

Silicon oil (storage pyritized preparations): Agar Scientific Ltd, 66a Cambridge Road, Stansted, Essex CM24 8DA, UK (tel. 44 279 813519; fax 44 279 815106).

Silicone oil: Dow Corning® silicone fluid (a clear colourless polydimethylsiloxane with a refractive index of about 1.403) is often used. The silicone fluid can be purchased with a variety of viscosities and mixed to produce the 2000 cs viscosity required as a mounting medium (e.g. mixing Dow Corning® 200/1000 cs silicone fluid and 200/12 500 cs silicone fluid in the relevant proportions). Supplier: BDH Limited, Industrial Chemicals Group, PO Box 11, Freshwater Road, Dagenham, Essex RM8 1RF, UK.

Silicone rubber glue: generic term for domestic sealant adhesives for mounting specimens on slides prior to wafering, available generally, which are used for filling and sealing around windows and basins etc.

Sodium polytungstate: (safe alternative to zinc bromide) – Sometu, Falkenried 4, D-1000 Berlin 33, Germany or PANGEA UK, 185 Oxford Road, Calne, Wiltshire SN11 8AL, UK.

Stable isotope equipment companies include:

ThermoQuest Corporation (for Carlo Erba and Finnigan products), 355 River Oaks Parkway, San José, California CA 95134-1991, USA (tel. 408 577 1053, fax 408 577 1641, web: http://www.thermoquest.com).

Finnigan Corporation (for Finnigan products), 355 River Oaks Parkway, San Jose, California CA 95134, USA (web: http://www.finnigan.com).

Carlo Erba Instruments (for Carlo Erba products), Strada Rivoltana, 20090 Rodano, Milan, Italy (tel. 2 95059272, fax 2 95059276).

Tracor/Tremetrics (for Carlo-Erba products), Grand Avenue Parkway, Austin TX USA (tel. 800 876 6711, fax 512 251 1597; web: http://ceinstruments.it).

Micromass UK limited (for VG-Fisons products), Floats Road, Wythenshawe, Manchester M23 9LZ, UK (tel. 44 161 945 4170, fax 44 161 998 8915; web: http://www.micromass.co.uk).

Stewart containers: ('Snapware' range of sealable, transparent containers for curation and specimen conservation, see Chapter 35): Wadden Marsh Way, Purley Way, Croydon CR9 4HS, UK.

Super glue: generic term for cyanylacrylate adhesives for preparation of wafers, available generally, in a range of viscosities.

Taxon v. 3.1: palynological database, freely available from R. Ravn at: Aeon Biostratigraphic Services, 6501 Shale Circle, Anchorage, AL 99516, USA.

TILIA & TILIAGRAPH software: Dr Eric C.

Grimm, Illinois State Museum, 1920 South 10 1/2 Street, Springfield, IL 62703, USA (email: grimm@museum.state.il.us).

Tungsten wire: (pure, 1.0 mm diameter, available in 5 m lengths) – GOODFELLOW CAMBRIDGE LTD, Cambridge CB4 4DJ, UK (tel: 44 0 1223 568068, fax 44 0 1223 639000).

Ward's Liquid Bioplastic (casting resin): Ward's Scientific Inc., PO Box 92912, Rochester, New York 14692-9012 USA (tel. 1 800 962 2660, fax 1 800 635 8439).

Water sampler: LaMotte Model JT-1, PO Box 329, Chestertown, Maryland, USA.

Index